BIOMECHANICS

SPORT INJURIES

FITNESS

EVALUATION

NUTRITION

WEIGHT MANAGEMENT

EXERCISE SCIENCE

Exercise science is the study of human movement and the body's response to exercise. It is an examination of systems, factors, and principles involved in human development within the context of society. Relevant fields in the study of exercise science include anatomy, physiology, biomechanics, motor learning and control, and sport psychology and sociology.

FOUNDATIONS OF
EXERCISE SCIENCE
STUDYING HUMAN MOVEMENT AND HEALTH

P. Klavora, PhD

Faculty of Physical Education and Health
University of Toronto

Sport Books Publisher

Design by My1 Designs and Maifith Design

National Library of Canada Cataloguing in Publication

Klavora, Peter
    **Foundations of exercise science : studying human movement and
health / Peter Klavora.**

Includes bibliographical references and index.
ISBN 0-920905-84-6

    1. Exercise--Physiological aspects. 2. Human mechanics. 3. Physical
education and training. I. Title.

QP301.K53 2004   612'.044   C2003-904023-2

Copyeditors: Gordon Leighton, Fred Unwalla, Patricia MacDonald
Proofreader: Patricia MacDonald

Distribution worldwide by
Sport Books Publisher
278 Robert Street
Toronto, ON M5S 2K8
Canada

http://www.sportbookspub.com
E-mail: sbp@sportbookspub.com
Fax: 416-966-9022

Printed in Canada

Dedication

To Tatjana, the most important person in my life.

Thank you for your continued encouragement and devotion.

Your love, trust, and constant inspiration make all the difference.

To all students I taught.

Your constant challenge in and out of class made me a better listener and teacher.

To all athletes I coached.

Coaching you made me realize that, in life, experience and research is far superior to scientific research alone.

P. K.

Contributing Authors

This book was written first and foremost with the student in mind. It was completed with the efforts of various present and former professors from the Faculty of Physical Education and Health at the University of Toronto, in collaboration with several graduate and undergraduate students in the same field of study. It was important that this book be user-friendly, and this collaborative effort among students and professors allowed this text to achieve a degree of accuracy and clarity, while remaining sensitive to the needs of students. Because the student writers had fresh experiences with the subject matter, and were still familiar with what it meant to be a young high school student with a keen desire to learn, their input was invaluable in the process of completing this text. All along during the preparation of this text, several teachers and students provided valuable feedback at various levels. The result is a book that makes expert knowledge about topics and issues in physical and health education available to students – an engaging and palatable resource for students and teachers alike.

 B. Akesson A. Anderson M-J. De Souza R. C. Goode P. Klavora T. Lam L. M. Leith

 M. Locke P. Maione M. Plyley U. Skonieczny P. Tiidus G. Wells I. Yim

Authors

Akesson, B., Prof. Emerita, Univ. of BC (2)
Anderson, A., PhD, OISE, Univ. of Toronto (1)
Klavora, P., PhD, Univ. of Toronto (3-10, 12-13, 15-18, 22-23)
Lam, T., BPHE, D.C., Univ. of Toronto (8, 13)
Leith, L. M., PhD, Univ. of Toronto (14, 19-20)
Locke, M., PhD, Univ. of Toronto (6, 9, 12)
Maione, P., BPHE, Univ. of Toronto (10-12, 17-18, 22-23)
Skonieczny, U., BPHE, Univ. of Toronto (15)
Tiidus, P., PhD, Wilfrid Laurier Univ. (21)
Tupling, S., PhD, Univ. of Toronto (7)
Wells, G., PhD, Univ. of Toronto (3-5)
Yim, I., BPHE, Univ. of Toronto (6, 10)

Contributors

De Souza, M-J., PhD, Univ. of Toronto (12)
Forsyth, B., BA, Univ. of Toronto (11)
Goode, R. C., PhD, Univ. of Toronto (9)
Plyley, M., PhD, Brock Univ. (3-5)

Academic Reviewers

De Souza, M-J., PhD, Univ. of Toronto (11-12)

Elliot, D., PhD, McMaster Univ. (16-18)
Goodman, J., PhD, Univ. of Toronto (9)
Lockwood, K., PhD, Brock Univ. (7)
Rogers, C., PhD, Univ. of Toronto (11, 13)
Su, J., M.D., Dip. Sport Med. (8)
Thomas, S., PhD, Univ. of Toronto (3-6)
Wolfe, E., PhD, OISE, Univ. of Toronto (7)

Teacher Reviewers

Boardman, S., South Carleton High School (7)
Childs, J., Grenville Christian College (2-7)
Da Ponte, M., Nantyr Shores Secondary School (6)
Harker, T., Harbord Collegiate (2-8)
Murray, R., Appleby College (1-7, 9-12)
Powles, J., Trinity College (1-23)
VanderZwaag, K., Woodland Christian High School (2-7)
Wakelin, R., Univ. of Toronto Schools (11-12)

Student Reviewers

Najemnikova, E., BPHE, Univ. of Toronto (2, 5-7)
Purushotham, D., Univ. of Toronto (1-7, 14-23)
Rolfe, D., BPHE, Univ. of Toronto (4, 9-12, 15)
Slatkovska, L., BPHE, Univ. of Toronto (1-3, 8, 13-23)

Preface

The road of life is long and winding, with obstacles confronting us at every turn. We never really know what awaits us around the next bend, but we learn valuable lessons along the way to help us cope with the hurdles that we inevitably encounter on our journey. Just like the in-line skaters on the cover of this book, you will travel a long road filled with ups and downs, highs and lows, thrills and disappointments, victories and defeats. Each of these experiences will teach you something different, contribute significantly to your knowledge base, and build upon your immense capacity to learn.

By the time we reach high school, many of us think we know all there is to know about life and the world in general. But although we have experienced a lot by the time we become teenagers, a lifetime of learning is still ahead of us. Learning is an ongoing process that never really ends – it begins the day we arc born and continues until we take our last breath – yet we often shut our minds to new ideas and different ways of viewing things. We encourage you to keep an open mind when reading this book and to explore the potential of new and different ideas that may enrich your life.

Although many roads have been paved ahead of us, we must discover and uncover new paths to follow in the pursuit of learning, knowledge, personal improvement, excitement, and self-fulfillment. And just as in-line skaters must be equipped with the proper gear – skates, helmets, and protective equipment – you need the right tools as you progress along life's path facing diverse challenges. Armed with knowledge and an open mind to learn, this book will teach you the foundations of human movement and in turn the science of physical and health education. It will enable you to confidently progress along the road of life.

PhysEddie

Follow me. Together we will explore the exciting world of exercise science....

Contents

Contributing Authors *vi*
Preface *vii*
Foreword *x*

CHAPTER 1
Introduction to Health and Wellness *1*

UNIT 1:
The Biological Basis of Human Movement **15**

CHAPTER 2
Human Anatomy: The Pieces of the Body Puzzle *17*

CHAPTER 3
Muscle Structure and Function *61*

CHAPTER 4
Muscles at Work *77*

CHAPTER 5
Energy for Muscular Activity *95*

CHAPTER 6
The Heart and Lungs at Work *109*

CHAPTER 7
How Do I Move? The Science of Biomechanics *129*

CHAPTER 8
Out of Harm's Way: Sport Injuries *169*

UNIT 2:
Human Performance **195**

CHAPTER 9
Physical Fitness *197*

CHAPTER 10
Evaluation in Physical and Health Education *231*

CHAPTER 11
The Nutritional Connection *261*

CHAPTER 12
Weight Management: Finding a Healthy Balance *295*

CHAPTER 13
Substance Use and Abuse
317

CHAPTER 14
The Mental Side of Human Performance *337*

UNIT 3:
Motor Development *361*

CHAPTER 15
Growth and Development
363

CHAPTER 17
Information Processing in Motor Learning *415*

CHAPTER 16
Movement Intelligence: A Vast Store of Skills *391*

CHAPTER 18
Motor Learning in Practice: Skill Acquisition *435*

UNIT 4:
Physical Activity and Sport in Society *461*

CHAPTER 19
Physical Activity and Sport Issues *463*

CHAPTER 21
Career Opportunities in PHE *523*

CHAPTER 20
Society, Culture, and Sport *489*

UNIT 5:
Beyond the Gym Class *535*

CHAPTER 22
Introduction to Research Methods *537*

CHAPTER 23
Introduction to Statistical Concepts *557*

References and Suggested Readings *575*
Key Words Index *580*
Credits *585*

Foreword

Imagine that you are sitting at home on a Saturday night and have just tuned in to the hockey game. What do you see? Mats Sundin skating at breakneck speed? Fancy footwork and a great move to elude a defensive player? A powerful slap shot that finds the top corner of the net? A triumphant waving of arms and sticks as players celebrate a goal? Perhaps you even notice the crowd cheering, the head coach appearing just a little more at ease, or the opposing team offering encouragement to their goalie.

The more you watch, the more you appreciate the remarkable amount of action that follows every goal that a player scores. While that may be obvious, something even more remarkable is perhaps less obvious. Although trophies, records, and titles may be the simple goals of any hockey player, what goes on inside an athlete such as Wayne Gretzky is much more complex and fascinating than meets the eye.

The mark of any champion may be found in his or her perseverance and dedication to training for excellence. Whether this means winning a medal, or struggling through adversity to reach an individual or team goal, victory comes with a price. Take NHL player Grant Marshall as an example. In 1990, he broke his neck in a junior game and was not expected to realize his dream of playing in the NHL. But Marshall defied the odds – and just helped the New Jersey Devils win the Stanley Cup. Most hockey fans are familiar with Gretzky's dedicated training regimen. As a young boy, he practiced shooting pucks in his backyard for hours every day. But how did this very basic exercise contribute to his outstanding ability on the ice? How did such simple drills maintain and improve his skill level throughout the crucial stages of growth and development?

And who can forget the courageous effort of Silken Laumann, who, after sustaining a serious leg injury just prior to the 1992 Olympics, showed the world that hard work and determination (and a lot of skill) can pay off. Not only did this Canadian rowing champion complete her race, she also succeeded in securing a bronze medal just months after the injury many thought would prevent her from even walking again and possibly crush her Olympic dream.

What was going on within Silken's body as she gracefully powered her boat through the water? How did she ensure that she had enough energy to last the entire length of the course? Are we all capable of that level of endurance, or did Laumann possess a unique supernatural trait? And where did she find the energy to pace herself for a race?

This raises a range of other questions – where did this energy come from? Was it derived from the food she ate? How did her body store and allocate energy to support long, tiring races and short sprints for the finish that require quick and powerful bursts of energy?

Successful performances also require some degree of muscular training. What muscles did Gretzky develop to make him a fast and aggressive skater? Do these muscles bear unusually large amounts of stress? Hockey players are particularly prone to knee and back injuries; what is it about the sport that makes its athletes so vulnerable? Do drugs or treatments exist that may prevent such mishaps?

And while we are on the topic of drugs, how do steroids and other substances influence athletic performance? Does an athlete's requirements for training change with drug use? What is the best way to train? It seems that Gretzky devoted his entire childhood to becoming arguably the best hockey player in the world. Could he have achieved the same results using a different training regimen?

Then again, maybe an athlete's ability has little to do with years of practice. Certain laws of physics can be applied to sport, so it may be that Laumann knew something about hydrodynamics that gave her a competitive advantage. Maybe she understood the proper technique required to maximize speed in the water while minimizing drag. After all, principles of biomechanics have

Known as "The Great One," Wayne Gretzky had fun as the whole world watched him become a household name in Canada and around the world. Born in Brantford, Ontario, in 1961, Wayne went on to dominate and re-write the NHL hockey record books. With four Stanley Cups, a career 1,016 goals, 2,223 assists, 3,239 points (including playoffs), and an Olympic gold medal as the executive director of the Canadian Olympic hockey team, Wayne Gretzky is a proven winner. He remains a true Canadian sports hero.

been used by sports scientists for many years in areas such as gymnastics, pole vaulting, and cycling.

In a league full of talented players, how did Gretzky manage to win so many face-offs? Was it remarkable reflexes that he was lucky enough to be born with, or did he have to develop this ability? If you analyze one of Gretzky's face-offs on tape, it appears as though he is actually moving before the referee drops the puck.

As an outstanding individual player, Gretzky's talents were not limited to his phenomenal physical skills: he was also a master of strategy. It is one thing to score the most goals in a season, but quite another to also lead the league in assists. Just imagine trying to set up your teammates for a goal every time you step out onto the ice. You must always be thinking one move ahead of the opposition in order to orchestrate a successful play. What went on in that brilliant mind that was always conscious of every player on the ice? Did Gretzky ever get nervous or lose his focus?

There must be days when athletes just don't feel like they can perform up to their potential. Every athlete is prone to such doubts over a career. But how was Laumann able to stay motivated to train and return to form for the Olympic Games after a devastating injury? What did it take to remain competitive year after year with the same focus and drive? How did Gretzky rise to the occasion in a big game, while others wilt under the pressure? With the salaries that many professionals are bringing in these days, the motivation to perform might be found in their back pockets.

When you review the number of games Gretzky played in a season, year after year, with different teams and different teammates, the questions arise: How did he stay "up" for every game? Did he ever relax and perform only marginally? What made the difference? And did Laumann have personality characteristics that allowed her to endure more pain than the average person? Rowing has one of the highest $\dot{V}O_2$max levels of any sport – top competitors must develop a high training capacity and also a high threshold of pain. Did this experience and years of training

help her endure and overcome a devastating injury that would have ended the career of most athletes?

What made the difference with these two athletes? These personality characteristics certainly helped both rise to stardom in their respective sports – time after time they excelled against the best competitors the world could offer. What made the difference? Was it because they could afford the best coaches, trainers, and equipment?

This brings up the issue of money. Where do astronomical sums of cash fit into the broader picture of sport? Do large salaries make players excessively greedy, to the point that they are willing to strike, risking the loss of an entire season of play? Does this change how the fans perceive players? Does this aspect detract from the beauty and tradition of sport by placing it in the hands of capitalism and big business?

And speaking of fans, how do we, as spectators, view sport, and how does it affect our lives? Every Canadian has certainly had some degree of exposure to hockey, rowing, and other sports. Increasingly, as women and minorities seek the opportunity to play, and citizens' coalitions band together to prevent televised violence, sport has become a focus of political and social issues.

As you can see, a single glimpse into the world of sport can generate discussion over a variety of subjects. And that, specifically, is the purpose of this textbook. The chapters that follow expose you to a variety of perspectives associated with physical and health education. You are most likely familiar with the sporting and physical activity aspects of PHE courses; however, this course is designed to provide a unique opportunity for students to apply sports-related ideas to associated areas including medicine, sociology, physics, and business.

With the expansion of your knowledge in this area, you should be motivated to strive for a higher quality of life through your own level of physical fitness. Rather than simply telling you that healthy living is desirable, we will show you why. For this reason, the following chapters are structured so that you have the opportunity to apply the knowledge you learn.

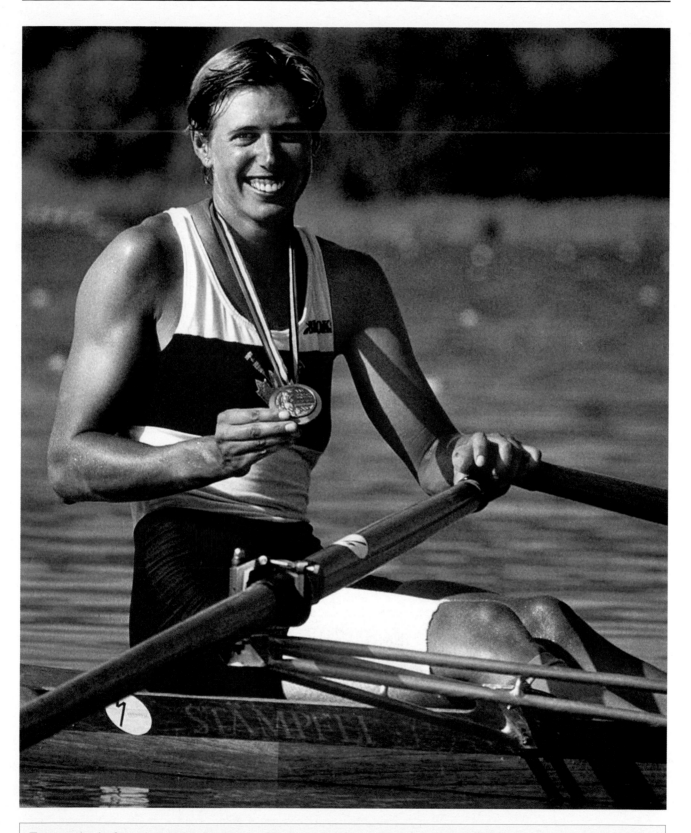

Ten weeks before the 1992 Olympics, Silken Laumann suffered a severe leg injury during training. She made a remarkable recovery and went on to win a bronze medal at those Games. She also won a bronze medal at the 1984 Olympics, a silver medal at the 1996 Olympics, and was a world champion in 1991. Silken Laumann is a model for many athletes: she believed in herself and refused to give up, triumphing in the end against all odds to become a household name in rowing in Canada and around the world.

In This Chapter:

Definitions and Dimensions *2*

Health and Wellness Is a Personal Journey *5*

Wellness Is Your Personal Responsibility *6*
    Family Influences *7*
    Media Influences *9*
    Social / Peer Influences *10*
    Cultural Influences *12*

Summary *13*

Introduction to Health and Wellness

After completing this chapter you should be able to:

- define health and its various dimensions;

- describe the factors influencing your personal health and wellness;

- discuss the value systems that affect decisions about your personal health and wellness;

- demonstrate an understanding that health is a personal responsibility and lifelong journey.

Health is an important resource for living, but it is very specific to people's lives.

To achieve good health it is important to personalize the information presented to make it relevant to your daily life. Throughout this chapter, and subsequent chapters, consider the ways health and wellness is expressed in your own life and the ways you set out to contribute to your health through, for example, physical activity, spending time with friends and family, enjoying time to contemplate the world around you, and challenging yourself to reach new heights.

Definitions and Dimensions

Health can be defined as "the capacity to lead a satisfying life, fulfill ambitions, and accommodate to change." This modern definition of health recognizes that health is a dynamic, ever-changing process of trying to achieve one's individual potential. There are six dimensions of health: physical, social, mental, emotional, spiritual, and environmental. These dimensions are interdependent but interact and overlap with each other to produce health.

Wellness, on the other hand, can be defined as the combination of health and happiness. It is the concept of achieving balance in one's mental, physical, emotional, social, environmental, and spiritual life.

Examine the health and wellness pie (Figure 1.1) to reflect on the various dimensions of health that are part of our lives. To help you reflect on each dimension of health from your own perspective consider the statements included in each section of the pie (Figure 1.1).

Physical health I have lots of energy and can get through the day without being overly tired. I find time to be vigorously active almost daily.

Social health I like to meet and interact with people. I am a good listener. I participate in a variety of social activities.

Emotional health I find it easy to laugh about things in my life. I take positive steps to cope with stress. I feel good about myself.

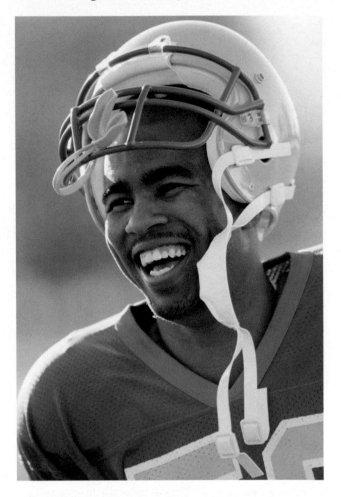

Environmental health I try to conserve natural resources. I believe it is important that everyone have opportunities to participate in physical activity pursuits regardless of culture, socioeconomic status, and race. Sport is a safe place to play (safe = free from discrimination, ridicule, and abuse).

Mental health I am ready to learn from life's challenges. I consider the alternatives and choices I have to live a healthy life.

Spiritual health I have hopes and dreams. I am passionate about a number of different things in my life and society. I take time to enjoy nature and the beauty around me. I take time to think about what is important in my life – who I am, what I value, where I fit in, and where I am going.

Discussions with young people about health often centre on not just individual health, but the quality of their relationships with varied environments. In other words, to what extent is the individual coping with the many interactions and transitions that are occurring in his or her life? Adolescence presents many new challenges:

- *An increase in autonomy and individual identity.* I am doing more on my own and I make more decisions about what I want to do;

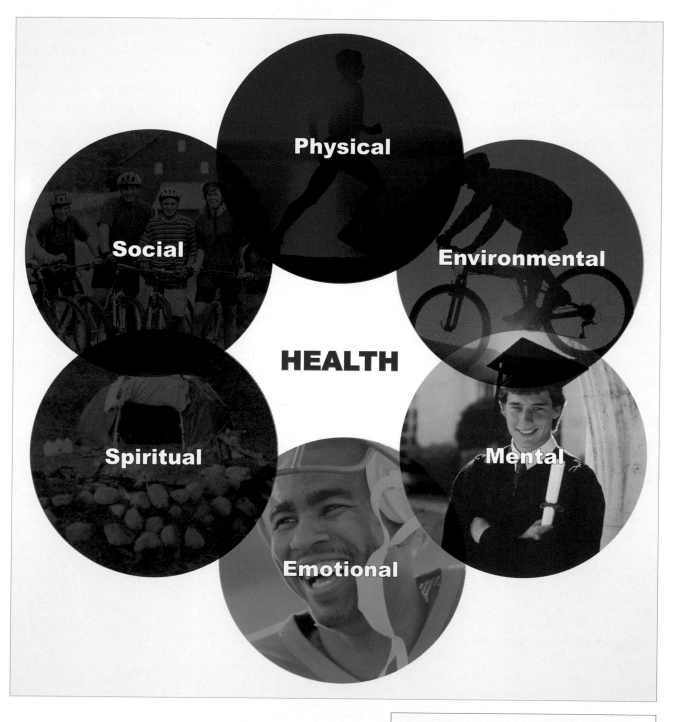

Figure 1.1 The health and wellness pie.

- *An increase in responsibilities.* I am more reliant on myself to accomplish what needs to be done;

- *An increase in industry.* I can participate in more challenging and sophisticated tasks at school and in work settings;

- *Intensification of relationships.* I am engaged in relationships with peers and intimate others that are emotionally, mentally, and physically more intense; and

- *Changes in body structure.* I will grow physiologically in ways that enable me to reach new levels of achievement and participation in a wide variety of experiences.

Dimensions of health that focus on adolescent transition might fall under the headings of being, belonging, and becoming (Figure 1.2).

Being Who am I? What do I stand for and believe in about myself and other people and things? Who am I becoming as a person?

Belonging To what organizations and groups (school, ski club, drama club, choir, etc.) do I connect with and feel a sense of belonging and affection?

Becoming Achieving personal goals, hopes, and aspirations. What accomplishments am I striving for? What goals have I set for myself? ("practical becoming" – work, school, volunteering; "leisure becoming" – activities that promote relaxation and stress reduction; "growth becoming" – activities that promote knowledge growth and skills that enable me to adapt to change).

These transitions are exciting opportunities for self-expression, leadership, and citizenship. It is important that we think of health as emerging new opportunities to participate in shaping the future and in the growth of society. Health should be understood holistically, i.e., in terms linked to the individual's capacity to interact positively with his or her physical and social environment and not simply the absence of disease. Health is related to the quality of one's life, i.e., the degree to which a person enjoys the important possibilities in his or her life. It is the recognition that health is directly related to people's ability to cope with the challenge of change in varied situations that led to the World Health Organization's definition of health as the "capacity to lead a satisfying life, fulfill ambitions, and accommodate to change."

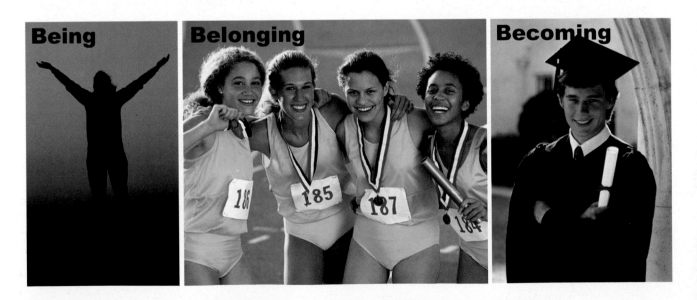

Figure 1.2 The adolescent transition focuses on being, belonging, and becoming.

Health and Wellness Is a Personal Journey

Health and wellness encompasses a lifestyle that includes the joys of physical activity as an integral part of daily living (Figure 1.3). Although we

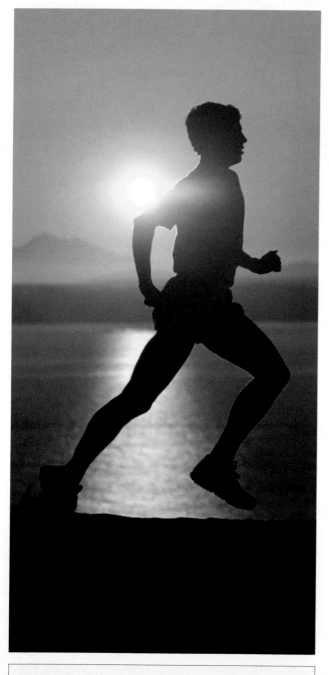

Figure 1.3 Integrating physical activity into your daily life is essential for optimal health and wellness.

ultimately make the decisions about our own health and how we choose to live our lives, these choices are not made in isolation from the environments in which we live. Numerous factors that have a strong impact on our outlook on health include family influences, the media, culture, or society. It is this perspective on health that will largely guide our lifestyle habits and behaviours throughout our lives. But the achievement of health is not a single event; attaining and maintaining health and wellness is an ongoing process, and indeed, a resource for everyday life.

Making healthy choices such as participating in regular physical activity, avoiding smoking, developing healthy relationships, and following good nutritional advice are all important guidelines to consider. But it is equally important to remember that these are simply guidelines, and it is up to you to find out what combination of factors creates a healthy balance for you. Moderation is a word many professionals like to use when talking about health; whether referring to nutrition or exercise, too much (or too little) of anything is a potential problem. From the average citizen to the most successful athlete, we must all find this balance in our lives to achieve optimal health. Consider the two personal stories in the box on the next page.

Chris' views about health might be considered a little old-fashioned – if you're not sick, why worry about your health. This view is what health professionals refer to as a *reactive* or *curative* approach to health. In other words, as long as you don't have some disease or illness, you can be considered relatively healthy. When you do get sick, seek a cure specifically for the illness. Chris would probably argue that Erin's efforts to live a healthy life haven't done much good because they both get sick despite their very different health habits. On the surface, both Chris and Erin appear to enjoy the same level of health; but according to more modern versions of health, Erin has adopted lifestyle habits that, in the long run, will enable Erin to do more than avoid and recover from illness. Erin is taking what health professionals call a *proactive* approach to healthy living. Erin is asserting much more control over how she leads her life. Although Chris' attitude towards life appears to be care-free and fun-loving (that is, free from responsibility for health care), in reality it is Erin's life choices that are enabling her to be free to live a life that is referred to as wellness.

Wellness Is Your Personal Responsibility

Wellness encompasses elements of a person's life that extend beyond his or her micro-biological or medical condition. Wellness is reflected in the way a person chooses to live his or her life. Wellness is therefore dependent on the individual's capacity

Two Views on Health

Chris is an avid snowboarder. Most evenings and weekends throughout the winter months, Chris can be found hanging out on the hills with friends, trying out new tricks. Although snowboarding is a mentally and physically challenging activity, Chris' overall lifestyle habits are less beneficial. Because many of his friends smoke, Chris has also become a smoker. Most mornings, Chris avoids breakfast and snacks throughout the day on fries, soft drinks, candy bars, and coffee. Late nights, excessive smoking, and poor nutrition have, on more than one occasion, left Chris so fatigued that his attendance at school and assignment completion have suffered. Most winters Chris gets a cold, and just this last winter, suffered through a bout of the flu. Chris' philosophy on health is: "If you're sick, take a few pills; otherwise, have fun and enjoy yourself! I'll quit smoking later. For now, it's something me and my friends enjoy doing together; besides, it's

more fun doing stuff with them than it is doing homework."

Erin is also a dedicated snowboarder. Like Chris, Erin works hard to perfect new moves and enjoys the physical and mental challenges of snowboarding. Erin also weight trains two or three times a week at a local fitness centre, and works out on the StairMaster three times a week. Although many of her friends smoke, and have at some point or another tried to persuade her to smoke, Erin has made a conscious decision not to start. Erin is careful to eat a variety of fresh fruits and vegetables on a regular basis. Fries and soft drinks are an occasional substitute for what Erin refers to as a "power meal – pasta, low-fat meats, veggies, and juice – a meal that gives me energy and will build my strength and stamina."

Like Chris, Erin usually gets a cold at least once a winter, and also suffered from the flu this past season. Erin's philosophy on health is: "I'm building for the future. What I do for my body today lays the foundation for a lifetime of involvement in healthy activities." Erin would prefer to be out on the hills than in school, but admits school is okay: "I get to be with my friends, and the teachers aren't bad. I even like some of the stuff we have to learn, especially in physical and health education."

to interact effectively with his or her environment, and to build and maintain physical, mental, social, and spiritual well-being throughout his or her life span. Wellness involves having a deep understanding of what it means to care for oneself in relation to others, and one's environment. In short, wellness is making informed choices and taking responsibility for the way we live our lives. Thinking back to Chris and Erin, Erin was able not only to make conscious decisions about how to live a smoke-free life, but was also able to deal with pressures coming from friends and the media to start smoking. Erin is deliberately working towards certain goals and ambitions. Her value system guides the decisions that are made about her individual living habits. The way Erin behaves shows her dedication to following a personal wellness plan.

Not everyone has a clear sense of what it means to be healthy and how to achieve wellness. This confusion is partly influenced by our families, the media, our peers, and the culture in which we live. A closer look at the influence these factors have on health and wellness will help us understand more about the lifestyle choices we make.

Family Influences

Our parents teach us a great deal about health and wellness. A simple example is the advice our parents give us to stay healthy: "Wear a coat outside or you'll catch a cold." Traditional family attitudes and actions send strong messages about health, well-being, and a general sense of life satisfaction (Figure 1.4). Families that value physical activity, for example, introduce their children to sports, games, and recreational pursuits that they enjoy at an early age. Most young people today get their start in dance, hockey, tennis, volleyball, skiing, and swimming because of their parents' interests/

Figure 1.4 Positive family attitudes and actions send strong messages to children about the value of physical activity at an early age.

attitudes and enthusiasm for these same activities (Figure 1.5).

Although many children express an interest in an activity because of prominent role models, it will be the parents' willingness to support their children's physical pursuits that will enable optimal development to occur. Tiger Woods is a prime example of how parental encouragement, guidance, and the willingness to support the development of high-performance skills have resulted in the emergence of a great champion. Countless households throughout the world devote time and money into giving their children the opportunity to experience the joy of participation. However, only an extremely small percentage go on to play their sport of choice at the professional level.

Supportive parents see participation in physical activity as an opportunity to develop more than epidemiological health. They see opportunities for their children to develop self-esteem, self-confidence, skill potential, perseverance, humility, friendship skills, teamwork, respect for others, dedication to goals, communication skills, and to share good times with others. Physical activity is embedded in a more holistic perspective on health. In other words, health is the capacity of the individual to interact with his or her environment, and to work towards fulfilling his or her potential.

Alternatively, families that push their children to compete for rewards outside of the physical, mental, social, and spiritual benefits of activity cause their children to withdraw prematurely from participating in, and gaining benefits from, sport and physical activity. Physical activity for the sake of activity, and for the sake of living a more energetic and satisfying life, is what engaging in physical activity and wellness is all about.

Figure 1.5 Parents introduce children to sports, games, and recreational pursuits.

Media Influences

The media has "hyped," commercialized, and distorted interpretations of what it means to be an accomplished performer, and what is to be expected from participating in sport and other physical pursuits. Sports coverage in the media has sensationalized many sports and sporting events, making athletes celebrities, role models, and international heroes (Figure 1.6). Unfortunately, sports coverage has also converted the pursuit of athletic excellence into a marketplace for the sale of clothing, beverages, training equipment, and personal health-care products. One of the greatest distortions that has emerged as a result of the commercialization of sport has been body image (Figure 1.7). Stereotypical versions of

the ideal body shape and size have resulted in drug abuse, eating disorders, and a host of other mental and physical problems. The countless hours of training, conditioning, and coaching are downplayed by advertisers who suggest that there are shortcuts to success or, at least, the "look" of success.

The pursuit of health and wellness has nothing to do with the style of clothing you wear, the shampoo you use, or whether or not you have "buns of steel." Wellness is more about finding out who you are. Wellness is about the journey towards personal improvement and aspiring to achieve your individual potential. Media coverage would have us believe that the pinnacle of achievement comes from beating the competition, being the toughest, and gaining

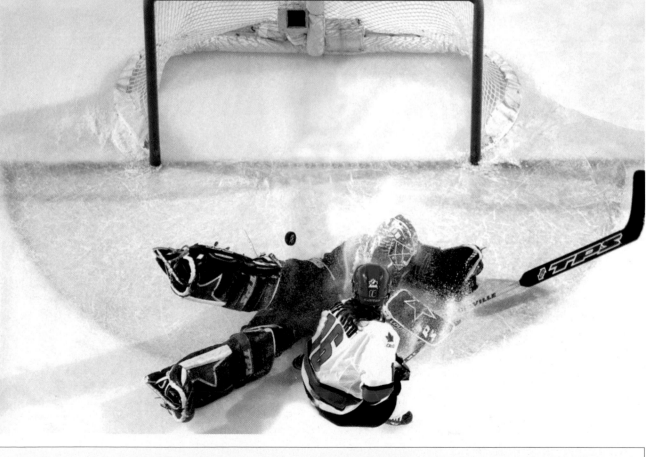

Figure 1.6 Jayna Hefford's winning goal in the women's gold medal game at the Salt Lake City Olympics represents positive media influence.

Figure 1.7 Computer-generated images of models are negative media influences.

multi-million dollar contracts to play a sport while advertising corporate products. Why then do so many high-performance athletes have substance abuse problems and dysfunctional relationships, and suffer a number of other social and mental disorders such as depression, excessive aggression, and feelings of alienation and loneliness? Wellness is about achieving a balance in one's life, a balance among the mental, physical, social, emotional, and spiritual elements of your life.

Erin made a decision to pursue an interest in snowboarding according to her rules and values, not someone else's. Someday Chris will also have to examine what beliefs and values will guide his life. Images of the sporting life can undoubtedly be motivational. But how these images and commercial products are consumed must ultimately be judged by each individual in relation to his or her personal goals and values.

Social / Peer Influences

Choose your friends wisely (Figure 1.8). Chris' friends turned Chris on to snowboarding, but also persuaded him to adopt some lifestyle habits that are problematic. Erin's friends were also trying to convince Erin to smoke, but Erin's resistance skills and strong convictions to training and healthy

Figure 1.8 Negative social influences.

living habits prevented Erin from taking the first puff of that cigarette.

Many people decide to become active participants in sport and recreational pursuits because of the social benefits incurred in meeting new people, and in spending time with old friends (Figure 1.9). Social interaction is one of the most compelling reasons for committing to an active lifestyle. It is therefore important that we seek to establish and maintain these social networks, and to foster related healthy activities within these communities. Those committed to healthy active living will have opportunities throughout their lives to engage in a variety of active challenges with people of all ages, backgrounds, and levels of ability. Sport and recreational pursuits are a common language. It is not unrealistic for a person to play tennis with a person who is from another country, who is older or younger than him/herself, who is from a different culture, or who may have a physical or mental disability. Participation in sport, recreation, and leisure pursuits can be a common experience shared among all people.

Figure 1.9 Positive social influences.

Cultural Influences

Views about health have evolved over time, and are understood differently across cultures. North Americans tend to think about disease from a scientific point of view. Disease is more likely to be understood as a biological, neurological, or emotional imbalance or deficiency. Much of the medical research conducted in Western societies has traditionally dealt with the treatment of organs (heart, lungs, skin, kidneys) and systems (digestive, respiratory, immune, skeletal, and nervous) and the diseases that affect them (heart disease, cancer, arthritis, AIDS), in isolation from each other, and from the person and the environment in which they live and work (Figure 1.10). Increasingly, a more holistic approach to the study of health and health care is emerging.

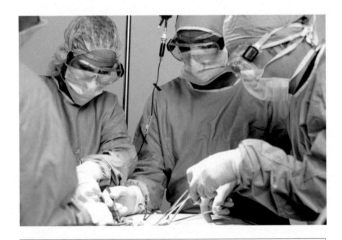

Figure 1.10 In Western culture, medicine deals largely with the treatment of organs.

Holistic approaches to health recognize the importance of personality; whether you are extroverted, assertive, and energetic, or passive, calm, quiet, and introverted; whether your job or school work is meaningful and productive, or demoralizing and unrewarding; and whether you live in a poverty stricken and racist community, or have the opportunity to live your life with dignity and respect. Remember, the World Health Organization's definition of health is the "capacity to lead a satisfying life, fulfill ambitions,

and accommodate to change." Contemporary concerns about health must go deeper and broader than body chemistry and cell activity to include social, economic, and educational opportunities to live a healthy life.

We do not live in a vacuum. Whether people have access to affordable and safe opportunities to be active may be a key determinant of health. In other words, high rates of obesity may be due to the fact that it is more difficult to be active in neighbourhoods and schools than ever before. How easy is it to fit activity into a crowded schedule? How expensive is it to join an exercise facility? Do students have opportunities to enrol in health and physical education programs or are they crowded out with compulsory requirements?

In Eastern and many aboriginal cultures, health has a strong spiritual quality. Disease is often understood in terms of the individual's spiritual harmony with oneself and/or his or her environment. Different systems are at work. In the oriental culture, they speak of chi, which refers to the flow of energy within the body. Different stimulations on various parts of the body can overcome specific blockages to a person's chi. The individual is also expected to play an active role in his or her healing process. Tai Chi, yoga exercises, meditation, and acupuncture are common and often effective ways to energize the body, refresh

Figure 1.11 Aboriginal sweat lodges represent places of spiritual awakening.

the mind, and overcome certain illnesses. Other cultures chant, take herbal tonics and remedies, and participate in special prayers to prevent and alleviate the symptoms of illness. Aboriginal cultures in Canada also have formalized methods of healing. The sweat lodge has for centuries been a place of spiritual awakening and vision (Figure 1.11). The medicine wheel symbolizes the need for a strong spiritual connection to the earth and to heaven.

Beliefs about health are a powerful part of each person's heritage. It is only fitting that our multicultural society finds ways to respect the beliefs and practices of others. Perhaps as the cultures mingle, we will create hybrid versions of health and healing, and discover new ways for us to participate actively in achieving and maintaining our health.

Summary

Health is multidimensional. Like Chris and Erin you must be prepared to make informed decisions that relate to all the various dimensions of health. Where and from whom you get your information will influence how you choose to live. As you explore the various aspects of physical and health education, consider the social and cultural underpinnings that affect perspectives and decisions about health. Look for the origins of your value systems – family, friends, the media, and the society (economic, geographic, ethnic, and racial) in which you live. The journey towards health is a lifelong adventure. The knowledge, skills, and values you build today will help you make important judgements along the way.

Key Words

Becoming	Environmental health	Social health
Being	Health	Spiritual health
Belonging	Mental health	Wellness
Emotional health	Physical health	

Discussion Questions

1. What health problems do you predict Chris will face in the future?

2. What has guided Erin's decisions to be smoke free, eat well, etc.?

3. What kinds of supports from family, friends, and the community are needed to adopt a healthy lifestyle?

4. How does culture influence views on what it means to be healthy and to take care of your health?

5. What do you do if your friends have poor health habits?

6. Many people think healthy living means giving up a lot of things (giving up high-calorie foods, giving up spare time for workouts, giving up smoking and drugs). What does living a healthy lifestyle enable you to *do*?

A Career in Kinesiology/ Personal Training

NAME: Matt Galbraith
OCCUPATION: Kinesiologist/Personal Trainer
EDUCATION: Human Kinetics and a minor in Nutritional Sciences, University of Guelph

What do you do?

Human kinetics is concerned with understanding capacities for, and limits of, human movement at different ages. It also encompasses the role of physical activity in human health. In addition to my university education, I also completed the necessary national certifications needed to legally prescribe exercises as a personal trainer. In the fall of 2002 I started my own personal training business called ProActive Health Solutions. As a kinesiologist/personal trainer, I design, develop, and monitor exercise, rehabilitation, and specific conditioning programs for individual clients interested in improving fitness, health, physique, or performance. In particular, I clearly instruct clients on the development of correct technique and breathing patterns during all phases of an exercise movement. It is the job of a personal trainer to maximize the efficiency and safety of every workout.

What is unique about your job?

Personal training is a very unique and flexible occupation. Exercise venues are variable and can include commercial fitness centres, the client's home, private personal training studios, and medical and wellness centres, as well as sporting arenas, outdoor parks, practice fields, and aquatic environments, such as community pools. It is a profession that enables me to utilize my education in the development of effective exercise prescriptions, while also providing me with the opportunity to interact socially, instructing and motivating a wide variety of interesting clients.

What was your motivation for pursuing this field?

When deciding on post-secondary education, I selected a university program that reflected my interests, which included athletics and physical fitness. While studying at the University of Guelph, I started personal training on a part-time basis at a local physiotherapy clinic and was also involved in teaching an introductory weight training class. I found the flexibility and the numerous everyday challenges accompanying a career in personal training enjoyable. After completing my degree I decided to further pursue this rewarding occupation.

How competitive is the field?

Personal training has rapidly become a serious profession, with its image growing impressively as a result of the publicity surrounding the trainers of the rich, famous, and glamorous. Many graduates of physical education and allied courses aspire to make personal training a career, but often end up disillusioned when they discover that simply having a university degree does not translate into immediate success. The personal training field is extremely competitive and although education is the cornerstone of a good trainer, profitability may rely on being able to market and manage a business better than the competition. In addition, an impressive academic background is only useful if the trainer is able to clearly communicate that knowledge to the client.

What career advice would you give to students interested in this area?

Any students aspiring to become a kinesiologist/ personal trainer should enroll in a post-secondary program majoring in kinesiology or exercise science. An interest in physical fitness and health is essential; however, one should also have an aptitude for science, especially anatomy and physiology. It is also highly recommended that an interested student start gaining practical experience through volunteering or part-time work. This allows the student to become familiar with the occupation and understand how the education is applicable. It is also important for anyone interested in a fitness profession to keep fit and in good condition with regular training, as personal trainers act as role models for healthy living.

What other career options are available to students interested in this area?

Other career options available to students interested in this area include leading aerobics or group exercise sessions, athletic therapy, biomechanics, ergonomics, cardiopulmonary rehabilitation, exercise physiology, physical/occupational therapy, and strength and conditioning instruction. These careers cover a wide range of physical education fields, from achieving and maintaining health and fitness, to safety and injury prevention, and finally to care and rehabilitation for individuals with injuries or various health conditions.

The Biological Basis of Human Movement

- **Human Anatomy: The Pieces of the Body Puzzle**

- **Muscle Structure and Function**

- **Muscles at Work**

- **Energy for Muscular Activity**

- **The Heart and Lungs at Work**

- **How Do I Move? The Science of Biomechanics**

- **Out of Harm's Way: Sport Injuries**

In This Chapter:

Terms and Concepts Worth Knowing 19
  Anatomical Position *19*
  Directional Terms *19*
  Planes of the Body *19*
  Joint Movements *20*

The Musculoskeletal System 23

Bones of the Human Body 24
  Bone Shape *24*
  Bone Classification *24*
  Bone Composition *25*
  Effect of Fitness on Bone *25*
  The Human Skeleton *25*

Joints of the Human Body 32
  Classification of Joints *32*
  Joints of the Pectoral Girdle *36*
  Joints of the Upper Limb *37*
  Joints of the Pelvic Girdle *38*
  Joints of the Lower Limb *39*

Muscles of the Human Body 42
  Muscles of the Face *42*
  Muscles of the Neck and Back *43*
  Muscles Connecting the Humerus and
    Scapula to the Axial Skeleton *46*
  Muscles of the Arm *48*
  Muscles of the Forearm *49*
  Muscles of the Hand *49*
  Muscles of the Pelvic Girdle *50*
  Muscles of the Thigh *51*
  Muscles of the Leg *52*
  Muscles of the Foot *54*
  Muscles of the Abdomen *54*

Summary 58

CHAPTER 2

Human Anatomy: The Pieces of the Body Puzzle

After completing this chapter you should be able to:

- demonstrate an understanding of the basis for anatomical description and analysis;

- use correct anatomical terminology when describing the human body and performance;

- describe the various parts of the skeletal and muscular systems and the ways in which they relate to human performance;

- demonstrate an understanding of the organization and complexity of human anatomy.

The human body has fascinated the human mind for centuries. What enables us to run, jump, and throw? How are we able to move our fingers with such remarkable dexterity? What are the structures that allow us to perform the myriad of tasks we do? The study of the structures that make up the human body, and how those structures relate to each other, is called **human anatomy**. Questions concerning human anatomy continue to capture the curiosity of human beings world-wide, because it is a subject that binds all humans together. An understanding of how our bodies are structured to perform is important if we are to gain our full potential, especially in the world of sport and physical activity.

It is important to realize that structure often determines function; the structures of the human body are well-designed for efficient movement. You have probably marvelled at the strength of the human skeleton that is able to withstand great impact and stress, not to mention its light weight that allows movements to be swift and active. The human body is undoubtedly a strong, flexible, well-oiled machine, able to move and perform with astonishing efficiency (Figure 2.1). But what structures allow some power lifters to lift weights two or three times their own body weight? How does Donovan Bailey run a distance of 100 metres under 10 seconds?

In fact, how are we able to stand upright and move against gravity and other forces? The science of anatomy attempts to shed light on these and other questions, as well as to provide answers based on the complex and intricate structure of the human body.

Many systems make up the human body. Some of them are the respiratory, urogenital, cardiovascular, nervous, endocrine, digestive, and musculoskeletal. The cardiovascular and nervous systems are essential to the musculoskeletal system and are presented in Chapters 6 and 17, respectively. In this chapter we will deal with the musculoskeletal system.

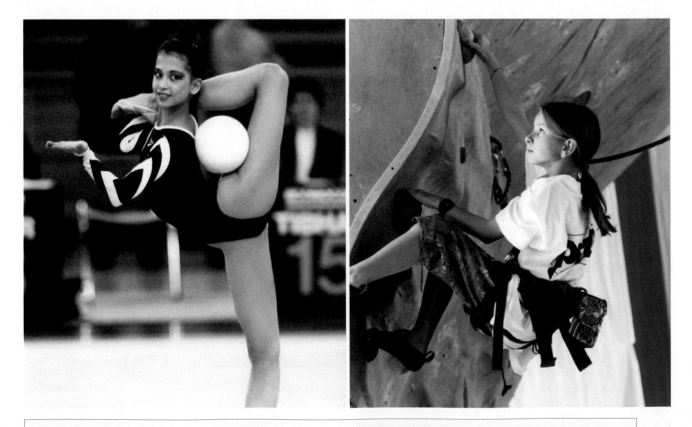

Figure 2.1 The human body is capable of moving gracefully and performing very challenging tasks.

Terms and Concepts Worth Knowing

In order to describe anatomy with clarity, there is a certain language or terminology to be learned. The language of anatomy may be difficult to grasp at first because it is largely unfamiliar to you; but once you gain a general understanding of the word roots, suffixes, and prefixes commonly used in anatomy, the terminology will become increasingly meaningful. For example, if you know that *myo* refers to muscle and that *cardio* pertains to the heart, you can reach the conclusion that *myocardium* refers to the muscle of the heart. The knowledge of some basic terms and concepts is invaluable to improving your understanding of anatomy.

Anatomical Position

Of particular importance to studying anatomy is the basic **anatomical position**. It is used in all anatomical description, specifying the locations of specific parts of the body relative to other body parts; it can best be learned by you, the student, in the following position: standing erect, facing forward, arms hanging at the sides with palms facing forward, legs straight, and heels and feet together and parallel to each other. The anatomical position is universally accepted as the starting reference point for describing the human body (Figure 2.2).

Directional Terms

In the anatomical position, your nose is **medial** to your eyes, your ears are **lateral** to your cheeks, your skin lies **superficial** to your muscles, your heart is **deep** to your ribcage, your lips are **anterior (ventral)**

Front to Back

The terms "ventral" and "dorsal" were used originally to describe positions in four-legged animals. In bipedal humans (two-legged animals such as ourselves) the terms "anterior" and "posterior" are used. However, the terminology "ventral" and "dorsal" may appear in some texts.

to your teeth, your back is **posterior (dorsal)** to your abdomen, and your lips are **superior** to your chin. Also, the hands are **distal** to the arms, and the arms are **proximal** to the hands. The terms proximal and distal are also used to describe nerves and blood vessels, proximal meaning "toward the origin" and distal meaning "away from the origin." A person lying on his back is **supine** and when lying face down is said to be in a **prone** position (e.g., when preparing to perform a push-up).

Each of the terms described here indicates the location of a body part or position in relation to another part of the body, giving a clear indication of where body parts may be found. If you want to locate the abdomen, for example, you would say, "The abdomen is **inferior** to the thorax," rather than saying, "The abdomen is below the thorax." It is important to note, however, that directional terms are based on the assumption that the body is in the anatomical position (Figure 2.2).

Planes of the body

In addition to directional terms, there are certain planes (imaginary flat surfaces) that need to be defined and understood,

Figure 2.2 The anatomical position.

Directional Terms

Superior – *Nearer to the head*
The head is superior to the thorax.

Inferior – *Nearer to the feet*
The stomach is inferior to the heart.

Anterior (Ventral) – *Nearer to the front*
The quadriceps are anterior to the hamstrings.

Posterior (Dorsal) – *Nearer to the back*
The hamstrings are posterior to the quadriceps.

Superficial – *Nearer to the surface of the body*
The skin is more superficial than muscle.

Deep – *Farther from the surface of the body*
The heart lies deep to the ribs.

Medial – *Nearer to the median plane*
The nose is medial to the eyes.

Lateral – *Farther from the median plane*
The eyes are lateral to the nose.

Distal – *Farther from the trunk*
The hands are distal to the arms.

Proximal – *Nearer to the trunk*
The arms are proximal to the hands.

which divide the body for further identification of particular areas. These terms always refer to the body in the anatomical position. For an individual standing in the anatomical position, the point at which the median, frontal, and transverse planes intersect represents the body's centre of gravity (centre of mass).

The **median plane** or **midsagittal plane** is a vertical plane that bisects the body into right and left halves; the **sagittal plane** is any plane parallel to the median plane; the **frontal plane** or **coronal plane** is any vertical plane at right angles to the median plane; and the **transverse plane** or **horizontal plane** is any plane at right angles to both the median and frontal planes (Figure 2.3).

These planes can also be used to describe different movements or actions, being described as sagittal, frontal, or transverse plane movements when they occur in a plane that is parallel to one of these planes. For example, a forward roll would be considered a **sagittal plane movement** because the forward and backward motion is parallel to the sagittal plane. Other sagittal plane movements include cycling and running. Similarly, movements that are lateral, or side-to-side in nature, can be described as **frontal plane movements**; some good examples are cartwheels, jumping jacks, and side-stepping. Can you think of any activities that would be considered **transverse plane movements**? How about a twist performed by a

diver, or a pirouette in ballet?

Although many movements do not occur in any one plane, large movements and movements that occur at joints can often be described as being sagittal, frontal, or transverse plane movements; therefore, these reference planes still remain useful for describing human movement.

Joint Movements

Most movements are often found in pairs: for every movement, there is generally a movement that is opposite to it. There are exceptions, but the following descriptions apply to most joints and are illustrated in Figure 2.4.

Flexion–Extension

This usually occurs in a sagittal plane. In general, **flexion** reduces the angle between two bones at a joint and **extension** increases it. Consider the elbow joint when a biceps curl is performed. Lifting the weight requires flexion (reducing the angle at the joint), while lowering the weight involves extension (increasing the angle at the joint). These terms are modified in certain actions, for example, at the ankle joint, where the terms *dorsiflexion* (motion bringing the top of the foot toward the lower leg or shin) and *plantar flexion* ("planting" the foot) are used.

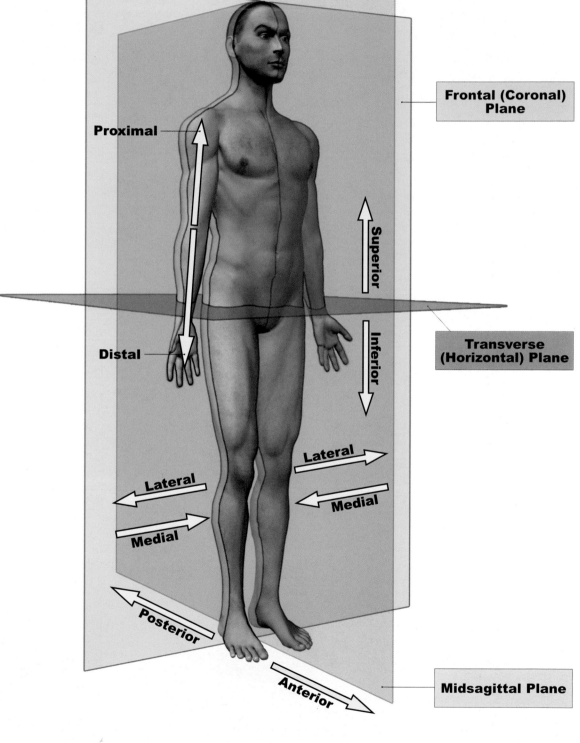

Figure 2.3 Anatomical position, directional terms, and planes of the body.

Flexion

Extension

Abduction

Adduction

Circumduction

Rotation

Pronation

Supination

Inversion

Eversion

Dorsiflexion

Plantar Flexion

Figure 2.4 Major body movements around joints.

Abduction–Adduction

In general, **abduction** is movement away from the midline of the body and **adduction** is movement toward the midline of the body in the frontal plane. The motions of the arms and legs during a jumping jack are examples of these two types of movements.

Circumduction

When flexion–extension movements are combined with abduction–adduction movements, a cone of movement occurs, but does not include any rotation. Tracing an imaginary circle in the air with your index finger while the rest of the hand remains stationary produces **circumduction**. The tip of your finger represents the base of the cone, while your knuckle forms the apex of this conical motion. This movement can occur at other moving body segments such as the hip and shoulder.

Rotation

A bone may also rotate along its longitudinal axis. To illustrate this action, flex your right elbow, place your left hand on your right shoulder and now rotate your right arm so that your hand is carried towards your abdomen. This movement toward the median plane is called **medial** or **internal rotation**. When you rotate your arm back to the original position or out laterally, this is called **lateral** or **external rotation**.

Pronation–Supination

This movement is used to describe movements relative to the forearm and hand. When the palm is moved to face anteriorly, this is **supination** (you can hold a bowl of soup); when the palm is moved to face posteriorly, it is **pronation**. These actions are required when turning a door knob, opening a jar, or performing a topspin shot in tennis.

Inversion–Eversion

This movement is relative to the sole of the foot. When the sole is turned inward (as when you "go over" on your ankle) it is inverted: this movement is called **inversion**. Injuries are common at the ankle joint, occurring when the joint is severely inverted beyond its normal range of motion. When the sole is turned outward or away from the median plane of the body, it is everted: this movement is called **eversion**.

Dorsiflexion–Plantar Flexion

The movement of the ankle so that the dorsal surface of the foot moves superiorly is called **dorsiflexion**. It is the opposite of **plantar flexion** that draws the foot inferiorly in the anatomical position. These actions occur when standing on the toes or using the pedals of a car while driving.

The Musculoskeletal System

The musculoskeletal system is composed of three distinct yet interdependent components: the bones, the joints, and the muscles. While each provides its own unique contribution, it is the interaction of these systems that allows human movement to occur. The bones form a rigid skeletal framework with numerous joints that can be moved as a result of the forces produced by the attaching muscles. As the muscles pull against the bones, the bones act as levers that can produce diverse movements in all directions. These three major components work together to make the human body strong, efficient, and capable of moving with grace.

Bones of the Human Body

The bones of the human body provide the supporting framework and protection for the vital organs of the body – living tissue complete with blood supply and nerves. Remember how painful it is to hit your shin on something firm and sharp?

Bone Shape

Bone can be classified by shape as short (e.g., bones of the wrist and ankle) that serve as good shock absorbers, long (like the femur of the thigh and the humerus of the upper arm) with proximal and distal enlargements, flat (like the bones of the skull and scapula) that largely protect underlying organs and provide areas for muscle attachment, irregular (like the bones of your face and vertebrae) that fulfil special functions, and sesamoid (shaped like a pea and found in tendons). The structures and shapes of the bones of the human body allow them to perform specific functions more effectively (Table 2.1).

Bone Classification

The amount of mineral content in bone varies with one's age, but also with the specific bone in the body. Bones that are more porous have a smaller proportion of calcium phosphate and carbonate, and greater non-mineralized tissue. According to the degree of porosity, bone can be classified into two general categories. Bone that has low porosity is called cortical bone (Figure 2.5). It is less flexible and can resist greater stress. In contrast, spongy or cancellous bone has a relatively high porosity with more non-mineralized tissue. Spongy bone

Table 2.1 Bone classifications.

Shape	Examples	Skeleton
Long	Femur, tibia, fibula, humerus, radius, ulna, metatarsals, metacarpals, phalanges	Appendicular
Short	Carpals, tarsals	Appendicular
Flat	Scapula Clavicle Ribs, sternum Frontal, parietal, occipital, mandible	Appendicular Appendicular Axial Axial
Sesamoid	Patella	Appendicular
Irregular	Facial bones of skull, vertebrae Pelvis	Axial Appendicular

has a characteristic honeycomb structure, and provides more flexibility. Cortical bone is largely found in long bones (such as the bones of the arms and legs) that are required to be stronger to resist greater stress, while spongy bone is found where shock absorption and a better ability to change shape are important (e.g., vertebrae). Typically, long bones have a marrow cavity filled with red marrow in children and yellow marrow in adults.

Bone Composition

Bone is very strong for its relatively light weight. What gives bone this important characteristic? The major components of bone are calcium carbonate, calcium phosphate, collagen, and water. The two calcium compounds make up approximately 60-70 percent of bone weight, providing much of the bone's stiffness and resistance to pressing or squeezing forces. The collagen component (a protein) gives bone its characteristic flexibility,

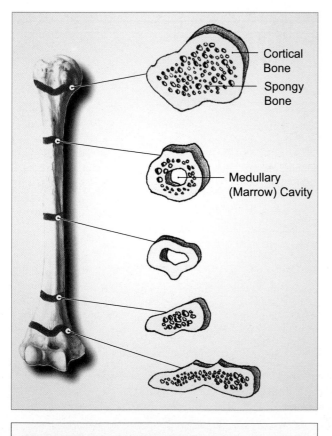

Figure 2.5 Transverse sections of the humerus, a long bone of the upper limb.

and contributes to its ability to resist pulling and stretching forces. The bones of children are significantly more pliable than those of adults. With aging, collagen is lost progressively and bone becomes more brittle. Although the human body as a whole is composed of about 60 percent water, bone only contains approximately 20 percent water (20-25 percent of total bone weight). Consequently, bones are stronger and more durable than many other structures, such as skin.

Effect of Fitness on Bone

Similar to muscles, bone also responds to the presence or absence of different forces with changes in size, shape, and density. When bones are subjected to regular physical activity and habitual loads, bones tend to become denser and more mineralized than the bones in people who are less active. This is revealed by the right-handed tennis player whose right forearm bones are denser than the left, as a result of using them more frequently. Similar changes can be found in throwers and runners in other sports. But just as forces acting on bone can increase bone density, inactivity works in the opposite direction, leading to a decrease in weight and strength. Loss of bone mass as a result of reduced mechanical stress has been noted in bed-ridden patients, inactive senior citizens, and astronauts.

The Human Skeleton

Approximately 206 bones make up the human skeleton. The skeleton (Figures 2.6 and 2.7) may be divided into axial and appendicular sections. The **axial skeleton** is composed of the skull, vertebrae, ribs, and sternum (the head, spine, and trunk), numbering 80 bones. The **appendicular skeleton** is made up of the pectoral (shoulder) and pelvic (hip) girdles, and the upper (arms) and lower (legs) limbs that are appended (hung) from the girdles. The appendicular portion of the skeleton consists of about 126 bones. While the axial skeleton serves mainly to support, stabilize, and protect vital organs of the body, the

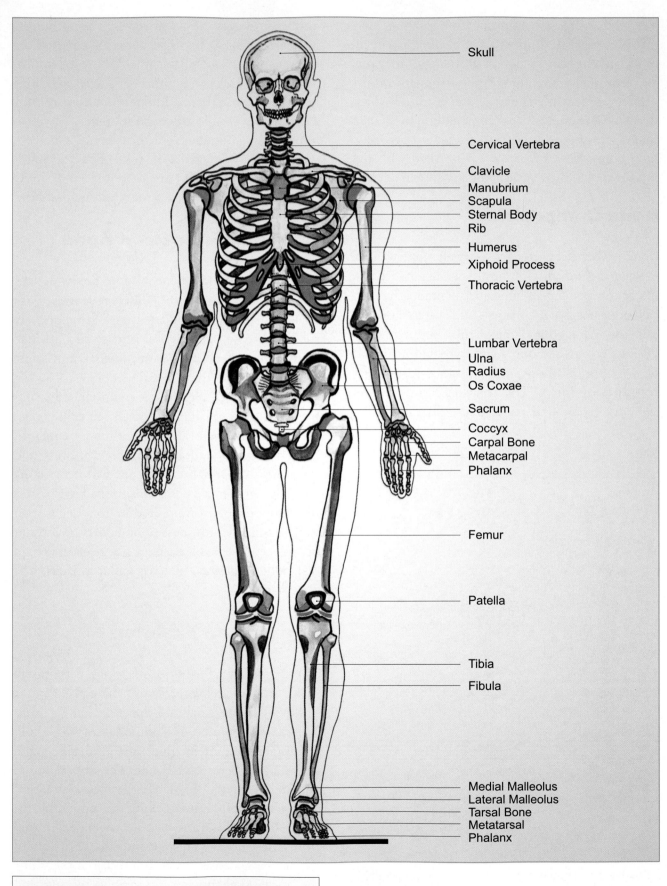

Skull

Cervical Vertebra

Clavicle
Manubrium
Scapula
Sternal Body
Rib
Humerus
Xiphoid Process
Thoracic Vertebra

Lumbar Vertebra
Ulna
Radius
Os Coxae
Sacrum
Coccyx
Carpal Bone
Metacarpal
Phalanx

Femur

Patella

Tibia
Fibula

Medial Malleolus
Lateral Malleolus
Tarsal Bone
Metatarsal
Phalanx

Figure 2.6 The human skeleton anterior view.

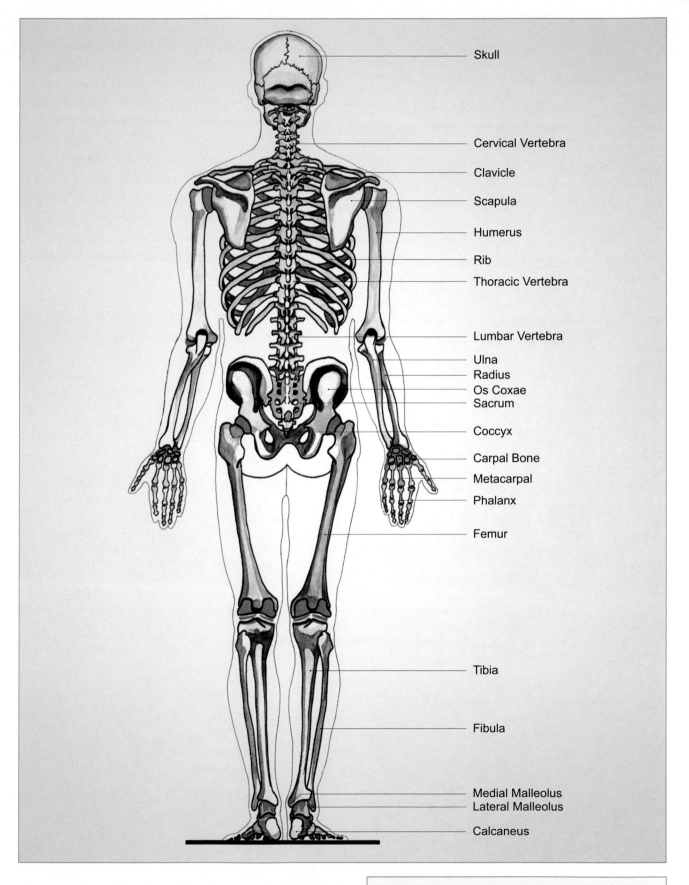

Skull

Cervical Vertebra

Clavicle

Scapula

Humerus

Rib

Thoracic Vertebra

Lumbar Vertebra

Ulna
Radius
Os Coxae
Sacrum

Coccyx

Carpal Bone

Metacarpal

Phalanx

Femur

Tibia

Fibula

Medial Malleolus
Lateral Malleolus

Calcaneus

Figure 2.7 The human skeleton posterior view.

appendicular skeleton is responsible for a large portion of the movements we perform.

Axial Skeleton

Skull The skull is divided into two major parts. The curved flat bones form the **calvaria**, or vault that protects the brain and brain stem. The irregular bones of the **face** give it its individuality, and provide protection for eyes, air passages, chewing, and entry of food into the body (Figure 2.8).

Calvaria The calvaria is formed by the **frontal**, **parietal**, **temporal**, **occipital**, and **sphenoid bones**. These may be fractured by blows to the skull (Figure 2.8), for example, as a result of being checked or hitting the skull on the ice when playing

hockey. The more fragile of the calvaria bones is the temporal bone and it overlies one of the major blood vessels supplying the membranes protecting the brain. If the temporal bone is fractured and displaced internally, it can cut the middle meningeal artery, resulting in an **epidural haemorrhage** (bleeding between the skull and the meninges, or protective covering of the brain; see Figure 2.8). This is a clinical emergency and bleeding must be stopped as quickly as possible so that blood collecting within the vault of the skull does not compress the brain, which is soft (the consistency of toothpaste) and easily damaged. A good reason for sport helmets, if you ever questioned their necessity.

Facial Bones The facial bones (Figure 2.8) include the **nasal** (nose), **lacrimal** (for drainage

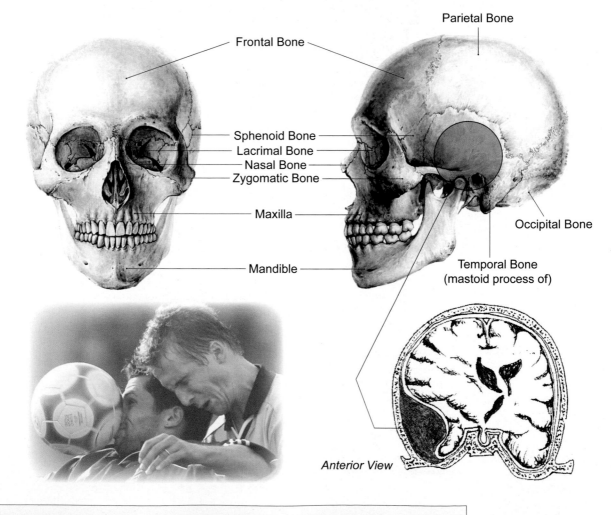

Figure 2.8 Anterior and left lateral view of the skull with epidural haemorrhage.

of tears), **zygomatic** (cheek bone), **maxilla** (upper jaw), and **mandible** (lower jaw) **bones**. Facial bones are the ones often broken in contact sports due to rough impact. Some fractures across the maxilla (upper jaw) can leave the lower face separated from the upper face.

Vertebral Column The vertebral column (Figure 2.9) is composed of up to 35 bones: 7 **cervical** (neck) vertebrae, of which the first 2 are named the **atlas** (C1) and the **axis** (C2), 12 **thoracic** (chest) vertebrae, 5 **lumbar** (lower back) vertebrae, 1 **sacrum** (midline region of buttocks) made up of 5 fused vertebrae, and 1 **coccyx** (tail bone) made up of 4 or 5 fused vertebrae.

Vertebrae are arranged in a cylindrical column interspersed with fibrocartilaginous (intervertebral) discs, forming a strong and flexible support for the neck and trunk. The vertebral column is also the point of attachment for the muscles of the back. The column has a snake-like form when viewed from the side with cervical, thoracic, lumbar, and sacral curves extending from the base of the skull through the entire length of the trunk. Not only does the column protect the spinal cord and nerves, it also provides essential support for the body and the ability to keep the body erect. The **intervertebral discs** absorb shock effectively when the load on the column increases, and allow the vertebrae to move without causing damage to other vertebrae or to the spinal cord.

Ribs and Sternum There are usually 12 pairs of **ribs**, made up of bone and cartilage that give strength to the chest cage and permit it to expand (Figure 2.10). The ribs are curved and slightly twisted making them ideal to protect the chest

C1
C2
C3
C4
C5
C6
C7

Cervical Vertebrae

T1
T2
T3
T4
T5
T6
T7
T8
T9
T10
T11
T12

Thoracic Vertebrae

L1
L2
L3
L4
L5

Lumbar Vertebrae

Sacrum

Coccyx

Lumbar Vertebra, lateral view

Lumbar Vertebra, superior view

Figure 2.9 Lateral view of the regions of the vertebral column.

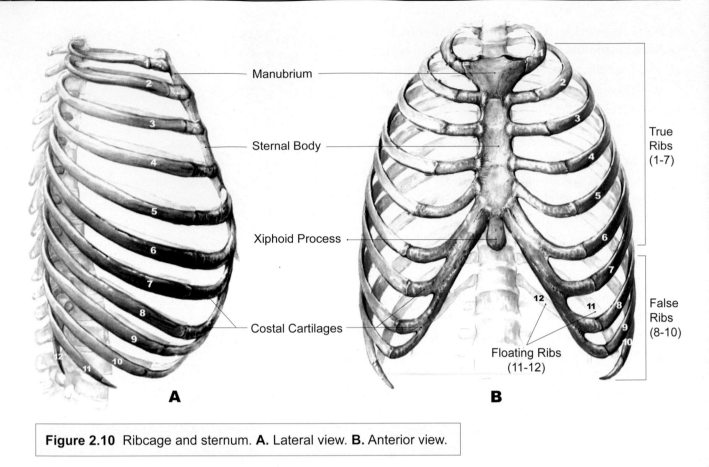

Figure 2.10 Ribcage and sternum. **A.** Lateral view. **B.** Anterior view.

area, effectively deflecting most blows that come its way. The upper 7 pairs (1-7) are the **true ribs** (attaching to both the vertebrae and the sternum), the next 3 pairs (8-10) are the **false ribs** (attaching to the sternum indirectly), and pairs 11 and 12 are **floating ribs**, so called because they only attach to the vertebral column. All 12 pairs of ribs articulate with the 12 thoracic vertebrae posteriorly.

The midline breast bone is called the **sternum**, comprised of three parts – the **manubrium**, **sternal body**, and **xiphoid process**. The clavicles and ribs 1-7 articulate with the sternum (Figure 2.10).

Appendicular Skeleton

Pectoral Girdle The bones of the pectoral girdle are the **scapula** (shoulder blade) and the **clavicle** (collar bone) (Figure 2.11). They are held to the chest wall by many muscles that allow the upper limb great mobility. A fracture of the clavicle is very common during falls or collisions during sport or everyday activities. The *sternoclavicular joint* between the sternum and clavicle is the only

bony joint between the axial skeleton and the pectoral girdle (Figure 2.15 A).

Upper Limb The arm (shoulder to elbow) bone is the **humerus**. From the elbow to the wrist the forearm is made up of the **radius** and the **ulna**, the radius being located on the thumb side of the hand. Therefore, when you pronate the forearm, the radius is actually crossing over the ulna. Try it yourself.

The **carpus** (wrist) is formed by two rows of four bones per row called **carpals** (Figure 2.11); from lateral to medial the proximal row contains the **scaphoid** (the bone most commonly fractured when you fall on the outstretched hand), **lunate**, **triquetral**, and **pisiform**; the distal row is made up of the **trapezium**, **trapezoid**, **capitate**, and **hamate** (The acronym **SLTPTTCH** representing the carpals from lateral to medial can be useful by remembering this sentence: *She Likes To Play, Try To Catch Her*). The distal row joins with the five **metacarpal** bones of the hand, which in turn articulate with the digits (fingers). All digits except the thumb are made up of three **phalanges** (singular = **phalanx**), *proximal*, *middle*, and *distal*. The thumb has only two phalanges, *proximal* and *distal* (Figure 2.11).

Pelvic Girdle The pelvic girdle is formed from the paired **os coxae** or hip bones (comprised of the ilium, pubis, and ischium) which join with the sacrum posteriorly and join each other anteriorly to form a basin-like girdle which supports the bladder and abdominal contents. On the lateral surface of the os coxae is a cup-shaped **acetabulum** for the head of the femur (Figure 2.12).

Clavicle (superior view)

Scapula (anterior view)

Humerus (anterior view)

Radius (anterior view)

Ulna (anterior view)

Carpal Bone (anterior view)

Metacarpal (anterior view)

Phalanx (anterior view)

Radius

Ulna

Scaphoid
Trapezium
Capitate
Trapezoid

Lunate
Triquetral
Pisiform
Hamate

1st Metacarpal

5th Metacarpal

Sesamoid Bone

5th Digit Proximal Phalanx

2nd Digit Middle Phalanx

3rd Digit Distal Phalanx

Figure 2.11 Major bones comprising the upper limb.

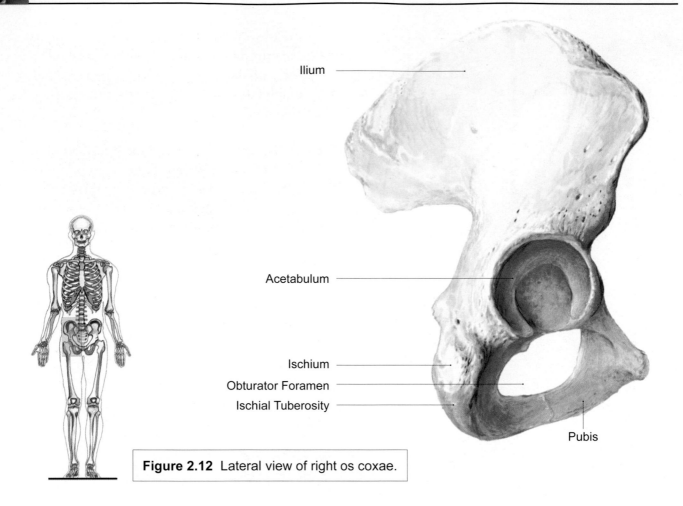

Ilium

Acetabulum

Ischium

Obturator Foramen

Ischial Tuberosity

Pubis

Figure 2.12 Lateral view of right os coxae.

Lower Limb The thigh (from hip to knee) bone is the **femur** (Figure 2.13). The **patella** (or knee cap) is a sesamoid bone in the tendon of the quadriceps muscles (thigh). From knee to ankle, the leg bones are the **tibia** and **fibula**. The tibia and fibula are held together very firmly by an *interosseous membrane* that provides stability and an area for muscle attachment. The distal ends of the tibia and fibula extend on the medial and lateral sides of the ankle (talus and calcaneus), forming a mortise into which the talus projects. These extensions can be felt subcutaneously and are commonly referred to as the "ankle bones" (Figure 2.13). Anatomists call them the **medial malleolus** and **lateral malleolus**.

The **tarsus** (ankle), like the wrist, is made up of several bones: the **talus**, resting on the **calcaneus** (heel bone), **navicular**, **cuboid**, and **1st (medial)**, **2nd (intermediate)**, and **3rd (lateral) cuneiforms** (*cuneiform* = wedge-shaped). The bones of the foot are the five **metatarsals**, in turn uniting with the

toes. The great toe has only two phalanges while the lateral four toes have three (Figure 2.13).

Joints of the Human Body

A joint is basically the point of connection between two or more bones. The stability and integrity of joints are maintained by strands of connective tissue called **ligaments**, which hold the bones together. Joints can be generally classified by the material that joins them.

Classification of Joints

There are fibrous, cartilaginous, and synovial joints. The latter are the most common in the body and have certain typical characteristics that will be described later.

Talus

Navicular

Intermediate Cuneiform

Lateral Cuneiform

1st Metatarsal

1st Digit
Proximal Phalanx

Femur
(anterior view)

Calcaneus

Cuboid

5th Metatarsal

5th Digit Middle
Phalanx

Lateral View of Right Foot

Patella
(anterior view)

Calcaneus

Talus

Tibia
(anterior view)

Cuboid

Navicular

Lateral Cuneiform

Intermediate Cuneiform

Medial Cuneiform

Fibula
(anterior view)

5th Metatarsal

Lateral Malleolus

1st Metatarsal

5th Digit Proximal
Phalanx

Medial Malleolus

Calcaneus
(dorsal view)

Talus
(dorsal view)

Navicular
(dorsal view)

Metatarsal
(dorsal view)

1st Digit
Distal
Phalanx

Dorsal View of Right Foot

Phalanx
(dorsal view)

Figure 2.13 Major bones comprising the lower limb.

Joints may also be classified according to their motion capabilities; some allow for a great deal of movement, while others are severely restricted. The joints which exhibit the least mobility are **fibrous** and **cartilaginous**. These joints can absorb shock but permit little movement, if any (e.g., interosseous ligaments). There are also slightly movable joints that are cartilaginous and can also attenuate applied forces (e.g., *intervertebral joints* and the *symphysis pubis*). The joints that allow the greatest amount of motion are the **synovial joints**, which have only slight limitations to movement capability, making possible a wide array of movements. The characteristics of synovial joints are presented in the box on the right. The following discussion will therefore focus on synovial joints.

Types of Synovial Joints

Synovial joints vary widely in structure and movement capabilities and may be classified in different ways – by the movements possible at the joint or simply by the axes around which the joint can be moved. The more common classification is based on the shape of the joint (Figure 2.14).

Hinge (Ginglymus) Joint This type of joint has one articulating surface that is convex, and another that is concave. Examples include the humero-ulnar joint at the elbow and the interphalangeal joints of the fingers.

Pivot Joint In these types of joints, one bone rotates around one axis. For example during pronation–supination of the forearm, the radius rotates along its long axis and the ulna remains fixed.

Condyloid (Knuckle) Joint The joint surfaces are usually oval as in the joint between your third metacarpal (bone of the hand) and the proximal phalanx (bone) of your third digit. One joint surface is an ovular convex shape, and the other is a

---

Characteristics of Synovial Joints

- There is a joint **capsule** lined with a **synovial membrane** that secretes the lubrication fluid for the joint. The capsule may or may not have thickenings called intrinsic ligaments that add support.

- There is a joint **cavity** surrounded by the capsule.

- There is a capillary layer of **synovial fluid** to lubricate the joint.

- Outside the capsule and not connected to it are **extrinsic ligaments** that support the joint and connect the articulating bones of the joint.

- Some joints have special features such as **articular discs, fibrocartilaginous labra** (singular = labrum) and **menisci** (singular = meniscus), and **intracapsular tendons**.

---

reciprocally shaped concave surface. At this joint, flexion–extension, abduction–adduction, and circumduction are all possible.

Saddle Joint The bones are set together as in sitting on a horse. This is seen in the carpometacarpal joint of the thumb. Movement capability at this joint is the same as the condyloid joint, but with a greater possible range of motion permitted.

Ball and Socket Joint A rounded bone is fitted into a cup-like receptacle. This is the kind of joint found at the shoulder and the hip where rotation in all three planes of movement is possible.

Plane (Gliding) Joint This joint permits gliding movements as in the bones of the wrist. The bone surfaces

Plane (Gliding)
Found in bones of the wrist and the acromioclavicular joint of the shoulder.

Pivot
Found in the atlantoaxial joint of the neck, and in the forearm during pronation–supination.

Ball and Socket
Found in the hip and shoulder.

Hinge (Ginglymus)
Found in the elbow.

Condyloid (Knuckle)
Found in the joints between the metacarpals and phalanges – except at the thumb.

Saddle
Found in the carpo-metacarpal joint of the thumb.

Figure 2.14 Typical synovial joints of the human body.

involved are nearly flat, so the only movement allowed is a gliding action. Another example of such a joint is the facet joints of the vertebrae.

The principal synovial joints of the body are presented in the following sections. While some of the terms may seem confusing, just remember that anatomical terms can be figured out by identifying the root words involved. Junctions of bones are called joints. Some fibrous joints (e.g., sutures of the skull) allow no movement, cartilaginous joints (e.g., intervertebral discs) allow limited movement, and synovial joints (e.g., elbow and wrist) allow a large range of movement. In synovial joints, bone ends are covered with smooth **cartilage**, and the entire joint is enclosed in a capsule filled with

synovial fluid. Ligaments and cartilage provide additional support.

Joints of the Pectoral Girdle

The pectoral girdle, comprised of the scapula and clavicle, has two joints. These joints are presented starting below.

Sternoclavicular Joint

This is the only joint connecting the pectoral girdle to the axial skeleton (the clavicle to the sternum). It is a true synovial joint strengthened by an intracapsular disc and extrinsic ligaments. This is important as this joint must absorb all

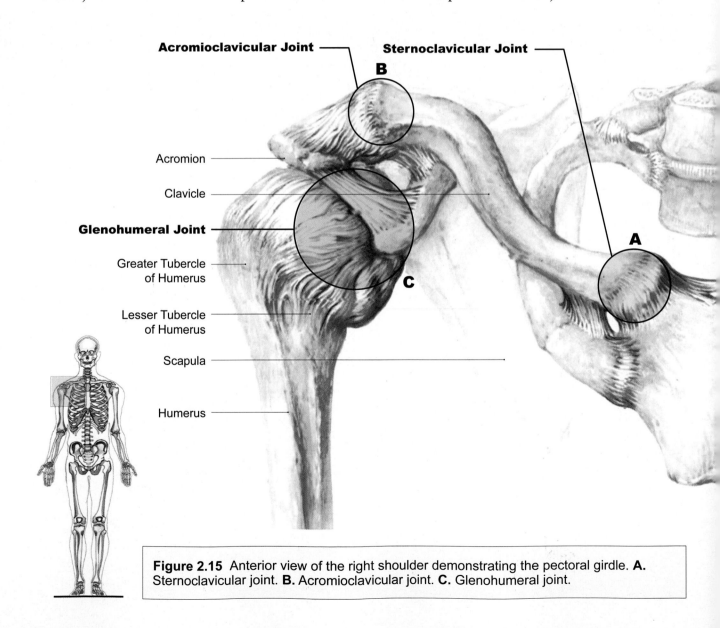

Figure 2.15 Anterior view of the right shoulder demonstrating the pectoral girdle. **A.** Sternoclavicular joint. **B.** Acromioclavicular joint. **C.** Glenohumeral joint.

forces transmitted to the upper limb in many activities, including many sports (Figure 2.15 A).

Acromioclavicular Joint

This joint unites the lateral end of the clavicle with the acromion process of the scapula. It is here that shoulder separations can, and often do, occur in sports such as hockey, baseball, and football (Figure 2.15 B).

Joints of the Upper Limb

Glenohumeral Joint

This is the joint between the upper limb and the scapula. Because we enjoy a wide range of movement at this joint, the compromise is a relative lack of stability. You have a large ball (of the humerus) articulating with a relatively shallow cup (of the scapula). The integrity of the joint depends on the rotator cuff muscles that **SSIT** on the greater and lesser tubercles of the humerus and cross the joint to attach to the scapula. These letters stand for the *Subscapularis, Supraspinatus, Infraspinatus,* and *Teres minor* muscles that hold

the head of the humerus firmly against the *glenoid fossa* of the scapula. This area is commonly injured by water polo players (Figure 2.15 C).

Elbow Joint

There are actually three joints at the elbow: (1) the **humero-radial joint** between the capitulum of the humerus and the head of the radius (Figure 2.16 A); (2) the **humero-ulnar joint** between the trochlea of the humerus and the olecranon process of the ulna (Figure 2.16 B); and (3) the **radioulnar joint** between the radius and the ulna (Figure 2.16 C). Flexion–extension occurs at the first two, and pronation–supination occurs at the radioulnar joint.

Joints of the Wrist

The distal radius articulates with the proximal row of carpal bones at the **radiocarpal joint** (between the radius and the carpals). Flexion–extension as well as abduction–adduction occur here (Figure 2.17). As well, there are **midcarpal** and **intercarpal**, **carpometacarpal**, and **intermetacarpal joints**. There are gliding joints between the bones of the

Figure 2.16 The right elbow joint. **A.** Humero-radial joint. **B.** Humero-ulnar joint. **C.** Radioulnar joint.

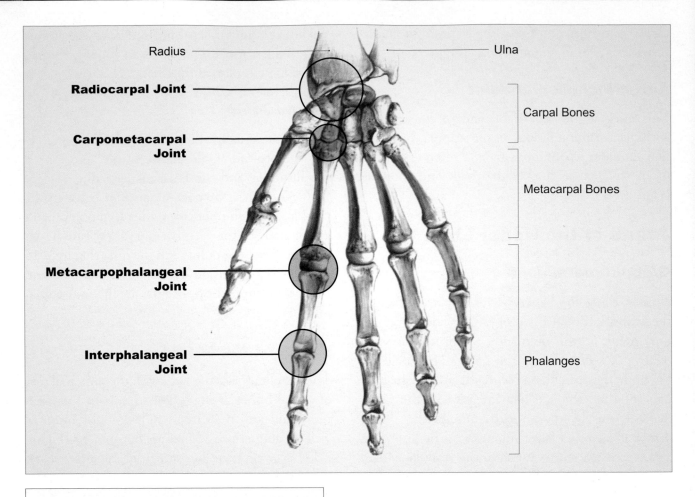

Radius — Ulna

Radiocarpal Joint —

Carpal Bones

Carpometacarpal Joint —

Metacarpal Bones

Metacarpophalangeal Joint —

Interphalangeal Joint —

Phalanges

Figure 2.17 Major joints of the wrist and hand.

carpus. The metacarpal of the thumb sits in the saddle of the trapezium and lies at an angle of 90 degrees to the palm of the hand. This allows the range of movement necessary for *opposition*, the ability to touch your thumb tip to each of your finger tips.

Joints of the Hand

The knuckles are the **metacarpophalangeal joints** (Figure 2.17). Flexion–extension and abduction–adduction can occur here, allowing us to manipulate our hands with amazing dexterity. Between the phalanges are **interphalangeal joints** (recall that there are three phalanges per finger, while the thumb has only two) that also permit flexion–extension (Figure 2.17).

Joints of the Pelvic Girdle

The hip bones (os coxae), comprised of the ilium, pubis, and ischium, together with the sacrum, form the pelvic girdle. It has two joints.

Symphysis Pubis

This is a fibrocartilaginous joint uniting the two pubic bones and completing the pelvic girdle anteriorly. It can soften just before giving birth to permit a wider opening for the baby.

Sacroiliac Joint

This joint unites the sacrum with the paired ilia (singular = ilium). It has both a fibrous and a synovial component. Minor displacement of the fibrous component can result in excruciating sacroiliac pain.

Joints of the Lower Limb

Hip Joint

Between the head of the femur and the cup (acetabulum) of the hip bone (os coxae) is the **hip** or **iliofemoral joint**. As in all ball and socket joints, movements of flexion–extension, abduction–adduction, and circumduction can take place here, allowing for the greatest range of motion and mobility (Figure 2.18).

The hip joint is the body's most stable synovial joint as it is provided with a deepened socket (via a lip or fibrocartilaginous labrum) and intrinsic and very strong extrinsic ligaments. In contrast to the shoulder joint, another ball and socket joint, dislocation of the hip joint even in the most aggressive contact sports is rare. Dislocation usually occurs when someone sitting in the front seat of a car is involved in a head-on collision and the knees are driven into the dashboard. The force

Figure 2.18 Anterior view of the pelvic girdle.

of impact can either dislocate the head of the femur posteriorly or drive it through the posterior lip of the acetabulum.

Knee Joint

Despite its very shallow receptor surface on the tibial plateau for the medial and lateral condyles of the femur, the **knee (tibiofemoral) joint** is a relatively stable joint with an incredible range of movement (Figure 2.19). It has additional structural supports from the **menisci** (shock-absorbing fibrocartilaginous discs), **anterior** and **posterior cruciate ligaments** (in the centre of the joint), **lateral** and **medial collateral ligaments** (extending from the sides of the femur to the fibula and tibia), and the musculature that surrounds it. The primary action here is flexion–extension such as when performing a squat or jump, but when the knee is flexed, medial and lateral rotation can also occur at the joint. Try it out yourself.

When You Sprain an Ankle

As with bone and muscle, all joints have a rich nerve supply. The muscles that pass over a joint and give it movement have the same nerve supply as the joints over which they act.

Question: When a joint becomes swollen (as in an ankle sprain) what causes the swelling? Why is this painful?

Answer: Trauma causes the synovial membrane of the joint to secrete fluid. This causes the swelling that results in stretching of the joint capsule which can activate pain receptors in the joint. When the joint becomes painful, the surrounding muscles may go into spasm. Once the inflammation is reduced, the pain will subside and the muscles will have to be remobilized with physiotherapy.

Figure 2.19 The right knee. **A.** Anterior view. **B.** Posterior view.

Figure 2.20 Ankle and foot joints. **A.** Dorsal view. **B.** Lateral view.

Ankle Joint

Several bones, the medial and lateral malleoli of the tibia and fibula, the head of the talus, and the calcaneus (heel bone), are involved in the **ankle (talocrural) joint** (Figure 2.20).

The talus is wedged into the mortise formed by the medial and lateral malleoli. Because the talus is wider anteriorly than posteriorly, when you dorsiflex at the ankle, you put the ankle into its most stable position. This is the reason for the forward cant in a downhill ski boot. The ankle is least stable in the "en pointe" position in ballet, putting great pressure on dancers' ligaments and tendons, and increasing the risk of injury.

Foot and Toe Joints

There are two rows of tarsal bones of the **transverse tarsal joint**. Movement between the proximal and distal rows of the transverse tarsal joint is inversion–eversion of the sole of the foot. This action enables you to adjust to uneven ground when walking or running. As in the hand, there are joints between the tarsal bones, metatarsals, and phalanges. They are strengthened by plantar ligaments that aid in maintaining the arch of the foot (weakened ligaments result in "flat foot," although you may be born with flat feet that cause you no discomfort).

Muscles of the Human Body

Muscles allow the skeleton to move. Most muscles are attached from one bone to another with a joint in between. The attachment closer to the centre of the body is the muscle's **origin** (also known as its *proximal attachment*). The attachment away from the centre of the body is the muscle's **insertion** (also known as its *distal attachment*). The origin of the muscle is usually attached to more stationary parts, whereas the insertion is attached to more mobile structures of the skeleton. Remember, muscles can only act on the joints they cross.

There are over 600 muscles present in the human body. It would be impossible to describe here all the muscles, so keep in mind that a short section in this chapter cannot do justice to the vast number and functions of these muscles. Only the major superficial muscles will be identified (Figures 2.24 and 2.25) as they relate to the bony regions discussed in the previous section.

Muscles of the Face

Facial muscles enable you to change expression and display your emotions outwardly; but most importantly, they allow you to close your eyes and your mouth (Figure 2.21). Closing the eyelids, as in blinking, acts to move tears across the cornea of the eye, keeping it moistened. When the eyeball is not kept moist, it will dry out and ulcerate, leading to discomfort and irritation, even blindness. People with paralysis of facial muscles will put artificial tears in their eyes to prevent this.

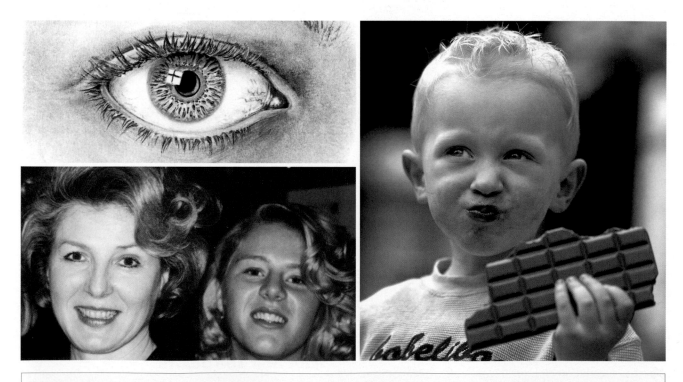

Figure 2.21 Facial muscles are essential for a variety of tasks, from smiling and blinking to chewing and speaking.

Facial muscles are also essential for opening and closing the mouth, thereby keeping food in the mouth and allowing you to move it between the teeth during chewing, to say nothing of forming words in speaking.

Muscles of the Neck and Back

The head sits on the first cervical vertebra (C1) called the atlas. To maintain this position there are muscles posterior, lateral, and anterior to the neck or cervical region that allow you to hold up your head, and also permit a wide range of movement. Try turning your own head while keeping your shoulders in a fixed position. The most important anterior pair of neck muscles are the **sternocleidomastoids** (Figure 2.22). Acting together, they are the muscles that allow you to flex your head towards your chest. Without them you cannot get up from a supine position (lying down). Individually, each sternocleidomastoid muscle tilts the face up and towards the opposite side.

Figure 2.23 Deep posterior back muscles.

Figure 2.22 Anterior neck with sternocleidomastoid muscles.

Posteriorly, there is a large muscle mass reaching in segments from the sacrum inferiorly, and to the skull superiorly, called the **erector spinae muscles** (Figure 2.23). They do what their name suggests – maintain your erect position. They are sometimes called the **anti-gravity muscles**. When someone faints, these muscles no longer function and the body falls face forward to the ground. Just imagine what it would be like if we were unable to keep our bodies upright – this ability to stand erect and walk on two feet is one feature that sets us apart from most other species.

Trapezius (upper fibres)

Deltoid

Pectoralis Major

Serratus Anterior

External Oblique

Brachioradialis

Wrist Flexor Group

Pectineus

Sartorius

Gracilis

Vastus Lateralis

Sternocleidomastoid

Pectoralis Minor

Biceps Brachii

Brachialis

Rectus Abdominis

Internal Oblique

Tensor Fasciae Latae

Adductor Group

Rectus Femoris

Vastus Medialis

Tibialis Anterior

Figure 2.24 Anterior muscles of the human body.

Trapezius (upper fibres)

Deltoid
Infraspinatus
Teres Minor
Teres Major

Latissimus Dorsi

Forearm Extensors

Gluteus Medius

Semitendinosus
Semimembranosus

Soleus

Rhomboid

Triceps Brachii

Brachioradialis

Erector Spinae

Gluteus Maximus

Biceps Femoris

Gastrocnemius

Figure 2.25 Posterior muscles of the human body.

Figure 2.26 Anterior muscles of the pectoral girdle. **A.** Anterior view. **B.** Lateral view.

Muscles Connecting the Humerus and Scapula to the Axial Skeleton

Anterior and Posterior Groups

Muscles acting to hold the pectoral girdle to the chest wall can be divided into anterior and posterior groups as follows.

Anterior Group   **Pectoralis major** has two heads. The clavicular head (attached to the clavicle) flexes and medially rotates the shoulder joint; the sternal head (attached to the sternum) extends the shoulder joint from a flexed position and medially rotates the shoulder joint. **Pectoralis minor** depresses and stabilizes the scapula. **Serratus anterior** steadies and holds the scapula forward (protracts it) against the chest wall (Figure

2.26). This frees the upper limb for actions such as rope climbing. These muscles as a group would also be required to perform the butterfly stroke in swimming.

Posterior Group Trapezius has three groups of fibres reflecting their relative positions. The *upper fibres* elevate the scapula, *middle fibres* retract the scapula, and *lower fibres* depress the scapula. Latissimus dorsi medially rotates, adducts, and extends the humerus, and teres major medially rotates the humerus (Figure 2.27).

Scapula–Humeral Region

The following muscles from the scapula to the humerus act across the shoulder joint. Their primary role is to stabilize the shoulder joint to allow full use of the upper limb.

Anterior Group Subscapularis adducts and medially rotates the upper limb. (Figure 2.27 C).

Superior and Posterior Group Supraspinatus initiates abduction of the upper limb at the shoulder joint. Infraspinatus and teres minor adduct and

Figure 2.27 Muscles of the back and scapula–humeral region. **A.** Superficial posterior muscles of the back. **B.** Posterior muscles of the scapula–humeral region, deep and lateral to latissimus dorsi. **C.** Anterior subscapularis muscle of the scapula–humeral region.

Clavicle

Acromion

Deltoid

Biceps Brachii

Triceps Brachii

Figure 2.28 The lateral muscles of the scapula–humeral region.

laterally rotate the upper limb at the shoulder joint. These muscles, combined with subscapularis, are the **SSIT** (rotator cuff) muscles of the shoulder (Figure 2.27 B).

Lateral Group   **Deltoid** has three functional groups of fibres. The *anterior fibres* flex and medially rotate the upper limb, the *middle fibres* abduct the upper limb, and the *posterior fibres* extend and laterally rotate the upper limb. All actions occur at the shoulder joint (Figure 2.28). The deltoid muscles are used extensively in paddling sports such as kayaking and canoeing.

Muscles of the Arm

Muscles of the limbs are primarily flexors or extensors. In the upper limb, the flexors are on the anterior surface of the arm, forearm, and hand, and the extensors are on the posterior surface.

Some muscles from the scapula to the forearm span the arm to reach the radius and ulna of the forearm.

The muscles with proximal attachments to the humerus are divided by a strong fascial sheet of connective tissue into anterior and posterior compartments.

Anterior Compartment   A muscle with two heads, both attached proximally to the scapula, the **biceps brachii** spans the arm to reach the radial tubercle of the radius. It is a powerful flexor of the elbow joint and supinator of the forearm (Figure 2.29 A). **Brachialis** is attached proximally to the anterior surface of the humerus and attaches distally to the coronoid process of the ulna. An important and powerful flexor of the elbow joint, it works along with the biceps brachii. To isolate brachialis in exercise, flex and pronate the forearm and perform repeated elbow curls.

Posterior Compartment Triceps brachii has three heads. The medial and lateral heads are attached to the humerus. They join with the long head from the scapula to attach distally to the olecranon process of the ulna. It is *the* powerful extensor of the elbow (Figure 2.29 B).

Muscles of the Forearm

The distal end of the humerus widens into lateral and medial epicondyles which provide attachments for muscle groups that act on the forearm and wrist.

The forearm muscles act on the elbow, wrist, and digits (fingers and thumb). Muscles attached to the medial epicondyle of the humerus are the **flexor–pronator** group (Figure 2.29 A) while those

attached to the lateral epicondyle of the humerus are the **extensor–supinator** group (Figure 2.29 B).

One muscle attached above the lateral epicondyle of the humerus is the **brachioradialis** muscle. It is on the extensor side of the humerus but, because it is positioned anterior to the elbow joint, it acts as an elbow flexor, especially when the forearm is partially pronated. You use this muscle when you shake hands with someone.

Muscles of the Hand

These muscles are divided into groups. The **thenar (palm) group** acts on the thumb and its metacarpal to abduct, flex, and oppose the thumb tip to the four remaining digits. The

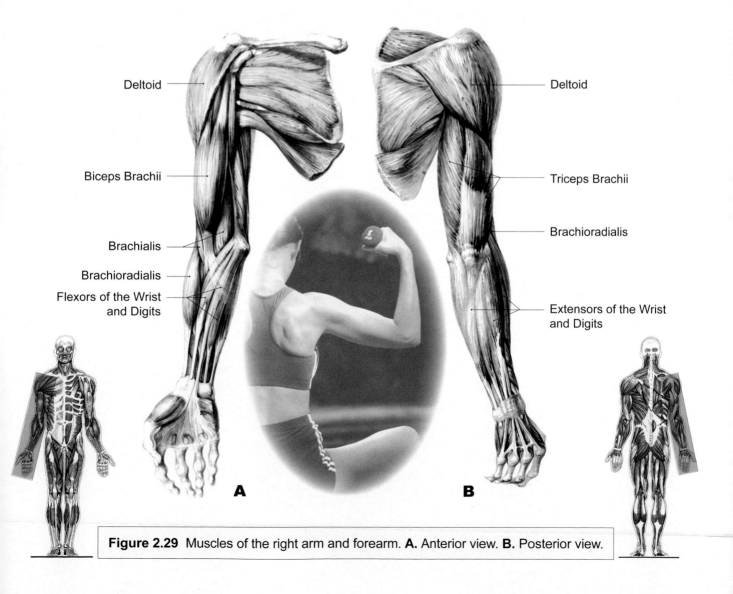

Deltoid

Biceps Brachii

Brachialis

Brachioradialis

Flexors of the Wrist and Digits

Deltoid

Triceps Brachii

Brachioradialis

Extensors of the Wrist and Digits

A

B

Figure 2.29 Muscles of the right arm and forearm. **A.** Anterior view. **B.** Posterior view.

hypothenar (little palm) group acts on the little finger and its metacarpal. Together the thenar and hypothenar muscles permit you to cup your hand as in holding a baseball. Between these two groups lie the **interossei** (between bones) and the **lumbrical** (earthworm) **muscles** that are referred to collectively as the **intrinsic** (within) muscles of the hand. Together they flex, extend, abduct, and adduct the fingers, positioning the digits for fine movements.

Muscles of the Pelvic Girdle

From the bony pelvis, muscles are attached that permit a wide range of movement in the lower limb; but here, stability and transfer of weight for walking are the prime focus, not the fine discriminatory movements that are necessary with the hands and fingers. Some of the muscles acting at the hip joint come from the abdomen; others come from the sacrum and external surface of the hip bone (os coxae).

Because the hip joint is a ball and socket joint, flexion–extension, abduction–adduction, medial and lateral rotation, as well as circumduction can all occur here. Try it yourself. Notice, however, that the movement here is more limited than at the shoulder joint.

Anterior Group   **Psoas major** (from the abdomen) and **iliacus** (from the iliac fossa of the pelvis) unite to form the **iliopsoas** muscle that crosses the anterior aspect of the joint and is the primary flexor of the hip, allowing you to bring your thighs up to your chest or your chest to your knees (Figure 2.30).

Posterior and Lateral Group   Large gluteal muscles cover the hip posteriorly. Put your hand on your hip and extend the joint. Feel the large muscle mass as it contracts. These are the three **gluteals**. The largest and most superficial posterior muscle, **gluteus maximus**, is the principal power extensor of the hip. **Gluteus medius** and **minimus** lie deep and lateral to maximus and in that order,

Psoas Major

Iliopsoas

Iliacus

Sacrum

Femur

Figure 2.30 Anterior muscles of the pelvic girdle.

Gluteus Medius

Gluteus Maximus

Figure 2.31 Posterior muscles of the pelvic girdle.

and have a very important role – they abduct the hip (Figure 2.31). This is a very important movement in normal gait, or walking (a skill that is required for so many physical activities). Deep to gluteus maximus are six little muscles that all perform the same job: they laterally (externally) rotate the hip.

Muscles of the Thigh

The thigh is divided very conveniently into three compartments: medial, anterior, and posterior. Like the arm, most of the muscles acting in these compartments are attached proximally to the pelvic girdle. Some will attach distally to the femur, others will span the entire length of the femur and attach to the bones of the leg.

Anterior Compartment The anterior group is the extensor group, also known as the **quads** or **quadriceps**. They are the **rectus** (*rectus* = straight)

femoris, **vastus lateralis**, **vastus intermedius**, and **vastus medialis** (Figure 2.32 A). The principal role of the quads is to extend the knee. To kick a soccer ball the knee must come into full extension for maximum distance, utilizing these leg extensors. The **sartorius** muscle lies anterior to the quads and acts to abduct and flex the thigh at the hip, and to flex the knee. You use this muscle to dance the limbo or to sit cross-legged on the floor.

Medial Compartment This group of medial muscles has one primary action – that is, to adduct the thigh towards the midline. This action prevents your leg from swinging too wide laterally as you walk. It is also the group of muscles you would use to stay on a horse. As their action implies, they are the adductor muscles comprised of **pectineus**, **adductor longus**, **adductor brevis**, and **adductor magnus**, as well as **gracilis** (Figure 2.32 B).

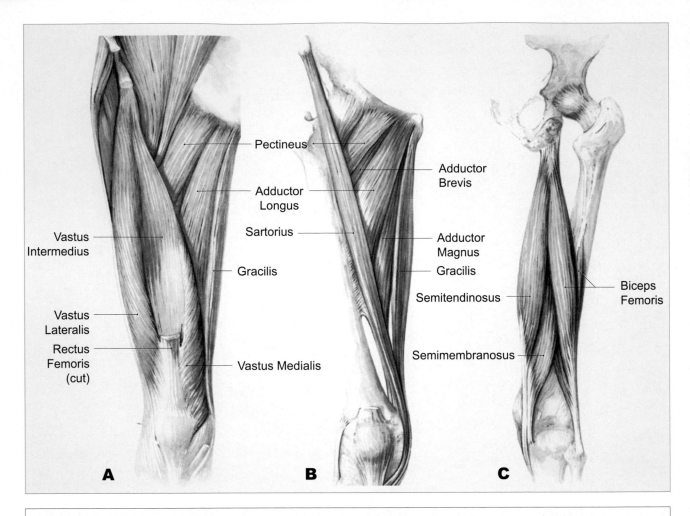

Figure 2.32 Muscles of the right thigh. **A.** Anterior compartment. **B.** Medial compartment. **C.** Posterior compartment.

Posterior Compartment The posterior group includes the muscles you know as the **hamstrings.** You may have thought the hamstrings were one muscle, but the group is actually made up of the **biceps femoris, semitendinosus,** and **semimembranosus** (Figure 2.32 C). Their role is to flex the knee and extend the hip with gluteus maximus. They are attached proximally to the ischial tuberosity (the bony part you sit on that gets sore when you sit on a hard chair for too long a time). Distally, the muscles cross posterior to the knee joint with the biceps femoris attaching to the head of the fibula and the semitendinosus and semimembranosus attaching to the tibia.

Muscles of the Leg

The joints of the leg are arranged in the opposite conformation to the arm. The extensors are on the anterior surface and the flexors are located posteriorly. Let's look at the compartments.

Nature is very kind to those studying anatomy. Again, as in the thigh, the leg muscles are grouped into compartments, but here into anterior, lateral, and posterior compartments.

Anterior and Lateral Compartments

Anterior Compartment These muscles do not cross the knee joint, but arise from the anterolateral surface of the tibia, the interosseous membrane between the tibia and the fibula, and from the anterior surface of the fibula. Their tendons cross anterior to the ankle joint and go to the medial side of the foot, and to the distal phalanges of the digits. They are primarily dorsiflexors of the ankle and extensors of the toes. The major anterior compartment muscle is **tibialis anterior** (Figure 2.33 A), which also functions to invert the sole of the foot. Loss of the nerve supply to these muscles results in foot drop.

Lateral Compartment   There are two muscles in the lateral compartment, the **peroneus longus** and **peroneus brevis** (Figure 2.33 A). Both muscles attach to the lateral surface of the fibula and pass behind the lateral malleolus to enter the foot. Because they cross behind the ankle joint they are plantar flexors of the ankle and the

evertors of the sole of the foot. For example, loss of the nerve supply to these muscles would mean you would have difficulty adapting your foot to uneven ground surfaces when running.

Posterior Compartment

Superficial Group   The large muscles of the calf are formed by the **gastrocnemius** and **soleus** muscles (Figure 2.33 B). Gastrocnemius has two proximal heads attached to the medial and lateral epicondyles of the distal femur. They come together to form a large muscle belly that attaches to the back of the calcaneus (large bone of the heel) in common with the tendon of soleus as the calcaneal tendon (**Achilles tendon**). These three are the principal plantar flexors of the ankle. Often, the medial head of gastrocnemius can be partially torn away from its attachment to the

Peroneus Longus

Tibialis Anterior

Peroneus Brevis

Gastrocnemius

Soleus

Achilles Tendon

A   **B**

Figure 2.33 Muscles of the right leg. **A.** Anterolateral compartment. **B.** Posterior compartment.

femur (e.g., during a game of squash when you are making very sudden starts, stops, and turns); it can be very painful, but the fibres will naturally reattach during the healing process.

Deep Group The deep muscles are the ones that assist in plantar flexion of the ankle, but their primary role is flexion of the toes. These tendons enter the foot by passing behind the medial malleolus of the tibia.

Muscles of the Foot

There are four layers of intrinsic foot muscles.

Together with the bones and ligaments, they are arranged to permit the foot to support the body on uneven ground. As a group, they permit flexion, extension, abduction, and adduction of the digits. The great toe (digit 1) is the primary lever in the "push-off" in walking, running, and jumping.

Muscles of the Abdomen

The anterior abdominal wall is a plywood-like trilaminar muscular wall. The triple layer is formed by, from superficial to deep, the **external oblique**, **internal oblique**, and **transversus abdominis** muscles (Figures 2.34 and 2.35). They reach

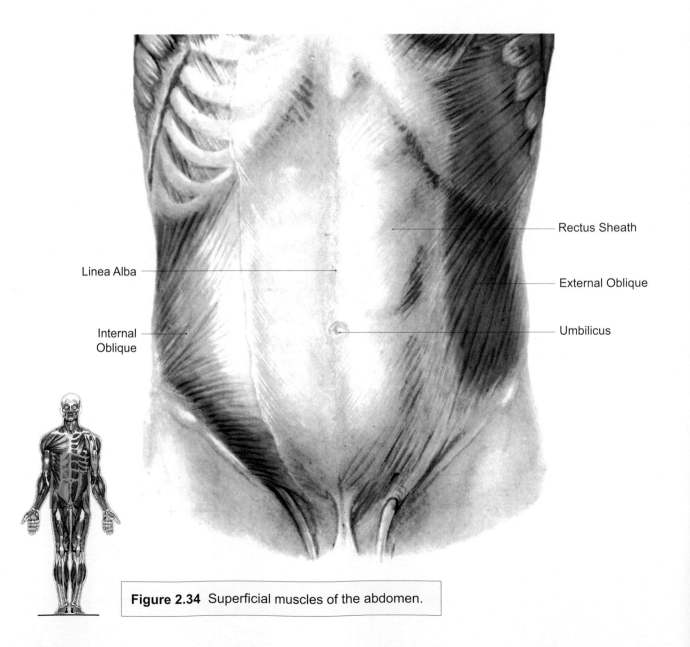

Linea Alba

Internal Oblique

Rectus Sheath

External Oblique

Umbilicus

Figure 2.34 Superficial muscles of the abdomen.

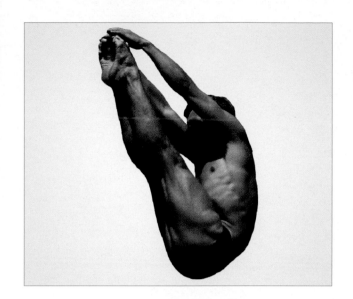

from the vertebral column, ribs, and hip bone posteriorly, to meet in the midline anteriorly at the **linea alba**. As the right and left muscle groups approach each other, they envelop paired midline muscles, the **rectus abdomini** (Figure 2.35). The obliques are important in lateral bending and in rotation of the trunk (e.g., in throwing the javelin). They also permit extension of the abdomen during forced inspiration, and allow the development of a pregnant uterus. They contract during forced expiration and help to expel fecal contents from the rectum. The rectus abdominis, the muscle used in sit-ups, is a powerful flexor of the anterior abdominal wall. Strengthening of the

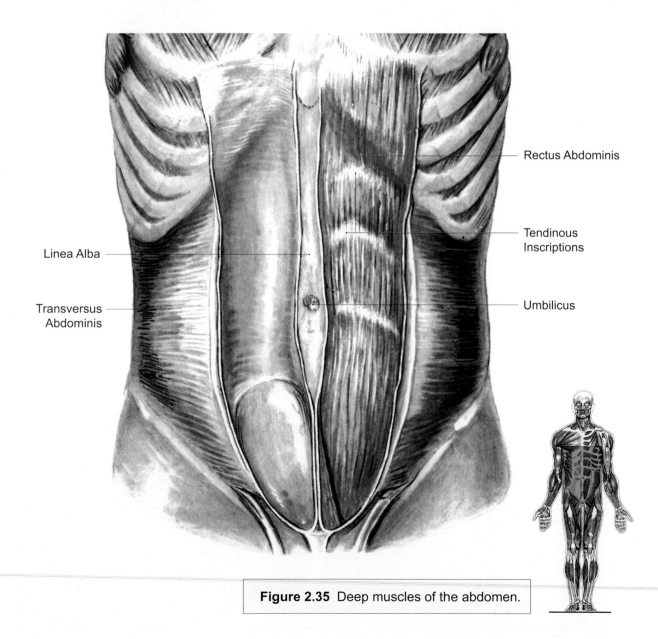

Rectus Abdominis

Tendinous Inscriptions

Linea Alba

Umbilicus

Transversus Abdominis

Figure 2.35 Deep muscles of the abdomen.

Table 2.2 Summary of major muscles and movements of the upper limb.

Joint	Action	Muscles	Sport or Activity
Shoulder	Flexion	*Pectoralis major, clavicular head *Deltoid, anterior fibres *Biceps brachii	Cross-country and downhill skiing, pull-through in freestyle swimming
	Extension	*Latissimus dorsi Teres major *Deltoid, posterior fibres Pectoralis major, sternal head	Iron cross formation in gymnastics, freestyle stroke, racquet positioning in tennis
	Abduction	*Deltoid Supraspinatus	Position in take-off in diving
	Adduction	*Pectoralis major Latissimus dorsi	Dance positions, cross-court shot in tennis
	Medial rotation	*Pectoralis major *Deltoid, anterior fibres Latissimus dorsi	Crossing one's arms, butterfly stroke in swimming, arm positioning in ballet
	Lateral rotation	*Deltoid, posterior fibres Teres minor Infraspinatus	Back stroke in swimming, lawn bowling, curling
Elbow	Flexion	Brachialis *Biceps brachii Brachioradialis	Weightlifting, shaking hands, positioning forearm to write, boxing
	Extension	*Triceps Anconeus	Pull stroke in paddling, backhand in tennis, painting a wall
Radioulnar	Pronation	Pronator teres	Volleyball spike, tennis serve, football pass
	Supination	*Biceps brachii Supinator	Fencing, volleyball serve, lawn bowling
Radiocarpal	Flexion–Extension	Forearm flexors and extensors	Baseball pitch, throwing a javelin
	Abduction–Adduction	Forearm flexors and extensors	Positioning wrist to maneuver a basketball or baseball
Metacarpo-phalangeal	Flexion–Extension	Forearm flexors and extensors	Position of wrist for throwing baseball, basketball, darts, javelin
	Abduction–Adduction	Forearm flexors and extensors Intrinsic hand muscles	Grasping a basketball or javelin, releasing a baseball or dart
Inter-phalangeal	Flexion–Extension	Intrinsic hand muscles Forearm flexors	Grasping an object, i.e., baseball, darts; releasing an object

* indicates prime movers

As you read the sports and activities listed in the table, try to imagine how the movements would be performed.

Table 2.3 Summary of major muscles and movements of the lower limb.

Joint	Action	Muscles	Sport or Activity
Hip	Flexion	*Iliopsoas Sartorius Pectineus Rectus femoris	Sprinting, climbing, gymnastics, diving
	Extension	*Gluteus maximus Semitendinosus Semimembranosus Biceps femoris Adductor magnus	Rising from a squat in weightlifting, running uphill, gymnastics
	Abduction	*Gluteus medius Gluteus minimus Tensor fasciae latae	Figure skating, gymnastics, hurdles
	Adduction	Adductor magnus Adductor longus Adductor brevis Gracilis	Equestrian events, cross-country skiing
	Lateral rotation	Obturator externus Obturator internus Piriformis Quadratus femoris	Figure skating, gymnastics, soccer
	Medial rotation	Tensor fasciae latae Gluteus medius Gluteus minimus	Gymnastics, ballet, diving
Knee	Extension	*Quadriceps femoris Tensor fasciae latae	Place kick in football, diving, gymnastics
	Flexion	*Biceps femoris *Semimembranosus *Semitendinosus Gastrocnemius Sartorius Gracilis Popliteus	Running, hurdles, rowing
Ankle	Dorsiflexion	*Tibialis anterior Extensor hallucis longus Extensor digitorum longus Peroneus tertius	Heel-toe walking, skiing
	Plantar flexion	*Gastrocnemius *Soleus Tibialis posterior Flexor hallucis longus	Push-off in sprinting, going "en pointe" in dance, gymnastics, diving
Transverse Tarsal	Inversion	*Tibialis anterior Tibialis posterior	Maintaining stability when walking on uneven ground
	Eversion	Peroneus longus Peroneus brevis	Maintaining stability when walking on uneven ground

* indicates prime movers

anterior abdominal wall is a very important part of back therapy, whereby the anterior wall muscles act to support the back.

Summary

Human anatomy deals with the structures that make up the human body, and how these various structures are related to one another. Having knowledge about the structures of the human body and their associated functions, the major bones, joints, and muscles that allow us to move, and an understanding of anatomical description and analysis, is important to realizing your full potential as an individual.

The bones, joints, and muscles that make up the musculoskeletal system allow numerous movements to occur, with varying degrees of motion capabilities, strength, and flexibility. Bones provide the structural framework necessary for support, muscles supply the power, and the joints supply the mechanism that allows human movement to occur.

While the human body is highly organized, intricate, and complex, it is structured precisely to respond to the demands of the world around us with astounding efficiency. Our ability to move and perform an almost limitless number of skills can be enhanced with knowledge of anatomy; and because structure determines function, knowing our structure can go a long way in improving the functions of those structures for performance in our everyday lives.

Key Words

Abduction	Flexion	Plane (gliding) joint
Adduction	Frontal (coronal) plane	Plantar flexion
Anatomical position	Hinge (ginglymus) joint	Posterior (dorsal)
Anterior (ventral)	Human anatomy	Pronation
Appendicular skeleton	Inferior	Prone
Axial skeleton	Insertion	Proximal
Ball and socket joint	Inversion	Saddle joint
Circumduction	Irregular bone	Sagittal plane
Condyloid (knuckle) joint	Lateral	Sesamoid bone
Deep	Lateral (external) rotation	Short bone
Distal	Long bone	Superficial
Dorsiflexion	Medial	Superior
Epidural haemorrhage	Medial (internal) rotation	Supination
Eversion	Median (midsagittal) plane	Supine
Extension	Origin	Synovial joint
Flat bone	Pivot joint	Transverse (horizontal) plane

Discussion Questions

1. Describe the anatomical position and discuss its relationship to the directional terms of the body.

2. What are the four major planes that bisect the body? Provide an example of a movement that occurs in each plane.

3. Define three types of movement and give an example of each for a specific joint in the human body.

4. List the six major types of synovial joints. Which synovial joints allow the greatest amount of movement? The least?

5. Outline the components and roles of the axial and appendicular skeletons.

6. List the five regions of the vertebral column from the most superior to the most inferior. In what region are the atlas and axis located?

7. What type of joint is the knee? What structures present at the knee provide additional support to this joint?

8. What muscles are primarily responsible for maintaining an upright posture?

9. The posterior group of leg muscles is commonly called the hamstrings. What three muscles combine to form the hamstrings? What role do they play?

10. List the four major muscles comprising the abdomen. Which layer is most superficial? Most deep? What actions do these muscles allow you to do?

In This Chapter:

Types of Human Muscle *62*

Skeletal Muscle *62*
    Properties *62*
    Muscle Teamwork *64*
    Structure *64*
    Muscle Fibre Types *69*

Nerve–Muscle Interaction *70*
    Motor Unit *70*

Intra-muscle Coordination *72*

Inter-muscle Coordination *72*
    Sport-specific Training *72*

Muscle's Adaptation to Strength Training *74*

Summary *75*

CHAPTER 3

Muscle Structure and Function

After completing this chapter you should be able to:

- describe the macro and micro structures of skeletal muscle;

- describe muscle contraction and explain the sliding filament theory;

- demonstrate an understanding of nerve–muscle interaction;

- differentiate among types of muscle fibres;

- describe group action of muscles;

- discuss muscle's adaptation to strength training.

61

Structure determines function. This is a statement that defines the essence of human anatomy and physiology. Muscle tissue – the contraction specialist – provides a prime example of how the structure of a tissue is well-adapted to perform a specific function. With approximately 660 muscles in the adult human body, comprising nearly half of our body weight, the importance of muscular activity is obvious. The various structures and types of muscle tissue support numerous life functions, such as ventilation, physical activity and exercise, digestion, and of course, pumping life-sustaining blood throughout the body via specialized cardiac muscle. The focus in this chapter will be on skeletal muscle, which permits voluntary movement, and is unique among other types of muscle in other important ways.

We often look at muscle as a single entity, but in so doing, fail to recognize the molecular complexity and hierarchical structure of this tissue. This specialized structure enables muscle to shorten and develop tension, allowing a myriad of human movements to occur. From movements as simple as waving good-bye or picking up a book, to more complex actions such as those required in athletics, the muscular system is vital to our daily functioning. But how does muscle activity integrate with the nervous system to produce movement? And what are the fundamental contractile properties of muscle?

Types of Human Muscle

On the basis of their structures, contractile properties, and control mechanisms there are three types of muscle in the human body: (1) skeletal muscle; (2) smooth muscle; and (3) cardiac muscle.

Most **skeletal muscle** is attached to bone and its contraction is responsible for supporting and moving the skeleton. The contraction of skeletal muscle is initiated by impulses in the motor neurons to the muscle and is usually under **voluntary** control.

Smooth muscle is under the control of the autonomic nervous system and is called **involuntary**. Smooth muscle forms the walls of blood vessels and body organs, such as the respiratory tract, the iris of the eye, and the gastrointestinal tract. The contractions of smooth muscle are slow and uniform and are very fatigue resistant. Smooth muscle functions to alter the activity of various body parts to meet the needs of the body at the time.

Cardiac muscle, the muscle of the heart, has characteristics of both skeletal and smooth muscle. Cardiac muscle functions to provide the contractile activity of the heart and has its own intrinsic beat. Like skeletal muscle, the contractile activity of cardiac muscle can be graduated; however, cardiac muscle is very fatigue resistant. Like smooth muscle, the activation of cardiac muscle is involuntary.

Although fitness training can benefit all three types of muscle systems, this chapter will deal primarily with the skeletal muscle.

Skeletal Muscle

Properties

Skeletal muscle refers to a number of muscle fibres bound together by connective tissue and is usually linked to bone by bundles of collagen fibres, known as **tendons**. Tendons are located at each end of the muscle (Figure 3.1 A). During muscle contraction, skeletal muscle shortens, and as a result of the tendinous attachments to bone, functions to move the various parts of the skeleton with respect to one another (joints) to allow changes in position of one skeletal segment in relation to another. Positioning several muscles on each "side" of a joint allows movement in several planes, and through graded activation the speed and smoothness of the movement can be graduated.

Skeletal muscles are capable of rapid contraction and relaxation. Intensive activity causes them to show early signs of fatigue. The assessment of the movement and the sequential pattern of muscle activation acting through joints to move

Origin–Insertion

In order for muscles to contract they must be attached to bones to create movement. This is accomplished by tendons, strong fibrous tissues at the ends of each muscle. The end of the muscle attached to the bone that does not move Is called the **origin**, while the point of attachment of the muscle on the bone that moves is the **insertion** (Figure 3.1 A). The origin tends to be the more proximal attachment (closer to the body), while the insertion is the more distal attachment (further from the body).

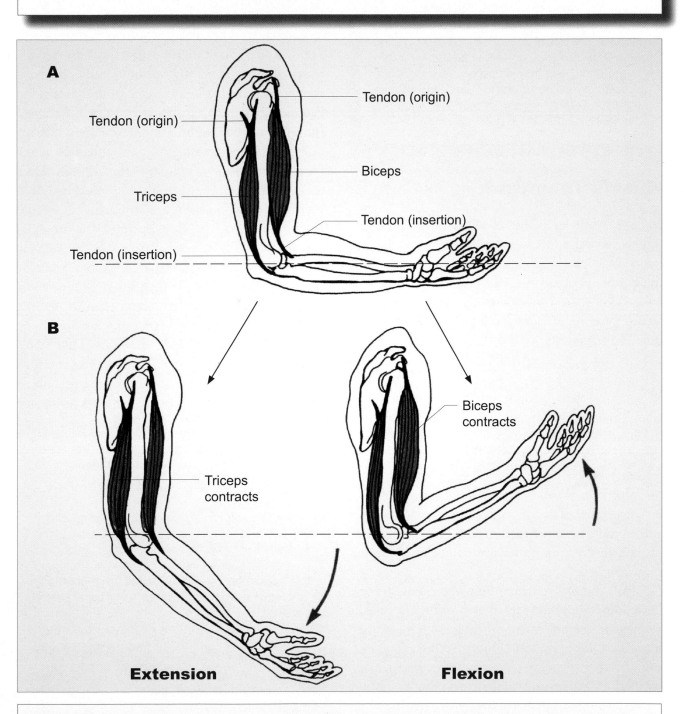

Figure 3.1 Bending or straightening the elbow requires the coordinated interplay of the biceps and triceps muscles.

body segments is termed **biomechanics of human movement** (see Chapter 7).

Muscle Teamwork

Muscles work in perfect synchrony. When one muscle contracts (draws together) to move a bone, the other relaxes, allowing the bone to move. The muscle or group of muscles producing a desired effect is known as the **agonist**, the **prime mover**. A muscle or group of muscles opposing the action is called an **antagonist**.

An agonist–antagonist relationship occurs between the biceps and triceps of the upper arm. When the biceps (agonist) contracts to bend the elbow, the triceps (antagonist) relaxes and allows the bend. When the triceps (agonist) contracts to straighten the arm, the biceps (antagonist) in turn relaxes (Figure 3.1 B).

The cooperation of biceps and triceps is typical of what takes place throughout the body. When entire groups of muscles get involved the interaction between agonist and antagonist muscles becomes more complex.

The muscles surrounding the joint being moved and supporting it in the action are called **synergists** (complementing the action of a prime mover). Other muscle groups called **fixators** will steady joints closer to the body axis so that the desired action can occur. For example, if you want to climb a rope hand over hand, the muscles holding your shoulder girdle tightly to your rib cage are fixators, enabling you to use the muscles acting over the shoulder, elbow, wrist, and finger joints to perform their job and pull you up the rope.

Structure

Skeletal muscle is comprised of numerous cylinder-shaped cells called **muscle fibres**, and each fibre is made up of a number of **myofilaments** (Figure 3.2). The diameter of each fibre varies between 0.05 and 0.10 mm, with the length being dependent mainly on the distance between skeletal attachments (in the case of the biceps, the length of a fibre is approximately 15 cm). Each cell (fibre) is surrounded by a connective tissue sheath called the **sarcolemma**, and a variable number of fibres are enclosed together by a thicker connective tissue sheath to form a bundle of fibres (Figure 3.2 B). Each fibre contains not only the contractile machinery needed to develop force (Figure 3.3), but also the cell organelles necessary for cellular respiration (see Chapter 5, Energy for Muscular Activity). Also located outside each fibre is a supply of capillaries from which the cell obtains nutrients and eliminates waste.

A large number of individual thread-like fibres known as **myofibrils** run lengthwise and parallel to one another within a muscle fibre. The myofibrils contain contractile units that are responsible for muscle contraction (Figure 3.2 D).

Muscle: The Contractile Machinery

Within each myofibril, a number of contractile units, called **sarcomeres** (Figure 3.3 A), are organized in series, i.e., attached end to end. Each sarcomere is comprised of two types of protein myofilaments: **myosin**, the so-called thick filament, and **actin**, termed the thin filament. Looking at the filaments in a cross-section, i.e., looking at the myofilaments end-on, we see that each myosin filament is surrounded by actin filaments (Figure 3.3 A). Examining the sarcomere longitudinally, i.e., length-wise, we see the distinctive banding pattern (striations) characteristic of skeletal, or striated, muscle (Figure 3.4). Projecting out from each of the myosin filaments at an angle of approximately 45 degrees are tiny contractile elements called **myosin bridges**; from this view, these elements look similar to the projections of oars from a rowing shell (Figure 3.3).

The Sliding Filament Theory   During the contraction of a muscle, it is the sliding of the thin actin filaments over the thick myosin filaments that causes shortening of the muscle to create movement. This phenomenon is called the **sliding filament theory**. It is far more complex than described here, but you should still be able to appreciate all the intricate anatomical structures involved with every move we make.

Myofibril

Muscle Fibre

Muscle Fibre Bundle

Muscle Belly

D   **C**   **B**   **A**

Figure 3.2   Components of skeletal muscle. **A.** Muscle belly (50 mm in diameter). **B.** Muscle fibre bundle (0.5 mm). **C.** Muscle fibre (0.05-0.1 mm). **D.** Myofibril (0.001-0.002 mm).

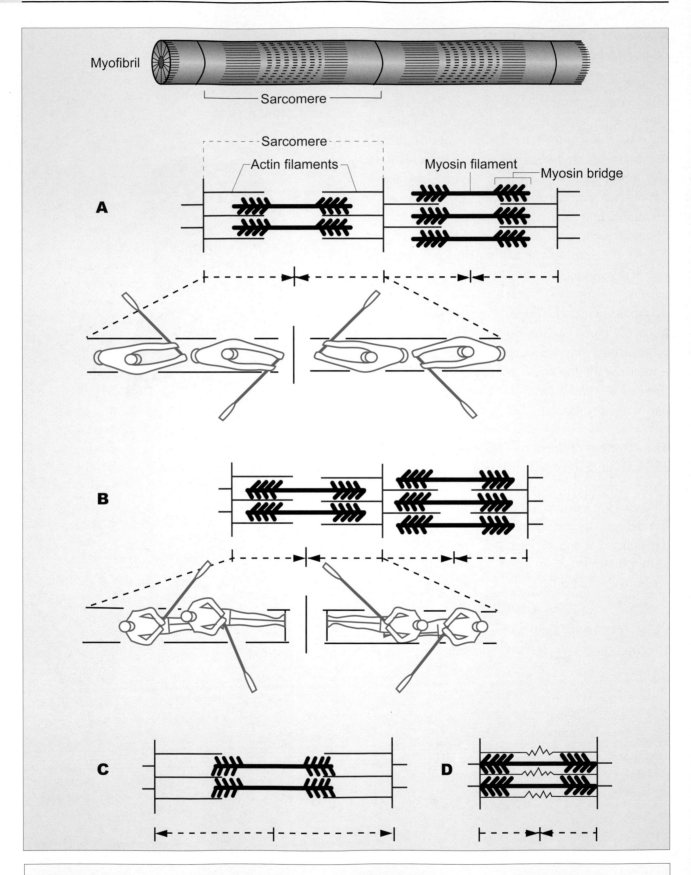

Figure 3.3 Longitudinal section of a myofibril and simplified representation of muscular contraction: **A.** At rest. **B.** Contraction. **C.** Powerful stretching. **D.** Powerful contraction.

Rowing Simulation When a signal comes from the motor nerve activating the fibre, the heads of the myosin filaments temporarily attach themselves to the actin filaments (Figure 3.3 D), a process termed **cross bridge formation**. In a manner similar to the stroking of the oars, and the subsequent movement of a rowing shell, the movement of the cross bridges causes a movement of the actin filaments in relation to the myosin filaments, leading to shortening of the sarcomere. A single "stroke" shortens the sarcomere by approximately 1 percent of its length, and the nervous system is capable of activating cross bridge formation at a rate of 7-50 per second. Since the sarcomeres are attached to one another in series, the shortening of each sarcomere is additive. The total amount of fibre shortening amounts to some 25-40 percent of myofibril length.

To produce an efficient rowing stroke, the oars must be optimally placed, i.e., reaching far enough, but not too far; similarly, for optimal cross bridge formation, the sarcomeres should be an optimal distance apart. For muscle contraction, this optimal distance is 0.0019-0.0022 mm. When the sarcomeres are separated by this distance, an optimal number of cross bridges can be formed per unit time. If the sarcomeres are farther apart, or closer together, than this optimal distance, then fewer cross bridges can be formed, resulting in less force development. If the sarcomeres are stretched further apart, as occurs when the muscle is in a lengthened (i.e., extended or stretched) position (Figure 3.3 C), fewer cross bridges can form as the myosin projections have difficulty in reaching the actin filaments; this results in a decreased ability to produce force. When the sarcomeres are too close together, as would occur when the muscle is shortened (flexed), the cross bridges in fact interfere with one another as they try to form, resulting in a fewer number of effective cross bridges being formed, and again a decreased ability to develop force (Figure 3.3 D).

The distance between sarcomeres depends on the state of muscle stretch, which in turn is a product of the position of the joint. What this means to the development of muscle force is that maximal force is developed when an optimal number of cross bridges are formed, which occurs at an optimal joint angle. Thus, as muscle force depends on muscle length, maximal muscle force occurs at optimal muscle length. As a joint moves through its range of motion, the muscle(s) connecting the two segments of the joint will move from a stretched position to a compressed position, and therefore, at some point in the movement, will pass through a position, termed the optimal joint angle, at which the muscle is at optimal length for maximal force development (Figure 3.5). This means that there would be an optimal joint angle for maximal force development

Figure 3.4 High magnification view of a single sarcomere within a single myofibril. The characteristic "striped" appearance of skeletal muscle is a result of the arrangement of the actin and myosin strands.

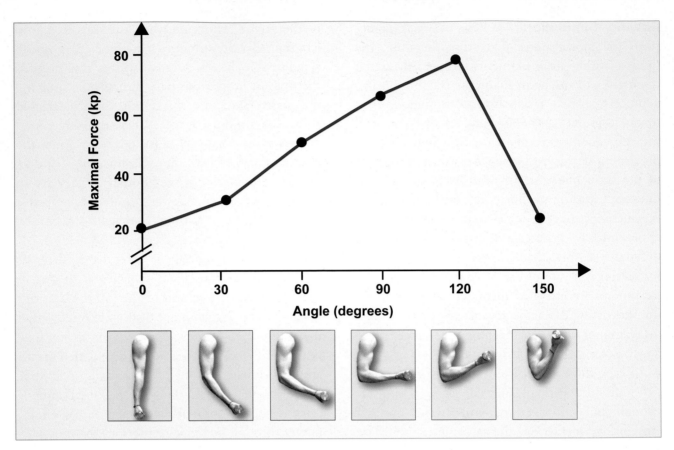

Figure 3.5 Maximal muscle force changes continuously throughout elbow flexion according to the joint angle.

Table 3.1 Relative involvement of muscle fibre types in sport events.

Event	Slow Twitch – Type I	Fast Twitch – Type II
100-m sprint	Low	High
800-m run	High	High
Marathon	High	Low
Olympic weightlifting	Low	High
Barbell squat	Low	High
Soccer	High	High
Field hockey	High	High
Football wide receiver	Low	High
Football lineman	High	High
Basketball	Low	High
Distance cycling	High	Low

for each movement of a joint. Knowledge of the joint angle at which maximal force can be developed is important in the development of optimal biomechanics of the movement.

Muscle Fibre Types

There are also different types of skeletal muscle fibres. Some fibres can reach maximum tension more quickly than others. Based on this distinction, muscle fibres can be divided into the categories of **fast twitch** (FT or Type II) (also called white fibres based on their microscopic appearance) and **slow twitch** (ST or Type I) (also called red fibres based on their microscopic appearance). FT fibres are more anaerobic, larger, fatigue faster, and have a faster contraction speed than ST fibres. This makes these fibres ideal for actions that are short and require quick bursts of power and energy, such as sprinting or jumping. On the other hand,

events that require endurance, such as long-distance running, swimming, or cycling, depend on the smaller, slower contracting, fatigue-resistant ST fibres that rely on oxygen (Table 3.1). There are also fibre types that fall in between these extremes with characteristics of both fibre types. Thus, Type II is further divided into Type IIa and Type IIb fibres. The distinction between the two is mainly in their contractile strength and their capacity for aerobic-oxidative energy supply. The Type IIa fibres have greater capacity for aerobic metabolism and more capillaries surrounding them than Type IIb and therefore show greater resistance to fatigue.

The muscle fibre composition of an individual is dictated through heredity. The fibre composition of an individual cannot be *altered* by training, i.e., the transformation of a fibre from one type to another as a result of the training stimulus does not occur.

Most skeletal muscles, however, contain both FT

Fast Twitch (Type II) Fibres (large diameter)

Capillary Blood Vessels

Slow Twitch (Type I) Fibres (small diameter)

Figure 3.6 Muscle biopsy.

and ST fibres, with the amount of each varying from one muscle to another, as well as among different individuals. Therefore, individual performance differences occur as a result of varying percentages of the muscle fibre types, making some individuals suited to some activities more than others (that is not to say that training will not *improve* what fibres you do have).

Muscle Biopsy

Muscle fibre type is determined from a **muscle biopsy**. In this procedure, a small incision (about 5-7 mm) is made in the skin and fascia of the muscle following injection of a local anaesthetic into the muscle. A tiny piece of tissue is cut and removed from the muscle and then analyzed under a microscope (Figure 3.6). In addition to determining muscle fibre type, it is possible to study the metabolic characteristics of the muscle, and to assess changes in metabolic capability following various types of training programs.

Biopsy = *bio* (life) + *opsis* (sight)

Nerve–Muscle Interaction

As with bone, muscle is a living tissue, and as such, is richly supplied with blood vessels and nerves. Skeletal muscle activation is initiated through neural activation (Figure 3.7), and therefore, is under conscious control. The nervous system is organized at two levels – the **central (CNS)** and **peripheral (PNS) nervous systems**, with the central system being composed of the brain and spinal cord (Figure 3.7 A), and the peripheral system being made up of numerous nerves of various sizes (Figure 3.7 C).

The nervous system can also be divided in terms of function, namely motor and sensory activity. The sensory section (Figure 3.7 E) collects information from the various sensors located throughout the body and transmits the information to the brain where it is processed and acted upon. This sensory information is also stored away so that future responses to similar input can be acted upon more quickly. The motor section (Figure 3.7 D) is involved directly in conducting the signals from the CNS to activate muscle contraction (see Chapter 17, Information Processing in Motor Learning).

Motor Unit

Motor nerves extend from the spinal cord to the muscle fibres. Each fibre is activated through impulses delivered via its **motor end plate**. A group of fibres activated via the same nerve is termed a **motor unit**, the basic functional entity of muscular activity. A muscle can be composed of a different number of motor units and each motor unit can in turn consist of a different number of muscle fibres.

All muscle fibres of one particular motor unit, however, are always of the same fibre type (FT or ST fibres). Muscles that need to perform delicate and precise movements (the eye and finger muscles) generally consist of a large number of motor units (1,500-3,000), each containing only a few muscle fibres (8-50). Relatively unrefined movement, however, is carried out by muscles composed of fewer motor units with many fibres (approximately 600-2,000), each of which innervates up to 1,500 muscle fibres. In the tibialis anterior muscle, approximately 650 muscle fibres are innervated by each motor unit; in the gastrocnemius muscle, the number is approximately 1,600, and in the extensors of the back, it is about 2,000.

The specific number of fibres in a motor unit of any given muscle can vary. The biceps may be composed of motor units that innervate 1,000, 1,200, 1,400, or 1,600 fibres. Furthermore, each muscle fibre can be innervated by only one motor unit. This cannot be altered through exercise.

All-or-none Principle

Muscle movement is controlled by the motor nerve

impulses transmitted from the CNS and spinal cord out to the motor unit, which when activated causes the muscle fibres to contract. Whether or not a motor unit activates upon the arrival of an impulse depends upon the so-called **all-or-none principle**. This principle, discussed in more detail in Chapter 17, requires an impulse of a certain magnitude (or strength) to cause the innervated fibres to contract. The principle is analogous to firing a gun. Once a sufficient amount of pressure is placed on the trigger, the gun fires; pulling on the trigger harder will not cause the bullet to go faster or further.

Activation Threshold Every motor unit has a specific threshold that must be reached for such activation to occur. For the biceps muscle, for example, all of the 1,500 fibres that may comprise

a single motor unit will contract maximally providing the nerve impulse has reached a certain magnitude. However, if the nerve impulse does not reach the required magnitude, then none of the fibres will contract.

A weak nerve impulse activates only those motor units that have a low threshold of activation. A stronger nerve impulse will additionally activate motor units with higher thresholds. As the resistance increases, more motor units must be activated by stronger, more intensive impulses. An athlete needs increasingly more will power to exceed the excitatory thresholds of the motor units. This process is extremely fatiguing as a result of lactic acid accumulation in the muscle tissue and blood, the depletion of high-energy compounds, and the fatigue of the nervous system processes.

Figure 3.7 Sensory neurons transfer messages to the central nervous system, where they are analyzed and responded to by motor neurons. Activation of a motor unit and its innervation systems: **A.** Spinal cord. **B.** Cytosomes. **C.** Spinal nerve. **D.** Motor nerve. **E.** Sensory nerve. **F.** Muscle with muscle fibres.

Intra-muscle Coordination

The capacity to activate motor units simultaneously is known as **intra-muscle coordination**. Although it is impossible to use all the motor units of a muscle at the same time, many highly trained power athletes, such as weightlifters, wrestlers, and shot-putters, are able to activate up to 85 percent of their available muscle fibres simultaneously, thus generating great strength. Untrained individuals, on the other hand, can normally activate only up to 60 percent of their fibres.

Research has shown that under hypnosis a trained athlete can elevate the maximal force application for a given muscle by approximately 10 percent. The difference between assisted and voluntarily generated maximal force is regarded as the **muscle force deficit** of the muscle contraction. For untrained individuals, this deficit is much larger (approximately 20-35 percent).

Trained athletes have not only a larger muscle mass than untrained individuals, but can also exploit a larger number of muscle fibres to produce force. However, for this reason, such athletes are more restricted than untrained individuals in further developing strength by improving intra-muscle coordination. For this same reason, trained individuals can further increase strength only by increasing muscle diameter.

Inter-muscle Coordination

Any physical movement requires considerable effort by the muscles or muscle groups to master a given movement. This requires an optimal level of **inter-muscle coordination**.

The interplay between muscles that generate movement through contraction, the agonists or prime movers, and muscles responsible for opposing movement, the antagonists, is of particular importance to the quality of inter-muscle coordination. The cooperation between agonist and antagonist muscles during the bench press, for example, provides a useful illustration. From a supine position, an athlete explosively stretches his or her arms against a high resistance. During the movement, a considerable number of motor units in the triceps and in cooperating muscles are synchronously activated, while the motor units of the antagonist muscles relax.

The greater the participation of muscles and muscle groups, the higher the importance of inter-muscle coordination for strength capacity. To benefit from strength training, technically demanding sport-specific movements are often broken down into partial movements, so that the individual muscle groups responsible for these movements can be trained in relative isolation. The exercises used closely resemble the movement structure of the sport-specific movement, such that the training allows for the key muscle groups to be loaded relatively heavily.

Sport-specific Training

Consider the following exercises, which are beneficial to shot-putters: the bench press (Figure 3.8 A), lateral trunk curl (Figure 3.8 B), knee bend or squat (Figure 3.8 C), and heel or calf raise (Figure 3.8 D). An athlete whose muscles have been trained and developed in isolation using such exercises must subsequently engage in training that coordinates these muscles within the complete, sport-specific movement. Difficulties may occur if the athlete fails to develop all the relevant muscles in a balanced manner. For instance, a shot-putter who uses exercises that increase strength in only the arm and leg extensors, but not the trunk muscles, may experience major disturbances of inter-muscle coordination. As a result, performance may not improve or reach the level desired by the athlete.

High-level inter-muscle coordination greatly improves strength performance and also enhances the flow, rhythm, and precision of movement. Unlike an ordinary individual, a highly trained athlete is able to translate strength potential more effectively into strength performance through enhanced inter-muscle coordination.

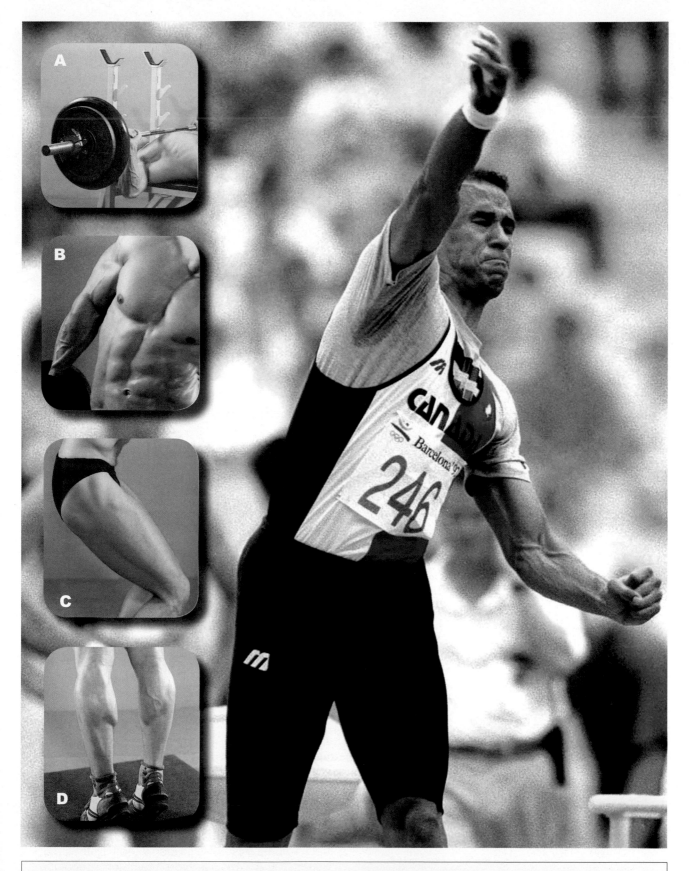

Figure 3.8 A shot-putter's training includes exercises that work several prime movers in isolation. **A.** Bench press. **B.** Lateral trunk curl. **C.** Knee bend or squat. **D.** Heel or calf raise.

Trainable vs. Non-trainable Factors

The performance capacity of muscle is determined by several trainable and non-trainable factors.

Trainable factors:

- fibre diameter
- intra-muscle coordination
- nerve impulse frequency
- inter-muscle coordination
- elasticity of muscle and its tendons
- energy stores of muscle and liver
- capillary density of muscle

Non-trainable factors:

- number of fibres
- fibre structure (ST or FT fibres)

Muscle's Adaptation to Strength Training

In strength training, an individual's performance improvements occur through a process of **biological adaptation**, which is reflected in the body's increased strength. Similar types of adaptation may occur in any form of training. Indeed, they are the building blocks for improved performance in any athletic activity.

In strength training, the adaptation process proceeds at different time rates for different functional systems and physiological processes. The adaptation depends on a variety of factors, in particular on intensity levels used in training and on an athlete's unique biological make-up. Specific substances of the metabolism, such as enzymes, adapt within hours; the energy supply in the liver and muscle increases at a more moderate pace, within 10-14 days, by which time the first adaptations in the cardiovascular circulation also occur (see Chapter 6). The muscle mass increases slowly, within four to six weeks, its growth caused by an increase in the structural proteins in the skeletal muscle fibres.

Recruitment of Muscle Fibres

Recruitment of muscle fibres during resistance work depends on the level of muscle tension. As the tension rises, more and more of the various fibre types are recruited into the movement as shown by the curves. Muscle tension below 25 percent of one's maximal resistance recruits mostly ST fibres. At higher resistance, FT fibres also become active. Furthermore, which fibre is involved depends upon the muscle force that needs to be mobilized, and also the rate of acceleration of the mass to be moved. High accelerations of small loads and low accelerations of high loads require the intensive involvement of the FT fibres. Also, it is primarily the FT fibres that generate the explosive-type movements requiring a lot of strength.

Summary

Muscles attached to skeletal bones work together and with tendons to enable body movement. Thin fibres called myofibrils constitute muscle, and end-to-end units called sarcomeres within each myofibril enable muscles to contract, causing movement in response to motor nerve stimulation.

Motor nerves extend from the spinal cord to muscles throughout the body, and each motor unit is specific to either fast twitch or slow twitch muscle types. FT fibres, which are anaerobic in nature and fatigue faster than ST fibres, are best suited for activities requiring short bursts of power and energy. Endurance events such as long-distance running, swimming, or cycling make use of the fatigue-resistant ST fibres that rely on oxygen. Motor units require threshold levels of nerve impulses before they can react – and some motor units have higher resistance thresholds than companion units in the same muscle.

Movement requires precise coordination of muscles and the muscle fibres themselves. Intra-muscle coordination is the ability to activate motor units simultaneously, while inter-muscle coordination refers to the synchronization of different muscles and muscle groups. Cooperation of the agonists and antagonists is necessary for smooth, controlled motion.

Key Words

Actin	Intra-muscle coordination	Prime mover
Agonist	Involuntary muscle	Sarcolemma
All-or-none principle	Motor end plate	Sarcomere
Antagonist	Motor unit	Skeletal muscle
Biological adaptation	Muscle biopsy	Sliding filament theory
Cardiac muscle	Muscle fibre	Slow twitch (ST) fibre
Cross bridge formation	Muscle force deficit	Smooth muscle
Fast twitch (FT) fibre	Myofibril	Striated muscle
Fixator	Myofilament	Synergist
Insertion	Myosin	Tendon
Inter-muscle coordination	Origin	Voluntary muscle

Discussion Questions

1. What are the three types of muscle found in the human body?

2. Describe the structure of a muscle from the largest structural unit to the smallest.

3. Explain how the sarcomere contracts, resulting in muscle shortening.

4. What are the three types of muscle fibres? Give two characteristics of each type of fibre.

5. Explain nerve–muscle interaction.

6. Discuss the differences between inter- and intra-muscle coordination.

In This Chapter:

Types of Muscle Contraction 78
    Static Contraction *78*
    Dynamic Contraction *80*
    Isometric Contraction *80*
    Auxotonic Contraction *80*
    Isotonic Contraction *81*
    Isokinetic Contraction *82*
    Concentric and Eccentric Contractions *83*
    Plyocentric Contraction *83*

Factors Influencing Muscle Contraction 83
    Joint Angle *83*
    Muscle Cross-sectional Area *84*
    Speed of Movement *86*
    Muscle Fibre Type *90*
    Age *91*
    Sex *91*

Summary 93

CHAPTER 4

Muscles at Work

After completing this chapter you should be able to:

- differentiate among the various types of muscle contractions;

- describe the factors that influence strength development;

- identify the components of strength;

- discuss the relationships among the various components of strength.

Muscle is an organ that creates movement. Its structure and function presented in the previous chapter can adapt according to some important training principles. These principles are designed to improve general and specific fitness, which is an important component of overall health. However, before we present the various principles of training in Chapter 9, you must become familiar with the various types of muscle contraction. You must also understand the concept of muscular strength, its components, and the interrelationships among these components, which provide the basis of training for fitness and athletic performance.

Types of Muscle Contraction

Several types of muscle contraction are relevant to a fitness and strength training program. The first distinction is made between static and dynamic contraction.

Static and dynamic work involves five types of muscle contraction: isometric, isotonic, auxotonic, isokinetic, and plyocentric. Each of these types of contractions is further divided into two forms of movement: concentric and eccentric.

> ### Did You Know?
>
> It is interesting to note that the terminology for major muscle contractions has been developed from the Greek language (Figure 4.1).

Static Contraction

Static contraction refers to a contraction in which the muscle tension or force exerted against an external load is equal or weaker, so no visible movement of the load occurs. Consider an athlete who attempts to flex an arm against the resistance of a fixed bar. Even if all energy and strength are mobilized, the athlete will not succeed in moving the arm or the bar. Nonetheless, the exerted muscle force is substantial.

In most sports, maximal static tension is rare. It may occur, however, in gymnastics (in the iron cross and hanging scale) or in wrestling and judo (in floor grips, holding techniques, and bridges). In general, most sport activities require low to **submaximal static contraction**. Sailing in close contact with the wind, shooting, and alpine downhill events often require static work over extended periods (Figure 4.2).

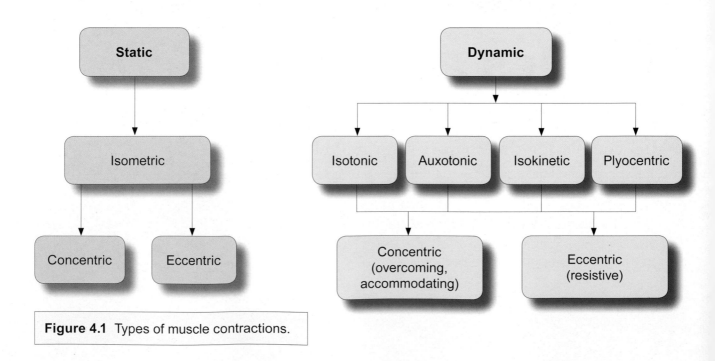

Figure 4.1 Types of muscle contractions.

A **B**

Figure 4.2 Static or isometric contractions. **A.** Activities requiring maximal static muscle tension. **B.** Activities requiring submaximal static muscle tension.

Dynamic Contraction

The neuromuscular system is said to work dynamically if internal and external forces are unbalanced. For instance, an athlete may be able to exert enough force to lift a weight through the full range of an exercise. When the external force (gravity of a weight or object) is smaller than the internal force generated by the athlete, the latter will be able to resist, and the result will be movement. Thus, a **dynamic contraction** involves movement.

Isometric Contraction

An **isometric contraction** (*iso* = same, *metric* = length) is one in which there is no visible change in muscle length, even though the muscle has undergone muscle contraction. In this case, the contraction is against a load which is beyond the capability of the muscle(s) to move, and therefore, no movement of the load occurs. We also know that considerable force has been produced by the tiredness that one feels. The issue here is that no external movement is registered. Isometric contraction is a static contraction.

Strictly speaking, no work is performed during an isometric contraction (work = force x distance); nonetheless, a relatively high amount of tension is developed and energy is used. Therefore, an isometric contraction is not defined by the work performed but by the rate of tension developed and by the duration over which the tension lasts.

When two individuals of equal strength compete in arm wrestling an isometric contraction occurs. There will be no movement of the hands until one individual fatigues (loses some of the cross bridges) and therefore can no longer maintain the status quo. For more on cross bridge formation, see Chapter 3.

Can you name other activities that are based on isometric contraction?

Auxotonic Contraction

Under normal circumstances, dynamic work is based on **auxotonic contraction** (*auxo* = increased, *tonos* = tension). Because of the continual change in joint angle and speed that occurs during dynamic work, the muscle needs to contract at either increasing or decreasing tension; the term auxotonic literally means "increased tension," although here it is used in the sense of "variable tension." The constant addition or subtraction of motor units recruited causes the muscle to adapt to constantly changing tension requirements. Auxotonic contraction is a dynamic contraction.

When an athlete bends the arms while holding a barbell, the mass of the barbell obviously remains unchanged during the entire range of movement. The strength needed to perform this movement is not, however, constant, but depends upon the physique of the athlete, the athlete's leverage, the angle position of the limbs, and on speed of movement (Figure 4.3). Also see Figure 3.5 on page 68 in Chapter 3.

Lateral arm raises, too, require greater strength initially, reaching a maximum at 90 degrees and then dropping constantly. When lifting the trunk from a horizontal position, an athlete needs to mobilize maximal strength at the beginning of the movement, gradually reach peak values, and then decline continuously towards zero.

The issue of changing muscle force or tension throughout a movement also poses a problem to those using free weights to train. What often happens is one of two scenarios. If the chosen load can be lifted throughout the complete range of motion, it provides adequate stress for training in the initial and final stages of the movement, but does not stress the muscle as much in the area of movement corresponding to optimal cross bridge formation. It is often in this area that the athlete wants to train, whether it is for the development of additional strength or the building of muscle bulk. If the load is chosen to provide training stress to the muscle in that part of the range of movement corresponding to optimal cross bridge formation, then the load is often too great for the individual to be able to move at either end of the complete range of movement. In this case, the individual often gets the bar moving by "bumping" it with

Figure 4.3 Muscle tension during elbow flexion varies according to the joint angle.

his thighs, and, at the end of the curl, lets it fall onto the shoulders. When lowering the bar, the first movement is to drop the bar until sufficient cross bridges can form to stop its falling, and the movement ends with the bar falling onto the thighs. Most often, the latter course of action is taken, and the result is that the individual does not train throughout the full range of motion, often resulting in the appearance that the arms can't be straightened! What one would like to have happen is that the muscle is optimally stressed throughout the range of motion. To do this, the load must be increased as the lift is made, and then decreased

as you pass the region where optimal cross bridge formation occurs, a difficult task to say the least when training with free weights.

Isotonic Contraction

Dynamic contraction is based on **isotonic contraction** (*iso* = same or constant and *tonos* = tension) only in exceptional cases. In an isotonic contraction, the muscle changes length but not its tension. For instance, an athlete achieves (an approximately) isotonic contraction when lowering an extremely heavy barbell at a slow and constant speed against maximal resistance.

In its pure form, however, this type of contraction is rarely encountered in sports and athletic events. The movement of any load involves continually changing joint angles, and these place changing demands on the level of tension required to move the load.

Isokinetic Contraction

In **isokinetic contraction** (*iso* = same or constant and *kinetic* = motion), the neuromuscular system can work at a constant speed during each phase of movement (despite the constantly changing leverage or torque) against a preset high resistance. This allows the working muscles and muscle groups to release high tension over each section of the movement range. This type of contraction is effective for strengthening the musculature uniformly at all angles of motion.

As in the auxotonic contraction, however, the precise amount of muscle tension release is always dependent upon the corresponding joint angle and the velocity of movement. This is accomplished, with varying degrees of success, by a number of expensive dynamometers, including the CYBEX,

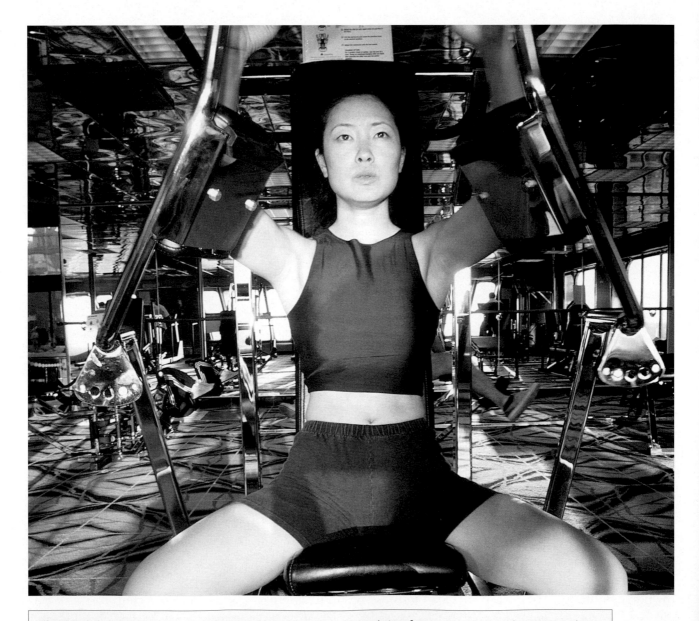

Figure 4.4 Isokinetic contractions are generated by a variety of very expensive dynamometers.

the KINCOM, and the LIDO, which keep the speed of movement constant electronically, and the HydraGym and Nautilus, which use mechanical means to produce movements which are "isokinetic" in nature (Figure 4.4).

The relatively constant speeds involved in swimming and rowing are similar to those produced in isokinetic exercise forms. For this reason, these sports use isokinetic training to increase performance levels. However, the majority of sports contain few pure isokinetic movements as they continuously require changes in velocity and force application throughout movements.

Isokinetic contractions are classified as dynamic contractions.

Concentric and Eccentric Contractions

A **concentric contraction** is one in which the muscle shortens as it goes through the range of motion; this is usually termed **flexion**. An **eccentric contraction** is one in which the muscle lengthens during the movement, and is usually termed **extension**. Again, let's use the arm curl with free weights as an example (Figure 4.3). The movement of the bar from the thighs to the shoulder region, flexion of the biceps brachii, is an auxotonic concentric contraction. The movement from the shoulder area back to the thighs, i.e., extension of biceps brachii, is an isotonic eccentric contraction.

Plyocentric Contraction

The last type of muscle contraction, a **plyocentric contraction**, is a hybrid contraction in that the muscle performs an isotonic concentric contrac-tion, but from a stretched position. The "pre-stretching" of the muscle is achieved by jumping off an object (box) from a height of 25-40 cm (depth jumping). This not only pre-stretches the muscles, but also sets off the **golgi tendon organ** reflex which functions to protect the muscle from too much stretch. The reflex causes the muscles to contract. Activities which utilize this type of contraction to train jumping ability include leaping and bounding, such as in plyometric training. Research has shown that this type of strength and power training leads to a greater increase in jump height than that developed by strength training alone.

Factors Influencing Muscle Contraction

There are numerous factors that can affect the force and power output of a muscle, including the individual's **state of health** and **training status**. Other factors that affect force and power output include: (1) joint angle; (2) muscle cross-sectional area; (3) speed of movement; (4) muscle fibre type; (5) age; and (6) sex.

Joint Angle

Let us again consider the example of elbow flexion during a barbell lift (Figure 4.3). Contraction of the elbow flexors is initially isometric (static). The muscle does not visibly shorten until after the internal forces generated by muscle flexing exceed the external forces of the barbell. As the arms flex at the elbow joints, the barbell is moved toward the shoulders. The barbell accelerates in proportion to the degree that the internal forces exceed the load of the barbell. A short phase of static work, often lasting only a few hundredths of a second, occurs between the dynamic work of concentric contraction and the lowering of the barbell. On lowering the barbell into its initial position, external forces exceed internal ones. The same muscles that previously were involved in lifting

Figure 4.5 Relationship between body weight and maximal load lifted for the combined clean and jerk and snatch events (data from the Seoul Olympics competition in weightlifting).

the barbell are now being stretched, and with the arms extended at the elbow joint, the barbell is lowered. Elbow flexors, which on lifting the load performed dynamic concentric contractions, are now involved in lowering the load by performing dynamic eccentric contractions. The greater the external force, the higher the speed at which the load is lowered. "Muscle teamwork" (agonist vs. antagonist) was discussed in Chapter 3.

An athlete doing knee bends performs an eccentric contraction during the flexing phase and a concentric contraction during the ensuing extension phase.

Athletic activities involving only one muscle or muscle group are rare. During each phase of movement, some muscles contract in a dynamic concentric mode, others in a dynamic eccentric mode, and some contract statically. For example, an athlete doing knee bends activates over 75 percent of the body's skeletal musculature to generate the total movement.

Muscle Cross-sectional Area

Human beings have always recognized the close connection between body mass and strength. The relationship between body mass and strength is indeed valid. The greater one's stature the greater one's strength – provided body mass is composed mainly of muscle and not fat. In other words, strength is determined by the volume of active body matter, that is, the entire body mass minus body fat. This mass is also referred to as the fat-free or lean body mass (see discussion on this topic in Chapter 12). This fact has been emphasized by the performances of weightlifters across various weight categories (Figure 4.5). The world record in the bantamweight division (56 kg) is greater than that in the flyweight (52 kg) division; and in the featherweight (60 kg) division it is higher than in the bantamweight division. The heaviest weights of all are lifted by athletes of the super-heavyweight category (in excess of 110 kg).

Maximal or Absolute Strength

From the above discussion we can conclude that the greater the active body mass, the greater the maximal or absolute strength. This general rule is based on the notion that strength depends to a

Figure 4.6 The larger the muscle cross-sectional area, the more force it can generate.

From Greek Mythology

The alertness and great strength of Hercules, the hero of Greek mythology, allowed him to perform extraordinary deeds. Even today, the name Hercules itself suggests a human being of giant stature and great physical strength.

high degree on the size of the muscle cross-section (Figure 4.6). However, this statement requires qualification. Because intra- and inter-muscle coordination, anatomical structure, as well as the elasticity of muscle also play an important part in the performance capacity of the muscle, it is possible for individuals of a small and lighter physique to possess a relatively high strength potential. For discussion on inter- and intra-muscle coordination, refer to Chapter 3.

Strength is also of critical importance to athletes who are not classified by weight but whose prime aim, nevertheless, is to overcome the resistance of a partner or equipment. Thus, wrestlers, judokas, and weightlifters competing in the highest weight category, as well as shot-putters, javelin throwers, and hammer throwers may all want to increase their strength by increasing muscle mass (and therefore total body mass). Weightlifters may also strive to increase their overall strength through an extreme thickening of the muscle fibres.

Relative Strength

The performance of athletes classified by weight (such as weightlifters), and athletes who must overcome their own body mass (such as jumpers,

runners, gymnasts, etc.), depends less on maximal strength than on the proportion of maximal strength to body mass. A gymnast, for instance, will be unable to perform an iron cross unless his neuromuscular system can generate approximately 10 Newtons of force per kilogram of body mass. The relationship between maximal strength and body mass is also referred to as **relative strength**.

$$\text{Relative Strength} = \frac{\text{Maximal Strength}}{\text{Body Mass}}$$

Consider the following example. Two athletes performing bench presses can lift a maximal barbell load with full arm extension. Suppose both are able to lift 100 kg (i.e., each develops equal maximal strength for the movement), but athlete A weighs 75 kg, athlete B 100 kg. Using the formula above, athlete B's relative strength is 1.0 (100 / 100 = 1.0), whereas athlete A's is 1.33 (100 / 75 = 1.33). It follows that the lighter athlete's (A) relative strength is higher than the heavier athlete's (B) (Figure 4.7).

Recreational athletes are usually interested in increasing their active strength by stabilizing their maximal strength and reducing body mass. Overweight athletes who want to lose superfluous fat also follow this method. It is of little use to competitive athletes, however, because a reduction of body mass is often linked with loss of muscle mass and therefore with a decrease in maximal and relative strength.

Another way to increase relative strength is to increase strength and stabilize body mass. As maximal strength is not only dependent upon muscle diameter, but also upon intra-

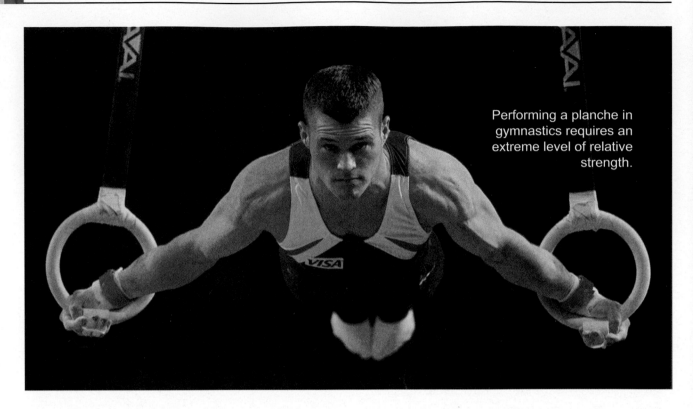

Performing a planche in gymnastics requires an extreme level of relative strength.

muscle coordination, this variation is often quite promising, provided that the correct and relevant training methods are chosen.

For young recreational athletes, the more favourable training programs are those that hold out the prospect of strength development in conjunction with a sensible and adequate increase in active body mass.

Speed of Movement

For movements occurring at fast velocities, the

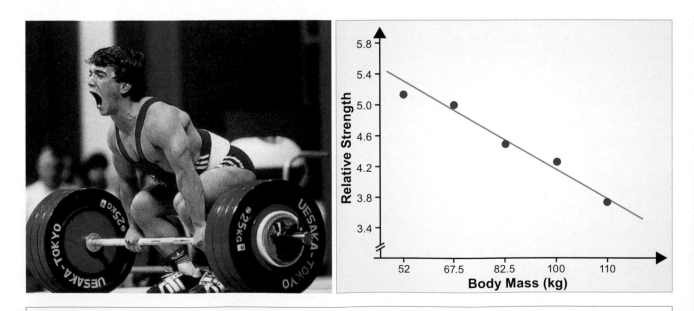

Figure 4.7 Relationship between relative strength and body weight based on the combined clean and jerk and snatch events (data from the Seoul Olympics competition in weightlifting).

cross bridges cannot couple and uncouple fast enough to establish and maintain a large number of cross bridges. This results in a decreased ability to develop force at fast velocities. This means that as the speed of movement is increased, the force that the muscle can develop is decreased.

Speed of movement is closely linked to the main components of strength: maximal strength, power, and muscle endurance. The relationships among these components also interact to affect speed of movement.

Maximal Strength

Maximal strength is the ability of the athlete to perform maximal voluntary muscular contractions in order to overcome powerful external resistances. It is the greatest force an athlete can exert for a given contraction of muscles, that is, the highest load the athlete can lift in one attempt or **one repetition maximum (1RM)**. A higher absolute strength is necessary for such activities as weightlifting, field events in track and field (shot put, hammer, discus, and javelin throws), and so on. Its importance for an athletic performance diminishes as the resistance that must be overcome in competition is reduced and as the period of competition increases.

Power

Power, often referred to as **speed–strength**, is the ability of an athlete to overcome external resistance by developing a high rate of muscular contraction. The ability to develop power is decisive in the speed of execution of individual movements performed in activities like high jump and long jump in track and field. It is also important for the achievement of high push-offs, throw or take-off velocity in ball games, for mastering of quick movement in individual activities, for starting and acceleration of sprinters and skaters, as well as for fast starts and accelerations in rowing and similar events.

Muscular Endurance

Muscular endurance or **strength endurance** is the ability of an athlete to resist fatigue in strength performance of longer duration. It determines performances in those endurance activities where exceptional resistance must be overcome over relatively longer periods of time, such as in rowing, swimming, and cross-country skiing.

Muscular endurance is also important in predominantly acyclic (non-repetitive) activities where high demands are placed on strength and endurance, such as gymnastics, wrestling, boxing, downhill skiing, and most games.

The Relationship Between Maximal Strength and Power

It is a well-known fact that top-class heavyweight weightlifters achieve outstanding results in tests measuring power, such as, standing high jump and long jumps, in 30-metre sprints, and other events that require speed and strength performance. This contradicts the deep-rooted notion that strength training and increases in maximal strength lead to slowed muscle performance (Figure 4.8).

Much research has been conducted to investigate this area in greater depth. The following is a summary of the results:

- The more internal force an athlete can generate to overcome external resistance, the more movement acceleration increases. If an athlete must mobilize as much as 90 percent of maximal strength to merely lift a barbell off the ground (i.e., to resist gravity), little strength reserve is left to accelerate the barbell lift. This means the movement must be performed at a relatively slow speed. If, however, the athlete needs to apply only 30 percent of maximal strength to lift the barbell off the ground, a high volume of strength is reserved for acceleration of the barbell. Indeed, the movement can then be performed explosively.

- The higher the external resistance to be overcome, the more important the maximal strength for power performance.

In general, high power output sports, such as 100-metre and 200-metre track events, high

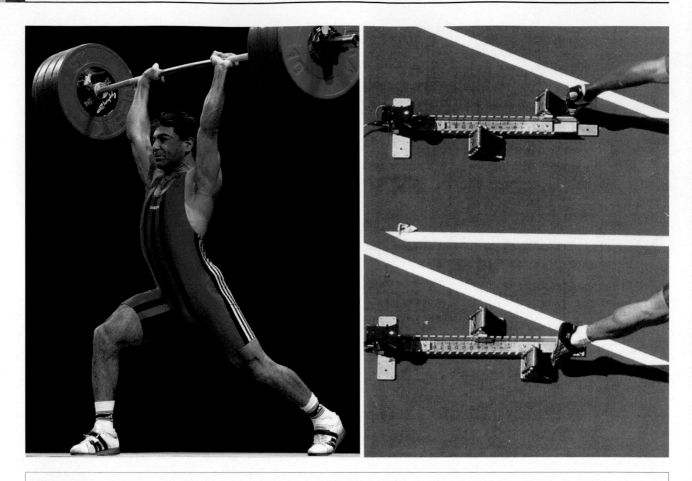

Figure 4.8 Heavy weightlifters and field event specialists in track and field are among the quickest athletes off the starting block. They also hold the world record in the standing long jump.

jump and triple jump, speedskating, and rowing, require the application of more than 25-30 percent of one's maximal strength, which in turn depends upon the use of ST and FT fibres (see discussion on muscle fibres in Chapter 3). FT fibres respond very effectively to high-resistance training, which generates an increase in diameter of the contractile elements (myofibrils) of the fibres. Furthermore, this type of training results in a progressive increase in the number of fast motor units that can be mobilized. This results in improved intra-muscle coordination (Figure 4.9).

Enlarged diameter of the FT fibres and improved intra-muscle coordination are beneficial to power performances, providing that the capacity of the FT fibres for fast contraction does not deteriorate following high-resistance training. This implies that, despite relatively slow movements during maximal resistance training,

the myosin and actin filaments must be able to retain their capacity for swiftly establishing cross bridge formation and, after completion of the contraction, removing the bridging formation. Coaching experience has shown that the high contraction speed of FT fibres can be maintained and even considerably increased if maximal strength training is carried out explosively at all times. It follows that a high level of maximal strength is an invariable prerequisite for fast movements in medium- to high-resistance training. Maximal strength training can thus be beneficial to the development of power.

The Relationship Between Maximal Strength and Muscular Endurance

The relationship between maximal strength and muscular endurance can be illustrated best with

Resistance Level	100%	95%	90%	85%	80%	75%
Table 4.1 Maximum number of repetitions as a function of resistance.						
Repetition Maximum	1	2-3	5-6	7-8	approx. 10-12	approx. 12-16

the following example. Athlete A is able to lift a 100-kg barbell, but partner B masters only 90 kg. If both athletes are challenged to clean and press a barbell of 85 kg as often as possible, athlete A will perform 7-8 repetitions and B only 2-3 repetitions. Using an 80-kg barbell, athlete A can do 10-12 repetitions and athlete B only 5-6. The comparison shows that the number of repetitions against high resistance is dependent on the maximal strength of the athlete. Table 4.1 shows the maximal number of repetitions possible for load levels of different resistance.

The maximal feasible number of repetitions of a particular load is referred to as the **repetition maximum (RM)**. If the RM of an exercise is 2-3, it can be deduced that an athlete can resist a force corresponding to approximately 95 percent of maximal strength capacity. If the athlete is able to perform maximally 7-8 repetitions with a particular weight, then this weight approximates

85 percent of maximal strength capacity.

Therefore, it is not always necessary that you work against maximal resistance (which may be very dangerous in most cases) in order to calculate your maximal strength capacity for a given exercise. Determining an athlete's maximal number of repetitions against submaximal resistance will produce an accurate assessment of maximal strength. However, as the number of repetitions increases (or as the level of resistance decreases), the RM becomes a less accurate criterion of maximal strength.

Issues Related to the Relationship Between Strength and Endurance It is a commonly held belief that the development of strength hinders and even impairs the development of endurance, and vice versa. The validity of this notion depends upon the type of training and event in question. Vigorous training

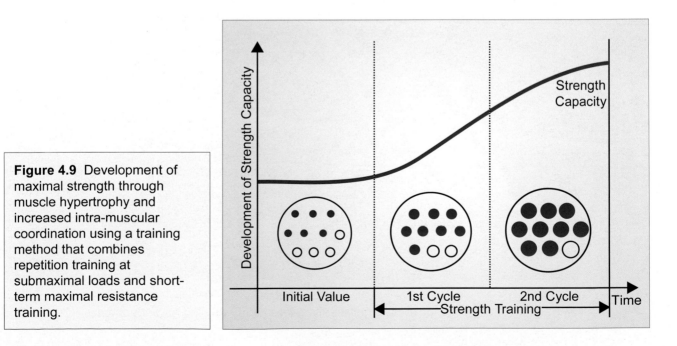

Figure 4.9 Development of maximal strength through muscle hypertrophy and increased intra-muscular coordination using a training method that combines repetition training at submaximal loads and short-term maximal resistance training.

for running long distances leads to an increase in cardiorespiratory fitness (increased aerobic power). However, the simultaneous decrease in the diameter of the fast twitch muscle fibres causes a corresponding decrease in muscle volume. These processes, then, result in increased endurance and decreased muscle strength.

Conversely, repetitive maximal strength training decreases endurance but increases strength. Thus, the training of a weightlifter or shot-putter is geared towards the development of maximal strength and power; endurance is hardly improved. However, unless a specific sports event requires the possession of a maximal level of endurance or strength, training should achieve a balance between strength and endurance (Figure 4.10).

Competitive athletes should be capable of coping with high-intensity, short-term anaerobic loads and at the same time, be able to master long-term low-intensity aerobic loads. The proof that such training is possible has been demonstrated in sports requiring both strength and endurance, such as Nordic events that combine cross-country skiing and ski jumping. A Nordic skier, however, will not normally achieve the distances of a skier specializing in jumping or approximate the times of a cross-country skier (Figure 4.11).

Thus, relatively high levels of both strength and endurance can be achieved either by training for strength and endurance in separate training sessions or by developing both in combination. Both methods can be used effectively. Using one method, an athlete doing four training sessions a week might devote two sessions to track exercises and two sessions to strength exercises. Using the other method, an athlete may develop a program that trains both strength and endurance within each session.

Muscle Fibre Type

Fibre type is another factor that will greatly affect muscle force output. In general, the greater the fast twitch fibre content of a muscle, the greater will be the force output, the overall speed of contraction, and the fatigability, when the muscle has been maximally activated. On the other hand, a muscle dominated by a slow twitch fibre population will be characterized as being capable of producing less force, will contract slower, but will have far superior endurance characteristics. Submaximal responses are much more difficult to predict, as we need to keep in mind the order of

Figure 4.10 Training for explosive power is significantly different than training for endurance.

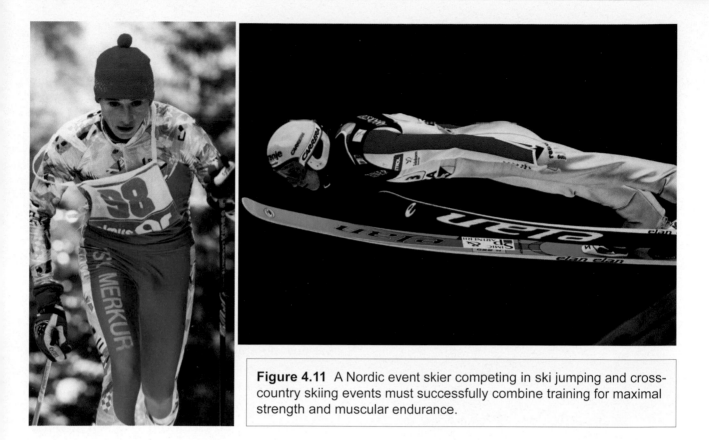

Figure 4.11 A Nordic event skier competing in ski jumping and cross-country skiing events must successfully combine training for maximal strength and muscular endurance.

fibre recruitment (discussed in Chapter 3) when examining submaximal activities.

Age

Aging has a significant influence on muscle force output. Research indicates that there is a selective loss of fast twitch fibres, mainly fast twitch glycolytic, with aging. Obviously, this loss will significantly affect the force generating potential of a muscle. What remains unknown at this time is why this loss takes place. It is possible that it is pre-programmed to occur with aging, i.e., **apoptosis**. Alternatively, the loss may represent a "use it or lose it" phenomenon. As people age they become less active which results in muscle atrophy (Figure 4.12).

Muscle loss has become a very real medical condition known as **sarcopenia** (Greek for "vanishing flesh"). Research shows that by age 70, sedentary individuals have lost 30 percent or more of the muscle they had at 30, the age at which muscle mass peaks. Muscle loss inevitably

means diminished strength and balance. These developments may lead to falls and fractures, a major cause of age-related disabilities.

Sex

From a physiological standpoint, men and women are more similar than they are dissimilar. Aside from the obvious distinctions between men and women, the average woman is approximately 70 percent as strong as a man of the same size. However, differences between the sexes may not be as great as is commonly thought. In fact, in some cases, the differences may not be at all what is typically assumed.

Strength-to-Weight Ratio

One of the major factors accounting for the physical performance differences between men and women is the ratio of strength to weight – where women are clearly at a disadvantage. Women do not have the physiological or structural capacity to develop the same strength and muscular bulk

Figure 4.12 Regular strength training can slow down muscle atrophy in elderly individuals.

Figure 4.13 Females are able to perform challenging tasks requiring maximal strength.

that men do, due to the ratio of muscle to adipose tissue. In general, women have less muscle tissue and considerably more adipose tissue. However, recent research has shown that a single fibre of the same diameter from a man and a woman produces similar amounts of force when activated by electrical stimulation. It follows that when adipose tissue is factored out of the equation and strength is looked at in terms of lean body mass, women are just as strong as men in total body strength (Figure 4.13).

Muscle Cross-sectional Area

The cross-sectional area of a muscle fibre is smaller in women largely because they have proportionally more Type I (slow twitch) fibres, while men have proportionally more Type II (fast twitch) fibres. Type II fibres are considered to be more conducive to increasing muscle size and strength, whereas Type I fibres are responsible more for muscular endurance.

Variation in Testosterone Level

A difference in testosterone levels is another significant reason accounting for the difference between men and women in the development of muscle size and strength. Men produce 20-30 times more testosterone than women, the anabolic hormone responsible for muscle growth.

Summary

When discussing exercise prescription for the development of general fitness among recreational individuals or the design of training programs for athletes, it is important to distinguish among the various forms of muscle contractions. In static contractions, tension develops in the muscle but it is insufficient to move the intended load. Dynamic contractions, on the other hand, involve movement.

Muscle contractions can be characterized further as either concentric or eccentric. A concentric contraction is one in which the muscle shortens as it goes through its range of motion (flexion); an eccentric contraction is one in which the muscle lengthens during the movement (extension). When there is no visible change in muscle length, even though the muscle has undergone muscle contraction, an isometric contraction is said to have occurred. It is important to know the functional value of training equipment that is designed to enhance specific muscle contractions.

Maximal strength is the highest load an athlete can lift in one repetition. This value is known as the athlete's one repetition maximum (1RM). Power refers to the ability of an athlete to overcome external resistance by developing a high rate of muscular contraction. Finally, muscular endurance is the ability of an athlete to resist fatigue in strength performance of longer duration. Many factors affect the force and power output of muscle contraction. Some of these factors, including joint angle, muscle cross-sectional area, speed of movement, muscle fibre type, age, and sex, were discussed in detail in this chapter.

Key Words

Apoptosis
Auxotonic contraction
Concentric contraction
Dynamic contraction
Eccentric contraction
Isokinetic contraction
Isometric contraction

Isotonic contraction
Maximal (absolute) strength
Muscular endurance
One repetition maximum
 (1RM)
Plyocentric contraction
Power

Relative strength
Repetition maximum (RM)
Sarcopenia
Speed–strength
Static contraction
Strength endurance
Submaximal static contraction

Discussion Questions

1. Identify the major types of muscle contraction and give two examples of each.

2. Discuss the major differences between static and dynamic muscle contractions.

3. Muscle cross-section influences the amount of force a muscle can generate. Explain.

4. List the factors that influence muscle contraction. Provide an example of each.

5. Differentiate between absolute and relative strength and give examples of each.

6. Discuss the differences between strength, power, and endurance sporting activities.

7. Briefly discuss the relationship between maximal strength and power. Present two examples.

8. Briefly discuss the relationship between maximal strength and muscular endurance. Present two examples.

9. What happens to muscular strength as one ages? Why?

In This Chapter:

The Chemistry of Energy Production 96

The Three Energy Systems 97
    Immediate Energy: The High Energy Phosphate System 99
    Short-term Energy: The Lactic Acid System 100
    Long-term Energy: The Oxygen System 104

Summary 106

CHAPTER 5

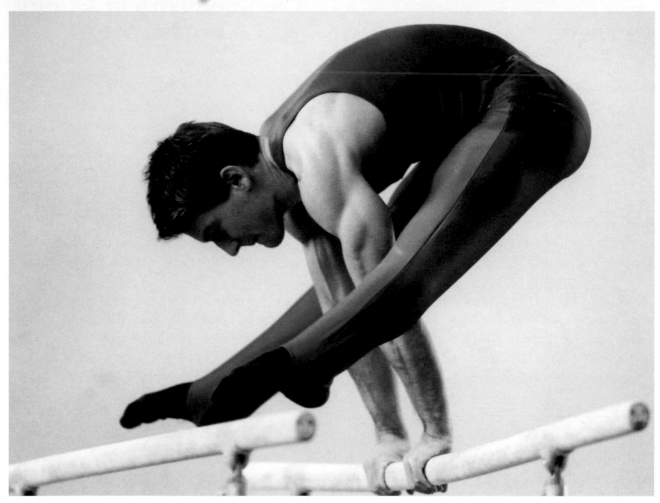

Energy for Muscular Activity

After completing this chapter you should be able to:

- use and understand the basic terminology of human metabolism related to exercise;

- describe the basic chemical processes the body uses to produce energy in the muscles;

- demonstrate an understanding of the body's three energy systems and their contribution to muscular contraction and activity;

- discuss the effects of training and exercise on the energy systems.

Humans are capable of performing amazing physical feats. Sprinters run down the track with astonishing speed and power; power lifters hoist hundreds of kilograms of weight, making it look effortless; swimmers traverse an entire lake or channel against the elements; hurdlers gracefully clear all obstacles in their way; and basketball players seem to defy the laws of gravity in their flight to the basket. While various combinations of physical ability, skill, and training are required to accomplish these feats, the common denominators in each case are the muscle activation patterns described previously, and the development of energy at rates, and in sufficient quantity, to meet the needs of the activity.

The energy needs for endurance events performed at relatively low intensity levels significantly differ from those requiring immediate power output performed at highest intensity levels. For effective planning of training programs coaches need to know the energy demands of their sport.

The production of a movement during contraction occurs as the muscle pulls on the bones through the tendonous attachments to the bones. Even a single contraction requires a significant input of energy. Just as a car requires the appropriate fuel to run efficiently, so too do our muscles require energy for maximal performance. However, depending on the activity in which you are engaged, the body will make use of different energy systems that have been adapted for supplying energy at the required rate and in the necessary amount for that particular activity, i.e., the body will produce energy at a higher rate (but for a shorter duration) during an activity demanding power than one requiring endurance, where energy is required in greater quantities, but at a low rate.

What are the body's primary sources of energy? What other fuels do we use? Why do our muscles produce energy differently under varying circumstances? These are some of the many questions that will be answered in this chapter. We will also explore some methods of testing and assessing energy production as well as the way the body adapts to exercise.

The Chemistry of Energy Production

All energy in the human body is derived from the breakdown of three complex nutrients: carbohydrates, fats, and proteins. The end result of the breakdown of these substances is the production of various amounts of the molecule **adenosine triphosphate (ATP)**, the energy currency of the body. ATP provides the energy for fuelling all biochemical processes of the body like muscular work or digesting food. The capacity to perform muscular work depends on sufficient energy supply at the required rate for the duration of the activity.

Energy is liberated for muscular work when the chemical bond between ATP and its phosphate subgroup is broken through **hydrolysis** according to the following biochemical reaction:

$$ATP \longrightarrow ADP + P_i + \text{Energy}$$

The breakdown of ATP into **adenosine diphosphate (ADP)** and a **free phosphate group (P_i)** is the fuel for contractile activity, i.e., the formation of cross bridges in working muscles (see Chapter 3, Muscle Structure and Function). The amount of energy released is about 38-42 kilojoules (kJ) or 9-10 kilocalories (kcal) per mole of ATP (Note: a **kilocalorie** is the amount of heat energy needed to raise 1,000 grams of water by 1 degree Celsius).

When the body performs physical work, it needs a continuous supply of ATP. The muscle has a small supply of ATP stored within it, satisfying initial requirements of the body, but the initial stores of ATP in the muscles are used up very quickly. Therefore, if activity is to continue, ATP must be regenerated. ATP is a renewable resource that can be regenerated by the recombination of ADP with a free phosphate. The metabolic process that results in the recombination of ADP and P_i to form ATP is termed **ATP re-synthesis**.

This reaction can occur at a very fast pace in the body. The re-synthesis of ATP is described by the following reaction:

$$ADP + P_i + \boxed{Energy} \longrightarrow ATP$$

The regeneration of ATP, however, requires the addition of energy, which is supplied through the breakdown of complex food molecules, such as carbohydrates and fats.

The Three Energy Systems

The production of ATP involves three energy systems, each of which produces ATP at a distinct

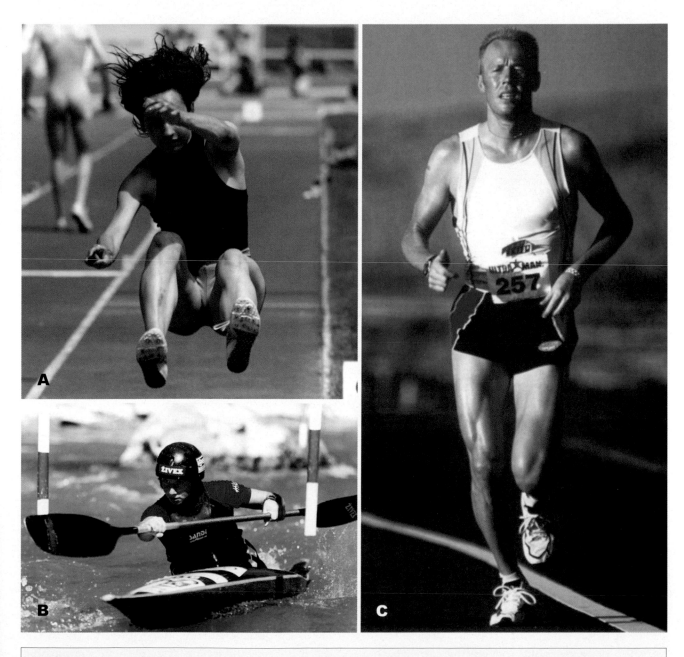

Figure 5.1 **A.** Immediate energy system activity. **B.** Short-term energy system activity. **C.** Long-term energy system activity.

Table 5.1 The roles of the three energy systems in competitive sport.

Energy Pathways	Anaerobic Pathways			Aerobic Pathway	
Primary Energy Source	ATP produced without the presence of O_2			ATP produced with the presence of O_2	
Energy System	Immediate Alactic	Short-term Lactic		Long-term Oxygen	
Fuel	ATP, CP	Glycogen, glucose		Glycogen, glucose, fat, protein	
Duration	0 s 10 s	40 s 70 s	2 min 6 min	25 min	1 hr 2 hr 3 hr
Sport Event	Sprinting 100-m dash Throwing Jumping Weightlifting Ski jumping Diving Vaulting in gymnastics	Track 200-400 m 500-m speed-skating Most gym events Cycling, track 50-m swimming	100-m swimming 800-m track Floor exercise gymnastics Alpine skiing Cycling, track: 1,000 m and pursuit	Middle-distance track, swimming, speedskating 1,000-m canoeing Boxing Wrestling Rowing Figure skating Synchronized swimming Cycling, pursuit	Long-distance track, swimming, speedskating, canoeing Cycling, road racing Triathlon
	Most team sports/racquet sports/sailing				

rate and for a given maximal duration: (1) the immediate or high energy phosphate system (anaerobic alactic system); (2) the short-term or glycolytic system (anaerobic lactic system); and (3) the long-term or oxygen system (aerobic system) (Figure 5.1). The main roles of the three energy systems in competitive sport are summarized in Table 5.1.

The three energy systems are designated as **aerobic** or **anaerobic**, depending on whether oxygen is needed by the system in the production of the energy. While oxygen is not needed by either the **high energy phosphate** or **glycolytic** systems, the **oxidative phosphorylation** system depends on oxygen to produce energy. Similarly, the two anaerobic systems can be separated on the basis of whether or not lactic acid is produced during the energy production. With the glycolytic system, lactic acid is produced as part of energy production (hence **anaerobic lactic**), but no lactic acid is produced during energy production by the high energy phosphate system (hence **anaerobic alactic**).

Figure 5.2 The immediate (alactic) energy system.

Immediate Energy: The High Energy Phosphate System

Many sporting activities, such as weightlifting, high jump, long jump, 100-metre run, or 25-metre swim, sometimes described as **high power output activities**, require an immediate high rate of energy production as intensive muscle activity is done over a short time interval. The primary fuel source for these activities is the **immediate** or high energy phosphate system. Under these conditions, creatine phosphate (CP), another high-energy compound in the muscle cell, can be broken down to produce phosphate and creatine. The free phosphate then bonds with ADP to reform ATP (Figure 5.2). As there is only a small amount of ATP and CP stored within each muscle fibre, and because this system produces energy at a very high rate, this system can only provide immediate energy for muscles in the initial 7-12 seconds of high-intensity activity.

This system is also known as the alactic energy source or the ATP-CP system.

Characteristics of the High Energy Phosphate System

The utility of the high energy phosphate system is that (1) it can produce very large amounts of energy in a short amount of time and (2) its rate of recovery is relatively rapid. The system can supply energy only until the intra-muscular stores of ATP are exhausted, and thereafter, for as long as there is a sufficient local supply of creatine phosphate to re-synthesize ATP from ADP. However, the total muscle stores of ATP are very small and are depleted after only a few seconds of high-intensity work. As the store of creatine phosphate in muscle is also small, it too is depleted rapidly during high-intensity work.

The initial concentrations of high energy phosphates in the muscle are limiting factors in an individual's ability to perform short-term high-intensity work. If the athlete must continue the activity for a period longer than 7-12 seconds of very highly vigorous work, or for 15-30 seconds of moderately intensive work, the high energy phosphate supply cannot provide all the energy for the activity. It is for this reason that a 100-metre runner often loses speed after only 80 metres as the store of high energy phosphates is exhausted and the body begins using another energy source, the short-term or glycogen energy source (Table 5.1 and Figure 5.3).

Similarly, in weight training, short-term sets (three of 30-second duration) during maximal strength and power training are dependent on stored ATP and CP as the primary energy source.

Short-term Energy: The Lactic Acid System

A second energy system results in the production of ATP at the expense of producing lactic acid, an unwanted by-product. This process is called **anaerobic glycolysis**. It involves the breakdown of glycogen (stored carbohydrate in the muscle) into pyruvic acid and ATP (Figure 5.3).

The **lactic acid system** uses a complex biochemical process called anaerobic glycolysis to release energy in the form of ATP by a step-wise breakdown of the carbohydrate fuels glycogen and glucose. During glycolysis, each step in the sequential breakdown (a total of 10 steps; Figure 5.4) involves a specific **enzyme** breaking down the chemical bonds of glycogen or blood glucose in the absence of oxygen (hence the term *anaerobic*). The last product in the series of breakdowns is termed **pyruvate**. When the rate of work is high, the pyruvate is converted into **lactic acid**. The exercise intensity at which lactic acid begins to accumulate within the blood is known as the **anaerobic threshold**. The anaerobic threshold can be thought of as the point during exercise when you begin to feel discomfort and a burning sensation in the muscles.

The source of substrates for the anaerobic energy system is carbohydrate. Glycogen (stored form of carbohydrate in the muscles and the liver) and blood glucose (circulating form of carbohydrate) are derived from the carbohydrates that comprise one's diet. Carbohydrates (pasta, rice, bread, potatoes, starchy foods, sweets; Figure 5.5) are the primary dietary sources of glucose and serve as the primary energy fuels for the brain, muscles, heart, liver, and various other organs. Once ingested, these foods are broken down into glucose by the digestive system. Glucose then enters the bloodstream and is circulated around the body. Some glucose stays in the blood, but most is stored in the liver and the muscles as glycogen. Glycogen consists of hundreds of glucose molecules linked together to form a chain. The process of forming glycogen from glucose is termed **gluconeogenesis**.

Characteristics of the Lactic Acid System

Lactic acid is the substance that makes your muscles "burn" when you exercise intensely (Figure

Figure 5.3 The short-term (lactic acid) energy system.

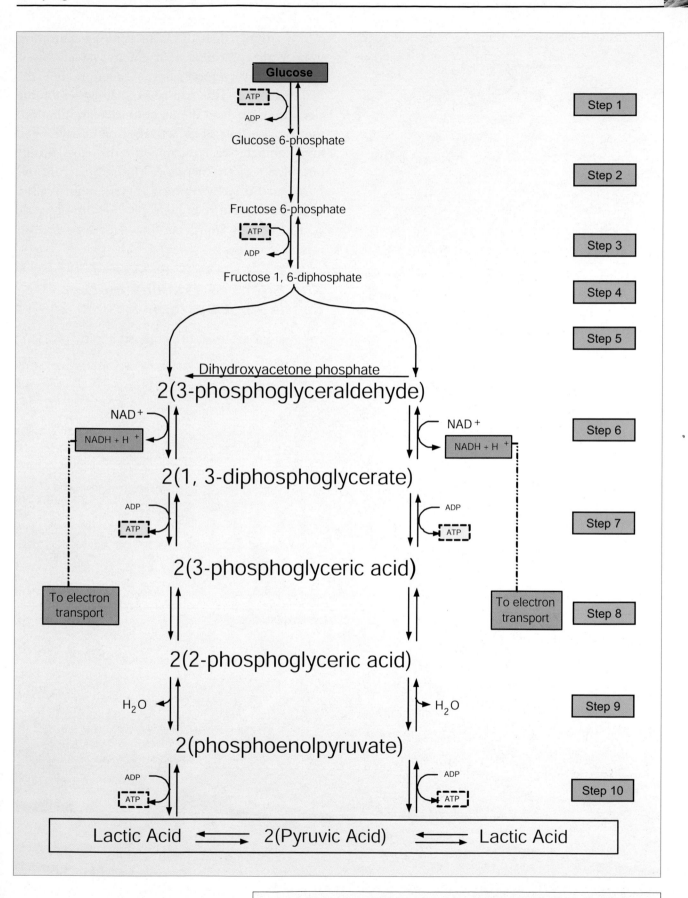

Figure 5.4 The highly complex metabolic pathways of glycolysis.

Figure 5.5 Food high in carbohydrates.

5.6). Not only does the lactic acid concentration impede the production of energy via glycolysis by inhibiting proper enzyme function, but the hydrogen ions also hamper transmission of the electrical signal at the neuromuscular junction, thereby limiting fibre activation. The hydrogen ions compete with calcium for the cross bridge binding sites (see Chapter 3, Muscle Structure and Function), thereby limiting the strength of fibre contraction. Thus, a high production of lactic acid ultimately limits continued performance of intense activities.

The Effect of Training on the Lactic Acid System

At any given level of work, the rate of lactic

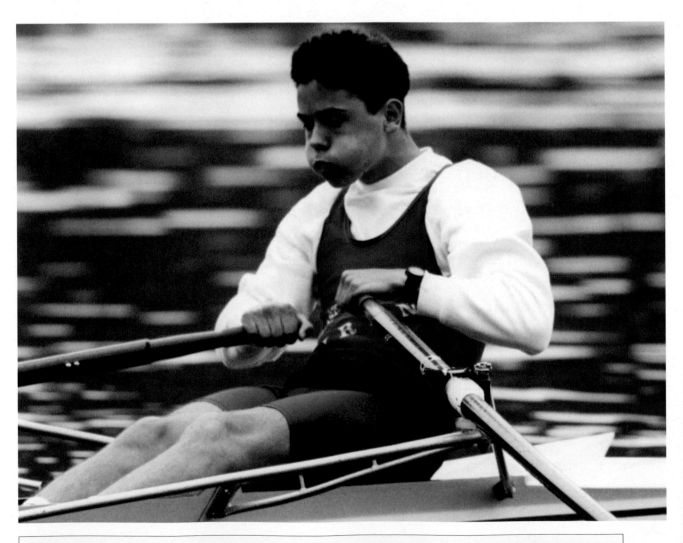

Figure 5.6 Extreme pain at the end of a rowing race is due to lactic acid concentration in muscles.

acid accumulation is decreased in the trained individual, i.e., the so-called anaerobic threshold is higher, meaning that the individual can work at a higher rate of activity before the accumulation of lactic acid begins.

During high-intensity exercise, the rate of lactic acid production can be decreased by decreasing the intensity of the activity, or by increasing the ability to "handle" the lactic acid. Decreasing lactic acid production at any given rate of work can be achieved by increasing the effectiveness of the aerobic system (described in the next section of this chapter), thereby lessening the need for energy from anaerobic sources. Note, however, that this is not a strategy that will work for sprint- or power-oriented performances as the rate of

energy demand for this purpose is always going to be higher than the ability of the aerobic system to provide ATP. For these types of performances, other adaptive responses are needed to manage the lactic acid production if higher or sustained levels of performance are to be achieved.

Endurance trained individuals are able to remove lactic acid faster from exercising muscle. Faster lactate removal will allow people to continue to exercise at higher intensities for longer periods of time. Major factors that can lead to an increased rate of lactate removal from the muscle following training are (a) an increased rate of lactic acid diffusion from active muscles (requires an increase in the capillary supply to the muscle in order that the lactic acid can be diffused into the circulatory

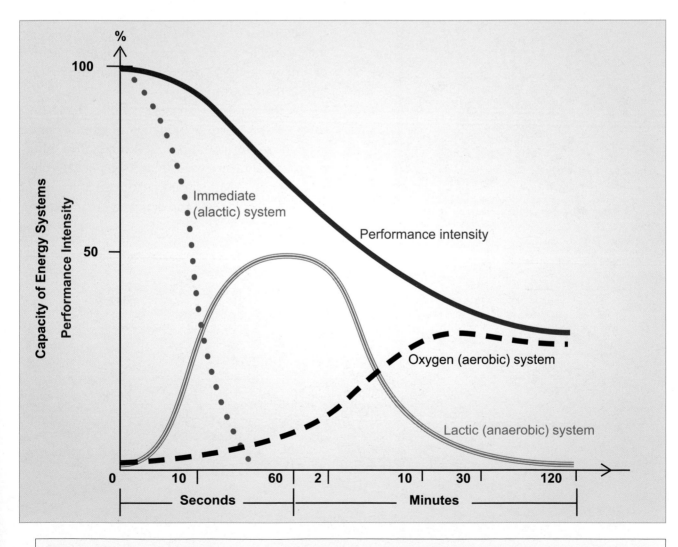

Figure 5.7 The role of the three energy systems during an all-out exercise activity of different duration.

system); (b) an increased muscle blood flow; and (c) an increased ability to metabolize lactate in the heart, liver, and non-working muscle fibres. Key elements in this adaptation process are changes in the cardiovascular system – the development of more capillaries and the expansion of the body's ability to deliver an increased blood flow to the working muscle either through an increased cardiac output, or by the re-distribution of blood flow to the muscle. Blood flow is increased in trained individuals through an increase in the number of blood vessels in the muscle, more red blood cells, greater total blood volume, and greater efficiency of the heart (see Chapter 6, The Heart and Lungs at Work).

Long-term Energy: The Oxygen System

The **oxygen** or **long-term** energy system is the most important energy system in the human body, as it represents the primary source of energy for a broad range of activities. Most daily activities use energy provided by the aerobic system. Exercise performed at an intensity lower than that of the anaerobic threshold relies exclusively on the aerobic system for energy production. Thus, during aerobic activities, blood lactate levels remain relatively low.

For intensive work of 2-3 minutes' duration, approximately half the energy is supplied from **anaerobic metabolism** and the other half from **aerobic metabolism** (Figure 5.7). As the duration of the activity increases, the relative contribution of the aerobic system to the total energy requirement increases. The aerobic system is the primary source of energy (70-95 percent) for exercise lasting longer than 10 minutes.

In the aerobic system, a complex biochemical process known as **oxidative phosphorylation** is used to re-synthesize ATP. Oxidative phosphorylation takes place in cell organelles called **mitochondria**. Mitochondria contain a system of enzymes, coenzymes, and activators that carry on

Figure 5.8 The long-term (oxygen) energy system.

an extensive breakdown of fuels, providing large quantities of ATP.

The aerobic energy system is the primary energy system used in exercise provided that (a) the working muscles have sufficient mitochondria to meet energy requirements; (b) sufficient oxygen is supplied to the mitochondria; and (c) enzymes or intermediate products do not limit the rate of energy flux through the aerobic energy production system, called the **Kreb's cycle**. The Kreb's cycle is a metabolic process where pyruvic acid is metabolized, as are other fuel sources including glucose, fat molecules, and protein.

Characteristics of the Oxygen System

The aerobic system is highly efficient. For example, the energy yield from the aerobic breakdown of a glycogen molecule is approximately 12 times more efficient than that of the anaerobic system breakdown of the same molecule of glycogen. Even more energy is derived from the utilization of fats. When fats are oxidized (note fats cannot be broken down anaerobically), the energy yield may be increased by more than 4.5 times the yield from carbohydrates. Thus, fats are an important energy source for athletic events that require large outputs of energy over a long period of time as they provide nearly limitless energy supplies to the human body. At the end of the aerobic breakdown of carbohydrates and fats, water and carbon dioxide are given off as the metabolic by-products (Figure 5.8).

Cori Cycle Another important feature of the oxygen system is its ability to remove lactic acid from the muscle. As indicated earlier, the removal of lactic acid from muscle tissue is important for the maintenance of skeletal muscle function. The removal of lactic acid allows the muscle to continue to contract and allows for exercise to continue. The aerobic system allows for removal of lactic acid through the conversion of lactic acid back into usable glucose. Lactic acid, once produced in the muscle fibre, passes out of that fibre and is taken to the liver to be metabolized back into pyruvic acid and then glucose. This process is called the **Cori cycle** (Figure 5.9).

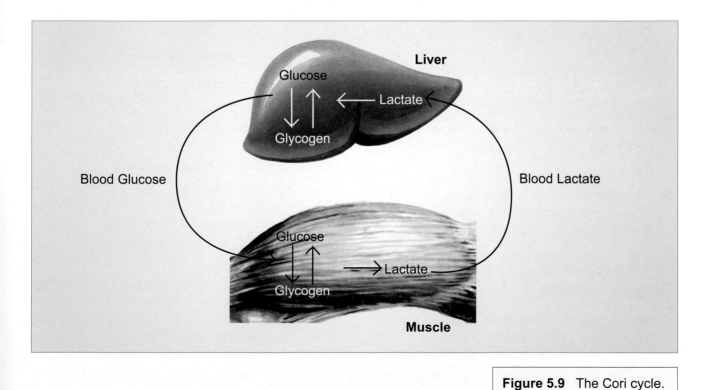

Figure 5.9 The Cori cycle.

Limitations of the Oxygen System

There are, however, two limitations of the aerobic energy system. First, the system requires continuous and adequate supplies of oxygen and fuel sources that are necessary for aerobic metabolism. Second, the rate of ATP utilization must be relatively slow to allow the process to meet the energy demands. Therefore, the aerobic system is well suited for low- to moderate-intensity activities.

Aerobic Power

The power of the aerobic system is generally evaluated by measuring the maximal volume of oxygen that can be consumed in a given amount of time during maximal effort (units of L/min). This measure is called **maximal aerobic power** or **$\dot{V}O_2$max**, and is most often expressed relative to body mass to yield a measure that describes the efficiency of the working body (units of ml/kg/min). The average sedentary, healthy, 20-year-old male will have a $\dot{V}O_2$max of 40-44 ml/kg/min, and the average sedentary 20-year-old female has a value of 36-40 ml/kg/min. In comparison, the values of trained athletes will reach values of 80-90 ml/kg/min for males and 75-85 ml/kg/min for females.

Factors that contribute to a high aerobic power include:

(1) a high arterial oxygen content (the amount of oxygen carried in the blood);

(2) an increased cardiac output (the amount of blood that the heart can pump per minute); and

(3) a larger tissue oxygen extraction (the amount of oxygen taken up by the cells as the blood flows through the tissue).

The Effect of Training on the Oxygen System

Endurance exercise is the most effective method of training for eliciting adaptations in the aerobic oxidative energy system. Endurance training consists of repeated, sustained efforts of long duration several times per week. Examples of endurance exercise include running, swimming, or biking for 40 minutes or more at a heart rate of 130-140 beats per minute. Endurance training has four major effects on aerobic metabolism:

(1) it increases vascularization within the muscles so that there is an enhanced delivery of nutrients and oxygen to the muscle;

(2) it increases the number and size of mitochondria within the muscle fibres;

(3) it increases the activity of the enzymes involved in the aerobic metabolic pathways; and

(4) it results in the preferential use of fats over glycogen during exercise, which saves the muscles' rather limited store of glycogen.

Endurance training increases the maximal aerobic power of a sedentary individual by 15-25 percent regardless of age. Genetics plays a large role in determining the rate of adaptation, with some individuals adapting quickly and others more slowly. Age also plays a role in the training adaptation in that an older individual adapts more slowly than a younger person. Maximal aerobic power peaks between the ages of 18-25 and declines at a rate of 0.5-1.5 percent per year after that.

Summary

Energy for muscular activity depends on a supply of ATP that can be broken down into ADP and phosphate. All the body's biochemical processes and energy systems require adequate ATP. The three energy systems are designated as aerobic or anaerobic, depending on whether oxygen is needed by the system in the production of energy.

Activities that involve intense muscle activity over a short time interval (e.g., weightlifting, 100-metre dash) require an immediate high rate of energy production. The primary fuel source for these activities is the high energy phospate system, or ATP-CP system. This energy system can produce large amounts of energy in a short time, with a relatively rapid recovery rate.

A second energy system called anaerobic glycolysis results in the production of ATP at the expense of producing lactic acid – the substance that makes your muscles "burn" when you exercise intensely. Anaerobic glycolysis involves the breakdown of glycogen (stored carbohydrate in the muscle) into pyruvic acid and ATP. The point during exercise when lactic acid begins to accumulate in the blood is known as the anaerobic threshold.

The oxygen, or long-term, energy system is the most important energy system in the human body, as it represents the primary source of energy for a broad range of activities. Most daily activities use energy provided by this highly efficient aerobic system. In the aerobic system, a complex biochemical process known as oxidative phosphorylation is used to re-synthesize ATP.

The body's energy production is one of the more complex factors affecting athletic capacity, especially with athletics involving high-endurance requirements such as running, swimming, cross-country skiing, and rowing. Trained individuals are able to utilize ATP and remove lactic acid more efficiently than untrained individuals, and endurance training can significantly improve the aerobic energy system.

Key Words

Adenosine diphosphate (ADP)
Adenosine triphosphate (ATP)
Aerobic metabolism
Anaerobic alactic
Anaerobic glycolysis
Anaerobic lactic
Anaerobic metabolism
Anaerobic threshold

ATP re-synthesis
Cori cycle
Enzyme
Gluconeogenesis
Glycolytic system
High energy (immediate)
    phosphate system
Kreb's cycle

Lactic acid
Lactic acid system
Maximal aerobic power
    ($\dot{V}O_2$max)
Mitochondria
Oxidative phosphorylation
Oxygen system
Pyruvate

Discussion Questions

1. What are the differences between the three energy systems?

2. List one advantage and one disadvantage of each of the three energy systems.

3. Give an example of three activities or sports that use each of (a) the high energy phosphate system; (b) the anaerobic glycolytic system; and (c) the aerobic glycolytic system as its primary source of energy (one sport for each energy system).

4. What is the most important source of fuel in the body for all types of energy production, a substance also known as the energy currency of the body?

5. Distinguish ATP turnover from ATP re-synthesis.

6. Describe how each of the three energy systems could be trained most efficiently.

In This Chapter:

Cardiovascular Anatomy *110*
    The Heart *110*
    The Peripheral Circulatory System *115*
    Red Blood Cells *116*

Cardiovascular Physiology *116*
    The Transport of Carbon Dioxide *116*
    Oxygen Uptake *117*

Respiratory Anatomy and Physiology *118*
    Structure *118*
    Function *120*

**Exercise Effects on the Cardiovascular and
  Respiratory Systems *122***
    Cardiac Output *122*
    Capillary Supply *122*
    Blood Volume *124*
    Ventilation *124*

Exercise and Environments *124*
    Altitude *124*
    Temperature *125*

Summary *126*

CHAPTER 6

The Heart and Lungs at Work

After completing this chapter you should be able to:

- explain the function and control of the cardiovascular and respiratory systems;

- describe the relationship between the cardiorespiratory system and energy production;

- explain the measures that are used to evaluate and describe the various components of the cardiovascular and respiratory systems;

- describe the acute and chronic effects of physical activity on the body;

- analyze the effects of different environmental conditions on the body during physical activity.

During an average human life the heart will beat about three billion times, beginning at conception and continuing until death. The heart is one of the first organs to begin functioning and is often associated with life and death. This life-sustaining organ that pumps blood throughout our bodies is only one part of our circulatory system. The others – blood vessels (the passageways) and blood (the transport medium) – complete the transport system that delivers supplies to the tissues that need them for survival and growth. Oxygen is perhaps the most important supply to be delivered at rest and during exercise.

The systems of the body, however, are by no means independent of one another. Pulmonary structure and function are closely linked with the cardiovascular system; without getting oxygen into the body through breathing (ventilation), diffusion, and gas exchange in the lungs, there is no oxygen to transport to the body's tissues. Thus, the body's systems must work together in order to function most efficiently.

Because cardiovascular function is so vital to our existence, it is important to be aware of the advantages that can result from training, and their implications for health. Exercise offers numerous benefits and enhanced cardiovascular function is one of them. Understanding the changes that occur during exercise will enable you to train more effectively for performance and will improve your cardiovascular health. How are blood flow and blood volume controlled? What is actually involved in the transport of oxygen? And what role does hemoglobin play in oxygen transport? The answers to these and other questions will be presented in this chapter; this material will provide the foundation you will need to attain and maintain optimal cardiovascular health.

Cardiovascular Anatomy

The primary role of the cardiovascular system is supplying the muscles and organs with the oxygen and nutrients that they need to function properly, and removing metabolic by-products from areas of activity. Optimal functioning of the cardiovascular system is critical for human performance. The anatomy and physiology of the heart and the blood vessels are described in this section.

The Heart

Structure

The heart is an organ comprised of striated muscle that serves to pump blood through the human body. The heart pumps blood through the body by using two different pumps, called **ventricles** (Figure 6.1). The blood comes to the heart from the peripheral organs. The right ventricle receives deoxygenated blood from the body and pumps it to the lungs, and the left ventricle receives oxygenated blood from the lungs and pumps it to the rest of the body. Since the **left ventricle** has to pump blood through the entire body, it is larger and its muscle walls are stronger than that of the **right ventricle**, which only has to pump blood a short distance to the lungs. The heart has two smaller chambers called **atria** (singular = atrium). These smaller pumps receive blood from the body (**right atrium**) or the lungs (**left atrium**) and then pump the blood into the right and left ventricle, ensuring that the ventricles have a sufficient supply of blood for distribution to the lungs and other areas of the body, respectively.

Function

The heart contracts in a constant rhythm that may speed up or slow down depending on the need for blood (and oxygen) in the body. For example, if you start running, your leg muscles will need more oxygen to do the work of running. Therefore your heart will have to pump more oxygen-carrying blood to those working muscles and will have to beat more rapidly in order to supply that blood. The beating of the heart is governed by an automatic electrical impulse that is generated by the sinus node. The **sinus node** is a small bundle of nerve fibres that are found

Figure 6.1   Chambers and valves of the heart.

The heart works like an efficient pump.

in the wall of the right atrium near the opening of the **superior vena cava** (see Figure 6.5). The sinus node generates an electrical charge called an **action potential** that causes the muscle walls of the heart to contract. The atria contract before the ventricles contract, which allows for the blood to be quickly pumped into the ventricles from the atria and then from the ventricles to the lungs and the body. The sinus node determines the rate of beating of the entire heart (Figure 6.2).

Blood Pressure

Blood pressure is an important measure of cardiac function (Figure 6.3). There are two components to the measure of blood pressure. The first component is the pressure in the ventricles when they are contracting and pushing blood out into the body. This is called **systole**. *Systolic pressure* provides an estimate of the heart's work and the strain against the arterial walls during the contraction. In healthy young adults the normal range of systolic pressure is around 120 mm Hg.

The second component of blood pressure is used to describe the pressure in the heart when it is in the relaxation phase of the cardiac cycle (the ventricles are relaxed and being filled with blood) and is called **diastole**. *Diastolic pressure* is used as an indicator of peripheral blood pressure (the blood pressure in the body outside the heart). It provides an indication of the ease with which the

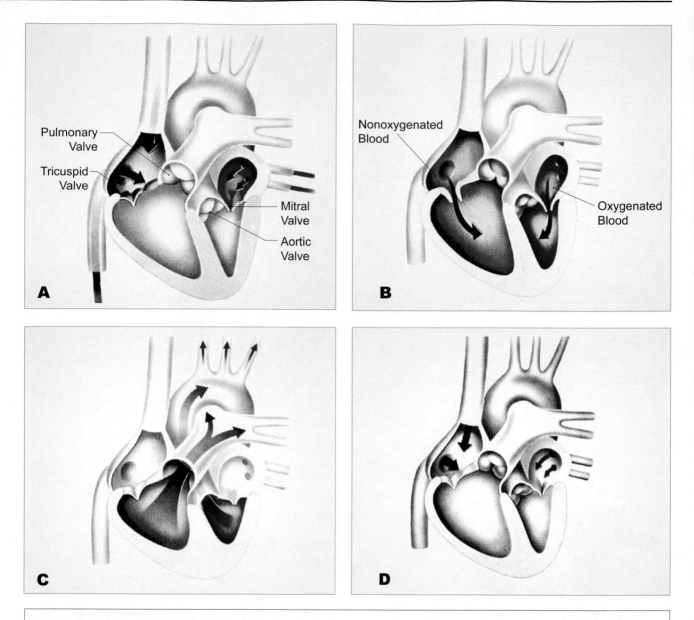

Figure 6.2 The finely tuned cardiac cycle. **A.** As the heart relaxes in diastole, both atria and ventricles simultaneously fill with blood. **B.** The atria, squeezing into systole, force blood into the ventricles. **C.** As the ventricle compartments fill with blood, they contract, thereby ejecting blood to the lungs and body. **D.** The atria and ventricles relax as the cycle begins anew.

blood flows from the arterioles into the capillaries. The normal diastolic pressure in healthy young adults is about 70-80 mm Hg.

Cardiac Output

The amount of blood that is pumped into the aorta each minute by the heart is known as the **cardiac output** (measured in litres per minute). Cardiac output is then the product of stroke volume (measured in litres per minute) and heart rate (measured in beats per minute) and is therefore representative of the quantity of blood that flows to the peripheral circulation. Cardiac output can be described by the simple equation presented below:

Cardiac Output = Stroke Volume x Heart Rate

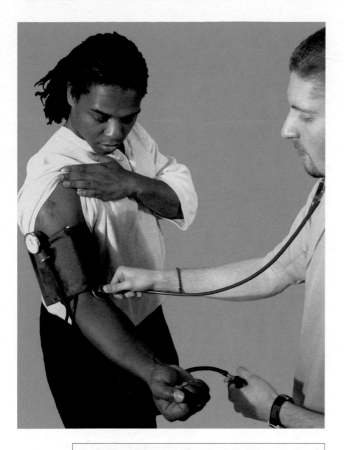

Figure 6.3 Measuring blood pressure.

Stroke Volume The amount of blood that is pumped out of the left ventricle with each heartbeat is the **stroke volume**. The stroke volume of the heart is measured in millilitres (1 litre = 1,000 ml). A typical stroke volume for a normal heart is about 70 ml of blood. Regular exercise and sports training can serve to increase stroke volume.

Heart Rate The rhythmical contraction of the walls of the heart is commonly known as a **heartbeat**. **Heart rate** is the number of times the heart beats in one minute and is measured in beats per minute (bpm). At rest the normal heart rate of an adult can range from 40 bpm in a highly trained athlete to 70 bpm in a normal healthy person. During intense exercise, the heart rate may increase to up to 200 bpm and occasionally even higher. The maximum expected heart rate for most people can be estimated by using the following equation:

$$\text{Maximum Heart Rate} = 220 - \text{Age (in years)}$$

Intensity of Work The intensity of aerobic exercise can be estimated by measuring heart rate as the two are highly related. The higher the intensity of exercise the higher the heart rate per

Figure 6.4 A. Measuring the carotid pulse. **B.** Measuring the radial pulse.

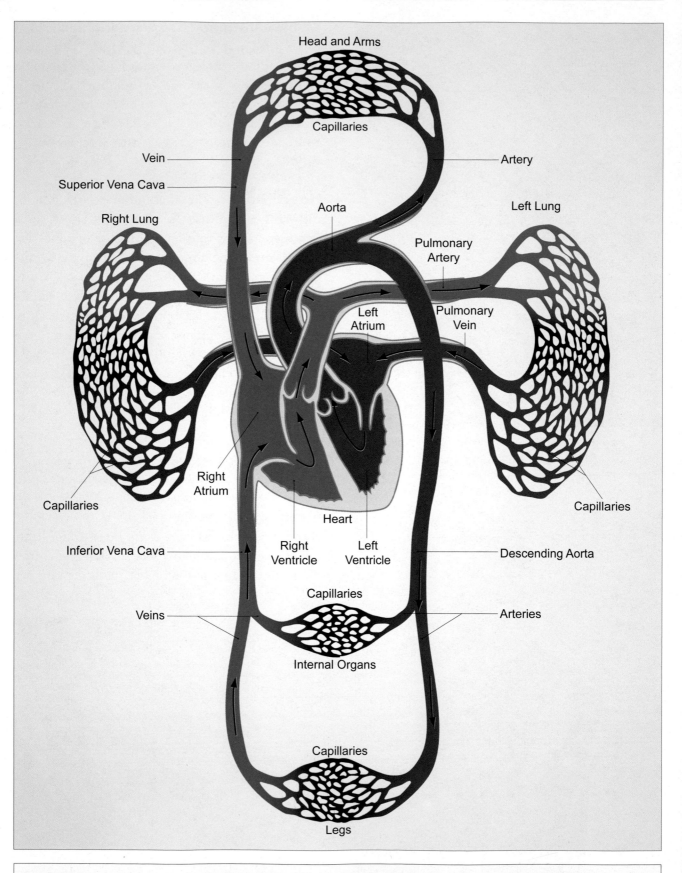

Figure 6.5 Circuitry of the heart and cardiovascular system. Oxygenated blood is shown in red, deoxygenated blood in blue.

minute. Since heart rate is a measure that is easily obtained, it becomes very practical for estimation of intensity of work and/or exercise. The heart rate can easily be measured by feeling the carotid or radial pulses with the middle three fingers as in Figure 6.4. By placing two or three fingers and applying light pressure between the trachea and the sternocleidomastoid muscle in the neck you can feel the carotid pulse. Then count the number of beats in 10 seconds and multiply the figure by 6 to get the number of beats per minute.

For example, a count of 17 beats in 10 seconds multiplied by 6 would result in a heart rate of 102 beats per minute. This elementary procedure allows you to quickly determine how hard you are working without any specialized equipment.

The Peripheral Circulatory System

All of the larger blood vessels of the body are made up of tubes comprised of layers of tissue. Smooth muscle cells that allow them to contract or relax also surround the fibrous tubes of the arteries, arterioles, venules, and veins. This enables the vessels of the peripheral circulatory system to regulate blood flow and alter the pattern of circulation throughout the body.

The peripheral circulatory system is comprised of the vessels that carry blood away from the heart to the muscles and organs (lungs, brain, stomach, intestines), and then return the blood to the heart. The vessels that carry blood away from the heart are called arteries and the vessels that return blood to the heart are called veins (Figure 6.5).

Arteries

As the **arteries** carry blood away from the heart they branch into smaller and smaller vessels called **arterioles**. The arterioles also branch into smaller and smaller vessels until they are comprised of vessels that are about the width of one red blood cell. At this point they are called **capillaries** (Figures 6.5 and 6.11). The capillaries are small vessels composed of only endothelial cells that allow for the exchange of oxygen and nutrients from the blood to muscles and organs and also allow blood to pick up the waste products and carbon dioxide from metabolism.

Veins

As the blood begins to return to the heart, the capillaries connect to form larger and larger vessels called **venules**. The venules then merge into larger vessels called **veins**. Veins have an additional feature that facilitates the return of blood to the heart sometimes against the pull of gravity. In comparison to arteries, veins have **valves** that open with the flow of blood in the

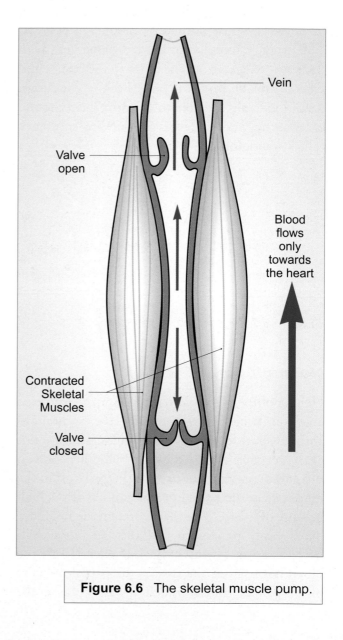

Figure 6.6 The skeletal muscle pump.

direction of return to the heart (e.g., from the knee to the hip), and close to prevent blood flow in the opposite direction (Figure 6.6). Blood can be pushed through veins by smooth muscle that surrounds the veins, contraction of the various skeletal muscles (or muscle groups), or to a minor extent by the pumping action of the heart.

Red Blood Cells

Red blood cells, or **erythrocytes** (Figure 6.7), are specialized cells (approximately 8μm in diameter) that are present in the blood. Other components of blood include **white blood cells** and a clear fluid called **plasma**. The percentage of the blood that is made up of red blood cells is called the **hematocrit** which normally is about 45 percent. The primary function of the red blood cells is to transport oxygen from the lungs to the tissues and carbon dioxide from the body back to the lungs. Red blood cells are able to perform this function because they contain an oxygen-binding substance called **hemoglobin**.

Figure 6.7 The red blood cell.

Hemoglobin

Hemoglobin is a molecule made up of proteins and iron. Each hemoglobin molecule can bond to and transport four oxygen molecules. The amount of oxygen that is carried by the blood depends on the **partial pressure of oxygen (PO_2)**. Thus, in the lungs where the partial pressure of oxygen is high because of the fresh air that is present, hemoglobin binds easily to oxygen and the red blood cells become saturated with oxygen. However, once the blood has reached the tissues, the partial pressure of oxygen is usually much lower, because the

metabolism of the body uses up the oxygen that is present. When the partial pressure of oxygen is lower, oxygen unbinds (dissociates) from hemoglobin and is diffused to the tissues where it is used to produce energy. The difference in the amount of oxygen that is present in the blood as it leaves the lungs and the amount of oxygen that is present in the blood when it returns to the lungs is called the **arterial–venous oxygen difference (a–v O_2 difference)** and is measured in millilitres of oxygen per decilitre of blood (i.e., ml O_2/100 ml blood). This is an important physiological measure of the amount of oxygen that is being used by the body. If the a–v O_2 difference increases, it means that the body is using more oxygen. A typical a–v O_2 difference at rest is about 4-5 ml O_2/dl of blood, while at exercise the a–v O_2 difference may increase to 15 ml O_2/dl of blood.

The total mass of red blood cells in the circulatory system is regulated within very narrow limits. New red blood cells (**reticulocytes**) are produced in the bone marrow. The principal factor that stimulates red blood cell formation is the circulating hormone **erythropoietin (EPO)**. EPO is secreted in response to low oxygen levels (when one is at high altitude; Figure 6.8) and also in response to exercise. Thus, exercise can increase the percentage of new red blood cells in the body. New red blood cells contain more hemoglobin than older red blood cells and thus can carry greater amounts of oxygen.

Cardiovascular Physiology

The Transport of Carbon Dioxide

Carbon dioxide (CO_2) is produced in the body as a by-product of metabolism. Once formed carbon dioxide diffuses from the cells to the blood where it is transported to the lungs via one of three mechanisms: (1) a small percentage of the produced CO_2 is dissolved in the blood plasma; (2) CO_2 also bonds to the hemoglobin molecule (remember that hemoglobin has unloaded its

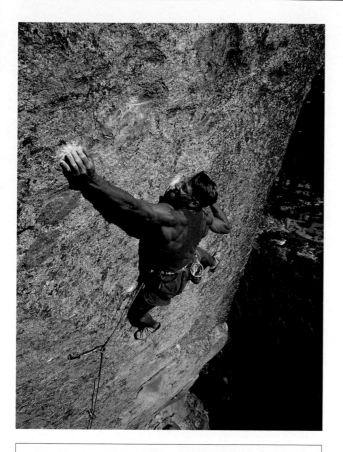

Figure 6.8 High altitude has an effect on EPO production which in turn generates a high production of red blood cells.

oxygen at the tissues so is capable of carrying CO_2 from the tissues to the lungs); and (3) CO_2 combines with water (primary mechanism) to form bicarbonate molecules (H_2CO_3) that are then transported through the body. This happens according to the following reversible reaction:

$$CO_2 + H_2O \longleftrightarrow H_2CO_3 \underset{\overset{\text{Carbonic}}{\text{Anhydrase}}}{\longleftrightarrow} H^+ + HCO_3^-$$

This reaction is also critical for the body's defence against changes in acidity.

Oxygen Uptake

Oxygen uptake is the amount of oxygen that is consumed by the body due to aerobic metabolism. It is measured as the volume of oxygen (in litres)

that is consumed ($\dot{V}O_2$) in a given amount of time, usually a minute. Oxygen uptake increases in relation to the amount of energy that is required to perform an activity; however, there is a limit to the amount of oxygen that the body can consume. One measure that is commonly used to evaluate the maximal volume of oxygen that can be supplied to and consumed by the body is **maximal aerobic power ($\dot{V}O_2$max)** (Figure 6.9).

The cardiovascular system can have an impact upon the amount of oxygen that is consumed by the body. For example, since the cardiac output determines the amount of blood that is delivered to the body, and blood is what carries oxygen to the tissues, any changes in cardiac output will alter the $\dot{V}O_2$. Changes in hematocrit (concentration of red blood cells) can also alter the oxygen uptake by increasing or decreasing the amount of oxygen that is supplied to working tissues. The ability of the tissues to extract oxygen (a–v O_2 difference) directly affects the oxygen uptake. Increases in a–v O_2 difference may arise due to an increased

Figure 6.9 Testing for maximal oxygen uptake or aerobic power.

number of mitochondria in muscles, increased enzyme efficiency in working tissues resulting in increased processing of oxygen, or for other reasons. Increased **capillarization** (number of capillaries in tissue) can affect the ability of the circulatory system to place red blood cells close to the tissues that are using the oxygen, thus increasing the ability of those tissues to extract the oxygen that is required due to a shorter diffusion distance.

Terminology Alert!

In most literature, the following terms are used synonymously with $\dot{V}O_2$max:

- aerobic power;

- maximal aerobic power;

- maximal oxygen uptake; and

- maximal oxygen consumption.

Cardiovascular limits ($\dot{V}O_2$max) can be described by multiplying the central component, cardiac output, by the effectiveness of peripheral factors (a–v O_2 difference). The central component primarily concerns the effectiveness of the heart and the ability of the lungs to oxygenate the blood. The peripheral factors include the ability of the body to extract that oxygen. Training can increase the maximal oxygen consumption of the human body by improving both the central and peripheral components. How this is accomplished will be presented in the next section.

Respiratory Anatomy and Physiology

One can survive without food for as much as several weeks, and without water for several days, but if one stops breathing for only three to six minutes, death is likely. The respiratory system is closely integrated with the cardiovascular system. Both these systems have similar functions in that they deliver oxygen and nutrients to the body, and remove carbon dioxide and waste products. The primary role of the respiratory system is to deliver oxygenated air to the blood and remove carbon dioxide, a by-product of metabolism, and to aid in acid–base balance.

Structure

The respiratory system includes the lungs, the several passageways leading from outside to the lungs, and the muscles that are responsible for the mechanical movements that move air into and out of the lungs. The two lungs are located within the thoracic cavity (the chest). Unlike most organs in the human body, the lungs are asymmetrical. The right lung is larger than the left lung because the heart takes up more space on the left side.

The air passages of the respiratory system are divided into two functional areas, the conduction zone and respiratory zone. The **conduction zone** consists of the anatomical structures through which air passes before reaching the respiratory zone. Air enters through the **nose** and/or **mouth**, where it is filtered, humidified, and adjusted to body temperature in the **trachea** (windpipe). The trachea branches into the **right and left bronchi** that enter the lungs and continue to branch into smaller and smaller tubes called **bronchioles**, and finally, the **terminal bronchioles**. The whole system inside the lungs looks so similar to an upside-down tree that it is commonly called the **"respiration tree"** (Figure 6.10).

The bronchioles continue to branch into the **respiratory zone**, the region where gas exchange occurs. The functional units of the lungs are tiny air sacs, known as **alveoli**. It is in these 300 million alveoli where gas exchange occurs. A single alveolus looks like a bubble. Alveoli are clustered in bunches like grapes, with a common opening into an alveolar duct, and each cluster is called an alveolar sac (Figures 6.10 and 6.12).

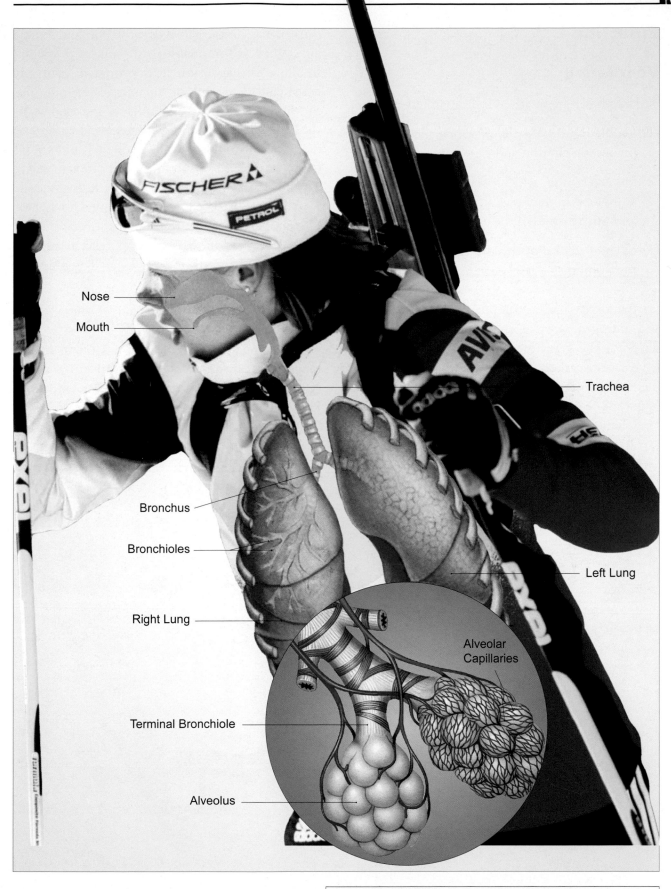

Nose

Mouth

Trachea

Bronchus

Bronchioles

Left Lung

Right Lung

Alveolar Capillaries

Terminal Bronchiole

Alveolus

Figure 6.10 The structure of the respiratory system.

Function

Ventilation

Several phases are involved in human respiration:

(1) **ventilation** or **breathing**, which includes two phases, inspiration and expiration;

(2) **gas exchange**, which occurs between the air and blood in the lungs and between the blood and other tissues of the body; and

(3) **oxygen utilization** by the tissues for **cellular respiration**.

Atmospheric air is composed mainly of oxygen and nitrogen, with a small amount of carbon dioxide. The gases of interest in respiration are oxygen and carbon dioxide. Ventilation involves the movement of air into (**inspiration**) and out of (**expiration**) the lungs.

Changes in the size of the thoracic cavity, and

thus of the lungs, allow us to inhale and exhale air. Lungs are normally light, soft, and spongy to allow for expansion in the thoracic cavity. It is the continual work of the muscles surrounding the thoracic cavity that results in the change in the thoracic cavity. These muscles include the **diaphragm** (Figure 6.12) and the **intercostal muscles**. During inspiration, the thoracic cavity expands via muscle contractions, causing the air pressure inside to be lowered, forcing a flow of air into the lungs. When the thoracic cavity shrinks during expiration via muscle relaxation, the increased pressure inside causes air contained in the lungs to flow out.

Gas Exchange in the Lungs

Gas exchange between the air and blood in the lungs occurs at the alveoli. Alveoli are only a single cell layer thick, thus facilitating gas diffusion. Each bubble-like alveolus is surrounded by a vast network of pulmonary capillaries (Figure

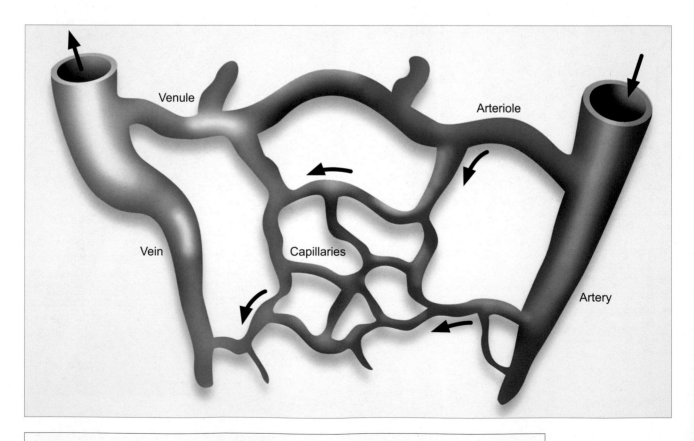

Figure 6.11   The network of pulmonary capillaries where gas exchange takes place.

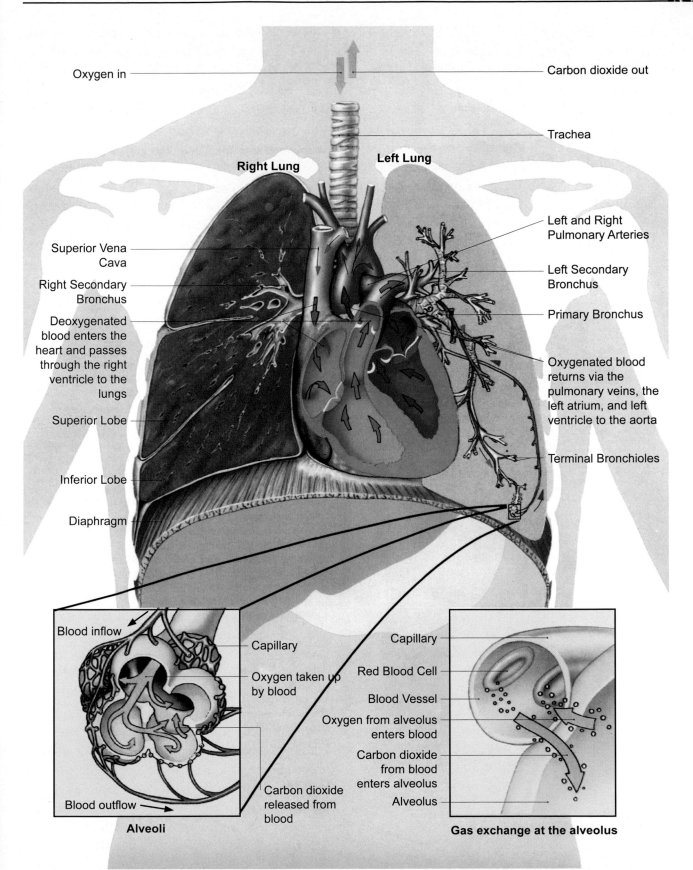

Oxygen in

Carbon dioxide out

Trachea

Right Lung

Left Lung

Left and Right Pulmonary Arteries

Superior Vena Cava

Left Secondary Bronchus

Right Secondary Bronchus

Primary Bronchus

Deoxygenated blood enters the heart and passes through the right ventricle to the lungs

Oxygenated blood returns via the pulmonary veins, the left atrium, and left ventricle to the aorta

Superior Lobe

Terminal Bronchioles

Inferior Lobe

Diaphragm

Blood inflow

Capillary

Oxygen taken up by blood

Blood outflow

Carbon dioxide released from blood

Alveoli

Capillary

Red Blood Cell

Blood Vessel

Oxygen from alveolus enters blood

Carbon dioxide from blood enters alveolus

Alveolus

Gas exchange at the alveolus

Figure 6.12 Gas exchange in the alveoli.

6.11). The atmospheric air, which has made its way into each alveolus, is rich in oxygen. The blood in the pulmonary capillaries is loaded with the waste product of carbon dioxide. This difference in concentration in these gases sets up ideal conditions for **gas diffusion**. Diffusion is the movement of molecules (gases) from a higher concentration to a lower concentration. Therefore, the oxygen from the atmospheric air diffuses through the alveolar membrane into deoxygenated pulmonary capillaries (Figure 6.12). Carbon dioxide diffuses in the opposite direction, from the carbon dioxide–rich pulmonary blood into the alveoli, where the concentration of carbon dioxide is lower. The carbon dioxide is exhaled. The oxygenated blood follows the pulmonary circulation to reach the heart's left ventricle, where it is distributed throughout the body via the systemic circulation.

Exercise Effects on the Cardiovascular and Respiratory Systems

Exercise can have many beneficial effects on the cardiovascular and respiratory systems. The cardiovascular system adjusts to meet the demands of exercise. These adjustments ensure an adequate blood supply to working muscles, the brain, and the heart, and ensure that heat and waste products generated by muscles are dissipated and removed. The benefits are important as they can lead to an improvement in quality of life by allowing people to do more with less effort, as well as by reducing disease and improving overall health and vitality. These benefits, known as exercise training effects, are presented in Figure 6.13, and discussed in this section.

Cardiac Output

The first effect of training on the cardiovascular system concerns changes in the heart (Figure 6.13 A). Endurance training has been shown to increase the size of the heart. The increase in heart size may arise due to an increase in the size of the heart cavities (ventricles and atria) as well as an increase in the thickness of the walls of the heart. The benefits to the cardiovascular system realized by an increase in heart size include: the larger atria and ventricles allow for a greater volume of blood to be pumped each time the heart beats; and the increased thickness of the walls of the heart (the walls of the heart are made up of cardiac muscle) allows for an increased contractility (rate of contraction) and also a greater emptying of the ventricles each time the heart beats. The end result is a greater cardiac output (heart rate x stroke volume) during each heartbeat and thus an increase in the efficiency of the heart.

Capillary Supply

Increased capillarization (number of capillaries in a given space) is another benefit that may arise as a result of endurance training (Figure 6.13 B). An increased capillarization allows for a greater surface area and reduced distance between the blood and the surrounding tissues, thus increasing diffusion capacity of oxygen and carbon dioxide, as well as easing the transport of nutrients to cells. An increased capillarization also occurs in cardiac muscle, reducing the possibility of cardiac disease and heart attacks. The a–v O_2 difference of the body can be improved by endurance training. Essentially this means that the body can be trained to extract more oxygen from the blood. This can be achieved because endurance training increases circulation (blood flow) to the capillaries that are next to muscle fibres, as discussed. This provides a greater surface area for the exchange of nutrients, oxygen, and carbon dioxide. Another factor that increases the ability of the body to extract oxygen is the ability of muscle cells to process oxygen through aerobic metabolism that occurs in mitochondria (see Chapter 5, Energy for Muscular Activity). Endurance training increases both the number and activity levels of mitochondria in muscle fibres.

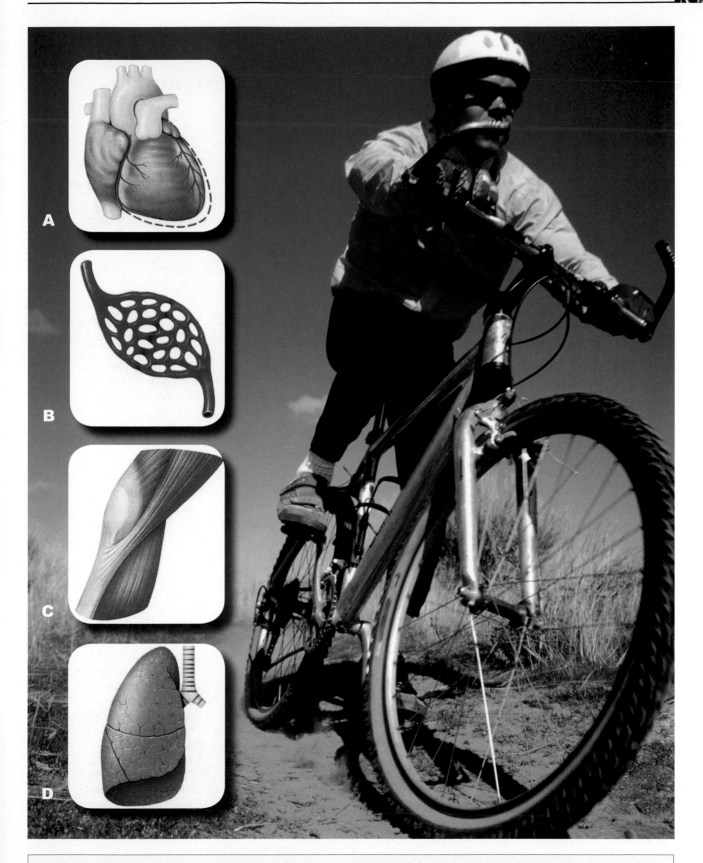

Figure 6.13 The dynamic exercise (aerobic) training effect on the cardiovascular and respiratory systems. **A.** Increase in the size of the heart. **B.** Increased capillarization. **C.** Increase in the amount of extracted oxygen from circulating blood in working muscles. **D.** Increased efficiency in gas exchange.

Blood Volume

Total blood volume has been shown to increase with training as the number and total volume of red blood cells are increased through stimulation of erythropoiesis (formation of new red blood cells) in the bone marrow. Both of these factors can have positive effects on the efficiency of the cardiovascular system, primarily by increasing the ability of the blood to carry a greater amount of oxygen and by decreasing the thickness (viscosity) of the blood. The amount of extracted oxygen from the circulated blood is significantly increased in the working muscles, thereby increasing their efficiency (Figure 6.13 C).

Ventilation

During dynamic exercise, breathing becomes deeper and more rapid. Ventilation increases with exercise in order to meet the increased demand of gas exchange. During exercise, ventilation can increase from 6 L/min at rest to over 150 L/min during maximal exercise. The increased air flow allows for more gas exchange to occur. With continuous dynamic activity such as running, swimming, cross-country skiing, and bicycling, the lungs become more efficient in gas exchange (Figure 6.13 D).

The Bohr Effect

During exercise, body temperature increases. An increased body temperature, in turn, promotes oxygen extraction. This phenomenon is known as the **Bohr effect**. It describes the reduced effectiveness of hemoglobin to hold oxygen. This phenomenon, accompanied by an increase in metabolic heat, carbon dioxide production, and lactic acid concentration, is important in vigorous exercise because even more oxygen is released to the working muscle tissue. However, in the alveoli the Bohr effect is negligible, thus allowing hemoglobin to maximally load with oxygen.

The Bohr effect is another example of an exercise training effect that occurs in the human body.

Exercise and Environments

In general, the environmental conditions under which exercise takes place do not change much. If the environment does change, it creates additional stresses on the various physiological systems of the body.

Two common examples of environmental changes are altitude and temperature.

Altitude

The air we breathe is primarily comprised of 79.04 percent nitrogen, 20.93 percent oxygen, and 0.03 percent carbon dioxide. At **altitude** the percentages of these molecules remain the same but the density of molecules changes. The term **thin air** is often used to describe the condition of air at altitude. Since the body requires a certain amount or volume of oxygen (obtained during each breath), a lower density of oxygen molecules per unit volume of air means a person at altitude must breathe more frequently or more deeply to obtain the necessary amount of oxygen. This **hyperventilation** is a hallmark of altitude exposure.

Although hyperventilation provides the necessary amount of oxygen to the body, it has

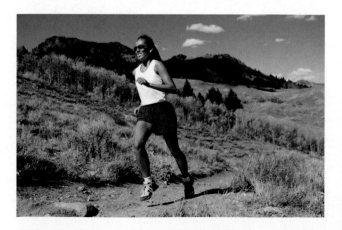

Figure 6.14 Exercising at altitude results in various positive physiological adaptations.

the negative consequence of "blowing off" a greater than normal amount of carbon dioxide, which changes the acid–base (pH) balance and thus influences other physiological systems and processes. With sudden or large changes in altitude, the body cannot always adequately adapt and **acute mountain sickness (AMS)** can occur. The symptoms and severity of AMS vary from a headache to cerebral or pulmonary edema, which can cause death.

One consequence of exercising at altitude is that the heart must work harder to compensate for the reduced amount of available oxygen. This partially explains the higher heart rates observed upon initial altitude exposure. However, given enough time, the body offsets the increased cardiac work by improving the oxygen-carrying capacity of the blood. This is accomplished by increasing both the number of red blood cells (*hematocrit*) and the amount of hemoglobin (the protein that carries oxygen) in the red blood cells. After a few weeks, these adaptations ease the work of the heart and homeostasis is restored (Figure 6.14). Athletes often train at altitude in hopes of acquiring these adaptations so that when they return to lower altitudes, they can derive the benefits of an increased oxygen-carrying capacity. Whether altitude training actually provides benefits is currently under investigation.

Temperature

While at rest, the body loses heat primarily through radiation. That is, heat warms the surrounding air and objects and is dissipated electromagnetically. During exercise heat must be released to maintain a constant core temperature. About 80 percent of the energy released during exercise is released as heat.

As heat builds up in the body, sweat glands produce sweat on the skin surface. As the sweat evaporates, heat is removed from the body. In humid conditions, when the air already holds a great deal of water, it becomes more difficult for the sweat to evaporate and heat tends to be stored in the body. Core temperature increases as

a result, along with the possibility of developing the potentially fatal conditions of **hyperthermia** or **heat stroke**.

Heat generated by the muscles is transported to the skin by the blood. During exercise in the heat, the circulatory system performs the dual function of delivering oxygen to the tissues as well as transporting blood to the skin (*peripheral vasodilation*) to allow for heat dissipation. Since these two events are mutually exclusive, athletes exercising in the heat often exhibit an increased heart rate at submaximal workloads to accommodate for the reduced blood flow to the muscles. This means that the heart will have to work harder than normal and maximal heart rate will be reached sooner. In addition, fluid loss through sweat will eventually lead to a reduced stroke volume which further compromises cardiac output. An athlete is therefore unable to work at the same absolute intensity under hot or humid conditions than when exercising in a normal environment.

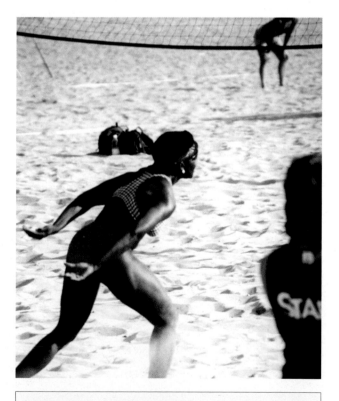

Figure 6.15 Fluid replenishment is vital to avoid the potentially dangerous effects of hyperthermia when exercising in the heat.

Since the body is sweating at a high rate, fluid replenishment is vital. If fluids are not replaced, core temperature will rise and hyperthermia may occur (Figure 6.15). Over time, the body can adapt to exercise in the heat by maintaining core temperature and minimizing increased heart rate, as well as increasing the ability to sweat and therefore lose heat.

Summary

The cardiovascular and respiratory systems are made up of interconnected organs that include the heart, lungs, and blood vessels, as well as the blood itself. These systems' four primary functions are the transportation of (1) oxygen from the lungs to the tissues; (2) carbon dioxide from the tissues to the lungs; (3) nutrients from the digestive system to other areas in the body; and (4) waste products from sites of production to sites of excretion.

Several key aspects of the cardiovascular system can be measured and monitored. Blood pressure (systolic and diastolic) is an important gauge of cardiac function. Heart rate is the number of times the heart beats in one minute, and the amount of blood pumped by the left ventricle with each heart beat is known as the stroke volume. Another factor, cardiac output, is the product of stroke volume and heart rate. Cardiac output represents the amount of blood that is pumped into the aorta each minute by the heart, and therefore indicates the quantity of blood that flows to the peripheral circulation.

Oxygen uptake is the amount of oxygen consumed by the body due to aerobic metabolism. One measure commonly used to evaluate the maximal volume of oxygen that can be supplied to, and consumed by, the body is maximal aerobic power, or $\dot{V}O_2$max, expressed in litres per minute. The difference in the amount of oxygen that is present in the blood as it leaves the lungs and the amount of oxygen that is present in the blood when it returns to the lungs is called the arterial–venous oxygen difference (a–v O_2 difference).

Key Words

Action potential	Diastole	Red blood cell (erythrocyte)
Acute mountain sickness (AMS)	Erythropoietin (EPO)	Respiratory zone
Altitude	Expiration	Reticulocytes
Alveoli	Gas diffusion	Right atrium
Arterial–venous oxygen (a–v O_2) difference	Heart rate	Right ventricle
	Hematocrit	Sinus node
Arteriole	Hemoglobin	Stroke volume
Artery	Hyperthermia (heat stroke)	Superior vena cava
Bohr effect	Hyperventilation	Systole
Bronchiole	Inferior vena cava	Terminal bronchiole
Bronchus	Inspiration	Trachea
Capillary	Left atrium	Valve
Cardiac output	Left ventricle	Vein
Conduction zone	Maximal aerobic power ($\dot{V}O_2$max)	Ventilation
Diaphragm	Plasma	Venule
		White blood cell

Discussion Questions

1. Describe the path and all related steps that a molecule of oxygen would take from the air in the lungs to a muscle cell.

2. Describe the path and all related steps that a molecule of carbon dioxide could take from a muscle cell to the air in the lungs.

3. Define and provide the units for blood pressure, heart rate, cardiac output, stroke volume, and arterial–venous oxygen difference.

4. List the ways in which training improves the effectiveness of the cardiovascular and respiratory systems.

5. Describe the two components of blood pressure. What do they measure?

6. What is hemoglobin? Where is it found? What is its purpose?

7. What is hematocrit?

8. Describe the ways in which carbon dioxide can be transported through the blood.

9. What is $\dot{V}O_2$max? What factors influence this measure? How is it affected by training?

10. Discuss the many benefits of exercise on the cardiovascular and respiratory systems.

In This Chapter:

Types of Study 130
    Quantitative Versus Qualitative
      Analysis 130
    Kinematics Versus Kinetics 132

**Biomechanical Models of Human
Motion 133**
    The Particle Model 133
    The Stick Figure Model 134
    The Rigid Segment Body Model 135
    Steps of Analysis 135

Types of Motion 135
    Linear Motion 135
    Angular Motion 136
    General Motion 136

Causes of Motion 136
    Calculating Moment of Force 138

Forces Represented by Vectors 141
    Net Force 141

Mass and Inertia Concepts 143
    Newton's First Law of Motion:
      Inertia 144

Force and Acceleration Concepts 145
    Newton's Second Law of Motion:
      Acceleration 145

**Impulse, Impact, and Momentum
Concepts 145**

Action–Reaction Concept 147
    Newton's Third Law of Motion:
      Reaction 147

Projectile Motion 147
    Maximizing Height and Range 149
    Taking Off and Landing at Different
      Heights 149

    Optimizing Range 150
    Air Resistance 150

Fluid Dynamics 150
    Fluid Drag Forces: The Dynamics of
      Air 151
    Skin-friction Drag 152
    Profile Drag 152
    Fluid Lift Forces 154
    Angle of Attack 154
    The Magnus Effect 155

Body Balance and Stability Control 157
    Equilibrium 157
    Balance 157
    Stability 157
    Factors Affecting Balance 158

Angular Kinetics 159
    Off-centre External Forces 159

**Conservation of Momentum Within the
Body 160**
    Rotations While Airborne 160

**Qualitative Analysis of Human
Motion 162**
    Skill Objective 163
    Analyzing a Skill 163
    Observation of Performance 164
    Error Detection and Correction 165

Summary 166

CHAPTER 7

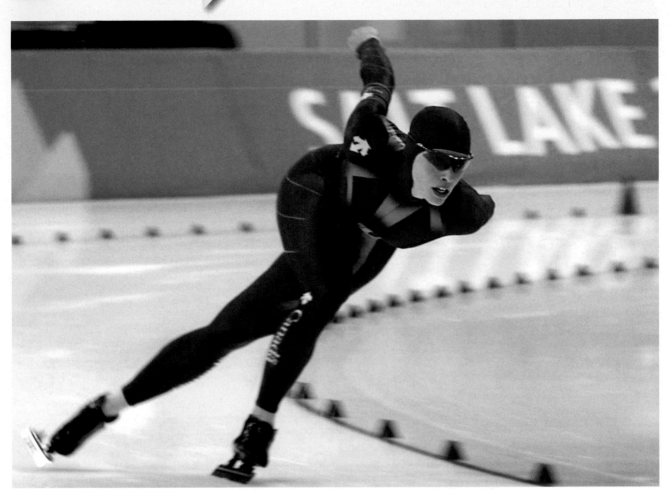

How Do I Move? The Science of Biomechanics

After completing this chapter you should be able to:

- distinguish between different types and causes of human motion;

- identify Newton's laws of motion and describe practical illustrations of the laws;

- describe the expected path and motion of a projectile;

- describe the conservation of momentum within the body, and explain why changes in the configuration of a rotating airborne body produce changes in its angular velocity;

- explain the role of friction in the context of fluid dynamics;

- evaluate qualitative analyses of human motion.

129

The capabilities of the human body seem endless. From a baby's first step, to an Olympic performance, we marvel at the wide range of human movements that are possible. We have all witnessed the powerful gymnast who explodes off the floor to perform three rotations in the air before landing on his or her feet, or the diver who twists and turns in the air before entering the water with delicate precision. But what causes these movements? How do we describe them? Are there limitations to what we can do? Biomechanics, one of the biophysical sciences which comprise the field of physical and health education, tries to describe the causes and effects of how the body moves.

Biomechanics is a science that examines the internal and external forces acting on the human body and the effects produced by these forces. It is considered a relatively young field of scientific inquiry, but many other scientific disciplines and professional fields make use of biomechanical considerations. People in various walks of life, including physical and health education, use the principles of biomechanics. Academic backgrounds in fields such as sports medicine, physical therapy, kinesiology, biomechanical engineering, and even zoology can offer important knowledge to the biomechanical aspects of the structure and function of living things.

For example, biomechanics allows us to understand why humans walk the way they do, what effect gravity has on the human musculoskeletal system, how mobility impairment in the elderly can be improved, and how a prosthesis can aid individuals with below-knee amputations. These are real concerns that can have a significant impact on the lives of many people. Sport biomechanists and engineers have also contributed invaluably to improving performances in selected sports, such as wheel and helmet designs for cycling, optimal body positioning for ski jumping during the flight phase, and the most effective technique for throwing a discus. Have you ever wondered why some golfers tend to slice the ball, or why pole-vaulting records have continued to fall since the introduction of fibreglass poles?

From playing surfaces and equipment, to shoes, biomechanics plays an important role in recognizing what practices are perhaps less effective and less dangerous, and how athletes optimize performance. Research continues to be conducted in an attempt to highlight these concerns, and provide more effective alternatives.

Obviously, research involving biomechanics is extremely diverse and multifaceted. From analyzing technique to developing innovative equipment designs, biomechanics has significantly added to our knowledge of human movement. Before the advent of fibreglass poles, clearing a height of 6 metres in pole vaulting would have seemed unreachable. Understanding the mechanical principles that underlie human movement can help answer questions related to human health and performance. This chapter will provide you with the foundation necessary to identify, analyze, and effectively answer questions related to the biomechanics of human movement.

Types of Study

Quantitative Versus Qualitative Analysis

Biomechanists spend a great deal of time devising techniques to measure those biomechanical variables that are believed to optimize performance. These scientists may investigate (1) the pattern of forces exerted by the foot onto the sprinter's starting block; (2) the sequence of muscle activity during running using electromyography; or (3) the three-dimensional movements of each body segment during a high jump using high-speed cinematography, or an automated motion analyzing system. These studies are examples of **quantitative analyses** of performance. A quantitative analysis is intended for use by researchers and will be left for further study.

Coaches and teachers do not always have available to them the necessary equipment to perform these analyses, and thus must rely on

Figure 7.1 Biomechanics can help us understand sport performances by suggesting better teaching and coaching techniques (A), comparing different techniques for performing the same skill (B), and improving error detection and correction techniques (C, D).

Kinematic Variables

Time

How long does it take to run a race, to swing a bat, to perform a karate chop, or to prepare to jump in volleyball? How long is a diver airborne before entering the water? *How long* refers to the temporal characteristics of a performance, either of the total skill or of its phases. It is a time interval calculated as the difference between the beginning and end of two instants of time.

Displacement

Displacement is the length and direction of the path an athlete traverses from the start to finish of a performance or portion thereof. Sprinters run 100 m east. Volleyball players jump 0.8 m up during a block.

Angular Displacement

Angular displacement measures the direction of and smallest angular change between the rotating body's initial and final position. In standing up from a chair, the knee joint and hip joint both rotate through approximately 90 degrees but in opposite directions (i.e., clockwise and counter-clockwise). A diver performing a front 1½ dive would have an angular displacement of 180 degrees clockwise or counter-clockwise.

Velocity

Velocity is the measure of the displacement per unit time. Velocities can be calculated as instantaneous, that is, occurring over a very small time interval, or as average, where the time interval is longer (i.e., the time it takes to run a complete race). During the 1996 Olympics, Donovan Bailey reached a peak velocity of 12.1 m/s (down the track), while his average velocity was (100 m / 9.86 s) 10.14 m/s (down the track).

Angular Velocity

Angular velocity is the measure of angular displacement per unit time, or how fast a body is rotating. The rotation of the arm about the shoulder joint during the delivery swing of a bowling ball has a lower angular velocity than the same movement in a fastball pitcher.

Acceleration

Acceleration is the rate of change of velocity. Success in many sports activities depends upon the athlete's ability to increase or decrease speed and/or direction rapidly, such as changes of direction in basketball or football, or stealing a base in baseball, or sprinting a 100-metre dash, or throwing a shot, or decreasing the velocity of a ball when catching in handball.

Angular Acceleration

Angular acceleration is the measure of change in angular velocity per unit time. During a giant swing, a gymnast begins from a handstand and swings once around the bar. The gymnast accelerates clockwise on the way down, but experiences deceleration clockwise during the up phase.

---

any information they can readily obtain, visual or aural, to assess performance. This type of analysis is known as a qualitative analysis. A qualitative analysis requires a framework within which skilled performances can be observed, a set of principles within which movement can be analyzed, a checklist to use when identifying errors, and techniques to use to correct errors in performance. Good qualitative analyses lead to good quantitative analyses.

Whether they are working with developing or advanced athletes, biomechanists can provide coaches and instructors with (1) knowledge on how a skill is done; (2) a basis for the comparison of techniques; (3) better teaching and coaching techniques; and (4) improved ability to detect and correct errors in performance (Figure 7.1).

Kinematics Versus Kinetics

The study of kinematics describes spatial and timing characteristics of motion of the human body and its segments. These variables are used to describe both linear and angular motion (see box *Kinematic Variables*). They answer four questions: how long? how far? how fast? and how consistent was the motion?

Kinetics, on the other hand, focuses on the various forces that cause a movement: that is, the forces that produce the movement and the resulting motion. The forces, which act on the human body, can be **internal** or **external**. Internal forces refer to forces generated by muscles pulling on bones via their tendons, and to bone-on-bone forces exerted across joint surfaces. External forces on the body refer to those forces acting from without, such as the force of **gravity**, or the force from any body contact with the ground, environment, sport equipment, or opponent. In general, internal forces *cause* individual body segment movements, while external forces *affect* total body movements.

Biomechanical Models of Human Motion

Biomechanics has been defined as the science that examines the internal and external forces acting on the human body and the effects produced by these forces. For example, a hockey player skating down the ice is generating internal forces in the leg muscles during each skating stroke. The net result of all of these internal muscle forces is a sequence of pushes against the ice with the skate blade. With each push against the ice, the ice pushes back upon the hockey player (note, the ice is an external force) and as a result the skater experiences forward movement. Other external forces also act upon the skater such as gravity, the weight of the hockey stick, or an opposing player who gives the skater a body check into the boards. Each of these external forces in turn has an effect upon the motion of the human body. A body check, for example, causes the hockey player to crash into the boards.

While we can visualize the hockey player crashing into the boards, the actual human body with all its bones, muscles, connective tissue, and internal organs is too complex for most biomechanical analyses. Anatomical differences exist between people due to race, age, sex, health, and lifestyle. Furthermore, all body tissues undergo shape deformations during sport movements. Moreover, the human body is multi-segmented such that the same total body or limb movement can be performed using different segment movement sequences. And finally, most sport skills occur in three dimensions, a fact which adds a great deal of complexity to understanding and observing human movements.

To make the study of human movement possible, biomechanics has adopted three simplified models of human motion analysis: the particle, stick figure, and rigid segment body models.

The Particle Model

The **particle model** is a simple dot representing the centre of mass (see box *Centre of Mass*, page 143) of the body or object (Figure 7.2 A). Particle models are used when the human body or object is airborne and in flight. When the body is airborne it is already free from its surroundings. Most often, gravity (see box *Gravity*, page 144) is the only external force acting on the body through its centre of mass. For objects that possess a relatively large velocity, such as baseballs, javelins, and discuses, the surrounding air will also apply a force to the object (see Figure 7.13, page 151). This external force, known as air resistance, will also affect the motion of the object.

Since particle models involve only the centre of mass of an object, they are limited to bodies in flight. In sport, these include any ball or object which is thrown, struck, hit, or kicked, as well as the human body in flight such as during diving, high jumping, or tumbling. In all of these examples, the object or body is said to be a projectile.

Figure 7.2 Three models used to represent the diver pictured above. **A.** Particle model. **B.** Stick figure model. **C.** Rigid segment body model. Choice of model is based on the type of biomechanical analysis to be made.

The Stick Figure Model

For athletes who are in contact with the ground or other earth-bound objects (i.e., diving board) a **stick figure model** is used to represent their bodies (Figure 7.2 B). Body segments are represented by rigid bars (sticks) linked together at the joints. Stick figures indicate approximate body segment positions, their connections, and size. External forces, represented by vectors, can be shown acting on the stick figure at the appropriate locations.

Stick figure models are used to represent the total body configuration for gross motor skills that occur in two dimensions. Sprint starts, running, and somersaults are good examples. They cannot easily represent small or fine local muscle movements, such as the grip on a baseball. Nor can they represent longitudinal rotations, either total body twisting movements or segment rotations such as pronations. Total body skills, which occur with many three-dimensional movements, are also difficult to draw.

A sequence of stick figures representing either the total body or portion thereof is known as a **composite diagram** (Figure 7.3). Composite diagrams give a quick picture of the body actions involved in a skill. To our mind's eye they resemble our visual impression of a skill. However, because the stick figure links have no volume the stick figure cannot be truly individualized to the athlete.

The advantage of the stick figure over the particle model is that multiple force vectors can be drawn on the free body diagram. These vectors can represent gravity or air resistance forces acting at the centre of mass, and reaction forces (described later in the chapter) acting on the body wherever contact is made with the environment. Some of these forces may create moments of force, and thus indicate rotation of the body or its

Figure 7.3 Composite diagrams provide a pictorial overview of the performance. However, if the motion does not occur in the two-dimensional plane of the diagram, then accurate measurements, such as angular velocity of the golf club, will be difficult.

segment parts (Figure 7.9, page 142).

The Rigid Segment Body Model

For sophisticated three-dimensional (3D) analyses, biomechanists employ a **rigid segment body model** in which each body segment is represented as an irregularly shaped 3D volume (Figure 7.2 C). The shape deformation of body segments during vigorous activity adds to the complexity of these analyses.

Steps of Analysis

There are three preliminary steps that must be completed before any human or object motion can be described using the three biomechanical models.

Step 1

Identify the system to be studied: in other words, isolate the object of analysis from its surroundings (e.g., arm, leg, tennis racquet, or total body of a runner) (Figure 7.4).

Step 2

Identify the frame of reference (or coordinate system) in which the movement takes place (e.g., a runner changes his position relative to the ground and to some starting point; Figure 7.4). While many sport movements are usually described as occurring in two dimensions (running, somersaulting), most sport activities (or components) actually occur in three dimensions.

Step 3

Identify the type of motion that is occurring, the **body planes** in which movement takes place (sagittal, frontal, and transverse, see Chapter 2), and the **axes of rotation** about which rotational motion occurs (either through a joint or the total body).

Types of Motion

Human movement is composed of a number of fundamental types of motion. We differentiate between linear, angular, and general motion.

Linear Motion

Linear motion occurs when all parts of the body move the same distance, in the same direction, and at the same time, such as a toboggan run, a skater's glide, or a sprinter (Figure 7.5 A). Another term often used for linear motion is **translation**, which refers to movement of the body as a unit without individual segment parts of the body moving in relation to one another.

    Rectilinear motion occurs when the movement follows a straight line (a 100-metre sprinter's movement); a **curvilinear motion** occurs when the

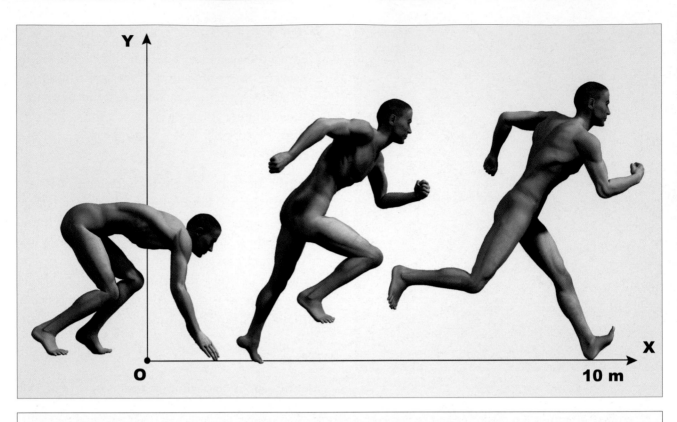

Figure 7.4 Identifying the system and reference frame. The system is the total body of a runner. The reference frame is the two-dimensional xy plane with the origin at the start line.

movement path is curved (a ski jumper's flight).

Angular Motion

When a body moves on a circular path and in the same direction, then the body is experiencing **angular motion** or **rotation**. The line about which bodies rotate is called the axis of rotation. A good example of this type of motion is a gymnast executing giant swings on a high bar (Figure 7.5 B).

Body segments also experience angular motion about their joints as they flex, extend, and longitudinally rotate. Twisting somersault dives, shot put, and an automobile's wheels turning around their axes are good examples of angular motion.

General Motion

A combination of linear and angular motion (i.e., body moving linearly and rotating simultaneously)

is referred to as **general motion**. This is true for most athletic and many everyday activities (e.g., gymnastics floor routine, wrestling, a diver falling downward while simultaneously rotating in a somersault; Figure 7.5 C).

Causes of Motion

The cause of motion of the human body is the application of internal and external forces. A force is any action, a push or pull, which tends to cause an object to change its state of motion by experiencing acceleration. If an object is not accelerating then it experiences a state of constant **velocity** (note: rest or no motion is just the state of constant "zero" velocity).

There are two types of motion resulting from the application of a force, linear motion and angular motion. Forces that act through a body's centre of mass will cause linear motion, such as

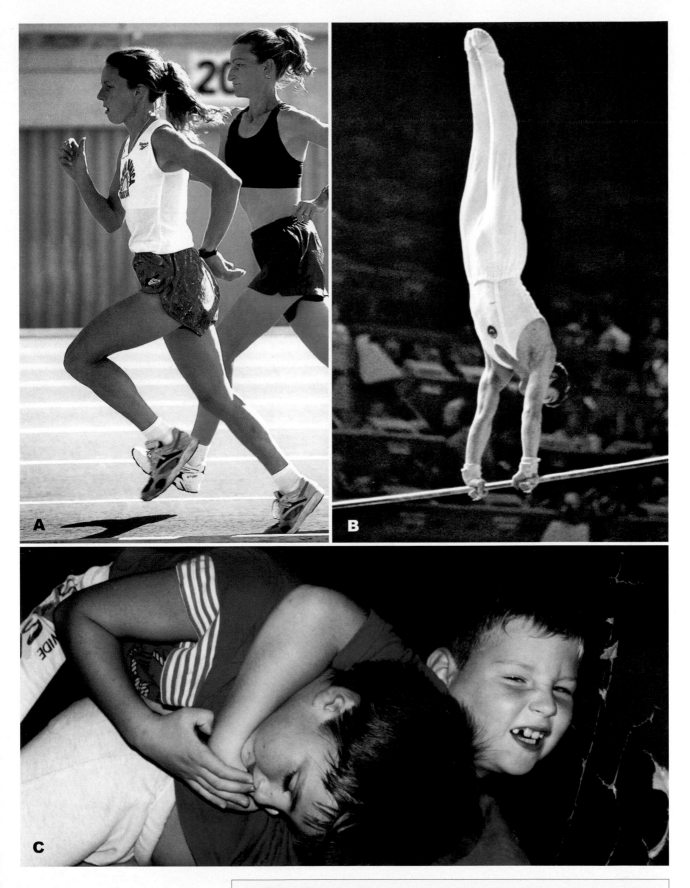

Figure 7.5 Types of human motion. **A.** Linear. **B.** Angular. **C.** General.

throwing a ball or pushing a cart (Figure 7.6 A).

Forces that do not go through the centre of mass or pivot point of an object cause a rotation about an axis of rotation. These actions cause the object to change its state of angular motion by experiencing an angular acceleration. When a force causes angular motion the effect is known as a **moment of force** or **torque**. Moments of force are generated to open a door, flex a joint, or move

an opponent (Figure 7.6 B).

Calculating Moment of Force

Consider a balanced teeter-totter (Figure 7.7 A). If each person was to sit alone on the teeter-totter, this would cause the teeter-totter to rotate about its axis, the **fulcrum** of the teeter-totter. Each person creates a moment of force by applying his or her

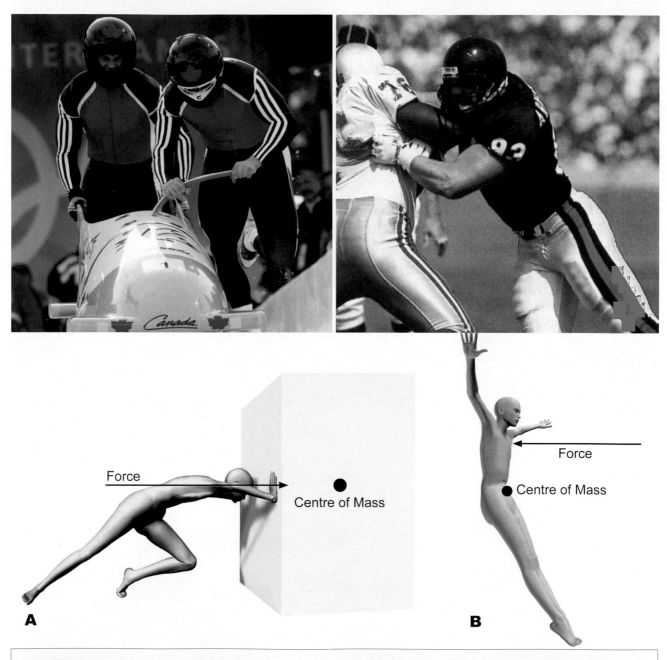

Figure 7.6 Causes of linear and angular motions. **A.** Linear motion results when the forces are applied through the centre of mass. **B.** Angular motion results when forces are applied away from the centre of mass.

Figure 7.7 Factors affecting the moment of force. **A.** Balanced teeter-totter. **B.** Increasing the moment arm by leaning back. **C.** Increasing the applied force by adding a friend.

weight away from the axis of rotation. However, if the moments of force created are equal then the teeter-totter will be balanced (Figure 7.7 A).

What could you do to unbalance the teeter-totter? One method is to lean back, away from the fulcrum, increasing the distance from the fulcrum to the point of application of your weight vector (Figure 7.7 B). The shortest (perpendicular) distance from the axis of rotation to the line of action of the force is known as the **moment arm (D)**. Therefore, by increasing the moment arm, you can create more moment of force and rotate the teeter-totter in your direction.

Another method to unbalance the teeter-totter would be to ask a friend to join you on your side of the teeter-totter (Figure 7.7 C). In this case, you have increased the applied force acting on the teeter-totter and thus have increased the moment of force your side creates.

Thus two factors, moment arm and magnitude of force, influence the magnitude of the moment of force which can be generated. The magnitude of the moment of force is calculated by using the equation:

Moment of Force = Moment Arm x Force

Levers

Levers are simple mechanical devices that augment the amount of work done by an applied force. A lever is a rigid body (i.e., long bone) that rotates about a fixed point (i.e., joint) called an axis (A) or fulcrum. Acting on the lever is a resistive force (R, i.e., weight of a limb segment) and an applied force (F, i.e., muscle contraction). There are three classes of levers, first, second, and third, which differ by placing the fulcrum, resistive force, and applied force respectively between the other two. They are presented in the box *Lever Systems and Muscle Actions*.

The teeter-totter is just one example of a lever. There are many levers found in the human body and in sport skills. Can you think of examples for each type of lever?

Lever Systems and Muscle Actions

Functions of Levers

Levers perform different functions. Some levers help to balance forces and resistive loads. In other levers, the application of a relatively small amount of force can overcome a relatively large resistive force (i.e., crowbar). Finally in some levers, the application of a force results in the lever (and resistive force) moving quickly through a large range of motion (i.e., forearm flexion).

First Class Levers When the applied force and the resistance are located on opposite sides we speak of **first class levers**. The applied force and resistance may be at equal distances from the axis, or one may be further away from the axis than the other.

In everyday life, the teeter-totter in Figure 7.7 is an example of a first class lever. In the human body, flexion and extension of the head about C1 is an example of a first class lever. The simultaneous action of agonist and antagonist muscle groups (see Chapter 3) on opposite sides of a joint axis is another. During contraction, the agonists provide the applied force and the antagonists supply a resistance force.

Second Class Levers The applied force and the resistance are on the same side of the axis in a **second class lever**, and the resistance is closer to the axis. In everyday life, a wheelbarrow or a nutcracker may serve as examples of second class levers. In the human body, second class levers are hard to find. Contraction of the calf muscles to raise the body onto the toes – the fulcrum is at the distal end of the metatarsals – serves as an example.

Third Class Levers A **third class lever** exists when the applied force and the resistance are on the same side of the axis, but the applied force is closer to the axis. In everyday life, a screen door with a spring closing or snow shoveling can serve as third class levers. Most muscle–bone lever systems of the human body are examples of third class levers during concentric contractions. Forearm flexion may serve as an example: the biceps, attaching to the bone at a short distance from the joint centre, supplies the applied force; the weight, at much greater distance from the joint centre, supplies the resistance.

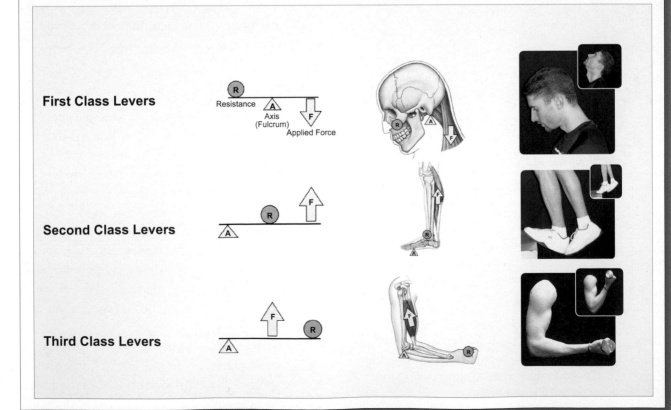

First Class Levers

Resistance · Axis (Fulcrum) · Applied Force

Second Class Levers

Third Class Levers

Your Levers at Work

Think of your throwing arm as a lever when you throw a baseball properly. Your elbow becomes a fulcrum, multiplying the speed of your slowly contracting triceps muscle and the forearm muscles. As you throw:

- Bend wrist and fingers (flexors)
- Straighten elbow (triceps)
- Straighten wrist and fingers (extensors)
- Bend elbow (biceps)

To add power to your throw, change the centre of gravity during the windup. Shifting your weight to your back leg lowers your centre of gravity. As you go through the movement of the pitch, the centre of gravity shifts forward and up as your weight is shifted from the back leg to the front leg. A higher pitcher's mound – it is raised by 25.4 cm – further adds to the ball's speed through the force of gravity.

Forces Represented by Vectors

In biomechanics physical variables such as time, speed, and force are classified either as scalar quantities or vector quantities. A **scalar quantity** has only magnitude, such as the length of time it takes to run 100 metres or the speed posted on a road sign (i.e., 100 km per hour). A **vector quantity** has both magnitude and direction. Force is a vector quantity because it has magnitude (large or small) and direction. The force of gravity of an object is always directed down, towards the centre of the earth.

Vector quantities are represented by arrows called **vectors**. The end with the straight-line segment is called the tail of the vector, while the end with the arrow head is called the head of the vector (Figure 7.8 A). The head of a vector points in the direction of the variable (i.e., force) the vector represents. The length of the vector is proportional to the magnitude of the variable. Vectors can be added together using the head-to-tail method. To add Vector B to Vector A, a vector identical to Vector B (same length and direction) is drawn with its tail beginning at the head of Vector A. The resultant vector, the sum of Vector A and Vector B, is directed from the tail of Vector A to the head of Vector B (Figure 7.8 and Figure 7.9).

When force (F) vectors are indicated on a stick figure, they are drawn pointing in the direction they act upon the body. By convention, gravity and air resistance are drawn acting from the centre of mass (Figure 7.9).

Net Force

The sum of all the acting forces is the **net force**. When all acting forces are balanced, or cancel each other out, the net force is zero and the body remains in its original state of motion (Figure 7.9 A). When a net force is present, the body moves in the direction of the net force with an acceleration

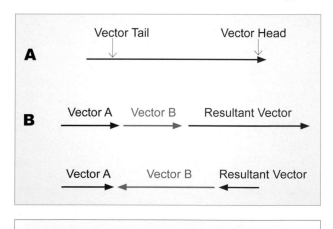

Figure 7.8 Simple vector algebra. **A.** A vector and its components. **B.** A resultant vector is based on vector composition which is done by adding or subtracting their magnitudes.

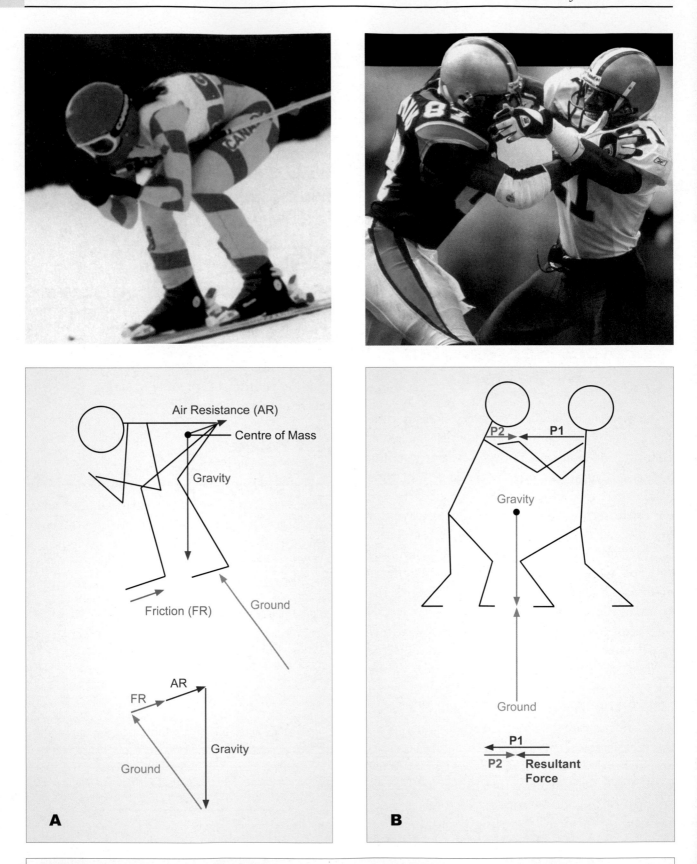

Figure 7.9 Calculating net external force using free body diagrams. **A.** The resultant vector is zero; therefore the skier is not accelerating. **B.** Since Player 1 (P1) is stronger than Player 2 (P2) the resultant vector between the linemen pushing on each other is not zero.

Centre of Mass

The point around which the body's mass is equally distributed in all directions is known as **centre of mass**, or centre of gravity (CG). The CG of a perfectly symmetrical object of homogeneous density is at the exact centre of the object. For example, the CG of a bowling ball or golf ball is at its geometric centre. If the object is a homogeneous ring (such as a ringette ring), the CG is located in the hollow centre of the ring.

Your centre of mass is not always found inside the body (as in the case of the skater). In general it is located about 15 cm above the groin area at approximately 55 percent of standing height in females and 57 percent in males.

The location of CG in the human body is of interest because a body behaves as though all of its mass were concentrated at the CG. Therefore, the force of gravity acting on this point of mass would be the same as the force of gravity acting on the total body. Or when the human body acts as a projectile, as in a long jump, the body's CG follows a parabolic trajectory, regardless of what the various segments of the body do while in the air.

Centre of mass outside of body

---

that is proportional to the magnitude of the net force (Figure 7.9 B).

Mass and Inertia Concepts

All objects have matter. The measure of how much matter an object has is its **mass**. Do you know your mass in kilograms? Where is your centre of mass? (For answers see boxes *Centre of Mass*, page 143, and *Weight Versus Mass*, page 144.)

Because objects have mass, they are also reluctant to change whatever they are doing. In other words, they are reluctant to change their state of motion from rest to motion or to moving faster or slower or to slowing down to rest. This property of objects is called **inertia**. Compared to a soccer ball, a tennis ball has less mass and therefore less inertia. If both are on the ground and have no motion, which ball would be easier

to kick and therefore change its state of motion? If both were traveling at the same velocity, which one would you rather stop (i.e., change its state of motion from moving to rest)?

Rotating objects also have a reluctance to change their state of angular motion: from rest to rotation, or rotating faster or slower or to slowing down back to rest. The inertia of rotating objects is measured by their **moment of inertia**, and depends upon their mass and how their mass is distributed about their axis of rotation. It is more difficult to change the state of rotation of a soccer ball, compared to a tennis ball, because it is more massive and its mass is found further away from any axis of rotation (i.e., the diameter of the soccer ball is larger). Similarly, layout dives are harder to perform than the same dive in the tuck position because the athlete's body parts are further away from the rotating axis (which passes through the athlete's centre of mass), giving the layout diver a greater moment of inertia (Figure 7.21 A, page 161).

Weight Versus Mass

There is a difference between mass (m) and weight (W). Mass is a measure of inertia, while weight is a measure of the force of gravity (g) acting on the body. Mass is measured in kilograms (kg), while weight is measured in Newtons (N). A person's weight varies directly with the magnitude of the acceleration due to gravity (9.8 m/s^2). Thus in space where there is no acceleration experienced due to gravity we weigh 0 N but have the same mass as we do on earth.

To calculate the weight the following formula is used:

$$W = m \times g$$

Gravity

Gravity is the force of attraction between two bodies, the magnitude of which is proportional to their masses and inversely proportional to the square of the distance between them.

For sporting activities (anywhere except outer space) gravity therefore represents a force of attraction between the masses of the athlete and the earth, which varies in magnitude according to the location on the earth. The closer the athlete is to the centre of the earth (polar regions, sea level) the greater the force of attraction. The further the athlete is from the centre of the earth (equator, mountains) the less the force of attraction.

At the 1968 Olympic Games, Bob Beamon became the one human on earth who could "fly." In the light air of 7,349-foot-high Mexico City, Beamon jumped longer than any other human in the history of track and field. His 8.9-metre jump was not broken until two decades later.

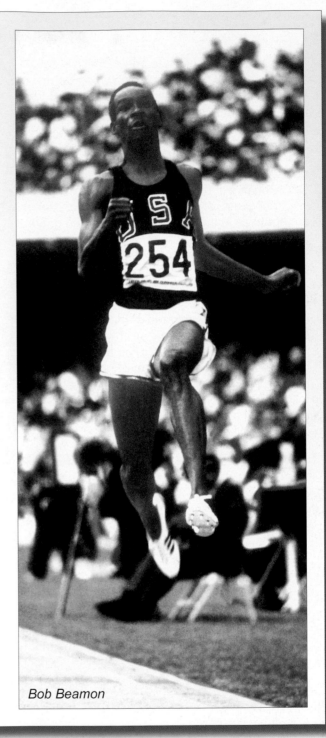

Bob Beamon

Newton's First Law of Motion: Inertia

Newton's first law of motion describes the relationship between inertia and force. It states: objects will not change their state of motion (i.e., they will continue to be at rest, or move with a constant velocity or in uniform circular motion about a fixed axis of rotation) unless acted on by an unbalanced external force (or moment of force). Thus, an object at rest will tend to stay at rest, and an object in motion will tend to stay in motion.

Football linemen, because of their large mass,

are difficult to move out of the way. A large force is required to change their resting state because of their large inertia. Similarly, once linemen are in motion it is difficult to stop them. Just ask any quarterback! Contrast this with young gymnasts who, because of their small mass (and thus inertia), require smaller amounts of force to manipulate their bodies during spotting.

Force and Acceleration Concepts

If external forces could overcome inertia and change the state of motion of a body, what would the relationship between the amount of force and the resulting change in motion be? Newton's second law of motion describes the relationship underlying this question.

Newton's Second Law of Motion: Acceleration

Newton's second law of motion states that for linear movements, the acceleration (a) a body experiences is directly proportional to the force (F) causing it, and takes place in the same direction as the force (F = m x a, where m is the mass of the body) (Figure 7.10). For angular movements, the angular acceleration of a body is directly proportional to the moment of force causing it, and takes place in the same direction as the moment of force.

Sprinters must experience a large external unbalanced force acting on their body mass at the start of a race in order to accelerate down the track. Similarly, at the end of the race, sprinters again experience a large unbalanced force but in the opposite direction to decelerate their bodies (m). When body checking, one hockey player applies an external unbalanced force into the opponent, accelerating the opponent into the boards. Divers experience a moment of force on their bodies when making contact with the diving board, thereby increasing the angular acceleration

about their axis of rotation (which passes through their centre of mass).

The various relationships between force, mass, and acceleration are shown in Figure 7.10.

Impulse, Impact, and Momentum Concepts

Another approach to quantifying the relationship between the external unbalanced forces and the resulting motion is to describe the amount of motion gained or lost by the body. During a race, a sprinter gains motion at the beginning of the race, maintains this motion during the middle portion, and loses this motion after crossing the finish line. While we cannot "see" the accelerations, we can "see" the changes in motion, caused by the application of external unbalanced force, thereby indicating the motion gained at the beginning and lost at the end of the race.

The product of a body's mass and its velocity is called **momentum**. Momentum is created by an **impulse**, the application of an internal force over a period of time. Momentum is lost through **impact**, the application of an external force over a period of time.

Impulse and impact are both associated with bodies changing their state of motion (speeding up, slowing down, changing directions) by experiencing large accelerations over relatively short periods (usually less than one second). Consider the changes in speed and direction in the broken-field running of a halfback in football, or a base runner trying to steal second base, or the movements of a dynamic basketball guard. Also consider collisions with other players (football tackles, hockey checks) or with the environment (landings in gymnastics). For most of these activities, the change in momentum is quick, and the time of force application is limited and often cannot be manipulated. Therefore, most changes in momentum in sport really depend upon the magnitude of the net external force acting on the body.

A

The greater the soccer player's force applied to a soccer ball that has the same mass, the greater the ball's acceleration.

B

As the mass of the soccer ball increases, it experiences less acceleration from a kick that has the same (constant) force.

C

As the mass of the soccer ball increases, the soccer player must generate an increased force to kick the ball if it is to assume the same (constant) acceleration.

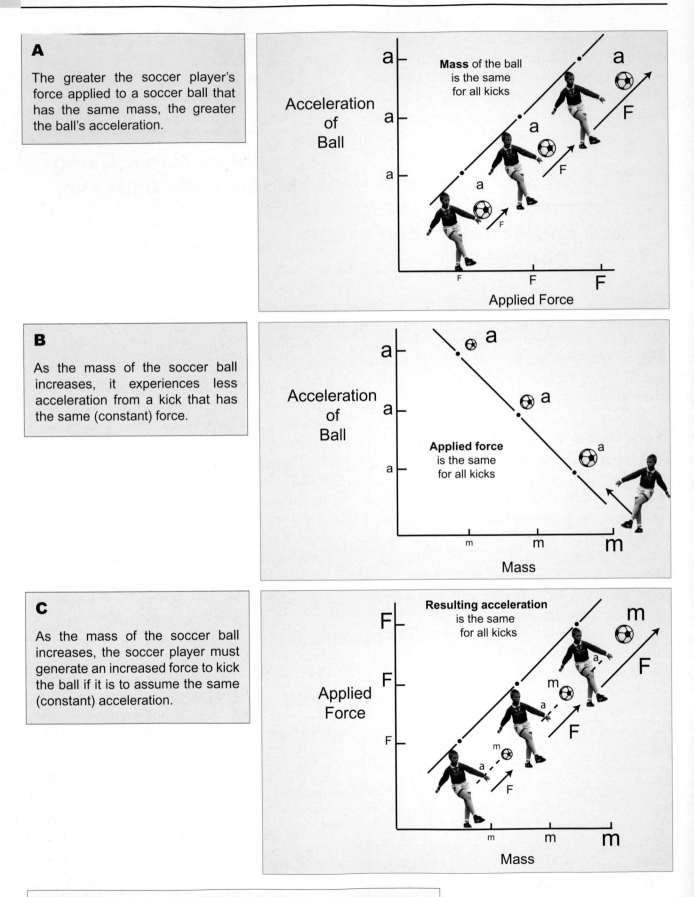

Figure 7.10 Relationships between force, mass, and acceleration.

For a sprinter, the time during which each foot is in contact with the ground is limited, and decreases with increased running speed. To increase impulse, a sprinter must increase the net external force per step. This implies reducing any retarding forces associated with initial foot contact with the ground and maximizing the propulsive forces during the push-off phase. Many sport skills have similar requirements, including all forms of running, jumping, striking, and throwing skills.

On the other hand, collision or impact skills can sometimes manipulate the time of contact and reduce the magnitude of the external force. In gymnastics landings, athletes can flex the joints of their lower limbs (ankles, knees, hips) to increase the time over which external impact forces from the ground act on their bodies and hence decrease the force. Hockey players can lean into a body check, which increases the time during which they can attempt to resist external checking forces. Similarly, when catching, ball players are able to cradle the ball, thereby increasing the time available to eliminate its momentum and reducing the force exerted by the ball on the athletes' hands. This concept illustrates what is commonly called having "soft hands" in sport.

Figure 7.11 The force from the blocks is the external force required to accelerate the sprinter through internal muscle actions.

Action–Reaction Concept

From where do the external forces that affect a sprinter, hockey player, and diver arise? Each of these athletes generates internal muscle forces, the sum of which interacts with their surroundings through some body part (often a foot). At every contact point where the resultant internal force is exerted, an external force from the surroundings is exerted back onto the body simultaneously. These two forces on the two different bodies are equal in magnitude but opposite in direction. This is Newton's third law of motion.

Newton's Third Law of Motion: Reaction

Newton's third law of motion, **action–reaction**

principle, states that "every action has an equal and opposite reaction." This law refers to the way in which forces act against each other. The sprinter exerts force onto the blocks, and simultaneously the blocks exert a force back onto the sprinter (Figure 7.11). The force from the blocks is the external force required to accelerate the sprinter. However, the magnitude and direction of this reaction force is completely under the sprinter's control, as it is simply the mirror image of the force resulting from the sum of all the athlete's internal muscle actions.

Newton's action–reaction principle applies to various forms of human movement. Several examples are provided in the box *I Push, You Push: Newton's Third Law of Motion in Action*.

Projectile Motion

Simply stated, any airborne object, including the human body, is a **projectile**. The centre of mass of a projectile will follow a **parabolic path** whenever gravity is the only external force acting on the object. Under this condition, the parabolic path followed is determined only as a function of the projectile's take-off velocity, both magnitude and direction, and acceleration due to gravity (Figure 7.12). If other external forces, such as air

I Push, You Push: Newton's Third Law of Motion in Action

In walking, an athlete moves the left leg and the right arm forward simultaneously. This results in the hips and shoulders twisting in opposite directions around the body's longitudinal axis. Similarly, a runner twists the upper and lower parts of the body and uses countermovements of the legs and arms. This achieves muscle forces approximately on the same plane when pushing off with either the right or the left leg and prevents twisting of the entire body. At the same time the stride length can be increased by twisting the hips. In cross-country skiing, the forward thrust is achieved through the countermovement of the poles in relation to the leg movements.

In athletic jumping events it is important to bring the body into a proper landing posture by applying appropriate action and reaction body movements. In the long jump, for instance, the jumper is initially extended. The upper part of the body is then brought forward around the hip joints, causing an action. The principle of reaction causes the lower part of the body to bend forward around the hip joints at the same time in order to achieve the longest possible jump (Athlete A). Poorer results are obtained by the athlete who is less skilled in following this principle (Athlete B).

Effective application of the action–reaction principle is also made in throwing and kicking. In handball, for example, the throwing action is carried out by moving the shoulder forward along with the throwing arm – action. To prevent the whole body from twisting, which is important for good throwing accuracy, the athlete twists the hips forward in the opposite direction – reaction. This also engages the powerful trunk muscles, which significantly increases the power of the throw.

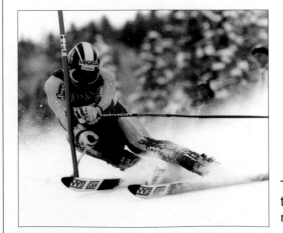

Twisting the upper part of the body in the opposite direction to that of the lower part of the body is the most natural way of negotiating the gates in slalom skiing.

Figure 7.12 Four projection paths at various angles with vectors. A baseball thrown at a 45-degree angle maximizes the landing distance.

resistance, act on the object, then the flight path is altered accordingly.

Skills involving some form of projectile have one of three objectives. A high jumper, for example, seeks the maximum vertical distance or **height** for the body. A javelin thrower, by contrast, tries to realize a maximum horizontal distance or **range**. Still others, such as basketball, involve projectiles that seek **accuracy**.

Maximizing Height and Range

Can we determine the conditions under which a projectile will attain a maximum height or range? Using the equations given in the box *Projectile Motion Equations*, we can deduce the following criteria for objects that take off and land at the same height:

1. To maximize the vertical distance (height) a projectile will achieve, one must maximize the take-off velocity and take off vertically (since

the maximum sine value is 1 and occurs at a 90-degree angle). Thus, high jumpers try to jump as vertically as possible, a difficult task given the high approach velocities they attain.

2. To maximize the horizontal distance (range) a projectile will achieve, one must maximize take-off velocity and take off at an angle of 45 degrees to the horizontal (since the maximum sine value is 1 and occurs at a 90-degree angle, and half of 90 degrees is 45 degrees). Baseball throws from the outfield as well as many throwing events in athletics (javelin, hammer, discus) try to achieve a take-off angle of 45 degrees (Figure 7.12).

Taking Off and Landing at Different Heights

Most sport activities involve taking off and landing at different heights (basketball jump shots, gymnastics dismounts).

Projectile Motion Equations

For projectiles that take off and land at the same height (or close enough) and for which air resistance can be ignored, the following equations describe the vertical (height) and horizontal (range) distances the projectile will traverse.

For

v = magnitude of the take-off velocity

θ = the take-off angle with respect to the horizontal

g = the acceleration due to gravity (a constant) = 9.8 m/s²

then

$$\text{Maximum Height} = \frac{(v \sin\theta)^2}{2g}$$

$$\text{Maximum Range} = \frac{v^2 \sin(2\theta)}{g}$$

The range a projectile will travel will increase if the take-off height is greater than the landing height, and decrease if the take-off height is less than the landing height. Objects which are to be thrown or struck should be released as high off the ground as possible by stretching all possible body parts. If the human body is the projectile, then a higher centre of mass can be achieved by elongating the body at take-off, and by raising as many body parts as possible which are not involved in accelerating the body. Golf shots taken from elevated tees travel farther, mainly because the shot is airborne for a longer period of time and can travel farther horizontally. Similarly, the elevated pitcher's mound, through the force of gravity, adds to the speed of the ball.

Air Resistance

Air resistance is another force acting on the projectile. As such, it will change the state of motion of the projectile and its path. The effects of air resistance on objects are discussed in the next section.

Optimizing Range

Of the four factors affecting projectile motion, (take-off velocity, take-off angle, difference in take-off and landing heights, air resistance), which is the most important in maximizing horizontal distance? Each factor does *not* work in

isolation. Increasing the take-off height compared to the landing height lowers the optimal take-off angle of 45 degrees. Skills that take advantage of air resistance in increasing range also have a lower optimal take-off angle. In most instances however, increasing the magnitude of the take-off velocity gains the greatest increase in horizontal distance.

For any projectile activity there are certain constraints, such as an athlete's height and air resistance. Given these constraints, scientists and coaches should be able to predict the optimal take-off angle for any given magnitude of velocity. As athletes get stronger and improve their technique, these values change.

Fluid Dynamics

All athletic events take place in a fluid environment, whether in water (underwater hockey), in air (cycling, sprinting), or in a combination of both (water polo, swimming). Some activities are largely unaffected (walking, gymnastics, dancing) by the fluid environment in which they occur, while for other activities and objects this environment is very important (running, cycling, skiing, speedskating, surfing, swimming, ping-pong, badminton shuttlecocks, baseballs, softballs, footballs, javelins).

Knowledge of the forces generated by the environment affects our understanding of how these skills are to be performed (i.e., which factors

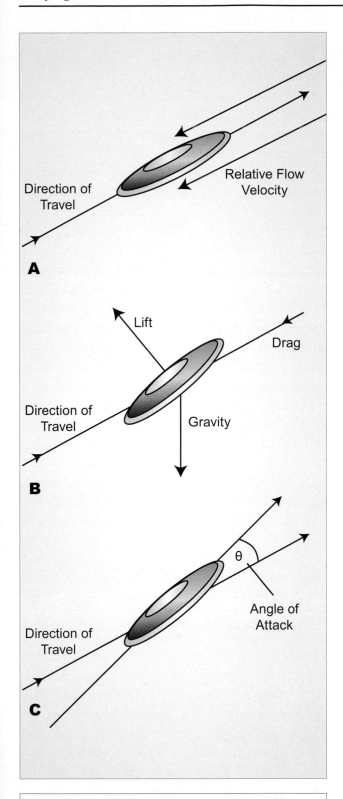

Figure 7.13 Effects of air resistance on a discus. **A.** Discus with direction of travel and relative flow velocity vectors superimposed. **B.** Free body diagram of discus, with lift, drag, and gravity vectors. **C.** Angle of attack (θ, is the angle between the direction of travel and the longitudinal axis of the discus).

affect them; Figures 7.13 and 7.14), and thus how they are taught and learned. For example, why does a cyclist pedal behind another in a race? What is "drafting" to a long-distance runner? Why does a ski racer adopt an egg position, but a ski jumper lean toward a prone position in flight? Why do swimmers "spiral" their hands through their underwater stroking? And what makes a curveball curve? These questions are answered in this section.

> **Did You Know the Air Around You Is a Fluid?**
>
> A fluid is a substance which flows – liquid or gas. When you move, you cause the air to flow around you. And, because air resists motion, it slows you down.

Fluid dynamics studies the forces and their effects on human movement through different environments. Fluid forces include **drag force** and **lift force**. Drag and lift forces are perpendicular to each other, produce different effects, are affected by different factors, and have unique applications to various sport movements. All fluid forces depend upon the flow velocity, that is, the motion of the fluid flowing past an object or the motion of the object through the fluid. Both concepts refer to the same variable, namely, the relative motion between the object and the fluid (Figure 7.13 A). In this section, only fluid forces acting in the air (**aerodynamics**) will be examined. **Hydrodynamics** (fluid forces acting in the water) is beyond the scope of this text.

Fluid Drag Forces: The Dynamics of Air

When cycling, we feel the air against our bodies acting directly opposite to our direction of motion. The faster we cycle, the greater the resistance. Intuitively, we know that if we flex at the hips and waist, presenting less surface area to the air, there is less resistance. The type of fluid force we are feeling is called **drag**. Although this force is acting on all surfaces of our bodies and the bicycle, we often simplify its representation by drawing a single vector acting at the centre of mass of the system (Figure 7.13 B).

There are two main sources of drag: form and skin friction. **Profile** or **form drag** is caused by the size of the object (or person) and the **air turbulence** produced by its shape as it moves through the air. **Skin-friction drag**, also known as **surface drag**, is caused by the surface roughness of the object (or person) as it moves through the air.

Both skin-friction and profile drag are proportional to the relative flow velocity, cross-sectional area, shape of the object, smoothness of the surface, and density of the liquid.

Skin-friction Drag

The fluid tending to rub (shear) along the surface of the body causes skin-friction drag (i.e., a friction force) parallel and opposite to the flow velocity. The layer of fluid next to the skin sticks to the body; however, the next layer is towed along and therefore slides relative to the innermost layer. The third layer is towed by the second and in turn tows the fourth layer. Eventually, a layer of fluid is reached in which no sliding occurs. The region of relative motion between adjacent layers of fluid is called the **boundary layer**. Two types of flow can occur within the boundary layer: **laminar flow** and **turbulent flow**.

If an object is small, streamlined, smooth, and relatively slow, then laminar flow will occur within the boundary layer. Laminar flow is a smooth, layered, flow pattern of a fluid around an object with no wake or other disturbance. Large bodies with rough textured surfaces will have greater skin-friction drag. Most human activities move too fast to allow laminar flow to occur. Therefore, surface skin drag is not the source of most of the drag encountered in sport activities.

Profile Drag

Profile drag is the main form of drag in skiing,

cycling, running, and all projectile events. Profile drag is the resistive drag against the object (Newton's third law of motion). It is characterized by turbulent flow in which the pressure on the leading surface of a body is greater than the pressure on the trailing surface. It is also known as **pressure** or **form drag**.

The velocity of air flow past the object is too fast for the air to follow the contour of the trailing side of the object, causing a "back flow" to occur at the surface of the object. This causes the boundary layer to separate from the surface contour, resulting in a large, turbulent, low-pressure zone to form behind the object. This region of low pressure, which is continually formed as the object moves through the fluid, contains eddies that must be pulled along with the object, increasing the amount of work done on the object.

Because drag increases as the square of speed, an object moving 10 times faster will produce 100 times more drag. In high-speed sports (skiing, cycling, bobsledding, etc.), where a fraction of a second decides who finishes first, athletes attempt to reduce drag as much as possible by streamlining their bodies to reduce their cross-sectional area (Figure 7.14).

Skiers in their low drag position can increase their velocity by as much as 50 percent – reaching downhill speeds of over 130 km per hour (Figure 7.14 A).

Sledding while supine decreases form drag. The luger's feet cut through the air first, presenting the smallest possible frontal surface area. This allows the air to flow much more smoothly over the body and head. The sleigh is also shaped for minimum form drag and maximum speed. The nylon skin-tight, rubberized bodysuit along with special "speed boots" decreases lugers' friction drag. The smooth, tightly woven surface of the suit reduces turbulence by allowing air to slide over it much more easily than it would over conventional clothing or even bare skin (Figure 7.14 B).

Bending parallel to the ice, arm(s) behind the back, decreases the form drag of a speedskater. The speedskater's "crouch" minimizes frontal surface

Figure 7.14 Drag forces generated by the environment have an effect on how various skills are performed most effectively.

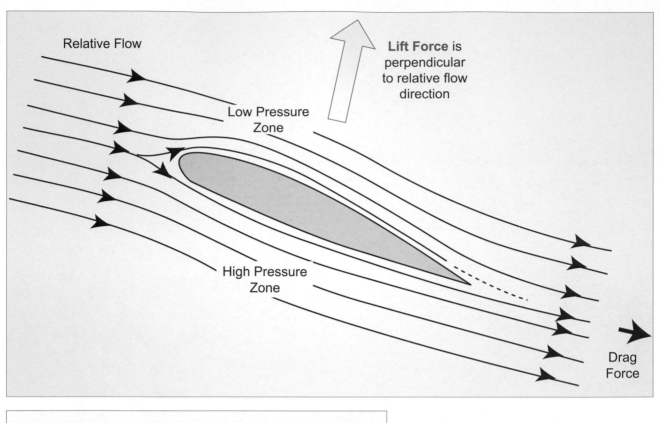

Figure 7.15 Aerodynamic lift force acting on an airfoil (wing).

area, thus significantly reducing wind resistance, and the position of the arms reduces turbulence, letting air flow more smoothly around the body (Figure 7.14 D).

Fluid Lift Forces

Fluid lift forces are always directed perpendicular to the flow velocity (not parallel as with drag forces). These lift forces can be directed (a) upwards (discus, javelin, Frisbee, ski jumpers, tennis balls, water skiers), (b) downwards (racing cars, sinker ball in baseball, or topspin in tennis), or (c) sideways (curveball in baseball).

How does lift occur? Consider the cross-section of an airfoil (a wing-shaped object) (Figure 7.15). Air flows faster over the upper curved surface than the lower flat surface, such that the difference in velocity across the surfaces results in a pressure difference between the two sides. The pressure difference results in a force directed from the high-pressure side to the low-pressure side. The inverse

relationship between flow velocity and pressure is **Bernoulli's principle**. The external force resulting from the pressure difference is perpendicular to flow velocity direction, and can thus change the motion of the object (Newton's first and second laws of motion).

Angle of Attack

The tilt of an object relative to the flow velocity is defined as the **angle of attack** (Figure 7.13 C). The angle of attack can mimic the effects of an airfoil by changing the pressure difference across

Aerodynamic lift force at work. Once airborne, the ski ju assumes the airfoil position with skis and body nearly parall maximum lift. The actual flight may last up to six seconds the jumper is never more tha metres above ground.

Why a Curveball Curves

The pitcher holds the index and middle fingers close together along the seams of the ball and twists the hand while releasing the ball to give it a very fast spin – approximately 1,800 revolutions per minute. The ball revolves 15 times in the less than 1/2 second it takes to reach the plate.

The ball's 108 stitches pull a thin layer of air with them as they spin. That layer makes the air on the bottom of the ball flow faster than the air at the top of the ball which produces the curve ball, i.e., Magnus effect at work.

Split finger fastballs, sliders, and screw balls all rely on different kinds of spin – and the Magnus effect – to change direction.

A major league pitcher can make a baseball curve up to approximately 43 cm from its straight path on its way to the plate.

the surfaces of the object. It is a function of the shape of an object and the flow velocity.

The angle of attack may change throughout the flight, which means the amount of lift will change as well. If the angle of attack increases too much, it approaches a critical maximum angle beyond which the lift force suddenly decreases as the drag force becomes dominant. At the critical angle, called the stall angle, the object falls earthward with no further forward motion. Frisbees, discuses, javelins, and airplanes all experience changing angles of attack.

The Magnus Effect

Any spinning projectile generates a lift force. A rotating body carries a layer of fluid with it as it spins. This boundary layer interacts with the fluid through which the body travels, such that if the layer is in the opposite direction to the flow velocity, the air stagnates and there is a zone of increased pressure. If the boundary layer is in the same direction, there is a zone of decreased pressure created. The net difference in the pressure on opposite sides of the body constitutes a force that changes the direction of the body along the pressure gradient.

Take an object that is spinning about an axis not aligned with the flow velocity vector (perpendicular is best), unlike a football in which the spinning axis and flow velocity are coincident. The pressure difference across opposite sides of such an object is such that changes in its flight path can be generated by a type of force known as a **Magnus force**, and the whole mechanism, the **Magnus effect**. The changes in path are always perpendicular to the flow velocity of the projectile.

Topspin restricts the horizontal distance a projectile will travel with no loss in take-off velocity. On the other hand, underspin or backspin will increase the horizontal distance, time in the air, or accuracy (golf, tennis, soccer, basketball) for a given take-off velocity.

For sidespins, a ball will curve towards the spinning side. More curve ("break") is noticed the longer the ball is airborne.

The Magnus effect is seen most readily in tennis, golf, ping-pong, and baseball (see box *Why a Curveball Curves*). In these activities, the projectile is small in size and mass, and can be given large take-off velocities and high spin rates,

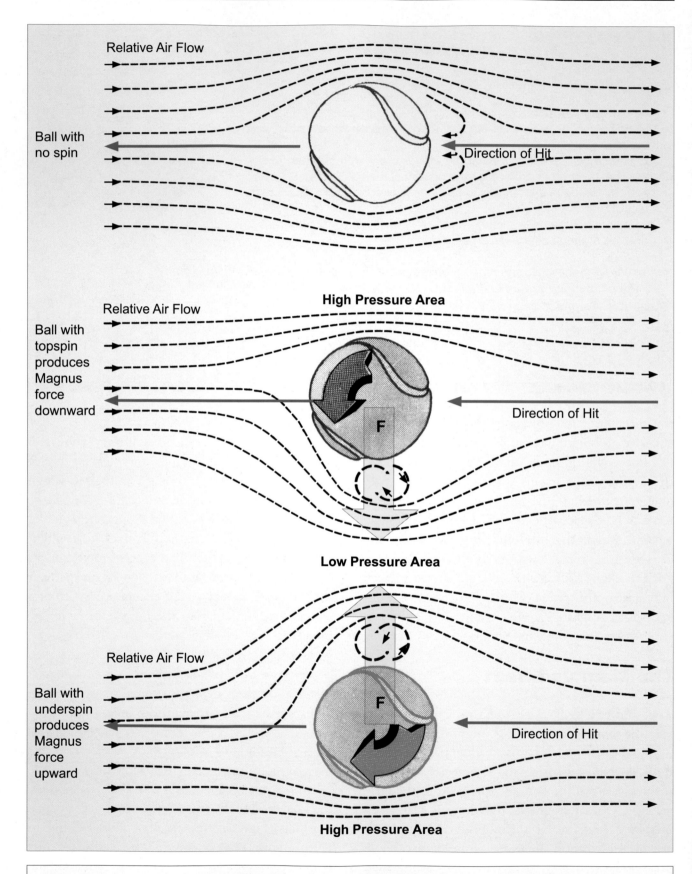

Figure 7.16 The uneven surface of a spinning tennis ball creates a Magnus force (F). The Magnus force is directed from high to low pressure.

all of which positively influence the Magnus force.

The uneven surface of a tennis ball pulls a thin layer of air along with it when it spins (Figure 7.16). That makes the air on one side of the ball flow faster (and more smoothly) than on the other side – it's like the spinning blades of a fan creating a breeze. The faster flow causes the air pressure on that side of the ball to drop – and the ball drops or curves into the area of lower air pressure.

Body Balance and Stability Control

Balance is a very important factor in athletic performance. In general, it depends upon the location of an athlete's centre of mass and how stable that centre of mass is. Stick figures are very useful tools in indicating body balance throughout an athletic performance (Figure 7.9, page 142).

Equilibrium

Equilibrium describes the state of a system that is not experiencing any change in its direction or speed. There are two states of equilibrium, static and dynamic. **Static equilibrium** describes the state of a system that is at rest. **Dynamic equilibrium** describes the state of a system that is moving with constant velocity (unchanging speed and direction). In Figure 7.19, the gymnast, lineman, and sprinter are in static equilibrium, while the kayaker, skier, and cyclist may be in dynamic equilibrium as long as their velocity is not changing.

Balance

The process whereby the body's state of equilibrium is controlled for a given purpose is called **balance**. To control the state of equilibrium we constantly (and often unconsciously) manipulate two factors. The first factor is our base of support, which is the area defined by the points of contact between the

body and the surface supporting it. The second factor is the location of our line of gravity which is an imaginary vertical line which passes through the centre of mass. If the line of gravity passes through some part of the body's base of support, then the body will be balanced (Figure 7.18).

Stability

Stability is a relative term and is a measure of the ease or difficulty with which equilibrium can be disturbed. A net external force is required to overcome the static equilibrium of a sprinter in the starting blocks or the dynamic equilibrium of a running back. A net external moment of force would be required to tip over a gymnast performing a handstand or to overturn a canoe or kayak.

At some critical time within most performances there is a trade-off between **maximizing stability** and **acquiring speed off a mark**. For example, sprinters must be able to move quickly at the start signal (i.e., to go into motion), and therefore it is desirable to be in an unstable equilibrium state. On the other hand, a football lineman or wrestler must be able to resist any external forces, and thus strives to be in a state of stable equilibrium.

Figure 7.18 Factors affecting balance.

Figure 7.19 Maintaining equilibrium and balance. Static equilibrium of **A.** a lineman's three-point stance; **B.** a gymnastics element; and **C.** a sprint start. Dynamic equilibrium of a **D.** kayaker; **E.** cyclist; and **F.** skier.

Knowledge of the ways stability can be altered, or the factors influencing it, are therefore pertinent to understanding a good performance in most sport skills.

Factors Affecting Balance

To *increase* the stability in a static equilibrium an athlete must:

(1) increase the base of support (Figure 7.19 A and B; lineman versus gymnast);

(2) increase the inertia (mass, moment of inertia) of the body – larger forces and moments of force would be required to move the body (Figure 7.19 A and B; lineman versus

gymnast);

(3) decrease the vertical distance between the centre of mass and the base of support (Figure 7.19 B and C; gymnast versus sprinter); and

(4) increase the distance between the point where a vertical line from the centre of mass intersects the base of support and the outside edge of the base of support (Figure 7.19 A and C; lineman versus sprinter).

To *increase* stability in dynamic equilibrium an athlete must:

(1) enlarge the body's base of support in the direction of external horizontal forces, which may be given or received (hockey checks);

(2) adopt a starting position in which the centre of pressure is close to the edge of the base of support whenever quick acceleration is important (kayaker, cyclist, or skier who wishes to turn quickly);

(3) lean backwards but keep normal frictional forces high to prevent slipping when slowing down or reversing directions in running; and

(4) use reflex movements to help regain loss of balance when tripping or falling (windmill action of arms of gymnasts falling off a beam), or to create a new base of support. The athlete can also use the angular momentum created, and perform a roll, thereby increasing the time required to exert the necessary force to regain an upright body posture (also temporarily increasing frictional forces between body and ground).

Angular Kinetics

Angular kinetics is concerned with the generation of rotations about an axis of rotation and the control of these rotations. All objects possess inertia and do not wish to start rotating, or if rotating, to change the quantity of rotation they have. However, if an external moment of force is applied to the object, then it will experience an angular acceleration, which results in a new state of motion (Figure 7.6 B, page 138). The greater the applied moment of force (action), the greater the change in the angular acceleration (reaction). This is another example of Newton's third law of motion: for every moment of force applied to one object, an equal moment of force is applied back to the other object at the same time.

The somersault serves as a good example of angular kinetics. It is found extensively in diving, freestyle skiing, and gymnastics, and is making headway in figure skating. For all these skills, the somersaulting motion is generated while the athlete is on the ground.

Off-centre External Forces

Any external force, which acts away from the body's centre of mass, will create a moment of force acting on the total body. This is so because all bodies, when airborne, rotate about an axis passing through their centre of mass. Usually the off-centre force is a reaction force from the ground or equipment (e.g., diving board), resulting from the internal muscle forces generated by the athlete.

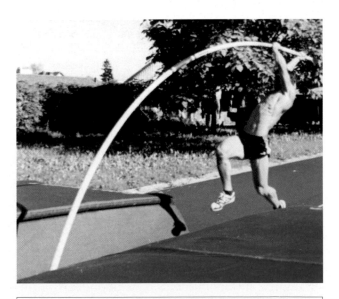

Figure 7.20 A pole-vaulter's movement exhibits rotation about the pivot point created by the planted pole.

However, if an athlete has forward momentum (i.e., running) and a pivot point is created, then some or all of the linear motion can be transferred into angular motion. Consider a pole-vaulter (Figure 7.20) who, upon planting his or her pole, creates a pivot point and rotates about that point. Similarly, how about the unfortunate runner whose foot gets caught in a hole in the ground and rotates forward about that pivot point upon hitting the ground.

Conservation of Momentum Within the Body

It is essential for athletes to make good use of the principle of conservation of momentum in turns, twists, and spins occurring in many sports. The mechanical properties of the human body permit great flexibility of its links to change the body form. In many movements, athletes can make skillful use of the fact that they can alter the magnitude of their mass moment of inertia during rotation. This applies to both the control of the rotation and to the successful execution of various complex forms of rotation in general.

Rotations While Airborne

Rotations in many sports are produced while the body is in contact with the ground. The initiated rotations will continue when the body is airborne. In the flight phase when the body can be regarded as a free moving system, angular velocity can be effectively controlled by skillfully changing the body posture and hence the mass moment of inertia. Once the body is airborne, only gravity and air resistance are acting on the body. Gravity acts through the body's centre of mass and cannot create a moment of force. Therefore, the amount of angular motion athletes have upon leaving the ground, their angular momentum, cannot be changed once airborne. An athlete's angular momentum is said to be conserved, constant, or uni-

form while airborne. This phenomenon is referred to as the **conservation of angular momentum**.

However, somersaulting athletes can change their body shape while airborne. Changes in body shape will decrease/increase their moment of inertia about the somersaulting axis, which will change their general resistance to rotating. If the moment of inertia decreases, then an athlete's body will have less reluctance to rotating and will begin to rotate faster (increased angular velocity). If the moment of inertia increases, then the body will have greater reluctance to rotating and will begin to rotate more slowly (decreased angular velocity). New motion is not being created or destroyed, but the speed with which the athlete is rotating changes with changes in the moment of inertia.

For example, in diving, athletes can perform a somersaulting dive in a layout, pike, or tuck position (decreasing moments of inertia about the body's sagittal axis) (Figure 7.21). Given an equal amount of angular momentum upon leaving the diving board, the angular velocity of these dives will be slow in the layout position (Figure 7.21 A), faster in the pike position (Figure 7.21 B), and fastest in the tuck position (Figure 7.21 C).

By changing their body posture during the final stages of the dive, divers have to control their angular velocity in such a manner that when entering the water their bodies have the lowest angular velocity. Only in this way is splashing reduced to a minimum.

The same phenomenon occurs in gymnastics and freestyle skiing. Similarly, in figure skating, athletes can change their moment of inertia about their vertical axis by going into the spin or jump with their arms and free legs as far away as possible from their axis of rotation. The spin or rotation of their jumps is increased by bringing their arms and legs tightly to the body's longitudinal axis of rotation (Figure 7.22).

Coaches have to be aware that rotations are generated and dissipated on the ground only. The illusions of changing rotational speeds are associated with changes in moments of inertia and not the amount of angular motion generated.

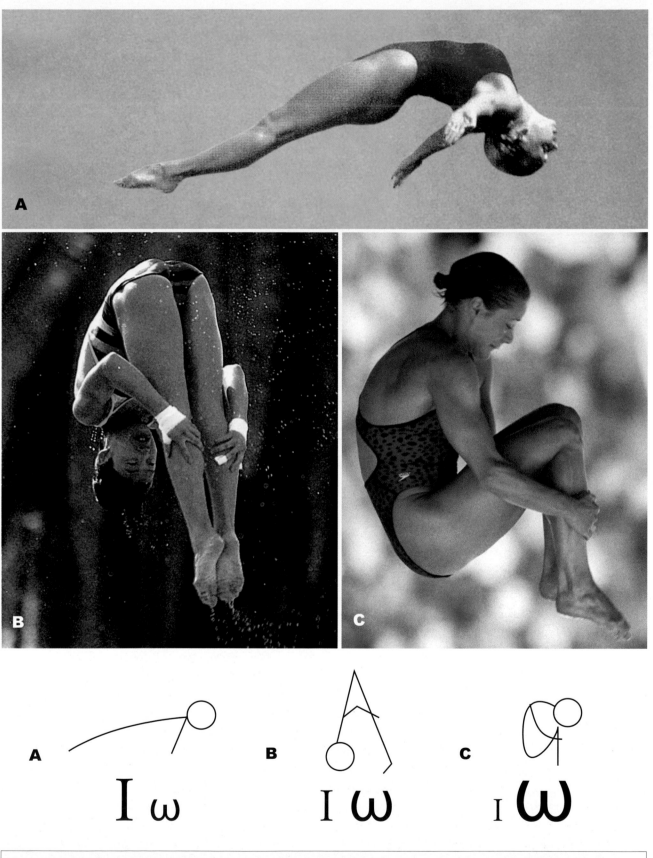

Figure 7.21 The inverse relationship between moment of inertia (I) and angular velocity (ω) for the **A.** layout; **B.** pike; and **C.** tuck position of a somersault in diving.

Figure 7.22 Figure skaters bring their arms in tight to the body to maintain high angular velocity during spins and jumps.

Qualitative Analysis of Human Motion

Qualitative analysis is the study of human motion, in the absence of measuring, by observing a movement and applying biomechanical principles in assessing a performance. A qualitative analysis is a subjective and yet systematic evaluation of a

movement or skill. It is based on direct visual observation of movement or its video recording. Although movements may be too fast to observe the skill accurately, this technique allows the instructor or coach to discover movement tendencies and to provide the athlete with immediate valuable feedback. This feedback is movement-specific and much superior to non-specific jargon-infected feedback like "don't fall," "rotate more," and "jump higher" (for more on types of feedback see Chapter 18).

The qualitative approach suggested here is generic. In this approach, the coach is asked to consider the objective of the skill, to analyze the skill biomechanically by identifying phases of the skill and the key criteria and movement patterns, to decide how the observation will be done, and to prepare, in advance, corrections for commonly occurring performance errors (Figure 7.23).

A qualitative analysis is dependent on the constraints or limitations of an event or performer. For example, rules, physical boundaries, equipment requirements, and the environment can all place constraints upon an event. Basketball is played on a specified court, with a ball of specified size, and with an established set of rules. Other constraints arise because of human limitations (such as body build, strength, power, endurance, and flexibility), skill level of the athlete and opponent, and any movement requirements which may precede or follow the skill. However, the generic qualitative analysis is independent of the nature of the skill, whether it is open or closed, discrete or continuous (for more on types of skills see Chapter 16).

Most importantly, however, the qualitative approach to movement analysis is based on instructors' thorough understanding of the movement or skill they are evaluating. This understanding comes from their vast experience with coaching or instructing the activity. Only then will they be able to assess accurately what is wrong or right in the performer's execution of the movement. It takes years of experience to develop a critical eye for correct assessment of techniques and their subtleties.

Qualitative analysis is based on a simple model

that integrates the four major aspects of quality instruction: preparation, observation, evaluation, and error correction (Figure 7.23).

Skill Objective

An objective can be described for all skills. It may be as simple as throwing an opponent in judo, or blocking an oncoming lineman in football. Secondary objectives may also exist, referring to the speed of the movement or the accuracy required. Skills with similar overall objectives will be governed by similar biomechanical principles, which in turn should simplify the analysis process for different skills.

For example, the performance purpose of many skills is to throw, strike, or kick an object for maximum horizontal distance (range). The mechanical purpose of these skills is therefore to release, strike, or impart to the object – at the instant of take-off – a maximal take-off velocity at the optimal angle of release (Figure 7.12). Accomplishing these biomechanical criteria will satisfy the performance objective.

Analyzing a Skill

Divide the Skill into Phases

All skills, whether discrete or continuous, can be

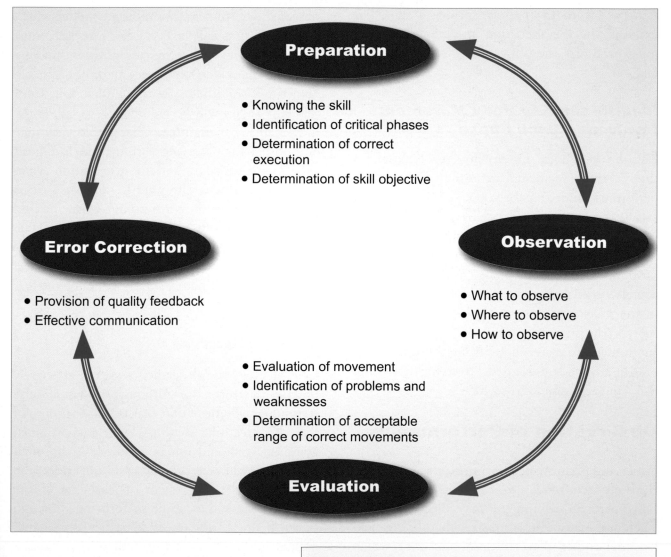

Figure 7.23 The integrated model of qualitative analysis.

divided into phases or subroutines (for more on subroutines see Chapter 16). These phases should make sense to the coach, as far as how he or she teaches the skill and how the sport defines the skill. One suggestion is that each phase relate to a change in the athlete's state of motion, that is, any time an acceleration occurs. Common names for phases include preparation, execution, and follow-through, although many skills include take-off, airborne, and landing phases, or push and pull phases.

Determine the Biomechanical Criteria for Each Phase

For each phase, identify the biomechanical criteria that cause the specific movement patterns associated with the performance of a skill. For example, in the execution phase, shot-putters must maximize the velocity of the shot prior to take-off.

Identify the Key Body Movements Involved in Each Phase

List the key body movements for each phase, that is, those segmental actions that should be performed and can be observed, and which satisfy the biomechanical criteria for that phase. Execution of these movements contributes directly to successfully accomplishing the biomechanical purpose of the discrete phase, and ultimately, the overall performance of the event. For example, in the preparatory phase of the soccer kick, the foot of the stance leg is placed beside the ball. In throwing a baseball in from the outfield, a sequence of body movements from the foot to the throwing arm should be seen.

Observation of Performance

Observing performances is a difficult task. Often, the skills occur too fast to see specific detail. Other body parts or equipment may block the view. There are many distractions on the playing field (weather, other players, time pressures) which may potentially interfere with a coach's ability

to observe an athlete's performance. To observe effectively, an observation plan must be prepared before arriving at the playing field. The plan identifies what, why, where, and how observation of the athlete's performance will occur.

What, Why, and Where to Observe

Before going to practice, a coach or instructor must identify the skill, or parts thereof, that he or she wishes to observe, and why. Specific elements of this observation plan include the phase of the skill to be observed, body movements, and related biomechanical criteria. Knowing what and why helps a coach stay organized with respect to observing the skills of all players.

Furthermore, knowledge of what will be observed determines the conditions under which the observation will take place. The coach must decide upon his or her viewing position, making sure that the athlete's body actions will be visible. Sometimes multiple views of the skill from different angles will be required to see all of the movements. For example, while a side view may be optimal for observing a runner, an overhead view might reveal important information when analyzing a discus thrower. In any case, it is important to keep the surroundings as uncluttered as possible and to minimize distractions. The instructor should estimate how many times the skill has to be viewed – enough to obtain an idea of "normal" performance, but not enough to elicit fatigue.

How to Observe

Coaches must use all of their senses to effectively observe a performance. Although our visual sense is dominant, information that is heard (timing of footfalls, breathing rhythms) or felt (spotting in gymnastics) should not be ignored. A thorough instructor will directly observe not only the athlete but also any tracks or traces he or she may have made during the performance (e.g., ski tracks, figure skating traces). Coaches often ask an athlete questions to confirm their observations, and if possible, videotape the observation, using slow motion replay to examine fast and/or small movement details which may otherwise be missed.

In general, any observation should begin with an analysis of the whole skill. The coach can then zoom in on the phase and body movements on which he or she really wishes to focus. An athlete must be given an adequate warm-up before demonstrating a particular movement to ensure a *normal* performance. When the athlete is ready, the coach should record his or her observations and/or provide immediate and specific feedback to the performer.

Error Detection and Correction

There are many reasons why athletes make errors. Sometimes the errors are psychological in nature, such as a lapse in concentration or fear of execution, or result from an error in judgement. Other errors occur as a result of lack of strength, power, endurance, or flexibility or because of poor habits. However, errors in technical performance can often be traced to athletes not maximizing or optimizing the biomechanical variables critical to the skill. In this case, coaches must be able to understand the biomechanics of the skill, identify which criteria are not being optimized, and direct their corrections to these biomechanical variables. Performing a biomechanical analysis beforehand will aid every technique used for error detection and correction.

In all cases, the coach must make corrections while keeping the athlete's physical and mental abilities, and level of competition, in mind.

Error Detection

The most common technique for error detection is visual, by using direct observation, analyzing videos, or observing traces or marks left by the athlete. Visual observation improves with practice. However, performing a biomechanical analysis of the skill beforehand will improve the chances of spotting where the error is occurring, particularly

concerning the phases of the skill and body parts used. Other error detection techniques include observing the outcome (placement of a golf shot) or follow-through (end of the tennis stroke), using a chart or checklist, or asking the athletes what they felt about their performance. The first two indicate which biomechanical variable was *not* performed well, and therefore suggest a phase or body part(s) on which to focus. The latter two are also useful if a prior biomechanical analysis has been done, because they will help athletes and coaches concentrate on critical variables.

One method to avoid is comparison with an ideal form or mental model. While these comparisons may be useful in conceptualizing a skill, everyone has a different body build (skeletal and muscular), which directly affects how he or she will look when performing a skill. By concentrating on the biomechanical variables, athletes will explore with their own bodies how to optimize these criteria. They will be able to concentrate on factors that are under their control, and not be drawn into adopting others' idiosyncrasies.

Good coaching includes asking athletes if given instructions were understood correctly, particularly under distracting environmental conditions, i.e., noise, distance, low visibility, etc.

Error Correction

Error correction is usually done verbally, although visual feedback (video, demonstration), repetition (drills), or mental imagery may also be used (for more on these concepts see Chapter 18). In all cases, corrections are being made to body part movements related directly to a biomechanical variable that satisfies the performance objective of the skill. If several errors have occurred, then begin with the earliest error, as this mistake may have introduced other errors in later stages of the skill. Correct only one or two faults before re-observing the skill. Accept that error correction is a multi-step ongoing process.

Good error correction is a communication skill as well as a biomechanical skill. When correcting, coaches should use positive and specific language appropriate to the age, developmental level, and competitive level of their athletes. Conscientious instructors ask for feedback to check if the correction instructions were received as intended, and they try to minimize any distractions in the environment before correcting any errors. Good coaches are also familiar with the latest technology and use it in their coaching (Figure 7.24).

Figure 7.24 In sports where there is a considerable distance between the coach and the athlete, a walkie talkie or other long-range communication device comes in very handy.

Summary

The focus of this chapter was biomechanics, or the *physics* of human movement. The major goal of research in the area of sport biomechanics is to help athletes optimize performance by describing human movement from both a kinematic and dynamic perspective. Biomechanists study movement with the aid of three computer-generated biomechanical models – the particle, stick figure, and rigid segment body models.

Motion in the human body, whether it's linear, angular, or general, is the result of the application of an external force (a push or pull). Newton's three laws of motion describe the relationships between inertia, force, mass, and acceleration. The fluid (i.e., air or water) through which an object or athlete moves generates drag and lift forces. Laws such as Bernoulli's principle and the Magnus effect influence characteristics of projectiles in flight (e.g., the path of a javelin or the spin on a tennis ball). When athletes are in flight, they can control their angular velocity by changing their body positions in the air. An object or athlete not experiencing any change in direction or acceleration is said to be in a state of equilibrium.

Coaches and athletes use qualitative analysis to evaluate skills for the purpose of detecting and correcting errors. A knowledge of biomechanical principles helps a coach determine the source of performance errors and how best to correct them.

Key Words

Acceleration	First class lever	Newton's second law
Action–reaction	Fulcrum	Newton's third law
Aerodynamics	General motion	Parabolic path
Angle of attack	Gravity	Particle model
Angular acceleration	Hydrodynamics	Profile (form) drag
Angular displacement	Impact	Projectile
Angular kinetics	Impulse	Qualitative analysis
Angular motion (rotation)	Inertia	Quantitative analysis
Angular velocity	Kinematics	Range
Axis of rotation	Kinetics	Rectilinear motion
Balance	Laminar flow	Rigid body segment model
Bernoulli's principle	Lever	Scalar quantity
Biomechanics	Lift force	Second class lever
Boundary layer	Linear motion	Skin-friction (surface) drag
Centre of mass (gravity)	Magnus effect	Stability
Composite diagram	Magnus force	Static equilibrium
Conservation of angular	Mass	Stick figure model
momentum	Moment arm	Third class lever
Curvilinear motion	Moment of force (torque)	Translation
Displacement	Moment of inertia	Turbulent flow
Drag	Momentum	Vector
Dynamic equilibrium	Net force	Vector quantity
Equilibrium	Newton's first law	Velocity

Discussion Questions

1. Define biomechanics. What other disciplines can benefit from studies in biomechanics?

2. Discuss three ways in which biomechanics can be helpful to teachers and coaches.

3. Apply each of Newton's three laws of motion to a skill, or portion thereof, relevant to a sport of your choice. Be specific in identifying forces, masses, accelerations, etc.

4. Briefly discuss how you would advise an athlete to maximize impulse and minimize the harmful effects of impact in a specific sport.

5. What factors affect the horizontal distance a projectile will travel? Which is most important?

6. Select a sport skill in which a light object is thrown. Discuss the effects air resistance will have on the projectile path of this object.

7. Identify three ways in which athletes decrease drag forces acting against their bodies.

8. Identify two sport skills in which lift forces have a large effect on the resulting motion. Explain this effect.

9. Differentiate between equilibrium, stability, and balance.

10. In a sport of your choosing, identify how an athlete maintains or loses his or her balance during the execution of a skill specific to that sport.

11. Identify the four aspects of qualitative analysis and apply them to a sport skill of interest to you.

In This Chapter:

Biomechanical Principles of Injury *170*

Injury Treatment and Rehabilitation *171*
  Healing Phases *173*

Pain: Nature's Warning System *174*

Soft Tissue Injuries *174*
  Contusions *174*
  Strains and Sprains *175*

Dislocations *179*
  Dislocation of the Shoulder *179*

Fractures *181*

Concussions *181*

Overuse Injuries *182*
  Tendonitis *184*
  Bursitis *184*
  Shoulder Impingement *187*
  Stress Fractures *187*

Injury Prevention *190*
  Protective Equipment *190*
  Warming Up and Cooling Down *190*
  Keeping Fit and Flexible *191*
  Eating and Resting to Avoid Injury *191*

Summary *191*

CONCUSSION

SHOULDER IMPINGEMENT

BURSITIS

LATERAL EPICONDYLITIS

HAMSTRING STRAIN

QUADRICEPS CONTUSION

ANTERIOR CRUCIATE TEAR

JUMPER'S KNEE

ANKLE SPRAIN

CHAPTER 8

Out of Harm's Way: Sport Injuries

After completing this chapter you should be able to:

- identify the factors associated with injury prevention;

- describe the common musculoskeletal injuries;

- demonstrate an understanding of the implications of various chronic and acute injuries and how to treat them.

The human body is designed to perform a wide variety of simple and complex movements and skills. Clearly, this ability relies on all its parts working together in harmony. An injury to one body part can disrupt the harmony of the entire body. Fortunately, many injuries are preventable.

With more people today participating in sport and physical activity for health, fitness, and fun, avoiding injury is a notable concern. Many people ignore the warnings and risks that accompany certain activities, believing that nothing can possibly happen to them. Even the most careful physically active person can experience a mishap, but following some specific guidelines can greatly decrease your risk of sustaining an injury. Whether you make a concerted effort to improve your skills and technique when exercising, recognize the hazards that exist around you, perform proper conditioning exercises, or demand safe and quality equipment, you can enjoy an enhanced level of safety and confidence in your physical pursuits. You must take responsibility for your own actions by making appropriate decisions that reflect your safety and personal health (Figure 8.1).

Despite our efforts to take all of the necessary precautions, all dangers can never be completely eliminated; accidents do happen and injuries do occur. While most injuries are minor and not life-threatening, knowing what to do if an injury occurs helps you deal with the situation quickly and correctly. An injury that is not cared for properly can easily escalate into a chronic problem that may plague your efforts to lead an active life.

Biomechanical Principles of Injury

The human body is made up of tissues or groups of cells that work together to perform a particular function. The four basic types of tissue are **epithelial** (e.g., skin), **muscle**, **connective** (e.g., tendons, bones, and ligaments), and **nervous**. Each type of tissue possesses unique mechanical characteristics. For example, bones are strong and stiff, whereas tendons are flexible so that joints can be mobile.

To best understand the biomechanical characteristics of tissue we examine its behaviour under **physical load** (see box *Forces Acting on Tissue*). Under load a tissue experiences **deformation**. This change in shape phenomenon can be visualized in the load–deformation curve in Figure 8.2.

Figure 8.1 Staying fit and active throughout your life requires attention to conditioning, healthy lifestyle choices, and safety.

Did You Know?

When developing a prosthesis for human parts, such as a hip joint, biomechanical engineers ensure that the prosthesis can handle loads as well as or better than the human tissue it will be replacing.

Characteristics of the Load–Deformation Curve

- Loads occurring in the elastic region do not cause permanent damage.

- Permanent deformation will occur if loads exceed the yield-level point.

- The area under the entire curve represents the strength of the material in terms of stored energy.

- The slope of the curve in the elastic region indicates the stiffness of the material. Stiffness is the resistance to deformation, where the greater the slope of the curve, the greater the stiffness of the structure.

Figure 8.2 Load–deformation curve of a bone.

The A-B segment of the curve represents the **elastic region** of the tissue structure. Elasticity is the capacity of a tissue to return to its original shape after a load is removed. For example, when you push your finger into your thigh the skin and the muscle underneath your finger become depressed. When pressure is removed the tissues return to their original shape.

Point B on the curve (**yield-level point**) signals the **elastic limit** of the tissue, where the **plastic region** begins. In this region increased loads cause permanent tissue deformation, resulting in micro-failure or injury to the tissue. Sprains and strains are good examples of such injuries. If the load continues to increase to the **ultimate yield point** (point C on the curve), **ultimate failure** of the tissue eventually occurs: a bone fracture or torn ligament. At this point the tissue becomes completely unresponsive to loads.

Injury Treatment and Rehabilitation

Treatment and rehabilitation are two directly linked aspects of recovery. During **treatment**, a patient receives care by a health care professional.

Tissue Responses to Training

Human tissue responds to training loads or stresses by becoming stronger. When training loads are at or near a tissue's *yield-level point* (Figure 8.2, point B), cells may divide to make new cells or to make proteins such as *actin*, *myosin*, *collagen*, or *elastin* to improve the mechanical properties of the tissue under **stress**. This muscle response is called the **positive training effect**.

Training overloads may cause microscopic injuries in various muscle regions, leading to sore muscles. In these situations, the muscle structures are *temporarily* weakened. It is important to let them recover before another workout. Research has shown that optimal training occurs at a level of tissue stress just below the yield-level point.

Early and correct treatment promotes the healing process and improves the quality of the injured tissue(s), allowing the person to return to activity more quickly. **Rehabilitation** involves a therapist's physical restoration of the injured tissue along with the patient's active participation by following prescribed rehabilitation guidelines on his or her own.

Although an individualized rehabilitation

Forces Acting on Tissue

Tissue is exposed to a variety of physical stresses during physical activity. These stresses are forces and moments acting as directional loads that generate **tension** (pulling), **compression** (squeezing), **bending**, **shear**, or **torsion**.

Tension

Compression

Tension   Compression

Bending

Shear

Torsion

program should be created for each athlete, knowledge of general guidelines for early treatment and rehabilitation can be useful for dealing with acute injuries in particular. Some of these guidelines will be presented in this chapter.

Healing Phases

The healing process begins immediately after injury and consists of three overlapping phases: the inflammatory response phase, the fibroblastic repair phase, and the maturation–remodeling phase (Figure 8.3).

Inflammatory Response Phase

The **inflammatory response phase** sets the stage for tissue repair. Inflammation begins at the time of injury, or shortly after, and may last from two to four days. The injured area may show signs of redness, swelling, pain, increased temperature, and loss of function.

To allow healing to begin, the injury must be protected and rested. **Cryotherapy** (ice or cold water immersion for 15-20 minutes at a time) limits the amount of swelling and decreases bleeding, pain, and muscle spasms. **Compression** is applied over the ice, usually in the form of an elastic bandage. During cold water immersion a compression bandage can be wrapped around the injured area. Finally, the area is elevated above the level of the heart to encourage the return of venous blood to the heart, thereby helping to decrease acute swelling and bleeding.

Follow the PRICE rule!

When dealing with an injury, follow these simple steps:

P — Protect
R — Rest
I — Ice
C — Compress
E — Elevate

Fibroblastic Repair Phase

The **fibroblastic repair phase** leads to scar formation and repair of the injured tissue. It begins within a few hours of injury, and may last as long as four to six weeks. A delicate connective tissue called **granulation tissue** forms to fill the gaps in the injured area. Fibroblasts produce **collagen fibres**, which are deposited randomly throughout the forming scar. In this second phase, many of the signs and symptoms seen in the inflammatory response subside.

During the fibroblastic repair phase, it is important to introduce controlled rehab-specific exercises that are designed to restore normal range of motion and strength to the injured tissue, as well as stressing the tissue to promote optimal tissue response (see box *Tissue Responses to Training*). Manual massage therapy and ultrasound help break down scar tissue. Protective taping or a brace is often used during this phase of rehabilitation.

Inflammatory Response Phase	Fibroblastic Repair Phase	Maturation–Remodeling Phase
2 – 4 days	hours – 6 weeks	3 weeks – years

Figure 8.3 The three phases of the healing process.

Maturation–Remodeling Phase

The **maturation–remodeling phase** is a long-term process of remodeling or realigning the scar tissue. It begins about three weeks after injury and may continue for as long as several years. Stretching and strengthening become more aggressive in this phase because the goal is to organize the scar tissue along the lines of tensile stress. Sport-specific skills and activities are usually included in rehabilitation.

Pain: Nature's Warning System

Pain is nature's way of telling us something is wrong. However, many athletes ignore pain altogether. Professional athletes in particular believe that a little pain is natural, and taking a few days off to nurse an injury makes you weak and vulnerable. As a result, they choose to mask the pain with medication, which allows them to play through an injury. While the pain may subside, the problem remains unaddressed (Figure 8.4). Continued participation will push injured tissues closer to ultimate failure, resulting in a need for surgical repair. Other serious consequences of using medication to mask pain include addiction and gastrointestinal complications.

Figure 8.4 Pain medication helps reduce discomfort, but fails to address the cause of the problem.

Having said that, the temporary use of certain medications to decrease pain and inflammation may be helpful and appropriate. One should always consult a physician prior to using any medication or supplement.

How long an athlete should rest an injury depends on the type and extent of the injury, and also varies among individuals. Pain is one of the most important indicators of when it is best to resume play. We all feel it, we all know when it is present, and we all know when it has subsided. If it is painful to walk on a sprained ankle, whether one day after the injury or weeks later, it is simply too early to resume all-out activities. Once pain has subsided, training and competing may be introduced with caution. The load placed on an injured structure should increase gradually. Overloading an injured area, or coming back too early, can set you back longer than the original injury, and an acute injury may eventually become a chronic problem.

Soft Tissue Injuries

Contusions

When a compression force crushes tissue, a **contusion** results. Commonly called a bruise, symptoms include discoloration and swelling. What some athletes call a "charleyhorse" is a contusion injury, often to the quadriceps muscle group on the front of the thigh. While most

---

Myositis Ossificans

In a severe contusion, abnormal bone formation may occur. This is called **myositis ossificans**. The most common sites are the anterior and lateral thigh. A 2- to 4-cm mass is often palpable. Referral to a medical doctor is needed.

Radiograph

Management of a Quadriceps Contusion

Acute Phase (first 24 to 48 hours)

- Apply ice and compression with knee flexed at 120 degrees for 20 minutes each hour for a minimum of 4 hours.
- Begin pain-free passive or active range-of-motion exercises.

Subacute Phase (2 to 5 days)

- Continue with ice and compression.
- Continue active range-of-motion exercises.
- Begin partial weight-bearing activities.

Full Weight-bearing Phase

- Continue with ice and compression.
- Range of motion should be full.
- Slowly return to previous activities and use protective padding to prevent reinjury.
- If there is still pain seek medical attention.

These are only general guidelines. Please consult a licensed health care practitioner for further details and individual situations.

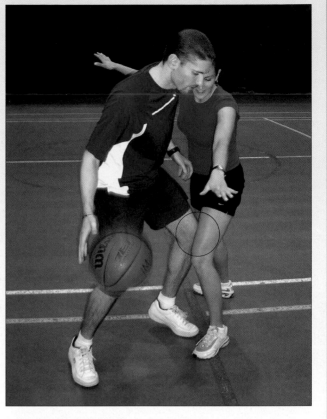

contusions are minor injuries, they can be serious and even life-threatening if the tissue involved is a vital organ such as the brain or kidneys.

Strains and Sprains

A **strain** occurs when muscle or tendon tissue is stretched or torn. A **sprain** results when a ligament or the joint capsule is stretched or torn, often from twisting movements or impacts that force the affected joints beyond their normal limits. Sprains and strains are classified into three grades based on the amount of damage to the tissues and the resulting pain and loss of function (Table 8.1).

Grade three sprains and strains result in complete rupture of the tissue and often require surgery. An example is an **anterior cruciate ligament tear**. The anterior cruciate ligament (ACL) and posterior cruciate ligament (PCL) crisscross the knee joint and give the knee stability. Of the two, the ACL is weaker and more likely

to tear, often when changing directions rapidly or slowing down after running or landing from a jump as in basketball. A loud popping noise often accompanies an ACL tear, which is very painful. The knee joint gives out and swells very rapidly.

Common Strains

Common muscles strained in the lower extremities include the adductors (pulled "groin"), quadriceps, hamstrings, and hip flexors (iliopsoas). In the upper extremities, muscles of the rotator cuff, which help stabilize the shoulder joint, are often vulnerable to strains.

Hamstring Strains   The hamstrings are the most frequently strained muscles in the body. The main mechanism of injury is rapid contraction of the hamstring muscles in a lengthened position. Most typically this occurs during sprinting or running (Figure 8.5).

Weak hamstring muscles compared with

Table 8.1 Grades of strains and sprains.

Grade		Strain	Sprain
1st	Description	A few muscle fibres have been stretched or torn	Ligament has been slightly stretched or torn
	Pain	Minor pain during isometric and passive movements	Minor pain during passive movements
	Range of motion	Decreased	
	Swelling	Minor	
	Weakness	Minor	
	Disability	Little or no loss of function	
2nd	Description	More muscle fibres have been torn	Ligament has been moderately stretched or torn
	Pain	Moderate pain during isometric and passive movements	Moderate pain during passive movements
	Range of motion	Decreased	
	Swelling	Moderate	
	Weakness	Moderate	
	Disability	Moderate loss of function	
3rd	Description	Muscle is completely torn	Ligament is completely torn
	Pain	No pain during isometric and passive movements*	
	Range of motion	May increase or decrease depending on swelling	
	Swelling	Major	
	Weakness	Major	
	Disability	Major	

* *When you completely tear a muscle, tendon, or ligament, the ability to feel pain in those structures is completely lost.*

Artificial Turf vs. Natural Turf

There is much debate about whether artificial playing surfaces are more dangerous than natural playing surfaces. Artificial surfaces provide greater friction, enabling athletes to run faster and change directions more quickly. However, these conditions also increase the loads placed on muscles, tendons, and ligaments, increasing the likelihood of sustaining a strain or sprain. Therefore, a trade-off exists between performance and potential for injury on artificial surfaces.

Management of an ACL Injury

Phase 1

- PRICE
- Range-of-motion exercises within pain-free limits
- Isometric exercises for quads, hamstrings, and hip adductors
- Cardiovascular exercise

Phase 2

- Continued range-of-motion exercises
- Unilateral balance activities
- Slow, controlled balance activities (using a wobble board)
- Slow, controlled calf raises and straight leg raises
- Cardiovascular exercise

Phase 3

- Maintain range of motion
- Functional strengthening exercises (squats, leg presses, lunges)
- Cardiovascular exercise
- Continued balance activities

Phase 4

- All the activities of Phase 3, with increased sport-specific activities, such as running (circles, cross-over steps) and jumping drills (hopping, bounding, skipping)

Surgery is often needed to repair a torn ACL. Your doctor replaces the damaged ACL with strong, healthy tissue usually taken from another area near your knee. Most commonly, a portion of the patellar ligament or hamstring is used. Your doctor threads the tissue through the inside of your knee joint and secures the ends to your femur and tibia.

After ACL surgery, rehabilitation exercises will gradually return your knee to maximal flexibility and stability. Building strength in the muscles around the knee joint (hamstrings, quadriceps, and calf) is important to stabilize the joint. Initially, a brace is usually required to protect the joint after surgery, but with successful rehabilitation knee braces are slowly weaned off.

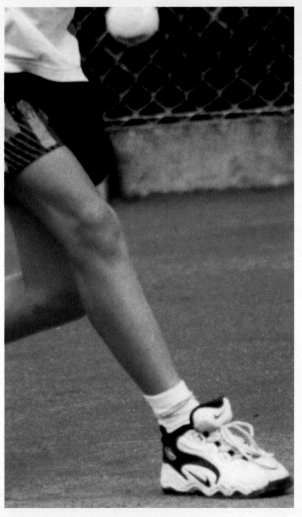

Anterior Right Knee

Femur

Posterior Cruciate Ligament

Lateral Meniscus

Lateral Collateral Ligament

Fibula

Anterior Cruciate Ligament

Medial Collateral Ligament

Medial Meniscus

Patellar Ligament (cut)

Tibia

These are only general guidelines. Please consult a licensed health care practitioner for further details and individual situations.

Avoiding Hamstring Strains

Below is an example of a balanced leg workout designed to avoid strength imbalances in the muscles of the thigh.

Exercise	Reps x Sets
Squats	10 x 3
Lunges	10 x 3
Hamstring curls	10 x 3

Posterior Right Thigh

Ilium
Femur
Biceps Femoris (long head)
Semitendinosus
Biceps Femoris (short head)
Semimembranosus
Biceps Femoris (short head)
Tibia
Fibula

SQUATS

(1) Place the bar on your shoulders. Stand shoulder-width apart. Point your feet slightly outwards.

(2) Slowly bend your knees and hips in unison. The bar should descend in a straight line.

(3) Continue until your thighs are just above parallel to the ground.

(4) Using your legs, push back up to the starting position. You should feel most of the weight on your heels.

HAMSTRING CURLS

(1) Set the machine so your knees line up with its centre of rotation.

(2) Lie on the padded surface.

(3) Slowly curl your feet towards your buttocks.

(4) Slowly lower your legs back to the starting position.

LUNGES

(1) Begin standing with legs together.

(2) Slowly take a step forward with one foot.

(3) Bend your knee, making sure you maintain your balance and your knee is in line with your toes.

(4) Return to starting position.

These are only general guidelines. Please consult a licensed health care practitioner for further details and individual situations.

Figure 8.5 Hamstring strains are very common among sprinters, and are often caused by muscle imbalances.

strong quadriceps are a main reason why hamstring strains occur so frequently. To reduce strength imbalances, rehabilitative exercises and strength and conditioning programs should emphasize the quadriceps and hamstrings equally. An example of a balanced workout program can be found in the box *Avoiding Hamstring Strains.*

Common Sprains

Ankle Sprains Ankle sprains are among the most common athletic injuries. You can sprain your ankle running, walking, dancing, or just stepping off a curb. Most common is the **lateral ankle sprain**. Lateral ankle sprains, or inversion sprains, occur when stress is applied (see box *Prevention of an Ankle Sprain*).

A "pop" or tearing noise is usually heard at the time of injury. The joint will swell rapidly and the person is usually unable to walk. Point tenderness will be localized over the anterior talofibular ligament and may extend over the calcaneofibular ligament.

Proper rehabilitation is important to prevent reinjury. Research indicates that a main reason why ankle sprains reoccur is decreased proprioception following the initial sprain. **Proprioception** is the ability to sense the position of a joint in space. Balance exercises, such as wobble board exercises, help improve proprioception. This component of rehabilitation is often neglected because people tend to think they are healed once the pain is gone. Unfortunately their proprioceptive abilities are not healed and they are more likely to suffer another injury.

Dislocations

If the forces acting on a joint are great enough to push the joint beyond its normal anatomical limits, a dislocation may occur. In a dislocation, the joint surfaces come apart. When the ligaments and other supporting structures of the joint are stretched and torn enough to allow the bony surfaces to partially separate, a **subluxation** has occurred. The joints of the fingers are the most commonly dislocated, followed by the shoulder. Dislocations may become chronic depending on the amount of damage to the ligaments and other supporting structures, and on the treatment and rehabilitation of the original injury.

Dislocation of the Shoulder

The shoulder joint is the most mobile joint in our bodies, but by virtue of this mobility it is also the most unstable. There are two basic categories of dislocations: partial and complete. A **partial dislocation**, or subluxation, indicates that the head of the humerus (ball) is partially out of the glenoid fossa (socket). A **complete dislocation** occurs when the head of the humerus is completely out of the socket. Of course, the greater degree of joint dislocation indicates greater

Figure 8.6 Falling and landing on an extended outstretched arm is one way to dislocate your shoulder joint.

Prevention of an Ankle Sprain

Prevention

- **Limit running on uneven surfaces.** Uneven surfaces increase the chance of ankle sprains.

- **Improve balance.** Even if you don't have an ankle problem, balance exercises can help prevent possible future injuries.

- **Wear proper well-cushioned shoes.** Shoes that are worn or that don't fit properly should be replaced. Wear shoes that provide stability, especially if you play a sport that requires a lot of changes of direction, such as basketball.

- **Monitor fatigue.** If you are feeling unusually tired, stop and rest.

- **Stay hydrated.** Water is a key lubricant that permits bones, muscles, and connective tissues to slide against each other.

- **Strengthen the ankle stabilizers.** An excellent way to strengthen the muscles, tendons, and ligaments around the ankle joint is to run along the shores of a sandy beach.

Lateral Right Foot

Fibula — Tibia

Lateral Malleolus

Anterior Talofibular Ligament

Calcaneofibular Ligament

| **ONE-LEGGED BALANCE** | **WOBBLE BOARD** | **ANKLE STRENGTHENING EXERCISES** |

(1) Stand on one foot while performing simple movements of the arms and non-weight-bearing leg.

* Try writing letters or numbers with your arms or free leg.

(1) Stand with your feet spread just inside shoulder-width on the wobble board.

(2) Balance.

* Try closing your eyes to challenge yourself.

(1) Tie some exercise tubing around the outside of your foot.

(2) Attach the tubing to something solid.

(3) Begin exercises with foot inverted.

(4) Slowly evert your foot. You should feel the muscles on the outside of your leg (peroneals) contracting.

* Perform 15-20 reps x 3 sets, three times a week.

These are only general guidelines. Please consult a licensed health care practitioner for further details and individual situations.

injury. A shoulder dislocation requires medical treatment to relocate the head of the humerus back into the glenoid fossa.

The most common type of shoulder dislocation occurs when the head of the humerus slips anteriorly. This can happen when you're falling backwards and you land on an extended outstretched arm (Figure 8.6). Because your arm is locked all the forces get transmitted to the front of the shoulder, causing the dislocation. The rotator cuff muscles help stabilize the joint, so a great deal of force is required for dislocations to occur.

Symptoms that occur with shoulder dislocations include swelling, numbness, pain, weakness, and bruising. In severe dislocations, the capsule that surrounds the shoulder joint can tear, along with muscles of the rotator cuff. An infrequent but serious complication of shoulder dislocations is injury to the brachial plexus. This is a group of nerves that exit from your neck and travel underneath the clavicle anterior to the head of the humerus. The brachial plexus innervates all the muscles of your chest, shoulder, arm, forearm, and hand. When the shoulder is dislocated forward, the brachial plexus may be injured.

Fractures

Bone fractures may be simple or compound. A **simple fracture** stays within the surrounding soft tissue, whereas a **compound fracture** protrudes from the skin. A **stress fracture** results from repeated low-magnitude training loads. Another type of fracture is an **avulsion fracture**, which involves a tendon or ligament pulling a small chip of bone away from the rest of the bone. Typically this occurs in children and involves explosive throwing and jumping movements.

Concussions

A **concussion** is an injury to the brain that usually develops from a violent shaking or jarring action of the head. The force of impact causes the brain to

Did You Know?

Helmets are a good idea for activities such as bicycling, in-line skating, and scooter riding. Skateboarders need special helmets that provide more coverage for the back of the head (especially for beginners who tend to fall backwards more often).

Research has shown that a properly fitted bicycle helmet offers up to 88 percent protection from brain injury (Figure 8.7).

Always replace helmets that have sustained a significant impact. Helmets are effective for one fall – one time use only! Also, avoid buying "used" helmets to ensure maximum protection.

bounce against the inside of the skull. This results in confusion and a temporary loss of normal brain function, such as memory, judgement, reflexes, speech, muscle coordination, and balance.

Approximately 20 percent of concussions occur in organized sports. They are common in hockey, football, boxing, and many other contact sports. Athletes with a previous concussion are three to six times more likely to suffer another one.

For years, coaches would urge an injured player to "shake it off" and return after a brief rest. This casual attitude has changed in recent

Figure 8.7 These kids are forgetting the most important piece of safety equipment – the helmet.

Concussion Awareness

Always assess airway, breathing and circulation.

All players who experience a concussion must be seen by a physician before the player can return to play.

Definition: Change in mental state (confusion) as a result of a trauma. May involve loss of consciousness.
Mechanism: Blow to the head, face or jaw. May result from a whiplash effect to the neck.

Types of Concussion

First Degree: Player experiences brief period of confusion. There is no loss of consciousness. Symptoms are completely gone in less than fifteen minutes.

Second Degree: Player experiences a loss of consciousness (however brief) or player experiences symptoms beyond fifteen minutes. *Player should see a physician immediately.*

Common Symptoms and Signs

Vacant Stare	Dizziness
Poor coordination	Ringing in the ears
Delayed responses to questions	Seeing stars
Nausea, vomiting	Sensitivity to light
Inability to focus	Sensitivity to noise
	Headache

Please note that some symptoms/signs may appear later so player should be observed even after symptoms/signs seem normal.

Mental Status Testing

For information only. Do not attempt to treat a concussion. Always have the player consult a physician.

Orientation: Does the player know what the exact time and place is? Does the player know the circumstances of the injury?

Concentration: Can the player spell "world" backwards?

Memory: Does the player know the score of the game?

Ontario Brain Injury Association   CANADA

Concussion Management

Any Loss of Consciousness – Initiate Emergency Action Plan and Call an Ambulance

➤ Rule out possible neck injury

➤ Remove the player from further play

➤ Do not administer medication

➤ Notify the parent or guardian about the injury

➤ The player does not return to play unless permitted to do so by a physician

Return To Play

The return to play process only begins after a physician has given the player clearance to return to activity. If any symptoms/signs return during this process, the player must be re-evaluated by a physician.

1. No activity, complete rest. Proceed to step 2 only when symptoms are gone and a physician has given the player clearance.
2. Light aerobic exercise such as walking or stationary cycling. Monitor for symptoms.
3. Sport specific training (e.g. skating).
4. Non-contact drills.
5. Full contact practices.
6. Game play.

Note: Player should proceed through the steps only when it has been demonstrated that there are no return of symptoms. This includes long term symptoms such as, fatigue, irritable behaviour or sleep disturbance. If any symptoms return the player should drop down to the previous level and **must be re-evaluated by a physician.**

Prevention

Players	**Safety Person/ Trainer**
• Make sure your helmet fits snugly	• Discourage checks to the head
• Get a custom fitted mouth guard	• Recognize signs and symptoms of concussion
• Respect other players	

These are only general guidelines. Please consult a licensed health care practitioner for further details and individual situations.

Figure 8.8 Hockey Canada Safety Program: Concussion Card.

years due to concussion-related retirements of Brett Lindros from hockey and Steve Young from football. Neurosurgeons and other brain injury experts emphasize that although some concussions are less serious than others, there is no such thing as a "minor concussion." The Canadian Hockey Association has developed a safety program using the "Concussion Card" to increase awareness of concussions (Figure 8.8).

Overuse Injuries

Overuse injuries are often the result of repeated microtrauma to the tissues, which do not have sufficient recovery time to heal. This accumulated microtrauma can result from poor technique, equipment that puts unusual stresses on the tissues, and the amount or type of training an athlete is

Preventing Lateral Epicondylitis

Lateral epicondylitis, commonly known as *tennis elbow*, tends to occur in people who play tennis or other racquet sports. The most common cause of this condition is improper technique or overuse. Below are a few things you can do to prevent it.

Prevention

- **Analyze your arm motions.** This is very important to reduce unnecessary stress on the lateral epicondyle. Always seek professional guidance whenever starting a new activity.

- **Exercise to strengthen your forearm extensors/supinators.** Use either exercise tubing or free weights.

- **Stretch after exercise.** Stretching keeps your muscles flexible and better able to tolerate eccentric loads.

- **Use compression straps.** Straps reduce the tensile load at the lateral epicondyle.

- **Apply ice.** Even if you do not feel discomfort after the activity it is important to ice.

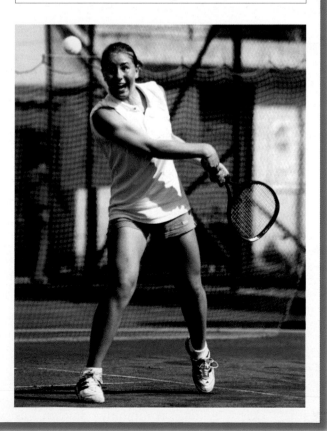

Posterior Right Arm

Triceps Brachii

Lateral Epicondyle of Humerus

Forearm Extensors

FOREARM EXTENSOR EXERCISE

(1) Begin with the wrist in maximum flexion.

(2) Extend the wrist.

* Perform 15-20 reps x 3 sets, three times a week.

SUPINATOR EXERCISE

(1) Begin with the forearm in maximum pronation.

(2) Supinate the forearm.

These are only general guidelines. Please consult a licensed health care practitioner for further details and individual situations.

doing. Common types of overuse injuries include tendonitis, bursitis, shoulder impingement, and stress fractures.

Tendonitis

A tendon is a type of connective tissue that connects your muscles to your bones. **Tendonitis** occurs when a tendon becomes inflamed initially, then weakened and degenerative, and is usually the result of a "microtrauma" in the tendon caused by excessive repetitive motions. Age can also contribute to the incidence of tendonitis because muscles and tendons lose their elasticity with age. Tendonitis produces pain, tenderness, and stiffness near a joint and is aggravated by movement.

Your risk of developing tendonitis increases if you perform excessive repetitive motions. For example, soccer and basketball players, runners, and dancers are prone to tendonitis in their legs and feet. Baseball players, swimmers, tennis players, and golfers are susceptible to tendonitis in their shoulders and elbows. The risk of developing tendonitis increases further if you use improper technique.

Tennis Elbow

Lateral epicondylitis, commonly known as **tennis elbow**, affects tendons of your forearm extensor/supinator muscles. These muscles attach to the lateral epicondyle of the humerus and are responsible for extending your wrist and fingers (see box *Preventing Lateral Epicondylitis*).

People who play tennis or other racquet sports may develop this problem. Contributing factors include excessive forearm pronation and wrist flexion during forehand strokes, gripping the racquet too tightly, improper size grip, excessive string tension, excessive racquet weight or stiffness, faulty backhand technique, putting topspin on backhand strokes, or hitting the ball off-centre.

Golfer's Elbow and Little League Elbow

Medial epicondylitis, commonly known as **golfer's elbow**, is similar to tennis elbow but it occurs on the inner side. This condition affects the tendons of the forearm flexors/pronators which attach to the medial epicondyle of the humerus. These muscles are responsible for flexing your wrist and fingers and pronating your forearm.

In severe injuries the ulnar collateral ligament and ulnar nerve can be injured. If the ulnar nerve is involved tingling and numbness may radiate into the forearm and hand, particularly affecting the fourth and fifth fingers. Other activities that can irritate the medial epicondyle include racquet sports and using a computer mouse.

Medial epicondylitis affecting the medial humeral growth plate in young children or adolescents is called **little league elbow**. This occurs primarily when young baseball players, usually around the age of 12-14, begin to throw curveballs. The excessive forces required to throw a curveball exceed the tissue tolerance of the medial epicondyle. For this reason teaching players under the age of 16 how to throw a curveball is discouraged.

Jumper's Knee

Pain affecting the infrapatellar ligament, known as **patellar tendonitis** or **jumper's knee**, is caused by repetitive eccentric knee actions, such as jumping in volleyball, basketball, and track and field events. The eccentric load affects the quadriceps during jump preparation, when the forces experienced are several times larger than the athlete's body weight.

Bursitis

Bursitis describes inflammation of the bursae. Like tendonitis, it results from overuse and stress. Your body contains more than 150 bursae – tiny fluid-filled sacs that lubricate and cushion pressure points between your bones and tendons (Figure 8.9). When they become inflamed, movement and direct pressure cause pain.

Bursitis is most common in the shoulder, elbow, and hip joints. Again, the mechanism of injury is excessive repetitive movements. For

Preventing Medial Epicondylitis

Medial epicondylitis, also known as *golfer's elbow*, occurs commonly in people who play golf or racquet sports. It also occurs frequently among people who use a computer mouse. Medial epicondylitis affecting the humeral growth plate in children or adolescents is called *little league elbow*. Listed below are a few things you can do to prevent this condition.

Prevention

- **Analyze your arm motions.** This is important to reduce unnecessary stress on the medial epicondyle. Always seek professional guidance whenever starting a new activity.

- **Exercise to strengthen your forearm flexors/ pronators.** Use either exercise tubing or free weights.

- **Stretch after exercise.** Stretching keeps your muscles flexible and better able to tolerate eccentric loads.

- **Apply ice.** Even if you do not feel discomfort after the activity it is important to ice.

Medial Epicondyle of Humerus

Brachioradialis

Forearm Flexors

Anterior Right Arm

FOREARM FLEXOR EXERCISE

(1) Begin with the wrist in maximum extension.

(2) Flex the wrist.

* Perform 15-20 reps x 3 sets, three times a week.

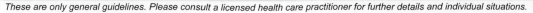

These are only general guidelines. Please consult a licensed health care practitioner for further details and individual situations.

Prevention of Jumper's Knee

Prevention

- **Maximize quadriceps and hamstring strength**. A balanced workout program is important to prevent injury.

- **Perform repetitive eccentric quadriceps exercises**. Gradually increase load to prepare the body to withstand repetitive loading.

- **Stretch after exercise**. Stretching keeps your muscles flexible and better able to tolerate eccentric loads.

- **Train on cushioned surfaces and wear well-cushioned footwear**. This decreases the forces acting on the knee.

- **Apply ice**. Even if you do not feel discomfort after the activity it is important to ice.

- **Seek medical treatment**. If you experience symptoms, seek medical attention to prevent future problems.

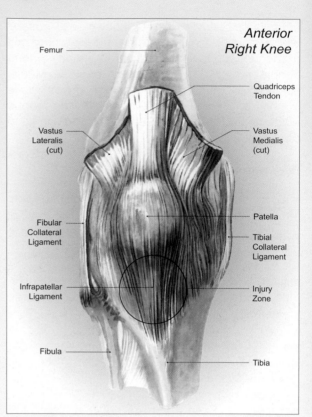

Anterior Right Knee

Femur — Quadriceps Tendon — Vastus Lateralis (cut) — Vastus Medialis (cut) — Fibular Collateral Ligament — Patella — Tibial Collateral Ligament — Infrapatellar Ligament — Injury Zone — Fibula — Tibia

SINGLE LEG SQUATS

(1) Balance on one leg.

(2) Slowly lower yourself, making sure your knee and pelvis are in good alignment throughout the exercise.

(3) Only go as deep as you are able to maintain form.

* Perform 10 reps x 3 sets, three times a week.

QUAD STRETCH

(1) Grasp your ankle.

(2) Slowly bring your foot to your buttocks.

* You may find it difficult on one foot, so try touching your belly button with your free hand.

These are only general guidelines. Please consult a licensed health care practitioner for further details and individual situations.

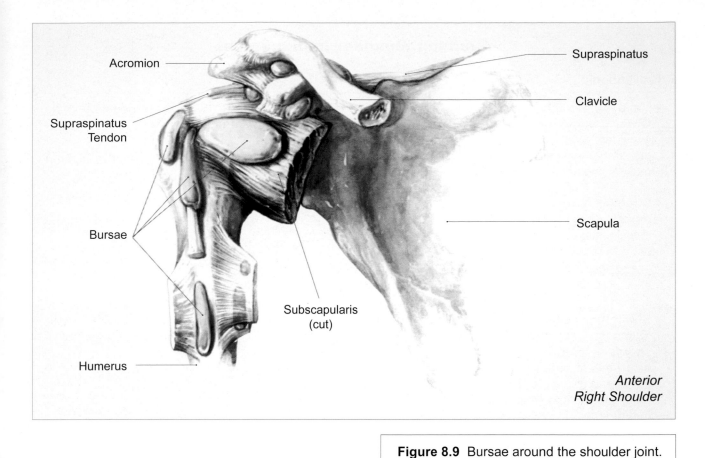

Labels in figure:
- Acromion
- Supraspinatus Tendon
- Bursae
- Humerus
- Subscapularis (cut)
- Supraspinatus
- Clavicle
- Scapula
- *Anterior Right Shoulder*

Figure 8.9 Bursae around the shoulder joint.

example, frequent extension of the arm at high speeds, such as in baseball pitching, can cause bursitis. Medical research indicates that you are more likely to develop bursitis with increasing age.

Shoulder Impingement

Shoulder impingement is a very common problem with athletes, industrial workers, and anyone who uses their shoulders repeatedly. Excess movement of the humeral head combined with a lack of space between the humeral head and the acromion causes inflammation in the bursae or rotator cuff tendons in the shoulder.

Muscle imbalances in the shoulder are largely responsible for development of shoulder impingement. The main culprit is weak shoulder depressors (lower fibres of the trapezius and serratus anterior) compared with the shoulder elevators (upper fibres of the trapezius). Likewise, a tight pectoralis major muscle may cause the humeral head to rotate anteriorly, increasing the potential for shoulder impingement.

Stress Fractures

A **stress fracture** is a special type of fracture that results from repeated low-magnitude forces. It begins as a small disruption in the continuity of the outer layers of cortical bone. With continued stress to the weakened bone, complete cortical bone fracture can occur. Stress fractures of the metatarsals, femoral neck, and pubis are common in runners who overtrain.

It is important to note the distinction between a stress fracture and shin splints, because the two terms are often used interchangeably. **Shin splints** describe pain that occurs along the inner surface of the tibia. Common causes include vigorous high-impact activity, training on hard surfaces, improper training protocols, poorly cushioned footwear, and having flat feet. Shin splints involve pain and inflammation without a disruption of

Avoiding Shoulder Impingement

Prevention

- **Make sure your shoulders are depressed when doing any exercises.** Elevating your shoulders while doing an activity decreases the space between the humerus and acromion, making impingement more likely.

- **Stretch the pectoralis major muscle.** A tight pectoralis major muscle may cause the humeral head to rotate anteriorly, thereby increasing the risk of shoulder impingement.

- **Strengthen the supporting muscles surrounding the shoulder joint.** These muscles help prevent anterior rotation of the humerus, thereby reducing the risk of shoulder impingement.

- **Reduce activity.** If your shoulders become painful reduce your activity levels.

- **Apply ice.** Even if you do not feel discomfort after the activity it is important to ice.

Acromion

Impingement Zone

Shoulder Joint Capsule

Coracoid Process of Scapula

Scapula

Humerus

Anterior Right Shoulder

EXTERNAL ROTATORS EXERCISE

(1) Begin with your arm flexed at your side, with your shoulder internally rotated.

(2) Rotate your arm out to the side like you are opening a door, making sure your shoulder is always depressed.

EMPTY CAN EXERCISE

(1) Begin with your arm straight at your side, making sure your thumb is pointing down to the floor.

(2) Abduct your arm slowly, making sure there is about 30 degrees of horizontal abduction and your shoulders are depressed.

LOWER TRAPEZIUS EXERCISE

(1) Lie on the ground or on a bench with your arms abducted to 90 degrees. Your palms should face the ceiling.

(2) Squeeze your shoulder blades together, making sure they are depressed and your palms are facing the ceiling.

These are only general guidelines. Please consult a licensed health care practitioner for further details and individual situations.

Preventing Shin Splints

Prevention

- **Limit running on hard surfaces.** Running on a variety of surfaces will force your supporting leg muscles to strengthen.

- **Join a running club.** Increasing mileage too quickly places excessive stress on the tibia. Proper training programs and technique are important. Guidance on this matter can be gained by joining a running club.

- **Seek medical treatment.** If you experience symptoms, seek medical attention to prevent future problems.

- **Address muscle imbalances.** Tight calf muscles and weak tibialis anterior muscles can decrease your ability to absorb forces.

- **Avoid biomechanical misalignment.** Anything from your toes to your head can affect the way you run.

- **Wear proper well-cushioned shoes.** Shoes that are worn or that don't fit properly should be replaced. Running shoes should be used for running, not basketball or tennis shoes.

- **Stay hydrated.** Water is a key lubricant that permits bones, muscles, and connective tissues to slide against each other.

- **Apply ice.** Even if you do not feel discomfort after the activity it is important to ice.

TIBIALIS ANTERIOR EXERCISE

(1) Use a weight or exercise tubing.

(2) Begin the exercise with your foot pointed away.

(3) Begin with the ankle in plantar flexion (point toes down).

(4) Slowly dorsiflex your ankle (point toes up).

* You should feel the muscle in front of your shin contracting.

* Perform 15-20 reps x 3 sets, three times a week.

CALF MUSCLE STRETCHES

Soleus Stretch

Gastrocnemius Stretch

Hold for 30 s and repeat.

Hold for 30 s and repeat.

(1) Begin with your knee bent while standing.

(2) Maximally dorsiflex your ankle until you feel a stretch.

(1) Begin with your knee straight while standing.

(2) Maximally dorsiflex your ankle until you feel a stretch.

Anterior Right Leg

Interosseous Membrane

Fibula

Tibia

Injury Zone

Lateral Malleolus

Medial Malleolus

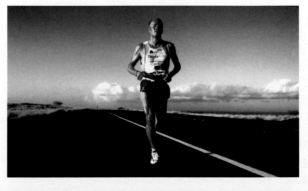

These are only general guidelines. Please consult a licensed health care practitioner for further details and individual situations.

the cortical bone. X-rays and possibly bone scans are therefore needed to properly diagnose a stress fracture.

Injury Prevention

Not every injury can be avoided, but if you take the necessary precautions and make note of preventative factors, it is possible to develop a viable plan for injury prevention.

Protective Equipment

It sometimes takes a serious injury or a mountain of clinical evidence to wake people up to the risks associated with certain activities. For example, professional hockey players (including goalies) used to play the game without protective head gear. Today, helmets and face masks are mandatory. The use of helmets in many sports such as in-line skating and cycling has also received greater attention in recent years, and rightfully so. The consequences of participating in such activities without the proper head gear can be debilitating and even fatal. Injury prevention, however, goes far beyond knowing the risks and preventative factors; knowing is not doing. It is up to you to take advantage of whatever safety equipment is available for the activity in which you participate (Figure 8.10).

Figure 8.10 Here is someone who is properly protected and ready to have fun.

Warming Up and Cooling Down

Most athletes perform some type of warm-up before training or in preparation for an event, including stretching, light jogging or other aerobic activities, and sport- or activity-specific motions. Warming up helps an athlete prepare optimally (physically and mentally) for a competition or workout (Figure 8.11). Most research advocates a thorough and well-planned warm-up to not only improve performance but also to help prevent injury.

The issue of cooling down is overlooked by many athletes. After completing a long and tiring workout, many people are content to sit down and rest to allow their bodies to recover. This may lead to muscle stiffness, a condition that may make you

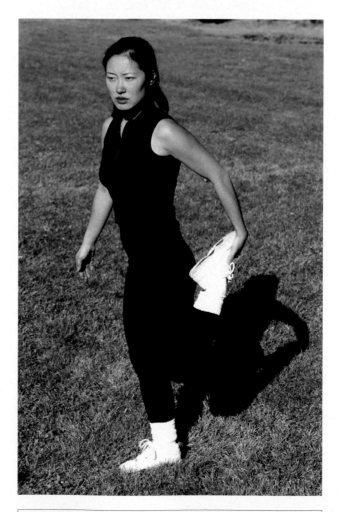

Figure 8.11 Stretching not only prepares your body but also your mind for physical activity.

more prone to injury the next time you take to the field or court. A short cool-down period removes lactic acid and other products of metabolism from the muscles and tissues, further reducing some of the stiffness and tightness that is often felt the next day. The cardiovascular system may also benefit from a gradual cool-down period since the abrupt lowering of an elevated heart rate is not ideal. So the next time you finish a long workout, don't just hit the showers; instead, walk a few laps and do some light stretching.

Keeping Fit and Flexible

As the saying goes, "use it or lose it." Seasonal athletes are well aware that training doesn't really end with the end of a competitive season. Sometimes the most important gains are made in the off-season. A fit athlete obviously has fewer adjustments to make at the beginning of a season than an athlete who is out of shape. The off-season is a time not only to develop and refine technical skills but also to maintain physical fitness (including strength, flexibility, and endurance). Most athletic injuries occur as a result of placing demands on a muscle or other tissue that is simply not prepared to withstand these demands.

The preseason claims many injury victims because many athletes do not stay in shape all year round. Some studies have shown that strength can be maintained with as little as one or two workouts a week at 90 percent of capacity. Fewer workouts are required to maintain aerobic capacity, so no excuses should be made for losing too much in the off-season.

Eating and Resting to Avoid Injury

Most athletes will agree that diet and rest play a major role, not only in enhancing performance but also in keeping the body well-tuned for injury prevention. In order to function most effectively, the body must be fed the proper nutrients and must receive adequate rest. Not meeting these conditions inevitably opens the door to potential

Figure 8.12 Resting and feeling a sense of accomplishment after a hard workout.

problems. Adhering to nutritional guidelines can prepare you for the stresses of physical exertion, and lower your risk of sustaining an injury (see Chapter 11 for details on nutrients, hydration, and pre-event meals).

Because training and competition involve putting forth great physical effort, muscles need rest from these physical demands to recuperate for the next training or competitive session (Figure 8.12). Muscles forced to endure heavy demands when inadequately rested may snap (literally) under pressure. Overtraining can be just as detrimental to your performance as not training enough (see Chapter 9).

Inadequate sleep may lead to mishaps that could have been avoided with proper rest and alertness. It is up to each person to discover what amount of sleep is best for him or her – there is no set number of hours that applies to everyone.

Summary

With more people participating in sport and physical activity for health, fitness, and fun, avoiding injury is a notable concern. Injuries occur based on the biomechanical properties of tissue, and where they are subjected to loads that exceed their elastic region.

Strains and sprains are common injuries. A strain occurs when muscle or tendon tissue is stretched or torn, and a sprain results when a ligament or the joint capsule is stretched or torn.

Another frequent sport injury is a contusion, or bruise, which occurs when a compression force crushes tissue. In a dislocation, either complete or partial (a subluxation), the joint surfaces come apart.

Bone fractures may be simple or compound. A simple fracture stays within the surrounding soft tissue, whereas a compound fracture protrudes from the skin. Overuse injuries are often the result of repeated microtrauma to the tissues. Examples include stress fractures, tendonitis, and bursitis. One potentially dangerous sport injury is a concussion, an injury to the brain that usually develops from a violent shaking or jarring action of the head.

Fortunately, we can train our bodies to make our tissues stronger and more resistant to defor-mation. We can also wear protective equipment, warm up and cool down before and after our ac-tivities, and make sure we perform the skill with good form in order to reduce our likelihood of injury.

No matter how hard we try to prevent them, injuries will always occur. The healing process begins immediately after injury and consists of three overlapping phases: the inflammatory response phase, the fibroblastic repair phase, and the maturation–remodeling phase. Many health care professionals have dedicated their lives to help us deal with problems resulting from injury. Doctors and various therapists can take us through treatment and rehabilitation programs that will help us return to our previous activities if not beyond.

Key Words

Anterior cruciate tear
Bending
Bursitis
Complete dislocation
Compound fracture
Compression
Concussion
Contusion
Cryotherapy
Deformation
Elastic region
Fibroblastic repair phase
Inflammatory response phase
Lateral ankle sprain

Lateral epicondylitis
Load
Maturation–remodeling phase
Medial epicondylitis
Partial dislocation
Patellar tendonitis
Plastic region
Positive training effect
PRICE
Proprioception
Rehabilitation
Shear
Shin splints
Shoulder impingement

Simple fracture
Sprain
Strain
Stress
Stress fracture
Subluxation
Tendonitis
Tension
Torsion
Treatment
Ultimate failure
Yield-level point

Discussion Questions

1. Define the load–deformation curve and use it to describe any injury.

2. What is the role of training with respect to injury prevention?

3. Describe the complications associated with pain medication.

4. What is the difference between a sprain and a strain?

5. What should you do immediately after an injury?

6. Compare and contrast a dislocation and a fracture.

7. Name and describe three overuse injuries.

8. What is the difference between bursitis and tendonitis?

9. How do you distinguish between a stress fracture and shin splints?

10. What are the benefits of warming up and cooling down?

A Career in Chiropractic Medicine

NAME: Dr. Borys M. Chambul
OCCUPATION: Doctor of Chiropractic Medicine
EDUCATION: BA, University of Washington (Physical Education and Psychology)
Canadian Memorial Chiropractic College (D.C.)

What does a chiropractor do?

A chiropractor is a healer who aims to improve and maintain health naturally. Rather than prescribing drugs or surgery, the chiropractor often uses spinal, cranial, and peripheral joint manipulation to restore normal function to the neuromuscular system. Some also use acupuncture and homeopathy. Chiropractic is holistic and preventative medicine. Practitioners tend to look at a patient's lifestyle as a whole, and often emphasize nutrition, exercise, and stress reduction.

Why did you choose a career in chiropractic medicine?

As a Varsity athlete, I suffered from a back and neck problem. I had tried traditional treatments, physiotherapy, and medication, but these did not work and I was forced to miss the second biggest meet of my university career. Later, at another meet, a teammate recommended a chiropractor who had been treating athletes. I had never heard of chiropractic medicine, but I responded to the treatment immediately and went out and won the discus event. After that, I was convinced that in this profession, I could be of help to athletes and other patients.

What do you like most about your profession?

People get better when they come for chiropractic care. There is a proportion of people who do not respond to traditional medical treatments, and I see their health improve with chiropractic treatment. My patients range from a three-week-old baby to a 94-year-old man. I treat people from all walks of life, including elite and Olympic athletes. I enjoy expanding my knowledge of the human body into so many different domains, and applying this knowledge to helping people.

What are the future job prospects for chiropractors?

The time is coming for chiropractors. People have been seeing chiropractors for years and feeling better, and now science is beginning to back up these findings with research studies. Chiropractors comprise the third largest group of medical practitioners in North America. There are over 65,000 chiropractors worldwide, and 40 percent of them are women. As people begin to demand a more active and preventative role in their own health care, chiropractors will be more in demand.

What advice do you have for students interested in chiropractic medicine?

Visit a chiropractor and see how he or she works. Take a tour of the chiropractic college in Toronto. It's a fantastic career for anybody who has a desire to help people get better naturally.

Note: *In 1978, Dr. Chambul won a gold medal at the Commonwealth Games in the discus event. He was the Commonwealth record holder in the discus from 1978-1982, and held the Canadian record from 1978-1992. He also held the National Championship meet record from 1980-2000 and was a two-time Olympian (1976 and 1980).*

A Career in Physiotherapy

NAME: Edison Au
OCCUPATION: Physiotherapist
EDUCATION: BSc, Queen's University (Life Sciences)
BScPT, University of Toronto (Physiotherapy)

What do you do?

While practicing sport and orthopaedic physiotherapy, I apply knowledge in biomechanics, anatomy, orthopaedics, tissue physiology, and pathology in the rehabilitation of musculoskeletal disorders. My goal is to restore or maximize a patient's functional level, usually following some sort of dysfunction or injury. This involves therapeutic exercise prescription, manual therapy, application of therapeutic modalities (ultrasound, electrotherapy, acupuncture, etc.), and patient education. Other physiotherapists may pursue areas of neurological (e.g., stroke or spinal cord injury rehabilitation) or cardiorespiratory (e.g., cystic fibrosis) specialization.

Why did you choose this profession?

For as long as I can remember, I have been interested in athletics and how it affects the human body. Being an active person and having suffered many injuries myself, I wanted a profession that would allow me to learn the intricate workings of sports injuries, how to treat them, and how to educate individuals interested in achieving maximal function. I also enjoy the challenge of addressing psychosocial issues that athletes endure when they are injured.

What are the future job prospects in the field?

In sport physiotherapy, good jobs are hard to come by. Otherwise, the job market for physiotherapists in general is fairly good, and will grow in demand as the population ages and more emphasis is placed on physical activity as a preventative medicine. The older people get and more active they wish to be, the more challenging it will be for physiotherapists to keep them on the go. Further specialization of physiotherapy will also continue to increase the profile and recognition of the profession.

What do you enjoy most about your profession?

Continually learning more about the intricacies of the human body, interacting with people, teaching them about how their bodies work, and developing progressive ways of healing them. There is nothing more satisfying for me than to see patients light up when you explain to them what is happening in their bodies and how to address it, then help them achieve a level of function that they did not think was possible.

What other career options are available to students interested in this area?

Besides physiotherapy, there are many other health-related professions out there that involve working in a hospital or clinic, which also provide similar interaction with patients and contribution to their well-being. A few examples include athletic therapist, chiropractor, dentist, doctor, exercise/recreation therapist, massage therapist, naturopathic doctor, nutritionist, nurse, occupational therapist, paramedic, pharmacist, physiotherapist assistant, radiation therapist, and x-ray technician.

What career advice would you give to students interested in entering this field?

Make sure that you talk to someone in the field and shadow them to get a feel of what each professional area covers, and learn about existing issues. Academically, start with a sound foundation in health sciences, which should prepare you for further training, and also inspire you to want to learn more about how the human body works. More than 50 percent of physiotherapy students have previous undergraduate work in kinesiology or physical and health education, which would be an ideal point from which to progress into a health science profession such as physiotherapy.

Human Performance

- Enhancing Health, Study, Work, and Play Through Physical Fitness

- What's My Score? Evaluation in Physical and Health Education

- The Nutritional Connection

- Weight Management: Finding a Healthy Balance

- Performance-enhancing Substances and Methods: Substance Use and Abuse

- The Mental Side of Human Performance

In This Chapter:

Definition of Terms 198

Components of Physical Fitness 200
    Muscular Strength 200
    Power 200
    Muscular Endurance 200
    Cardiorespiratory Endurance 203
    Flexibility 205
    Body Composition 208
    Psychomotor Ability 208

Components and Principles of Fitness Programs 209
    Training Components 209
    Principles of Fitness Training 213

Designing Fitness Training Programs 216
    Resistance Training 216
    Cardiorespiratory Training 221
    Combination Training 224

Summary 226

CHAPTER 9

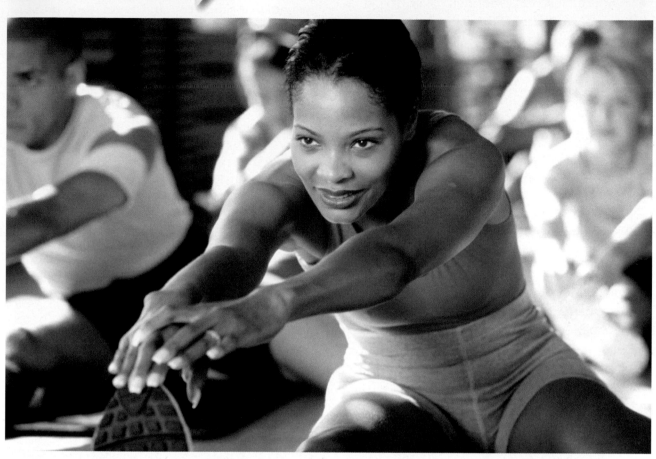

Enhancing Health, Study, Work, and Play Through Physical Fitness

After completing this chapter you should be able to:

- identify and discuss the various components of physical fitness;

- describe the contribution of physical fitness to overall health;

- evaluate the effects of various training methods on performance;

- examine your own physical fitness level and develop an awareness of personal fitness requirements;

- adapt physical fitness and activity programs to address personal needs.

The health, joie de vivre, and creativity of a well-developed personality depend to a great degree upon general fitness levels. Fitness is your functional readiness and level of effectiveness that are required for everything you do. It involves the ability to adapt to the demands and stresses of daily life and is directly related to the amount and intensity of your physical activity. The term fitness is used in many ways, and has many dimensions, including physical, emotional, social, and intellectual. The focus of this chapter will be on physical fitness.

Physical fitness is more than just a concept – it is a way of life. It incorporates many components important for health, such as cardiorespiratory endurance; flexibility; muscular strength, power, and endurance; and body composition. Each of these components offers unique benefits and advantages that affect your health in a positive way. Engaging in physical exercise provides numerous benefits that help you control your weight, manage stress, and boost your immune system, as well as protect you against disease. Not only does exercise help you look and feel good, but it allows you to have fun while achieving a state of health and vitality. Fitness need not be boring and monotonous, or restricted to running and cycling; there are many options available, and all you need to do is discover what activities interest you most. Exercise is one of the most important, and indeed, most controllable, factors affecting your general health.

General physical fitness forms the basis for sport-specific fitness and is ultimately related to it. High levels of general fitness are of utmost importance to athletes who strive to achieve high levels of performance. High levels of general fitness constitute important prerequisites for the effective and optimal development of sport-specific fitness. Both develop on the basis of the training principles governing exercise.

In order to get the most out of exercise and physical activity, you need the basic knowledge and an understanding about how to exercise properly and most effectively. This chapter will provide you with concepts related to components of fitness and equip you with basic knowledge governing training principles and their interrelationships.

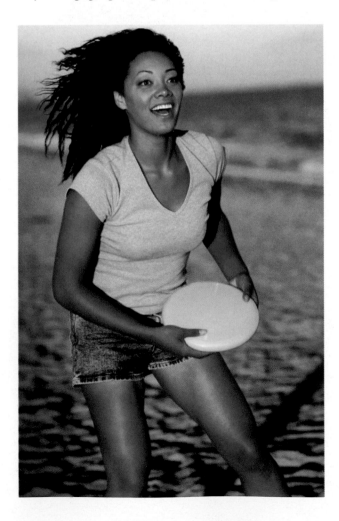

Definition of Terms

Physical fitness can be defined as the ability of the body to adjust to the demands and stresses of physical effort and is thought to be a measure of one's physical health. In contrast, **physical activity** is defined as "any movement carried out by the skeletal muscles requiring energy." The term **exercise** is considered to be a subset of physical activities that are planned, structured (usually repetitive bodily movements), and designed to improve or maintain physical fitness.

Although physical activity and physical fitness are related measures, physical fitness should be distinguished from physical activity. Physical fitness is an achieved condition which limits the

Muscular Strength

Psychomotor Ability

Muscular Endurance

PHYSICAL FITNESS

Body Composition

Cardiorespiratory Endurance

Flexibility

Figure 9.1 The components of physical fitness.

amount of physical activity that can be performed. A physical activity such as walking, cross-country skiing, or swimming might be considered exercise by an unfit person, while considered physical activity by someone who is very fit. The point is that a physical activity–exercise continuum exists. It demonstrates the specific nature of exercise and physical activity. How much activity, what type, how intense, and how often one should exercise are all important questions that should be considered before any exercise program is designed. In what follows, the terms exercise and physical activity are used interchangeably.

Components of Physical Fitness

Physical fitness is achieved when all of the physiological systems of the body are functioning efficiently to meet the physical demands of everyday activities. The components of physical fitness include muscular strength, muscular and cardiorespiratory endurance, flexibility, psychomotor ability, as well as body composition (Figure 9.1).

Muscular Strength

Muscular strength is commonly measured as a maximal value and can be defined as the ability of a muscle or muscle group to exert force against a resistance. Thus, strength and force are synonymous. The force generated by a muscular contraction may be applied against a movable object, as in weightlifting, or against a fixed object, such as the starting blocks in sprinting. Force is the product of mass times acceleration ($F = m \cdot a$) and when a force is applied through a distance (D), work (W) is accomplished ($W = F \cdot D$). It follows that the greater the mass of a muscle, the greater its capability of generating force (see Chapter 4). Think of sports that require great strength. Do the athletes that participate in these sports have large muscles?

Power

As defined in Chapter 4, **power** is the ability to overcome external resistance at a high rate of muscular contraction. It is the force that can be generated at speeds characteristic of the activity to overcome gravity (see discussion on gravity in Chapter 7) and thus accelerate the body or an implement. The ability to exert force is in turn dependent on muscular strength. Thus, power is an important derivative of muscular strength and is decisive in performance in most sports and many recreational activities (Figure 9.2; also see discussion on power in Chapter 4).

Muscular Endurance

Muscular endurance is defined as the ability of

Agonist–Antagonist Training

When planning training, care must be taken to include exercises that stimulate both the agonists (working muscles) and the antagonists (counter-acting muscles; see discussion on muscle teamwork in Chapter 3). A program that focuses only on increasing agonist strength tends to shorten the agonist muscles and weaken the antagonist muscles. This results in a change in the proportion of strength between agonists and antagonists which, under normal circumstances, is well balanced. This shift in strength equilibrium can result in impaired joint positions, and make articular cartilage and muscles (especially the tendons) prone to disease and injury.

Thus, a program that includes exercises to develop the biceps should also include exercises to enhance the triceps; trunk extensor training should be complemented with trunk flexor training. This approach to strength training is referred to as **agonist–antagonist training** (Figure 9.3).

To achieve a balanced development of strength your strength program must assure a balance between the training of agonists and antagonists.

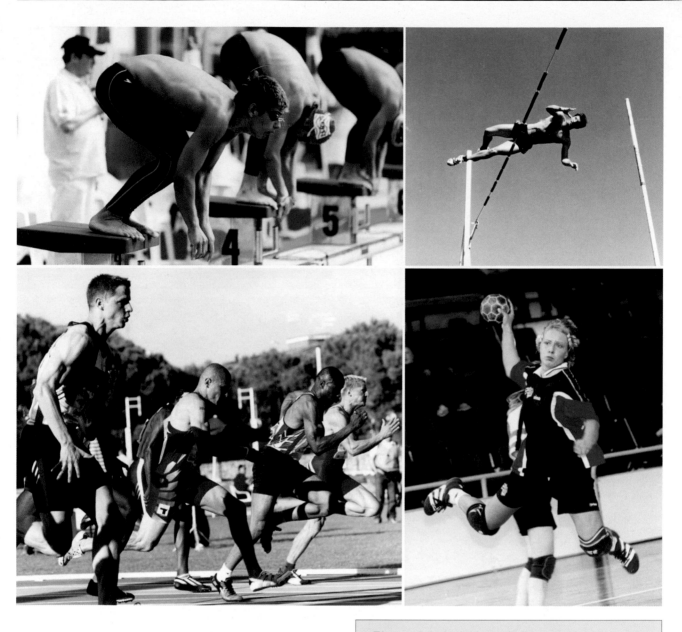

Figure 9.2 Activities requiring explosive power.

a muscle or muscle group to sustain a given level of force (static exercise) or to contract and relax (dynamic exercise) repeatedly at a given resistance. Static exercises involve sustained contractions, which often compromise blood flow. As a result, oxygen is rapidly used up and metabolic by-products accumulate causing fatigue. Performing a flexed arm hang will provide you with this experience. Your heart and lungs do not have much trouble performing during a flexed arm hang, but your arm muscles (local muscle group) feel a strong burning sensation and fatigue rapidly.

In contrast to static exercises, dynamic exercises involve continuous rhythmical contractions and relaxations that allow for oxygen to be continually delivered to the muscle and metabolic by-products to be removed. Thus, other physiological systems play a greater role and, depending upon intensity, fatigue may take longer to develop. For example, during cycling, in addition to your leg muscles requiring muscular endurance, your cardiorespiratory system is also involved. Exercises that employ large muscle groups for prolonged periods of time such as distance running, cross-

Figure 9.3 Agonist–antagonist training. **A.** Using partner-assisted exercises. **B.** Using free weights. **C.** Using one's own body weight.

country skiing, cycling, or swimming involve cardiorespiratory endurance, another important component of physical fitness (Figure 9.4).

Cardiorespiratory Endurance

As its name implies, **cardiorespiratory** (also called **cardiovascular**) **endurance** or **fitness** involves both the heart (cardio) and the lung (respiratory) systems. A major function of the cardiorespiratory system is to provide oxygen to the tissues. The maximal rate at which the body can take up, transport, and utilize oxygen is known as **aerobic power** or endurance which is expressed as maximal oxygen uptake or $\dot{V}O_2$max. $\dot{V}O_2$max is also the maximal rate of aerobic metabolism and is the single most important criterion of physical fitness (see discussion on aerobic power in Chapter 5).

Cardiorespiratory fitness is the ability to produce energy through an improved delivery of oxygen to the working muscles. It is needed for exertions over relatively longer periods of time regardless of the activity. It is intimately related to muscular endurance, as the working muscles rely on the oxygen supply sent by the pumping heart, delivered via the blood, and used by the muscles. The major improvements or training effects related to cardiorespiratory endurance were discussed in Chapter 5.

Maximal Oxygen Uptake ($\dot{V}O_2$max)

$\dot{V}O_2$max can be measured, estimated, or predicted in many ways. Measuring the $\dot{V}O_2$max of a person

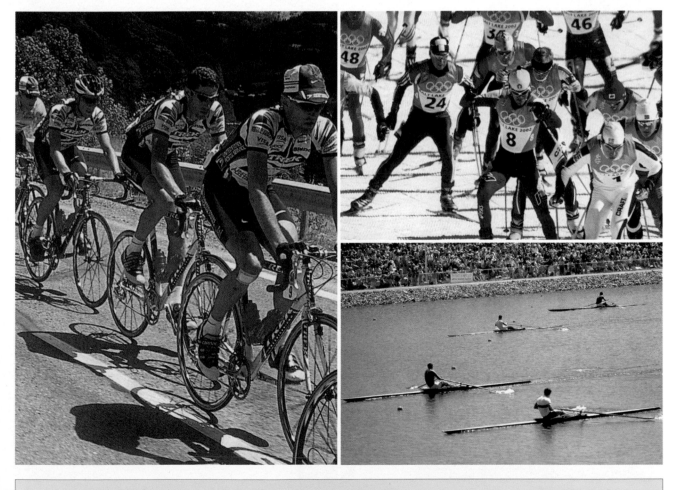

Figure 9.4 Performances in rowing, cycling, and cross-country skiing are based on muscular and cardiovascular endurance.

running on a treadmill involves having a person run at a given speed or workload for a few minutes (2-3 min) (Figure 9.5), while oxygen uptake or consumption is measured over a period of time (2-3 min) at each workload. The workload is gradually increased by increasing the speed or the treadmill slope. At each new workload, the individual demand for oxygen increases, i.e., as the workload is increased more oxygen is taken up by the lungs, delivered by the heart, and utilized by the muscles. However, eventually a point will be reached where the increased workload cannot be supported by an increase in oxygen uptake. Oxygen consumption is said to have reached a plateau or reached a maximal value. This plateau is known as one's $\dot{V}O_2max$.

Prediction of $\dot{V}O_2max$ With each new workload, as more oxygen is required, the heart will pump more blood, delivering more oxygen to the exercising muscles. Thus, at each new workload heart rate will also increase and eventually reach a maximal value. The linear relationship between heart rate and workload that exists over a given workload range is the basis for estimations or predictions of $\dot{V}O_2max$.

Absolute $\dot{V}O_2max$ $\dot{V}O_2$ is expressed in an absolute manner as a **volume per unit time**, litres per minute (L/min). In general, an **absolute $\dot{V}O_2max$** measurement is related to mass, especially muscle mass. Larger individuals usually have higher $\dot{V}O_2max$ values due to their greater muscle mass.

Figure 9.5 Testing for $\dot{V}O_2max$ can only be carried out in a laboratory setting.

Figure 9.6 Marathon runners are among the best when it comes to relative V̇O₂max.

For example, it is not uncommon for elite male rowers who are generally tall and muscular to have V̇O₂max values of approximately 6.0 L/min. In contrast, shorter and comparatively slighter runners might have V̇O₂max values of only 4.5 L/min.

Absolute measurements of V̇O₂max are useful for comparison within groups, but limited when comparing two groups that differ in mass or body composition.

Relative V̇O₂max To account for differences in mass, V̇O₂max can also be expressed in a relative manner, i.e., in relation to mass expressed in kilograms. Thus, when comparing two athletes playing different sports, it is often useful to divide their absolute V̇O₂max by their mass to obtain **relative V̇O₂max** values (Figure 9.6). When V̇O₂ is expressed relative to mass, the units used are expressed in **ml/kg/min**, thus indicating the consumed volume of oxygen in millilitres per kilogram of body weight per minute. Using our male rower and runner example, if the rower weighed 90 kg and the runner weighed 68 kg, then both have the same relative V̇O₂max, 66 ml/kg/min (this value was obtained by dividing their absolute V̇O₂max by their mass).

Flexibility

Have you ever wondered how gymnasts or ballet dancers perform the splits or arch their spines so far? This type of performance illustrates their ability to perform movements that require a great measure of **flexibility**.

Flexibility is defined as the ability of a joint to move through its full range of motion. Flexibility is determined primarily by joint structure and to a lesser extent by muscle elasticity and length.

Connective tissue is the most important part of muscle in terms of its flexibility. The main structural protein in connective tissues is **collagen**. Collagen fibres provide structure and support to tissues, ligaments, tendons, and joints. Collagen is a **triple helix** that can withstand very high tensile forces. In addition to collagen, another protein known as **elastin** provides an athlete with stretching ability.

A number of factors such as age, sex, and inactivity can affect flexibility. Just compare the level of flexibility of a young and active rhythmic gymnast (Figure 9.7) to that of an elderly person with arthritis. Flexibility promotes good joint health, slows joint deterioration, and generally improves quality of life for most individuals. It may

Figure 9.7 Rhythmic gymnasts are known for their extreme flexibility.

Figure 9.8 A. Active stretching. **B.** Passive stretching.

also prevent lower back pain and injuries as well as reduce the frequency and severity of injuries.

Active and Passive Flexibility

Flexibility can be active or passive. **Active flexibility** is the range of movement generated by individual effort, while **passive flexibility** is the range of movement achieved with the help of external forces (a partner, weight, rubber band, etc.). Passive flexibility exercises help achieve a wider range of movement than do active flexibility exercises (Figure 9.8).

Stretching Methods

There are three stretching methods: the static, dynamic, and proprioceptive neuromuscular facilitation methods.

Static Stretching Static stretching refers to holding a fully stretched position, such as the splits. Using this method, an athlete slowly relaxes the muscles to be stretched and holds himself/herself in a stretched position over 10-30 seconds. The process may be enhanced by an assisting

partner. The process is repeated four to six times for maximal efficiency.

Dynamic Stretching Dynamic or ballistic stretching refers to rapidly moving a joint through its full range of motion, such as the arm of a baseball pitcher. The method involves stretching with repetitive bouncing movements using small intervals, rather than just one pull. An athlete begins the first repetition over a relatively small range of joint motion, gradually increasing the amplitude range, reaching the maximal range after 10-20 movements. The process is then repeated three to five times, using body weight or an assisting partner (Figure 9.9).

Pre-stretching The pre-stretching or proprioceptive neuromuscular facilitation (PNF) method exploits the natural protective reflex of the muscle and its tendon sensors – the muscle spindles and golgi tendon organs. It is regarded as the most efficient stretching method.

The PNF method is carried out in three phases with a partner.

Strength Training and Flexibility

Some exercises may have a dual training effect by developing both strength and flexibility. Arm raising exercises from the mat, for instance, involve little stretching; when performed from the bench, however, the same exercise allows for a far larger range and thus promotes the stretching of the pectoral muscles in particular. Half-knee bends, if overused, cause the quadriceps to shorten; deep-knee bends help stretch them.

It is for this reason that weightlifters, who must often assume very deep squatting positions to clean or snatch heavy loads, have extremely elastic leg muscles. Similarly, competitive swimmers develop extreme flexibility in their shoulder girdles. Such examples show that, under certain conditions, the same exercises may develop both strength and flexibility. However, the movement range around a joint must always be exploited to its full capacity. If not, muscle stretching will not occur; indeed, the muscle may shorten, and strength training may then lead to impaired flexibility. To achieve optimal flexibility through strength training, you must exploit the full range of joint movement that can be achieved during any given exercise.

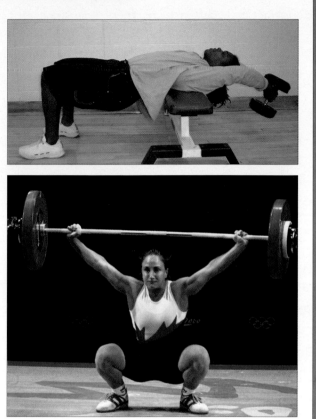

- During the first **active stretching phase**, the muscles to be stretched are actively pulled to the very limit of the movement range. This initial stretching movement should be performed slowly and continuously. This prevents the muscle spindles from initiating the stretching reflex and thus contracting the muscles.

Figure 9.9 Partner-assisted dynamic stretching.

- In the second **pre-tension phase**, the trainee exerts a full static resistance (a strong isometric contraction) against partner resistance for approximately seven seconds. This causes the tendon golgi organs to release inhibitory impulses which in turn cause an involuntary relaxation of the muscles to be stretched.

- In the third **passive stretching phase**, the partner pushes the body further into a stretched position almost to the point of pain. This final position is then held, with all muscles relaxed, for approximately six seconds. The partner's pressure must be applied slowly and constantly in order to prevent muscle spindles from initiating a reflex contraction, which may cause injury.

Body Composition

Body composition refers to the amounts of body constituents, such as fat, muscle, bone, and other organs, and is regarded as one of the major components of physical fitness. Of particular interest are percentages of lean body mass and fat body mass. Typically, an active physically fit individual has a lower percentage of body fat than an inactive unfit person. The large number of overweight young people in our society is a cause for concern. Any fitness program, strength or cardiovascular, should be designed with an aim to help reduce body fat. For detailed information about body composition, weight management, and the effects of obesity see Chapter 12.

Psychomotor Ability

Successful athletes appear to move effortlessly. In addition, they can respond easily or readily to changes in their surroundings. To accomplish this, athletes must monitor their environment, collect information, make decisions, and execute their movements. It is their **psychomotor ability** that allows them to complete these tasks quickly and accurately.

A high level of psychomotor ability serves to integrate the workings of the central nervous

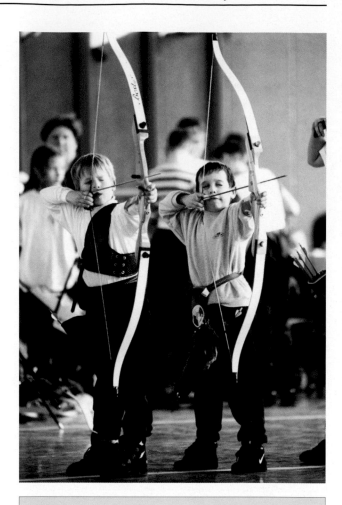

Figure 9.10 Archery requires hand steadiness as well as undivided concentration.

system with the more physical components of fitness. The body constantly monitors both its internal and external environments, collecting information and making decisions about what is relevant information and what is irrelevant information.

The psychomotor domain may seem an unimportant component of physical fitness; however, it is of utmost importance to effective functioning in all environments.

Psychomotor abilities are many. The most significant ones are reaction time and anticipation, visual skills, hand–eye coordination, perception, attention and concentration, balance, proprioception or muscle feeling, memory processes and recall, and decision making (Figure 9.10). These abilities are presented in more detail in Chapter 16.

Components and Principles of Fitness Programs

Fitness training programs are based on several closely related training components. These components follow well-established training principles that are intended to generate optimal adaptation and performance improvements of trainees. These components and their principles are the subjects of this section of the chapter.

The following interrelated training components should be considered when designing a comprehensive fitness program: training time, frequency of exercise, intensity of exercise, volume of training, work-to-rest ratio, and the type of exercise. Strength training also involves other components vital to effective training: the order of exercises used, number of repetitions per set and number of sets, and the recovery or rest periods between exercises.

Training Components

Training Time

Training time refers to the total time devoted to developing fitness. It is based on duration of each training session and the frequency of training during a week, month, or year.

Training Frequency

Training frequency depends on an individual's goals, abilities, and fitness level. Normally, an athlete undertakes 3-10 strength and cardiorespiratory training sessions per week, depending on the needs of his or her particular sports activity.

Depending on the overall goal of fitness training, recreational athletes normally perform 2-6 sessions per week. If the goal is to maintain certain levels of fitness, 2-3 sessions per week are sufficient; however, if the goal is to reduce weight or to increase strength and/or cardiorespiratory fitness, 4-6 sessions are necessary.

Training Volume

Training volume is one of the most important components of training. It refers to the sum total of work performed during a training session or phase of training and is measured in various units depending upon the type of activity. In cyclic movements (walking, running, swimming, and so on), the total distance (in metres or kilometres) in one workout or several workouts represents the volume of training.

For various strength exercises using body weight, the volume may refer to (a) the number of all repetitions of each exercise (20 push-ups) or (b) the sum total of all repetitions during a workout (for example, 200 repetitions using 10 different exercises within one circuit training session).

For weightlifting exercises using a barbell, the volume is calculated on the basis of (a) the sum total of all weight lifted per training session (for example, 4.5 tons using 8 exercises) and (b) the number of repetitions performed with a given load (for example, 6 x 80 kg, or 3 x 6 x 80 kg).

Training Intensity

Training intensity is probably the most important component of strength training. Generally, it characterizes the degree of stimulation intensity of exercise per unit of time. It is measured in various units depending on the type of activity, as follows:

Distance Covered: metres per second (m/s) and kilometres per hour (km/h) for cyclic activities, such as running, cross-country skiing, cycling, etc.

Resistance to Be Overcome: kilograms (kg) lifted per unit of time (kg/min; kg/30 min, etc.) in weightlifting using barbells, dumbbells, etc.

Frequency of Movements: rate per unit of time for acyclic activities, such as gymnastics, figure skating, diving, ski jumping, ball games, etc. (Figure 9.11).

Training intensity is always expressed as a

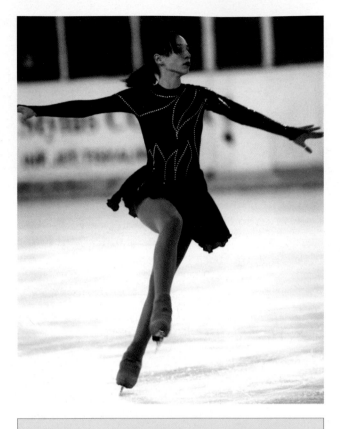

Figure 9.11 In figure skating, the intensity of training is measured by the total number of repetitions of a movement per unit of time (5 min, 10 min, 30 min, etc.).

Work-to-Rest Ratio

A **work-to-rest ratio** refers to the relationship between the phases of work and rest during training. It is not possible to work continuously without a break throughout a training session unless the intensity of exercise is relatively low. Generally, the lower the intensity of exercise per unit of time the shorter the rest periods required by the working trainee. Conversely, the higher the intensity of exercise per unit of time the longer the rest periods that must be scheduled.

A trainee's heart rate is normally used to determine the length of rest between individual sets and/or series of exercises. Depending upon the fitness level of the trainee, after an incomplete recovery period of about 30-180 seconds, the heart rate may drop to about 120-140 beats per minute, at which point exercising can resume.

Training intensity must always be considered in connection with the other components of training, such as the volume of exercise and type of exercises used. Some of these relationships are presented in Figure 9.12.

percentage of a trainee's personal best or 100 percent performance in the activity when converted to the units of measurement described previously. This performance becomes the benchmark, the starting point, for defining the various ranges of relative intensities used in planning workouts.

1RM

In strength training, for example, a 100 percent performance expressed in kilograms is the trainee's maximal performance in one repetition trial (**1RM**) for a specific lift or exercise (for more on 1RM see Chapter 4). The load intensity of strength training expressed as a certain percentage of the 1RM represents an athlete's necessary effort in training. Thus, the 100 percent performance or 1RM of the athlete becomes the starting point for defining the various ranges of relative intensities used in the planning of training.

How Much Rest?

In general, training programs (methods) designed to improve endurance require relatively short rests when the intensity of exercise is relatively low. Training programs (methods) designed to improve speed and power require exercising at relatively high intensity levels with extended rest intervals to allow almost complete recovery.

Type of Exercise

The type of physical exercises used in fitness programs is a decisive component for fitness development. Exercises may differ considerably in their spatial and dynamic structure, and in their complexity and difficulty. In strength training, for example, multiple possibilities of load selection can be achieved by exercises using an athlete's own body weight, partner exercises (Figure 9.13), and exercise with weights (i.e., dumbbells, round

Figure 9.12 Diagrams showing the relationships between **A.** intensity and volume of exercise and **B.** distance/time and speed of running.

Figure 9.13 Partner exercises are cheap, effective, and fun.

weights, barbells, body weight) and, of course, various strength training machines, such as Nautilus, Universal Gym, Hercules, etc.

In cardiorespiratory fitness training one can choose from running on the track, running in parks and on beaches (sand), running the bleachers, hill running, etc. Each running environment provides different intensity stimuli that can be effectively explored and incorporated in one's fitness program.

Warm-up and Cool-down

Loosening-up and relaxation exercises before training and after training facilitate physical and mental relaxation, and also reduce and sometimes eliminate the potentially harmful effects of training (Figure 9.14). The warm-up procedure prepares the body and mind for the exercise activity by:

(1) raising the body temperature, increasing respiration and heart rate, and increasing blood flow, metabolic rate, and oxygen exchange;

(2) increasing range of movement thus decreasing muscle tension and guarding against muscle, tendon, and ligament strains; and

(3) increasing central nervous system activity, which coordinates the trainee's movements, reduces the time of motor reaction, and improves coordination.

The cool-down procedure is particularly important after vigorous exercising. A proper cool-down helps a trainee recover more quickly by helping physiological systems return to their normal levels faster.

Other Components of Training

Other components of training that must also be considered include exercise speed, number of repetitions and sets, order of exercising, and number of exercises used.

Exercise Speed Exercise speed is particularly important. Lower exercise speeds promote an increase in the muscle diameter (for more on

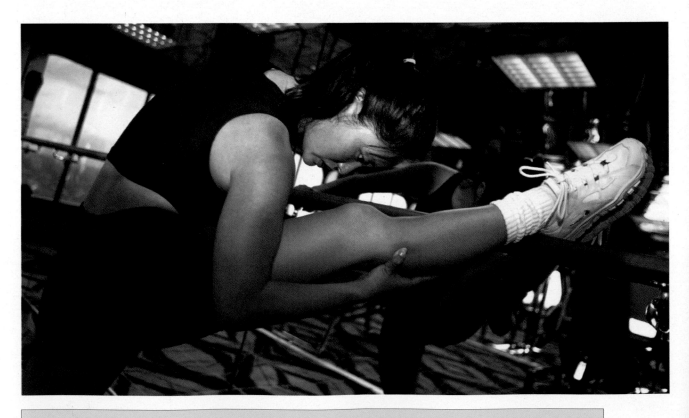

Figure 9.14 Loosening-up exercises are most beneficial after an exhausting exercise session.

muscle hypertrophy see Figure 4.9 in Chapter 4), whereas brisk exercise speeds develop power or muscular explosiveness.

Number of Repetitions The number of repetitions and sets used is dependent upon the training method chosen and a trainee's performance level and goals. Generally, a lower number of repetitions per set promotes development of maximal strength and power, i.e., 5-12 repetitions are recommended for the increase of muscle diameter, 1-3 repetitions are sufficient to improve intra-muscle coordination. A greater number of repetitions causes fatigue and is suitable for muscle endurance-type training.

Variety of Exercise The variety of exercise and the respective order of exercises within a training session must also be considered. The variety of exercises depends on the overall goal. Recreational athletes seeking to develop all-round strength of as many muscle groups as possible may train with over 40 different strength exercises.

Competitive athletes striving to develop strength capacities that are sport- or event-specific may find 3-5 exercises adequate. Weightlifters customarily include 8-12 different exercises in their regular training program. In comparison, bodybuilders use the greatest number of exercises by far in their training regimen, as they target almost all muscles of the body.

Principles of Fitness Training

Strength training is a fairly complicated process involving various pedagogical, biological, and psychological principles at many levels. Put into practice, these principles underlie a systematic approach to training and provide the necessary methodological guidelines. They should never be considered in isolation, but must be mastered and applied as a whole. They determine training in all its aspects: content, means, method, and organization. Training principles are not immutable laws, but in as much as they reflect general experience and successful practice, they embody values important to the coaches and

From Greek Mythology

In his youth Milon of Croton (disciple of Pythagoras, scholar, and multiple Olympic wrestling champion in ancient Greece) decided to become the strongest man on earth. To achieve this he lifted and carried a calf every day. As the calf grew and became heavier Milon's body adapted to the growing weight of the animal and became increasingly stronger. When the calf had grown into a bull and Milon a man, he had become the strongest man of his time.

athletes alike. Four of the more important training principles are presented in this section.

Progressive Resistance or Overload Principle

The **overload principle** is based on a simple observation: new and progressively higher training demands enable athletes to adapt their physical and mental functions to increase performance capacity. After a period of time, an overloaded muscle will increase its strength and at some point the level of stress that was previously considered stressful or an overload will no longer provide an adequate overload stimulus. Thus, what was once an overload has now become a "normal load." To ensure the muscles/systems are being adequately overloaded, resistance should be periodically increased. Hence the principle of **progressive resistance**.

There are various ways of increasing load, depending on one's fitness level and the particular method of training used. For example, training volumes that may be maximal for a beginner may not be sufficient for an advanced athlete even to

How to Overload

One way to determine whether to increase the load is by judging the number of times a given weight can be lifted before causing fatigue. For example, if one starts lifting 25 kg 10 times and, after training for a length of time (two to five sessions), one can lift the same weight 15 times, then to increase muscle strength, the load should be increased to what can be lifted maximally (until exhaustion) 10 times. This new weight will most likely be 30 kg. This ensures that the muscles are working in the overload zone and the "signals" that stimulate adaptation are being sent to the muscles.

maintain his or her current performance level or capacity.

Generally speaking, an increase in training load affects all training components. However, training volume and training intensity are of special importance. Training load can be increased gradually or abruptly.

Gradual Load Increase Increasing training load gradually in small steps is recommended for beginners and recreational trainees. The training load is increased from one training cycle to another in small steps. An example is shown in the box *How to Overload*. In general, all training and individual exercises should be performed to the point of fatigue. Gradual training load increase also depends on training frequency, volume, and intensity, in that order.

Explosive Load Increase Abrupt or explosive increase in training load is especially effective in more serious training for competition. To training athletes this method provides an important complement to gradual load increase. It requires a substantial increase in volume or intensity of training (or both) from one training cycle to another. Coaching experience has shown that much higher training load demands make explosive load increase highly effective.

Reversibility Principle

This principle implies the avoidance of long interruptions in the training process. Interruptions in training have a negative effect and result in stagnation or even decline of performance. With a loss of training time, cardiorespiratory and muscular endurance performance decline faster than maximal strength or power performance.

The loss in performance due to training interruption applies to coordination and technical and tactical skills and abilities, as well as to the overall standard of performance, because all these factors are interrelated.

An athlete's training experience also has a bearing on the stagnation process due to interruption in training. Athletes who have trained over many years are more resistant to performance loss than beginners. Highly trained athletes also tend to make up for loss in performance relatively quickly.

Specificity of Exercise Principle

Coaches often state "you play the way you practice" or "practice does not make perfect, it makes permanent." These statements are true and illustrate the principle of specificity. This principle states that the response(s) to exercise is specific to the nature or type of exercise performed. What this means is that if we wish to increase a particular fitness parameter, we must train that parameter in as specific a manner as possible. The principle of specificity applies to the specificity of strength, muscular and cardiorespiratory endurance, coordination, speed of movement, and motor patterns. Specificity should also take into account joint angles, neuromuscular components, and the speed of muscle contraction as well as the type of contraction. The point of this principle is that specific exercises cause specific physiological responses. Several examples of specificity are presented in the box on the following page.

Periodization of Training Principle

Periodization is a systematic division of the training year into periods that allow a coach to

When You Exercise for Performance, Be Specific!

- If you work out by pushing against immovable walls (static contractions), you will get strong at pushing walls but not at lifting weights, which requires dynamic contractions.

- It makes little sense for basketball players to practice shooting at an 8-foot basket if they have to shoot at a 10-foot one in a game.

- Running at 75 percent speed during training may help one learn what to do, but it provides little help when your opponent forces you to run at full speed.

- If one has to lift and/or move a 90-kg opponent, as in rugby, wrestling, or football, it makes little sense to work with a 70-kg dummy during training. Likewise, bench pressing 75 kg will not be suitable in terms of specific strength demand and will provide little help during a game/event situation.

- Sprinters are very good at running sprints or short distances. However, they are generally not very good at playing wide receiver in football due to the specificity of coordination (skill of catching the ball at full speed). In addition, running sprinters are also not very good at swimming sprints. Why? Specificity!

- Sprinters will do themselves little good if they train by running long distances.

prepare players to perform at their optimum during competition (Table 9.1). There are three major periods in the training year: preparatory (PP), competition (CP), and transition periods (TP).

The individual periods are further subdivided into macro-cycles (two to six weeks), micro-cycles (seven days), daily cycles (one to two training sessions), and training sessions (one to two hours).

The periodization principle can be applied to longer or shorter training cycles that are typical for high school and university sports schedules. Table 9.2 gives examples of possible periodization variations of different duration. Notice the changing relationships between preparatory and competition phases as the training cycles become shorter.

Preparation Period The prime objective of this period is the development of a high level of fitness on which the trainee can build in future periods. This stage is characterized by a gradual and progressive increase of volume of exercise (overload principle) at medium intensity levels.

Competitive Period One goal in the competitive period (league games, playoffs) is to maintain the level of fitness achieved in the preparation period. Both volume and intensity of fitness work are reduced as the main emphasis of this period is on sport-specific skill and tactics training.

Transition Period The transition period is relatively short, about two to four weeks, and is designed to offer the athlete a necessary break from

Table 9.1 Division of the training season into periods and sub-periods.

Periodization	Training Period						
	Transition	Preparation		Competition			
	Transition	General Preparation	Specific Preparation	Pre-competition	Competition	Taper	Playoff

Table 9.2 Periodization of training.

Training Cycle	Training Period			
	Transition (wks)	Preparation (wks)	Competition (wks)	
			1st stage	2nd stage
12 months (52 weeks)	5	32	9	6
8 months (35 weeks)	4	20	5	6
6 months (26 weeks)	3	13	5	5
4 months (18 weeks)	2	8	3	5

Ratio between preparation and competition periods:

12 months approx. 70% : 30%
8 months approx. 65% : 35%
6 months approx. 55% : 45%
4 months approx. 50% : 50%

competition and intensive training. However, it is recommended that this time be used for recreation and circuit training activities to ensure that strength and muscular and cardiorespiratory endurance do not drop significantly.

Designing Fitness Training Programs

The major fitness training methods are presented in Table 9.3. These methods are designed to develop various forms of specific and general fitness. Strength and muscular endurance are developed by strength training methods, whereas aerobic and anaerobic capacity or fitness are developed by cardiovascular training methods. If combined, the two methods can improve overall fitness.

Resistance Training

Station Training

Station or dynamic resistance training promotes the development of strength by using free weights (popular with serious athletes) and strength training exercise machines with constant or variable resistance (popular with recreational

athletes). **Station training** refers to the completion of all the sets of one exercise before moving to the next exercise. When performing a series of sets within a station, the same muscle groups are stressed over and over again. The optimal training stimulus for strength development is moderate to high intensity, 60-100 percent of 1RM. Therefore, this type of training requires relatively longer breaks between sets. And finally, it is important that any station training program be based on the agonist–antagonist training principle discussed at the beginning of the chapter.

The use of heavy free weights requires excellent lifting techniques, expert spotting, and well-maintained equipment. Since all of these requirements are rarely met in school programs, no further discussion on the method is provided here.

Circuit Training

Circuit training is an exercise program that allows an individual to combine specific exercises to achieve specific fitness goals. It embraces a number of carefully selected exercises designed to work all major muscle groups – legs, abdominals, arms, shoulders, back, and trunk – in one session. This aspect of circuit training is illustrated by the circuit training layout in Figure 9.15.

Table 9.3 An overview of fitness training methods and their effects.

Training Method	Training Effect
Resistance Training • Station training • Circuit training	Strength fitness Strength and muscular endurance fitness

Cardiorespiratory Training
• Endurance training
• Fartlek training
• Interval training
   - extensive interval
   - intensive interval
• Tempo or repetition training
	Aerobic fitness
	Aerobic fitness
	
	Aerobic* and anaerobic fitness
	Aerobic and anaerobic* fitness
	Activity-specific aerobic and anaerobic fitness

Combination Training • Combo circuit training • Cross training	Strength* and aerobic fitness Cardiorespiratory fitness

* *emphasized fitness development*

A circuit training program is a valuable and effective method of exercising used in many sports. By manipulating training components presented in previous sections you can improve strength, muscular endurance, and cardiovascular endurance to varying degrees. With creativity and originality, a circuit exercise program can be designed that is difficult enough to challenge athletes at various levels. It can also be easily and very effectively incorporated into school physical education and athletic programs, as well as provide a valuable approach to fitness development for anyone whose objectives are to improve general fitness or lose weight.

Circuit Training Variables The major variables of circuit training programs include the number of exercises, sequence of exercises,

Guidelines for Designing an Exercise Program

- Set ambitious but realistic goals for each training session; every effort should be made to fulfill them.

- Schedule training sessions and record the performance achieved.

- Take note of the relationship between load, fatigue, and recovery during the planning and performance stages of training.

- Increase the training load according to training load principles.

- To avoid injury, warm up before training and cool down after exercise.

- Increase the training load properly, bearing in mind the relationship between the various training components. Concentrate on essentials.

- Train over the whole year for several years. Avoid discontinuation of training, which may lead to stagnation and loss of performance.

- Monitor the quality of performance in each training session.

- Participate regularly in competitive contests. Compare the results achieved with the goals set.

#1 Arms/Shoulders

Dips

Stepping Exercises

Push-ups

Pull-ups

Legs Fixed

CIRCUIT

Jumping Exercises

Knee Bending Exercises

TRAINING

**Leg Raises
(Trunk Fixed)**

#3

Back

**Back Extensions
(Legs Fixed)**

Trunk Fixed

...up Exercise

...bdominals #4

Figure 9.15 General layout of a circuit training program.

number of trips around the circuit, number of repetitions, resistance levels, rest period between sets and circuits, and types of exercises.

- **Number of Stations** The circuit may consist of 6-18 stations of different exercises. Circuits with 8-12 stations are most popular. In a typical circuit exercise program, each muscle group may be successfully exercised by several different exercises. The number of exercises per muscle group depends on the trainee's needs and the training effect to be achieved.

- **Exercise Sequence** The loading of the main muscle groups changes as the trainee moves from one station to another. The sequence of exercises is arranged so that no two consecutive exercises involve the same muscle group. Thus, a set to develop the arm extensor muscles could be followed by a set to exercise the leg extensors. This, in turn, can be followed by exercises to develop the abdominals, and so on.

- **Number of Laps** A circuit is normally repeated one to three times. Competitive athletes may perform up to six laps during the preparation period.

- **Number of Repetitions and Level of Resistance** The number of repetitions per exercise depends on the objective of training: muscular endurance development requires 8-15 repetitions per exercise using 30-60 percent resistance; strength development requires 2-4 repetitions per exercise at 80-90 percent resistance.

- **Recovery Between Exercises** The recovery between exercises and laps depends on the training objectives: for muscular endurance development relatively short or no recovery is planned (the trainee moves from one exercise station to another with no interruption in exercising); for strength development the rest intervals are longer, allowing good recovery between exercise sets and circuit laps.

- **Types of Exercises** Circuit training can be carried out by using a great variety of means: own body weight, partner-assisted exercises, medicine balls, dumbbells, barbells, and exercise machines.

Popular Circuits The structure of three popular circuit training programs is shown in Table 9.4.

Table 9.4 General structure of three popular circuits designed for general or specific fitness development for school or club programs.

Variation 1
- 10-12 exercise stations
- 30 s on, 30-60 s off (perform as many repetitions as possible in 30 s; followed by 30 s recovery)
- instructor uses whistle to indicate start and end of exercising; commands can be pre-recorded
- trainee records number of repetitions achieved/station (example: 15/7)

Variation 2
- 10-12 exercise stations
- 10-15 repetitions at each station
- set exercise time to 10 minutes
- no recovery between stations
- trainee records number of laps and number of exercises achieved in the last lap (example: 2/7)

Variation 3
- 10-12 exercise stations
- 10-15 repetitions at each station
- no recovery between stations
- trainee records total time achieved per circuit (example: 8:27 min)

Cardiorespiratory Training

The interaction among the components of training, notably training volume and training intensity, is reflected in the various training methods, which characteristically use different ranges of relative intensity. The transition between these ranges of intensity is fluid and is reflected in the four basic training methods: endurance, Fartlek, interval, and repetition (Figure 9.16).

Endurance Training

Endurance training, also known as **continuous training** or **slow long distance (SLD) training**, involves training at approximately 40-60 percent of maximal performance ability over a long distance. Typically, SLD training is carried out without a break (Figure 9.17 A). The intensity and duration of exercise are typically "conversational," whereby the trainees are able to talk without undue respiratory distress.

The physiological benefits derived from SLD training primarily include enhanced aerobic capacity and development of staying power. Psychological benefits include increased determination and self-confidence, and the ability to resist fatigue and mobilize oneself for hard sustained work.

The major objective of SLD training is to develop a solid fitness base during the preparatory season. Many athletes use it in the transitory season as well. The SLD training method combined with Fartlek training (Table 9.5), discussed in the next section, forms the bulk of fitness training of many competitive and recreational athletes.

Fartlek Training

Fartlek is an endurance training method used by runners mainly during the preparatory season. It is designed to develop basic endurance using an extremely flexible training program that can be done just about anywhere, any time, and all year.

Table 9.5 Sample training week for a serious high school cross-country program during the preparatory phase of training.

Sunday	Monday	Tuesday	Wednesday	Thursday	Friday	Saturday
Rest	40-60 min SLD	40-50 min Fartlek training	40 min SLD	20-25 min extensive interval	40-50 min SLD	40-50 min Fartlek training

Table 9.6 Sample Fartlek training session for a high school cross-country program.

Preparation Phase	Main Body Phase	Conclusion Phase
• Stretch • 10-min easy run	• 100 m at race pace • 2 min easy • 250 m at fast pace • 3 min easy • 400 m at fast pace • 3 min easy • 50 m at all-out pace • 4 min easy • 300 m at race pace • 3 min easy • 600 m at fast pace	• 10-min easy run • Stretch

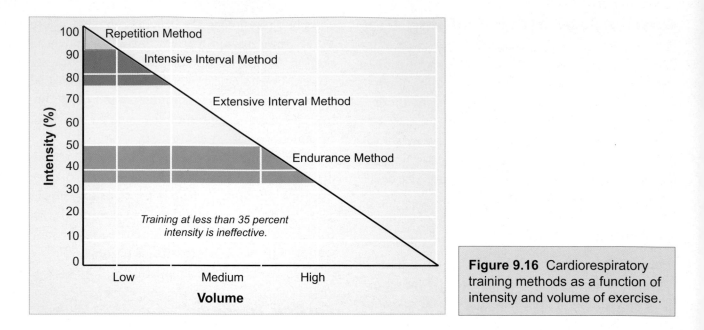

Figure 9.16 Cardiorespiratory training methods as a function of intensity and volume of exercise.

Fartlek combines long slow distance training, pace/tempo training, and interval training. It involves easy running, fast bursts of running of varying lengths, hill running, and running on the beach, parks, streets, etc. (Table 9.6). This basic format can also be applied to cycling, swimming, cross-country skiing, and skating. Because it is such a diverse workout you can create a Fartlek training program for yourself or challenge an exercise partner to come up with a new workout every other week.

Interval Training

Aerobic and anaerobic capacity or fitness (discussed in Chapters 5 and 6) are most effectively developed by interval training, which involves the systematic alternation of exertion and recovery. The constant repetition of physical stress causes continuous breakdown of high-energy substances in the working muscles, and at the same time generates an ongoing increase in the build-up of fatigue.

We distinguish between extensive and intensive interval training methods.

Extensive Interval This method requires the trainee to carry out a great number of repetitions of selected distance in one session (Figure 9.17 B) with a recovery period equal to the work interval, thereby keeping the work-to-rest ratio (W:R) at 1:1-2 between intervals and 1:2-4 between sets. Each exercise (running, cycling, swimming, or cross-country skiing) is repeated 20-30 times. The repetitions are divided into several sets (Figure 9.17 B). The training intensity in the extensive interval method is higher than in the previous two (SLD and Fartlek training). It is between 60-80 percent of the trainee's maximal performance

Commonly Asked Questions About Fartlek

- **What's in the name?** Fartlek is a Swedish word meaning "speed play" or "playing with speed."

- **How often?** Once a week almost all year round; more often (two or three times per week) during the preparatory season.

- **What intensity and how far or how long?** Depending on your feeling at the time, you can go as fast or as slow for as short or as long as you wish.

- **What rest?** For beginners, run slowly until you're breathing comfortably (conversational pace) before starting the next speed surge.

- **Where?** Fartlek can be done anywhere and in a variety of different ways.

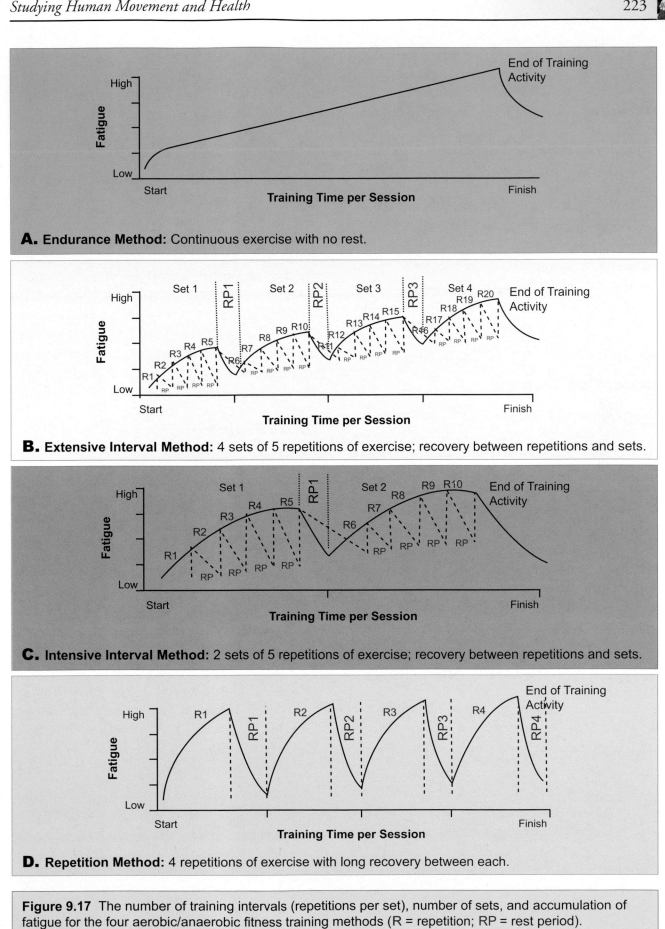

A. **Endurance Method:** Continuous exercise with no rest.

B. **Extensive Interval Method:** 4 sets of 5 repetitions of exercise; recovery between repetitions and sets.

C. **Intensive Interval Method:** 2 sets of 5 repetitions of exercise; recovery between repetitions and sets.

D. **Repetition Method:** 4 repetitions of exercise with long recovery between each.

Figure 9.17 The number of training intervals (repetitions per set), number of sets, and accumulation of fatigue for the four aerobic/anaerobic fitness training methods (R = repetition; RP = rest period).

capacity. This method predominately stresses the development of the aerobic energy system.

Intensive Interval This method features an overall lower training volume – each interval is repeated 10-20 times – than the extensive interval method, performed at a higher intensity level, 80-90 percent of the trainee's maximal performance capacity (Figure 9.17 C). Each interval taxes the individual close to VO_2max. Therefore it requires longer breaks: W:R is approximately 1:2-3 between intervals and 1:4-6 between sets.

Because intensive interval training is very demanding, it should not be practiced until a solid fitness base of aerobic training has been attained through previously discussed methods.

Repetition Training

Repetition or tempo training is conducted at maximal intensity levels. The method mimics competition pace and intensity and is therefore used by athletes in the final preparations for competition. The duration of exercise at all-out intensity level is normally longer than the ones in interval training. It often extends to the entire competition distance. Long recovery periods are needed between individual bouts, causing the W:R to be approximately 1:5 or longer (Figure 9.17 D). An example of a training week with repetition training is shown in Table 9.7.

Combination Training

Combination training programs offer multiple benefits for the trainee. They simultaneously develop both muscular and cardiorespiratory fitness.

These programs are particularly popular with recreational athletes, who use them all year round. Because of their general nature, serious athletes use them only in the transition period.

Combo Circuit Training

In addition to strength exercises, a circuit may include running laps between stations. The distance of the running segment may vary between 50-400 metres depending on the available facility and specific needs of the trainee. If, for example, a soccer or football team goes through a circuit program (using partner exercises, Figure 9.18) on the field, each run may involve running once around the track, i.e., 400 m; in comparison, a basketball team doing the same circuit on a basketball court may run once around the gym, covering only about 50 m.

Cross Training

Cross training involves activities that offer aerobic fitness benefits similar to those offered by running. In addition, it can also promote total body fitness and may help prevent overuse injuries. Runners often use this method when recovering from injuries.

Cross training is popular among competitive athletes during the transition period. To provide variety and prevent boredom and burnout, recreational athletes use cross training throughout the year.

Aerobic cross training may involve cycling, swimming, cross-country skiing, water running, and skating. **Muscular endurance cross training** may involve working on a rowing machine, StairMaster, cycling ergometer, and NordicTrack

Table 9.7 Sample training week for a serious high school cross-country program during the competition phase of training (one week prior to competition).

Sunday	Monday	Tuesday	Wednesday	Thursday	Friday	Saturday
Rest	40-50 min Fartlek training	40-50 min SLD	40 min extensive interval	20-25 min intensive interval	40-50 min SLD	20-30 min repetition

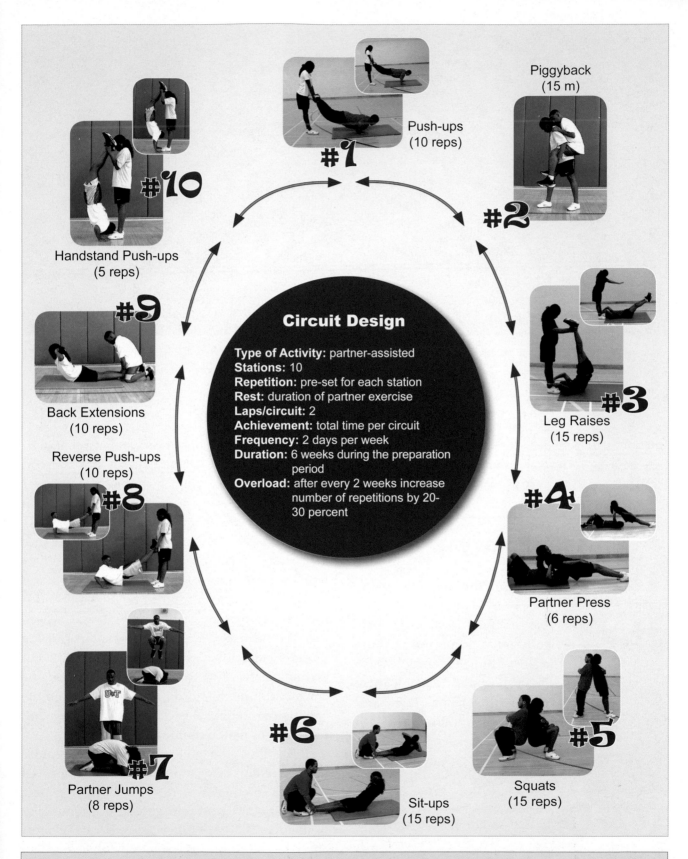

Push-ups
(10 reps)

Piggyback
(15 m)

#1

#2

Handstand Push-ups
(5 reps)

#10

#9

Back Extensions
(10 reps)

Reverse Push-ups
(10 reps)

#3

Leg Raises
(15 reps)

#4

Partner Press
(6 reps)

#8

#7

Partner Jumps
(8 reps)

#6

Sit-ups
(15 reps)

#5

Squats
(15 reps)

Circuit Design

Type of Activity: partner-assisted
Stations: 10
Repetition: pre-set for each station
Rest: duration of partner exercise
Laps/circuit: 2
Achievement: total time per circuit
Frequency: 2 days per week
Duration: 6 weeks during the preparation
period
Overload: after every 2 weeks increase
number of repetitions by 20-
30 percent

Figure 9.18 Sample circuit with partner-assisted exercises for high school varsity teams' general fitness development. For partner-assisted exercises it is important that team members form partner pairs of similar size.

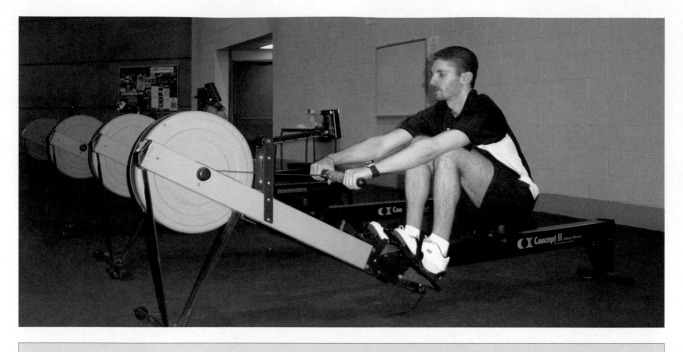

Figure 9.19 Working on a Concept II rowing machine requires little skill but provides great fitness benefits.

(Figure 9.19). **Activity cross training** may involve participating in several different activities (Figure 9.20).

Summary

The concept of physical fitness deals with factors that have a positive impact on your lifestyle, helping to maintain and significantly improve your health through active living. Physical fitness encompasses many components that are important for health, including strength, power, endurance,

Figure 9.20 Cross training involving many different activities is a good way to achieve total body fitness.

flexibility, body composition, and psychomotor abilities. Resistance training using free weights, exercise machines, your own body weight, or partner-assisted exercises can be used to develop and maintain muscular strength.

One measure of cardiorespiratory endurance is maximal oxygen uptake, or $\dot{V}O_2$max. $\dot{V}O_2$max represents the maximal volume of oxygen that can be supplied to and consumed by the body and is the most important criterion of physical fitness. Relative $\dot{V}O_2$max is a useful way of comparing the cardiovascular fitness of athletes across different disciplines. Cardiorespiratory endurance can be enhanced through four different types of training: endurance training, Fartlek, interval training, and repetition or tempo training.

Flexibility, the ability of a joint to move through its full range of motion, can be improved by three methods: static stretching, dynamic stretching, and proprioceptive neuromuscular facilitation (PNF). PNF is considered the most effective technique. Psychomotor abilities (e.g., reaction time, coordination, concentration, and balance) help an athlete monitor and respond to his or her environment.

How Fast Should I Go?

How much exercise is enough to maintain or improve health fitness? Two simple measures can be used to answer this question: the breath sound check and the talk test.

If you wish to maintain or improve your general health, moderate intensity activity is adequate. The **breath sound check** is an easy way to determine when this minimum level of activity has been reached. You want to reach your **ventilatory threshold**, which is the point at which you just start to hear your breathing. In other words, you should be able to hear your breathing when you perform aerobic exercise.

The **talk test** is based on the principle that you should be able to carry on a conversation while exercising. If you find that you have difficulty talking and are out of breath, you are working above the ventilatory threshold and have reached an anaerobic level.

To establish your ventilatory threshold, jog slowly or walk vigorously for one minute. Increase the pace until the sound of your breathing is audible, and maintain the pace that gives you that sound level. If you can hear your breathing and are able to talk, you are at or close to the ventilatory threshold. Individuals who participate regularly in physical activity have higher ventilatory thresholds and are able to do more before breathing sounds become audible, while less active individuals will hear their breathing much sooner.

On the other hand, if you want to participate in more vigorous activities such as hockey, squash, or track and field, you may be interested in rapid gains or larger improvements in your anaerobic threshold. The **anaerobic threshold** is the point at which your body's main source of fuel comes from your short-term energy store, the lactic acid system (see Chapter 5). While working at his level may not improve your health any more than moderate activity, it can improve your performance fitness. Programs designed to improve both health and performance fitness are possible.

When developing a strength or cardiovascular fitness program, several components must be taken into account, such as training time, frequency, volume, and intensity. Work-to-rest ratio depends on the training intensity and describes the amount of rest needed between the phases of a workout. The type of exercise, exercise speed, number of repetitions, and order of performance also must be considered when building an exercise program.

Several important principles offer training guidelines for athletes and coaches. The overload principle specifies that progressive resistance is required to increase performance as a muscle adapts to a given load. On the other hand, if load is decreased or training is interrupted, a loss in fitness gains will result. This outlines the reversibility principle. The principle of specificity requires that exercises be specific to the desired result. For example, a sprinter will not improve performance by running long distance. Finally, the periodization principle allows a coach to divide the training year into three periods (preparation, competition, and transition) and develop training regimens suitable for each stage.

A popular exercise method for both serious and recreational athletes is circuit training. Circuit training combines and manipulates exercises to achieve specific fitness goals. With combination circuit training, gains in strength, muscular endurance, and cardiovascular endurance can be achieved simultaneously.

Knowing how and when to exercise can have a significant impact on how enjoyable and rewarding your experiences are with physical fitness. The secret lies in putting together a fitness plan that is right for you as an individual. By setting realistic goals and following the training principles outlined in this chapter, you are well on your way to a lifetime of rewarding physical activity.

Key Words

Absolute $\dot{V}O_2$max
Active flexibility
Activity cross training
Aerobic cross training
Aerobic power ($\dot{V}O_2$max)
Agonist–antagonist training
Anaerobic threshold
Body composition
Breath sound check
Cardiorespiratory
    (cardiovascular) endurance
Circuit training
Collagen
Continuous training
Dynamic (ballistic) stretching
Elastin
Endurance training

Exercise
Explosive load increase
Fartlek
Flexibility
Gradual load increase
Muscular endurance
Muscular endurance cross
    training
Muscular strength
Passive flexibility
Periodization of training
    principle
Physical activity
Physical fitness
Power
Progressive resistance
    (overload) principle

Proprioceptive neuromuscular
    facilitation (PNF) stretching
Psychomotor ability
Relative $\dot{V}O_2$max
Reversibility principle
Slow long distance (SLD)
    training
Specificity of exercise
    principle
Static stretching
Station training
Talk test
Training frequency
Training intensity
Training time
Training volume
Ventilatory threshold

Discussion Questions

1. List the components of physical fitness described in this chapter. Explain how each dimension relates to physical fitness.

2. What is antagonist training? Why is it important that antagonist training be incorporated into a strength training schedule?

1. List the components of physical fitness described in this chapter. Explain how each dimension relates to physical fitness.

2. What is antagonist training? Why is it important that antagonist training be incorporated into a strength training schedule?

3. Describe the various methods used to promote muscular strength, muscular endurance, and cardiorespiratory endurance.

4. Distinguish between $\dot{V}O_2$max, absolute $\dot{V}O_2$max, and relative $\dot{V}O_2$max. List the appropriate units of measurement for each.

5. Why is flexibility work important for one's health? What are some of the established flexibility methods? Which of the methods is most effective?

6. Discuss the relevance of psychomotor abilities as a component of fitness.

7. Identify the principles of exercise training and explain how each dimension affects the planning of a fitness program.

8. Identify five components of an effective cardiorespiratory and muscular fitness program. Briefly explain the important characteristics of each component.

9. Describe the elements of a circuit exercise training program. How can you incorporate circuit training into your overall fitness regimen?

10. How can people improve their muscular and cardiorespiratory endurance in one workout?

A Career in Fitness

NAME: Paula Paunic
OCCUPATION: Fitness Consultant and Wellness Educator
EDUCATION: BPHE, University of Toronto (Physical and Health Education)
BEd, University of Toronto (Education)

What do you do as a fitness consultant and wellness educator?

As a fitness advisor and wellness educator in Saudi Arabia, I work in fitness facilities training the staff and consulting individuals from Saudi Arabia, and all around the world, on a holistic approach to health and fitness. I also assist in writing a wellness newsletter called "Heartbeat," as well as work closely with the medical department in the hospital, particularly with diabetics and hypertensives. I am also involved in teaching exercise to Saudi women, in Arabic, which involves a brochure being handed out by medical staff for women who are pregnant, including post-natal exercise. My job is very diverse and I create my own challenges.

How do you feel about your role in "exporting" fitness knowledge to another country?

It is extremely exciting, and it is also a challenge because fitness or exercise in Muslim countries can sometimes be forbidden, based on the way women dress, and the music they exercise to. This requires that I adapt everything I do to follow their religious beliefs, so as not to offend anyone. This is interesting because there are still many parallels: they are interested, and have enough contact with the Western world, that they see the need for exercise in taking care of their bodies. Saudi Arabia has one of the highest incidences in the world of diabetes and heart problems, and although there is still a lot of work to be done, it is exciting to be there.

Why did you choose to pursue a career in fitness and wellness education?

I actually went to university with a career in physiotherapy in mind, doing a lot of volunteer work in hospitals to accumulate the hours and experience necessary. I also worked in occupational therapy where I dealt with long-term care patients and terminally ill patients. I found that my personality was not suited to this work with people who were dying, because I became attached to the patients, and it was emotionally draining. My personal physician then suggested that I might be better suited to working with healthy people than with the very sick. My life has since changed, and I have not looked back; I have concentrated on keeping my patients healthy, and it is very exciting working with seniors across the board.

How did a degree in physical and health education benefit your career choice?

My degree provided me with the groundwork and the basis of knowledge, and allowed me to be credible and professional. I appreciated my experiences in physical and health education, which gave me a lot of practical as well as theoretical experience – theoretical alone is not enough to be competitive in the field. My experiences opened up many opportunities for me.

What do you see in the future for fitness consultants and wellness educators?

I see us working closer with the medical community, beyond traditional medicine. I see people actually looking to alternative medicines, in conjunction with the other traditional medicines that are out there. Instead of going directly to a doctor, we may go to see a naturopath, a physical educator, or a wellness educator to find out why we are getting sick – we may be under stress, or not sleeping well, or not eating right – rather than always going for that "pill." I think that is where we are headed – it has to be.

What advice would you give to students who are interested in pursuing a career in fitness or a related occupation?

First of all, it is important to get good grades in high school so that you can get into university or college to pursue your interests. Many people go to university without a clear idea of what they want to do, but the more experiences you have, the more opportunities that arise. Keep your interests varied, and aim for a broad range of experiences. Opportunity is not going to come to your door, you have to go after it – this means being creative, and taking a few risks. If physical education is something you are interested in, you have to live it, and believe in it, in order to be a good role model. Your own actions can facilitate positive lifestyle changes in other people.

In This Chapter:

Purposes of Testing and Evaluation 232
>Diagnosis   233
>Placement   233
>Prediction   233
>Motivation   234
>Achievement   234
>Program Evaluation   234

Norms – Your Reference Perspective 234

Reliability and Validity 235
>Reliability   235
>Validity   235

Assessing Physical Fitness 236
>Measuring Aerobic Capacity   236
>Measuring Body Composition   239
>Measuring Muscular Strength   243
>Measuring Muscular Power   244
>Measuring Muscular Endurance   247
>Measuring Flexibility   251
>Measuring Agility   254

Summary 257

CHAPTER 10

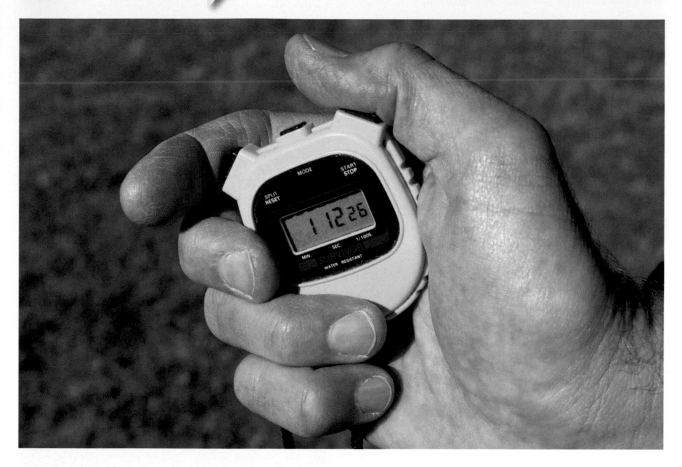

What's My Score? Evaluation in Physical and Health Education

After completing this chapter you should be able to:

- discuss the usefulness and application of testing, measurement, and evaluation;

- outline the criteria for the evaluation and selection of tests;

- describe a variety of practical and economical tests that are useful to the average physical education teacher and student in various performance areas;

- administer these tests to yourself and others in a reliable and valid manner.

In the field of human performance, testing, measurement, and evaluation serve an important purpose. We all make evaluative decisions on a daily basis, although the soundness of these decisions varies with the information we use to make them. In order to make accurate judgements, we must first accumulate relevant information, organize it, and evaluate this information in order to draw conclusions that support our eventual decisions. During election years, for example, numerous surveys are conducted in order to inform voters about how the candidates are faring in their campaigns. This provides us with relevant information that is applicable to the evaluation and decision process.

What would it be like to go through life without knowing what effect nutrition has on performance, or how smoking affects our health? It seems that virtually everything we do is based on research and testing that has been (or is being) done. Whether we make decisions concerning who we should vote for, what kinds of foods we should eat, what sport to pursue, or how much we should exercise, these decisions are only properly made with the aid of testing, measurement, and evaluation.

In order to effectively gather, sort, analyze, and evaluate relevant information before making a decision, you must determine whether that information is reliable, valid, and objective. Ultimately, the effectiveness of a decision can be traced to the relevance and quality of the information used to make the decision.

Take fitness appraisals as an example. In a society that has become increasingly preoccupied with issues of weight, health, and exercise, obtaining a precise evaluation of your fitness level is becoming correspondingly more important. People want to know how they can improve their health through exercise, which aspects of their fitness should be improved, and where they fit in with the rest of the population. The evaluation you receive from simple field tests (Figure 10.1) or modern laboratories can reveal whether your physical condition is consistent with good health, and can help you plan a program that is appropriate

for your level of fitness, making exercise more enjoyable and individually rewarding.

Purposes of Testing and Evaluation

Why is it important to have skill and knowledge in performing correct and effective measurement and evaluation? Some of the reasons are illustrated by Kevin's story (see box *Test For Success*). When Kevin decided to use testing to evaluate his performance, this provided him with motivation and the means by which he could easily and objectively monitor his improvement. Using specific tests to monitor your performance can be an ideal way to stay motivated and to work towards continual improvement. However, it is

Figure 10.1 Simple tests of flexibility can be good indicators of your general level of fitness.

Test For Success

Kevin loved to play basketball. If he wasn't doing homework or watching television, you could be sure he was shooting a few hoops outside in his driveway. But despite his love for the game and his willingness to practice for hours on end, he could not seem to make his high school basketball team. He had tried out for the team the previous two years and was one of the last players to be cut on each occasion. This left Kevin dejected and lacking confidence – he almost considered giving up basketball altogether.

Instead, the season continued and Kevin decided to sit in on a few of the team's practices with the permission of the coach. He watched carefully and made note of some of the tests and drills the team used to evaluate and improve their skills, and decided that he would use some of them to monitor his own performance during the off-season. When summer came around, Kevin was excited and had renewed interest in pursuing basketball.

Kevin decided to use a free-throw shooting test to begin, since shooting accuracy was one of his primary weaknesses. He simply recorded the number of free-throw shots he could make in 20 attempts. Most players on the team could make at least 14 out of 20 shots, so he set a goal of attaining this base level of achievement. His first day of practice, he only made 11 out of 20 shots. But persistent practice and steady improvement brought with it motivation; after just three and a half weeks, he was consistently making 16 out of 20 free-throw attempts–a higher percentage than many players on the team were shooting. Delighted with his improvement on the free-throw shooting test, he tried out another drill that tested his dribbling ability and ball control. He tested himself with several similar drills in the remaining summer months, until he felt he had improved adequately.

Finally, the basketball season arrived. Kevin was nervous about his chances this year, but the measurement and evaluation process he endured during the summer provided the challenge, stimulation, and confidence he needed to make the team. Kevin tried out for the team and not only made the roster, but cracked the starting line-up just three games into the season. He went on to have a very productive season and became a respected team leader.

important to remember that the most important consideration is the selection of valid tests that are reliable and meet your needs for time and effort.

Although there are many other reasons for testing we will focus on six general reasons to illustrate its importance to students, teachers, and researchers in the field of physical education and human performance.

Diagnosis

Once a test has been administered, the results may be evaluated to identify deficiencies or weaknesses in the subjects – in other words, to make a **diagnosis**. Whether it be a student, athlete, medical patient, or fitness appraisal subject, one can effectively use testing and measurement to determine areas that need improvement or require special attention.

Placement

One reason for testing and evaluating human performance is for the purpose of **placement**. Initial tests may be used in circumstances where it would be beneficial to group individuals on the basis of their skill level or ability, so that time is spent where it is needed. Grouping individuals together who share a certain characteristic makes the most efficient and effective use of time and energy.

Prediction

Specialized tests have long been used for the **prediction** of future events or results with varying degrees of success. Entrance exams for colleges and universities, personality inventories, and skinfold measurements all propose to predict some aspect of human performance. It is a challenging task to predict future events on the basis of past or present data, but tests and measurements assist us in getting one step closer to doing so accurately.

Motivation

How difficult would it be to get a classroom full of students to hand in assignments if they were not being graded or their marks had no special significance? Very difficult. Most individuals need the proper **motivation** if they are to put forth their full effort, and the measurement and evaluation process provides this challenge and stimulation (Figure 10.2).

Achievement

In order to effectively evaluate an individual's **achievement** level in an instruction or training program, it is necessary to establish a set of objectives that accurately and objectively measure it. In accomplishing this task, you must make use of the measurement and evaluation process which will indicate how an individual has fared at a particular task.

Program Evaluation

With increasing competition for funds and resources, **program evaluation** is becoming more useful, and something of a necessity. Program evaluations allow superiors to determine (according to established standards) whether or not a particular program has successfully achieved its objectives. For example, if you request increased funds for your fitness program, you must first demonstrate that the program is resulting in the improved fitness of your clients.

Norms – Your Reference Perspective

Humans are social beings, so we like to know how we compare to those around us. It sometimes isn't

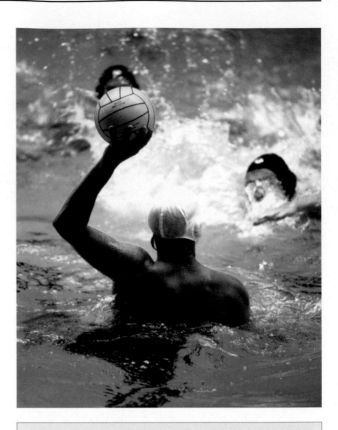

Figure 10.2 When we know our performance is being evaluated, we are motivated to put forth our best effort.

enough to know how we placed – we want to know who finished ahead of and behind us. Standardized tests often provide such information. For example, in order to evaluate your level of explosive power, a vertical jump test is administered. Your results are compared to **norm-referenced standards (norms)** that have been established after numerous previous trials, and you are able to obtain results that reflect your level of achievement relative to a clearly defined subgroup (e.g., people of the same age, sex, or class). In other words, you are able to determine how your performance compares with other males or females of the same age.

Norms can serve many purposes. A major benefit of using norms is that individuals can be effectively compared on a specific task with others who share important characteristics such as age and sex. For an athlete or coach who is interested in athletic talent identification, norms can provide him or her with an indication of whose performance is above average, and who is perhaps better suited for a different activity. Norms can also provide you with an indication of where improvements need to be made and where most of your efforts should be directed during training. They give you a starting reference point from which your performances can be compared.

Reliability and Validity

Reliability and validity are essential to testing, measurement, and evaluation. Testing involves careful planning in order to obtain results that are consistent and accurate (Figure 10.3). Thus, you must look for accuracy and consistency when making measurements, and the proper choice of instrument is the first major consideration. It is therefore necessary that you understand how to properly use a testing instrument, as well as to have some knowledge about the quality of the measurements it generates. A test or instrument that fails to demonstrate precision and reproducibility runs the risk of yielding faulty results.

Reliability

Reliability refers to the consistency or repeatability of test scores, data, or observations. A test is reliable if measurements are the same (or approximately the same) each time the test is administered to the same individual. This ensures that the test results are dependable and consistent. For example, if you test a student's running speed over a 15-metre distance each hour for four hours, you would expect similar (not exact) results for each trial.

Validity

Whereas reliability refers to the consistency of test scores or data, validity is a characteristic of the instrument or test being used. **Validity** is the degree of truthfulness of a test score, referring to the extent to which a test measures what it proposes to measure. Most people would agree that sit-ups are a valid measure of abdominal muscular endurance. But do sit-ups measure

upper body strength? Obviously not. In order to be deemed valid, a test must thus be reliable and relevant, and measure what it reports to measure.

Reliability and Validity

Both *reliability* and *validity* must be present if results are to be accurate and meaningful. A test can sometimes be valid in one circumstance but not in another, or reliable but not valid. For example, although total body weight is a reliable measure from day to day, it is not a valid measure of body fatness since the body is composed of tissues other than fat. Thus, it is incorrect to equate total body weight with body fatness. Always consider issues of reliability and validity when conducting tests or interpreting results.

Figure 10.3 When administering any test, accuracy and consistency are required to produce reliable results.

Assessing Physical Fitness

Attaining and maintaining a high level of physical fitness has various documented benefits that support leading an active lifestyle. This has led many people to begin exercise programs directed at improving their strength, endurance, agility, flexibility, body composition, and general quality of life. But how do you accurately determine your level of fitness? You may have seen, or experienced firsthand, fitness appraisals being done at health clubs or universities involving step tests or treadmills for endurance, grip strength tests, and sit-and-reach tests for flexibility, for example. But what do these tests actually measure? Do they provide you with an accurate indication of your actual level of physical fitness? It's important to set goals for yourself that make sense for you – fitness appraisals can be beneficial in this respect. This section will help you become more familiar with the various ways fitness is measured, how you can use the results of these tests to make personal changes in your life, and how you can administer these tests in a reliable and valid manner. Understanding the components of physical fitness (see Chapter 9) and how they can be measured will go a long way in assisting you in your own pursuit of physical fitness and health.

Measuring Aerobic Capacity

Cardiorespiratory endurance is a key component of physical fitness. It is what we are usually referring to when we say that someone is in "good shape" or "physically fit." The concept of cardiorespiratory endurance reflects an individual's aerobic capacity or aerobic power – in other words, the ability to supply oxygen to working muscles during physical exertion (see Chapter 5).

The most accurate and reliable measure of cardiorespiratory function is **maximal oxygen consumption** or $\dot{V}O_2max$, which is a measure of the amount of oxygen consumed per kilogram of body weight per minute of exercise. Measurement of aerobic capacity in the laboratory often involves a maximal exercise test on an ergometer (usually a treadmill or stationary cycle) in which the subject works at progressively increasing loads (intensity) until reaching exhaustion. Other reliable and valid testing protocols have been developed for estimating (predicting) $\dot{V}O_2max$; they are calculated from measurements of maximal or submaximal exercise performance, or submaximal heart rate. These **laboratory tests**, however, are rigorous and time consuming, and they often require expensive equipment such as gas analyzers, ergometers, and computerized metabolic systems. This puts lab testing of aerobic power out of reach for most schools.

Other simpler and more practical **field tests** have been devised to measure cardiorespiratory function. Popular field tests include running and step tests. **Running tests** require subjects to run a prescribed distance or run for a predetermined length of time; the time required to cover the distance and the distance covered in the allotted time, respectively, are the measurements used to evaluate aerobic capacity. The **step tests** involve stepping up and down steps of a certain height at a particular rate for an established period of time. Aerobic capacity is then estimated from the heart rate response or recovery heart rate following the activity – an individual with high aerobic power will return more quickly to a lower heart rate than a less "fit" individual. Make note of the fact that many step tests were devised for use by individuals of college age or above.

It is important when using field tests to employ standard distances, timers, and recording procedures for the most accurate results.

12-Minute Run–Walk Test

This test is satisfactory for both males and females from junior high school to college. Little equipment is required – a stopwatch, whistle, and distance markers are really all you need to complete the test. However, a course of specified distance will make counting the number of laps completed an easier task; the number of laps can then be easily multiplied by the course distance. Distance markers can also be used effectively to divide the course into quarters or eighths so that the tester can quickly and accurately determine the distance covered after 12 minutes have elapsed.

The goal of the test is simply to run or walk (or both) around the course as many times as possible in 12 minutes following the starting signal from behind a designated starting line. A spotter assigned to each runner should maintain an accurate count of each lap completed by the subject until the stop signal is given after 12 minutes. The runner should keep track of laps as well. The distance covered is calculated by multiplying the number of laps completed by the distance of each lap (including the incomplete lap). Spotter and subject can then reverse roles to complete the testing. If 12 minutes seems too long for a particular age level, 9-minute run–walk tests may also be appropriate. Evaluative norms for the 12-minute run are presented in Table 10.1.

Table 10.1 Fitness classifications based on distance covered (km) in the 12-minute run–walk test.

Fitness Category		Distance Covered by Age (years)		
		13 – 19	20 – 29	30 – 39
Superior	males	≥ 3.01	≥ 2.85	≥ 2.74
	females	≥ 2.45	≥ 2.35	≥ 2.25
Excellent	males	2.78 – 3.00	2.66 – 2.84	2.53 – 2.73
	females	2.32 – 2.44	2.17 – 2.34	2.09 – 2.24
Good	males	2.53 – 2.77	2.41 – 2.65	2.35 – 2.52
	females	2.09 – 2.31	1.98 – 2.16	1.92 – 2.08
Fair	males	2.22 – 2.52	2.12 – 2.40	2.11 – 2.34
	females	1.92 – 2.08	1.80 – 1.97	1.71 – 1.91
Poor	males	2.09 – 2.21	1.96 – 2.11	1.91 – 2.10
	females	1.61 – 1.91	1.54 – 1.79	1.53 – 1.70
Very Poor	males	≤ 2.08	≤ 1.95	≤ 1.90
	females	≤ 1.60	≤ 1.53	≤ 1.52

2,400-Metre Endurance Run

Participants are encouraged to complete the 2,400 metre distance in the shortest possible time. They should be informed that they may walk or stop and rest at any time if necessary.

Several runners may be timed at the same time by one timer. The time is recorded for each participant to the nearest second. Evaluative norms are presented in Table 10.2.

YMCA 3-Minute Step Test

All that is required for this simple test is a bench that is 12 inches in height, a metronome set at 96 beats per minute, and a watch or timer. It is an ideal test for testing large groups of people, particularly for the initial testing of unfit subjects. The subject should first listen to the metronome to become accustomed to the rhythmic beat. After becoming familiar with the beat and practicing the steps, the subject then begins the test. He or she steps to a rhythm of 96 beats per minute following an "up–up, down–down" pattern, which results in 24 steps per minute. This continues for three minutes, after which time the subject steps down and sits down in order that a tester can record the heart rate over one minute. This one-minute recovery heart rate is the score for the test.

Table 10.2 Norms (min:sec) for the 2,400-metre run for boys and girls, 14-17 years old.

Percentile	Boys				Girls			
	14	15	16	17	14	15	16	17
95	9:57	9:38	9:18	9:29	12:02	12:17	11:58	11:14
90	10:21	9:59	9:49	9:45	12:43	12:57	12:24	12:24
85	10:43	10:23	10:08	10:08	13:28	13:31	12:38	12:45
80	11:00	10:39	10:25	10:21	13:51	14:01	13:09	13:06
75	11:09	10:50	10:42	10:32	14:16	14:19	13:22	13:31
70	11:22	11:02	10:50	10:42	14:34	14:36	13:41	13:57
65	11:34	11:15	11:03	10:50	14:49	14:56	14:21	14:11
60	11:50	11:25	11:10	11:02	15:05	15:17	14:47	14:28
55	12:08	11:36	11:21	11:05	15:30	15:38	15:15	14:50
50	12:16	11:51	11:32	11:16	15:51	16:02	15:44	15:13
45	12:29	12:04	11:50	11:29	16:07	16:10	16:02	15:39
40	12:40	12:23	12:02	11:52	16:32	16:37	16:26	15:58
35	13:03	12:36	12:20	12:07	16:50	16:55	16:44	16:20
30	13:25	12:51	12:36	12:26	17:07	17:21	17:06	16:45
25	13:51	13:16	13:05	12:40	17:32	17:31	17:37	17:31
20	14:11	14:03	13:15	13:06	17:59	18:20	17:56	18:05
15	14:40	14:46	14:08	13:33	18:51	18:58	18:37	18:53
10	15:26	15:45	14:57	14:27	19:22	19:58	19:33	19:39
5	16:38	17:03	16:10	16:40	20:41	21:29	21:15	22:15

Queen's College Step Test

This test is satisfactory for males and females of college age or above. Bleachers or any stepping bench at a height of 16-17 inches is appropriate. A metronome and stopwatch are also needed to administer the test. Divide the group into pairs, with one partner being tested and the other counting the pulse rate. Before beginning, partners should familiarize themselves with pulse-counting procedures in order to perform properly (see Chapter 6).

Subjects step to a four-beat rhythm (up–up, down–down) for three minutes (Figure 10.4). Males step at 96 beats per minute (24 steps/min), while females step at 88 beats per minute (22 steps/min). After demonstrating and practicing at the required beat for about 15 seconds, begin testing. At the completion of the exercise, the subject remains standing and a heart rate is taken

for a 15-second period (5 seconds after exercise). Recovery heart rates are converted into beats per minute (bpm) (15-second heart rate x 4). The following equations can then be used to predict $\dot{V}O_2$max (ml/kg/min).

> **$\dot{V}O_2$max (males) = 111.33 – .42 (pulse rate in beats/min)**

> **$\dot{V}O_2$max (females) = 65.81 – .185 (pulse rate in beats/min)**

In terms of accuracy of prediction, one can be 95 percent confident that the predicted value will be within 16 percent of the subject's true $\dot{V}O_2$max. Predicted $\dot{V}O_2$max values can be obtained from Table 10.3.

Measuring Body Composition

Because obesity is a risk factor for various health conditions such as high blood pressure (hypertension), coronary heart disease (CHD), cancer, and Type II (adult onset) diabetes, the accurate assessment of body composition is an important measurement goal. Many people today are concerned with their total body weight; however, the focus should be on losing excessive body fat rather than on total weight alone. Although numerous height–weight tables and indexes are used to assess body composition (e.g., BMI, see Chapter 12), you must be careful when interpreting information from such sources. An athlete who is well-muscled, for example, may be considered overweight on a height–weight table even though he or she is actually quite lean. Indexes such as the BMI do not directly measure body fatness.

True measures of body composition (lean versus fat mass) involve the estimation of an individual's body fat percentage, requiring the determination of body density. A lean individual at a fixed body weight will have a higher body density (lower percent body fat) when compared to a fatter person

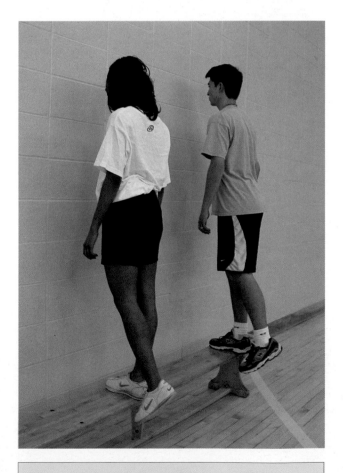

Figure 10.4 Participants follow an "up–up, down–down" stepping pattern for the step test.

Table 10.3 Predicted maximal oxygen uptake ($\dot{V}O_2$max) for the step test (ml/kg/min).

15-Second Heart Rate	Heart Rate (bpm)	$\dot{V}O_2$max – Females	$\dot{V}O_2$max – Males
30	120	43.6	60.9
31	124	42.9	59.3
32	128	42.2	57.6
33	132	41.4	55.9
34	136	40.7	54.2
35	140	40.0	52.5
36	144	39.2	50.9
37	148	38.5	49.2
38	152	37.7	47.5
39	156	37.0	45.8
40	160	36.3	44.1
41	164	35.5	42.5
42	168	34.8	40.8
43	172	34.0	39.1
44	176	33.3	37.4
45	180	32.6	35.7
46	184	31.8	34.1
47	188	31.1	32.4
48	192	30.3	30.7
49	196	29.6	29.0
50	200	28.9	27.3

of the same weight. Many methods of measuring body density and body fat percentage exist, including chemical analysis of human cadavers, hydrostatic weighing, volumetry (body volume), total body water, total body electrical conductivity (TBEC), and radiographic (x-ray) analysis. Most of these methods are obviously not feasible for most schools or individuals for measuring body composition, as they require special apparatus and/or complex procedures.

Skinfold measurements are one of the most feasible, reliable, valid, and popular methods used for estimating body composition. These tests involve measuring skinfolds (actually "fat folds") at particular sites on the body with special calipers (Figure 10.5). These measurements of

Figure 10.5 Skinfold calipers range in price, but more affordable plastic varieties are available for schools or organizations with limited budgets.

subcutaneous fat are based on the relationship that exists between fat located directly beneath the skin, and internal fat and body density. The sum of a set of skinfolds can be used as an indication of the relative degree of fatness among individuals.

YMCA Skinfold Test

This test requires skinfold calipers. The process involves taking skinfolds at the abdomen, suprailium (crest of the hip bone), triceps (Figure 10.6), and thigh. The following steps should be followed when taking skinfold measurements:

(1) lift skinfolds two or three times before placing the calipers for a measurement;

(2) place the calipers below the thumb and fingers and perpendicular to the fold to allow easy reading of the measurement; completely release the caliper grip before reading the dial 1-2 seconds later;

(3) repeat this procedure three times; the measurements should not vary by more than 1 mm; use the median value and allow at least 15 seconds between each measurement.

Figure 10.6 Caliper placement for measuring the triceps skinfold.

You must be aware that plenty of practice is required to obtain reliable and consistent results. You can convert the skinfold measures to percent body fat by using the following equations.

Four sites: abdomen, suprailium, triceps, and thigh:

Males
% fat = .29288 x (sum of 4) − .0005 x (sum of 4)^2 + .15845 x (age) − 5.76377

Females
% fat = .29669 x (sum of 4) − .00043 x (sum of 4)^2 + .02963 x (age) + 1.4172

Your body fat percentage can then be compared to norms for percent body fat (Table 10.4). However, in calculating your percent body fat, be aware that a standard error of estimate of up to 3.98 percent exists. Thus, a calculated percentage of 16 may actually range from 15.4 to 16.6.

Circumference (Girth) Measurements

The girth of various body segments can also be used to assess body composition. Using a cloth measuring tape, measurements must be made carefully at the correct sites and at right angles to the long axis of the body or specific body segment being measured (Figure 10.7). Plenty of practice is required to become an efficient tester.

Because obesity is characterized by large abdominal and hip girths in relation to chest circumference, these are particularly useful circumference measures to use. Some of the body sites most frequently measured include the:

- **neck** – immediately below the larynx;

- **chest** – in males, at nipple level; in females, measures are taken sometimes at the level of just above or just below the breasts (all measures of chest circumference should be taken at the end of an expiration);

- **hips** – from the maximal protrusion of the buttocks to the symphysis pubis;

Table 10.4 Norms for percent body fat in males and females.

Rating	Males		Females	
	18 – 25	**26 – 35**	**18 – 25**	**26 – 35**
Very lean	4 – 7	8 – 12	13 – 17	13 – 18
Lean	8 – 10	13 – 15	18 – 20	19 – 21
Leaner than average	11 – 13	16 – 18	21 – 23	22 – 23
Average	14 – 16	19 – 21	24 – 25	24 – 26
Fatter than average	17 – 20	22 – 24	26 – 28	27 – 30
Fat	21 – 26	25 – 28	29 – 31	31 – 35
Overfat	27 – 37	29 – 37	32 – 43	36 – 48

- **thigh** – the point of maximal thigh girth;

- **calf** – the point of maximal calf girth;

- **biceps** – the point of maximal circumference when the arm is (1) fully flexed and muscles fully contracted, and (2) fully extended and muscles fully contracted; and

- **abdomen** – measurements have been taken at different sites:

(1) at the level of the umbilicus (belly button) and iliac crests;

(2) at the point of minimal girth, half way between umbilicus and xiphoid process of sternum; and

(3) at the point of maximal abdominal girth; in women, about 5 cm below umbilicus.

Figure 10.7 Common sites used for girth measurements. **A.** Abdomen. **B.** Biceps. **C.** Thigh.

Measuring Muscular Strength

Strength is recognized as an important factor in human performance, particularly in the execution of physical skills. It can be defined as the maximum force that muscle can generate during a brief contraction against a single rigid resistance. Measures of strength involve tests that require one maximal effort for a given movement, often lifting an external weight or contracting against external resistance. An individual's body weight, however, has an impact on how "strong" he or she is deemed to be. For example, a 64-kg man who lifts 75 kg (75/64 = 1.17) is stronger (relatively) than a 90-kg man who lifts 95 kg (95/90 = 1.05). But the 90-kg man still possesses more **absolute strength** because he is able to lift a larger absolute weight.

Again, laboratory tests used to assess muscular strength require sophisticated equipment such as computerized dynamometers. Such an apparatus allows detailed measures of work, power, etc., but can be quite expensive. Although lab tests can be quite useful for physiotherapists, clinicians, athletic trainers, and rehabilitation centres, field methods are far more feasible for the average individual.

Grip Dynamometer

This is an isometric strength test that measures strength with a **grip dynamometer**. It is used to measure the grip strength of the hand, but has correlated well with total body strength. It is adjustable to fit the size of any hand. A needle

Table 10.5 Norms (kg) for grip strength of the dominant hand based on age.

Age	Males	Females
6	9.21	8.36
7	10.74	9.88
8	12.41	11.16
9	14.34	12.77
10	16.52	14.65
11	18.85	16.54
12	21.24	18.92
13	24.44	21.84
14	28.42	24.79
15	33.39	27.00
16	39.37	28.70
17	44.74	29.56
18	49.28	29.75

indicates scoring on the dial which is marked off in kilograms (0 to 100). The subject simply takes in a breath, and while exhaling, squeezes the device maximally to obtain a reading. This is completed three times to calculate an average score for each hand. Evaluative norms are presented in Table 10.5.

One Repetition Maximum (1RM)

One repetition maximum (1RM) refers to the maximum amount of weight an individual can lift just one time. 1RM tests can use values from the bench press or leg press. Dividing the 1RM values by the subjects' body weight allows you to make the strength measures equitable across weight classes. When testing for maximum strength, you must adhere to the following guidelines:

- have subjects warm up with stretching and light lifting;

- have subjects perform a lift below the maximum (a pre-test session may be useful);

- have subjects rest at least two minutes between lifts to prevent fatigue;

Maximal Strength – Muscular Endurance Relationship

It is neither necessary nor safe for an athlete or student to work against maximal resistance to calculate maximal strength capacity for a given exercise. Due to the close relationship between maximal strength and muscular endurance, determining an athlete's maximum number of repetitions against submaximal resistance will produce an accurate conclusion about maximal strength.

The relationship can be illustrated best with the following example. Student A is able to lift a 100-kg barbell, but partner B masters only 90 kg. If both students are challenged to clean and press a barbell of 85 kg as often as possible, student A will perform 7-8 repetitions and B only 2-3 repetitions. Using an 80-kg barbell, student A can do 10-12 repetitions and athlete B only 5-6 repetitions. This comparison shows that the number of repetitions against high resistance is dependent on the maximal strength of the athlete. The table below shows the maximal number of repetitions possible for load levels of different resistance.

The maximal feasible number of repetitions of a particular load is referred to as the **repetition maximum (RM)**. If the RM of an exercise is 2-3, it can be deduced that an athlete can resist a force corresponding to approximately 95 percent of maximal strength capacity. If the athlete is able to perform maximally 7-8 repetitions with a particular weight, then this weight approximates 85 percent of his or her maximal strength capacity.

Maximum number of repetitions as a function of resistance.

Resistance Level	100%	95%	90%	85%	80%	75%
Repetition Maximum	1	2 – 3	5 – 6	7 – 8	approx. 10 – 12	approx. 12 – 16

- increase weight on subsequent lifts by small increments (2.5 or 5 kg);

- continue procedure until subjects fail to lift a particular weight;

- record the last weight successfully lifted as the 1RM;

- divide the subjects' 1RM by their body weight.

If it takes more than five lifts to determine a subject's 1RM, consider retesting the subject the next day with a heavier starting weight.

Measuring Muscular Power

The term **power** is often (incorrectly) used as a synonym for the term strength. However, power specifically refers to the ability to release maximum force in the shortest possible time. Indeed time is the element that really distinguishes the two concepts. Activities that involve rapid muscular contractions such as the vertical jump, shot put, and standing broad jump require power to execute movements explosively. Many tests of power are easy to administer and are very practical in terms of time, effort, and equipment.

Standing Long Jump

This simple test can be used for both males and females from age six and up. All that is needed for the test is a floor or mat, a tape measure, and a marking material (chalk or tape) to indicate the distance jumped. Actually, it has never been easier to measure an athlete's explosive power in the legs using the standing long jump. Special standing long jump test mats have been made to make the test even simpler to administer (Figure 10.8). The special mat eliminates taping down measuring tapes to the gym floor and eyeballing the distance jumped since the measuring tape (in cm and in) is printed directly on a thick, durable rubber material.

The goal of a two-footed long jump is to jump horizontally as far as possible from a standing

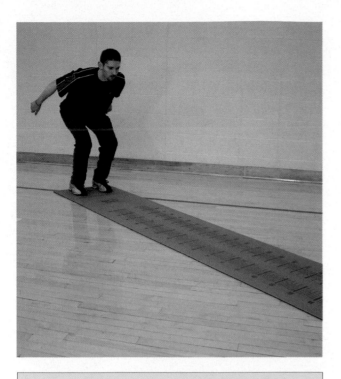

Figure 10.8 The rubber material of the mat provides excellent grip for take-off and effectively cushions landings, eliminating the fear that students may slip on a wooden floor or other slick surface.

start. Begin by standing with the feet about shoulder-width apart with the toes just behind the take-off line. Then bend the knees and swing the arms backwards and forwards in preparation for the jump.

After attaining a feel for the jump, extend the hips, knees, and ankles from a crouch position as a unit while simultaneously swinging the arms forward for the jump. In addition, the trunk should be leaning slightly forward at the instant of take-off and then upward as the arms swing in the direction of the jump. There should be no extra hop or step prior to the jump; it must be performed cleanly, with both feet entirely behind the take-off line. The key to a successful jump is coordinating all parts of the body during the jump – ankles, knees, hips, arms, and trunk.

The measurement of the jump is the distance between the take-off line and the heel touchdown (or other body part) closest to the take-off line. Accurate readings are quick and easy with a specialized test mat. Allow each student at least three trials to obtain an average score. Evaluative norms are presented in Table 10.6.

Vertical Jump (Sargent Jump)

Another simple test used to measure power in the legs is the vertical jump, satisfactory for males and females age nine and up. A measuring tape or yardstick, chalk, and a smooth wall at least 12 feet high is all that is required to complete the test. The subject simply stands sideways beside

Table 10.6 Norms (cm) for the standing long jump test.

Performance Level	Males			Females		
	Age (years)			Age (years)		
	15	16	17+	15	16	17+
Excellent	217 – 235	228 – 244	235 – 255	185 – 204	190 – 208	193 – 208
Above Average	206 – 216	217 – 227	223 – 234	173 – 184	177 – 189	178 – 192
Average	195 – 205	207 – 216	214 – 222	163 – 172	166 – 176	170 – 177
Below Average	176 – 194	196 – 206	200 – 213	150 – 162	153 – 165	157 – 169
Needs Improvement	131 – 175	169 – 195	168 – 199	124 – 149	121 – 152	128 – 156

the wall about an elbow's distance away (put the hand closest to the wall on your hip to determine this distance). Holding a small piece of chalk in the hand closest to the wall, the subject reaches up as high as possible with the heels on the floor and makes a mark on the wall (Figure 10.9 A). He or she then jumps as high as possible and makes another mark at the peak of the jump on the wall. It is important to bend the ankles, knees, and hips before explosively extending these joints from the crouch position for optimal power. Allow three trials of which the best score will count. The jump height is measured by subtracting the reach height from jump height.

Vertical Jump Test Mat Another special device has been developed to measure vertical jump height and power. The key feature in the design of this vertical jump test is a measuring tape feeder mounted on a rubber mat. This feeder allows the measuring tape to be fed through with minimal resistance as the athlete jumps, but stops the tape once the apex of the jump is reached (Figure 10.9 B). The length of measuring tape pulled through the feeder indicates the height of the jump, which is clearly displayed for recording. Evaluative norms are presented in Table 10.7.

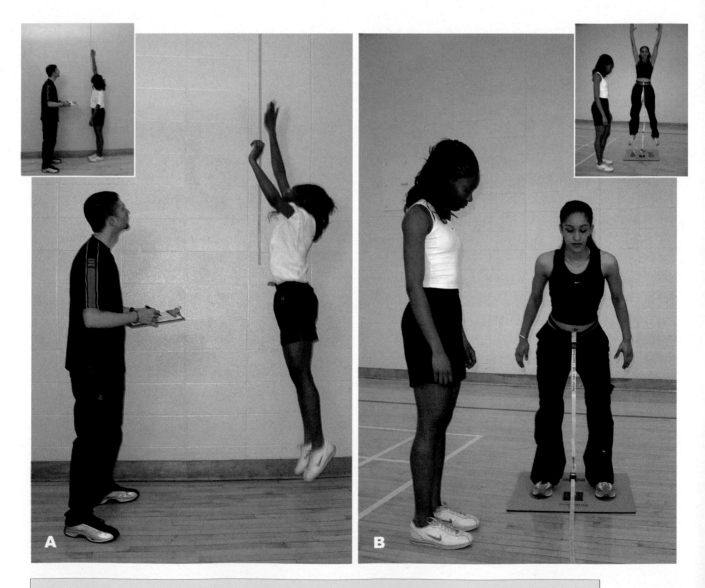

Figure 10.9 The vertical jump. **A.** Traditional sargent jump. **B.** Using a vertical jump test mat.

Table 10.7 Norms (cm) for the vertical jump test.

Performance Level	Males Age (years)			Females Age (years)
	15	**16**	**17+**	**15+**
Excellent	≥ 53.5	≥ 55.5	≥ 60.5	≥ 42.5
Above Average	46.5 – 53.0	48.5 – 55.0	52.5 – 60.0	36.5 – 42.0
Average	42.5 – 46.0	45.5 – 48.0	48.5 – 52.0	32.5 – 36.0
Below Average	37.5 – 42.0	40.5 – 45.0	43.5 – 48.0	28.5 – 32.0
Needs Improvement	≤ 37.0	≤ 40.0	≤ 43.0	≤ 28.0

Measuring Muscular Endurance

Muscular endurance is characterized by the ability of muscle to maintain tension or to execute repeated movements versus submaximal resistance over time. Whether measures of endurance are static (e.g., flexed arm hang) or dynamic (e.g., pull-ups), most tests of muscular endurance are actually quite practical. The scoring for such tests usually involves recording the number of repetitions completed for a particular exercise, or the length of time tension is maintained. Whether the test involves push-ups, sit-ups, bench presses, or squats, the ability to sustain muscular tension with repeated movements is what is being tested. It is important to note the difference between cardiorespiratory and muscular endurance. Muscular endurance, unlike cardiorespiratory endurance discussed earlier, refers to the endurance of skeletal muscle involved in activities, not the efficiency of the heart and lungs.

YMCA 1-Minute Sit-ups Test

This test is appropriate for males and females of most ages and requires subjects simply to perform the maximum number of sit-ups possible in one minute. The test is to be performed with bent knees, the feet flat on the ground shoulder-width apart, and the fingers behind the head (Figure 10.10). A partner holds the subject's feet during the test as he or she performs sit-ups to alternate sides (i.e., left elbow to right knee, right elbow to left knee, etc.). The total number of sit-ups performed in one minute is recorded to measure trunk endurance; repetitions are not to be counted if the fingers lose contact with the head. Evaluative norms are shown in Table 10.8.

Figure 10.10 The YMCA sit-ups test.

Table 10.8 Norms (number of repetitions) for the YMCA sit-ups test.

Performance Level	Age and Sex			
	13 Males	14 Males	15+ Males	13+ Females
Excellent	≥ 98	≥ 100	≥ 103	≥ 93
Above Average	87 – 97	90 – 99	92 – 102	83 – 92
Average	73 – 86	76 – 89	81 – 91	71 – 82
Below Average	55 – 72	58 – 75	61 – 80	54 – 70
Needs Improvement	≤ 54	≤ 57	≤ 60	≤ 53

Pull-ups and Flexed Arm Hang

Pull-up tests are popular for testing upper body muscular endurance. All that is required is a horizontal bar high enough from the ground that the tallest subject cannot reach the ground with his or her feet. An overhand grip (palms facing away) must be used. The test begins with the subject maintaining a straight arm hang (Figure 10.11 A). The subject's task is simply to pull him or herself upwards until the chin is above the bar (Figure 10.11 B); after each chin-up, the subject is to return to the starting position. This sequence is repeated as many times as possible to test muscular endurance of the arms and shoulder girdle. Evaluative norms are presented in Table 10.9.

The flexed arm hang is another effective test of muscular endurance, especially for participants who cannot pull their own body weight. In this test, two spotters assist the subject in attaining a flexed arm position (palms facing in) so the eyes are level with the bar (Figure 10.11 C). The subject is to hold this position as long as possible,

Figure 10.11 The pull-ups test. **A.** Starting position. **B.** Chin-up position. **C.** Flexed arm hang modification.

Table 10.9 Raw score norms (number of repetitions) for the pull-ups test for boys.

Percentile	Age				
	13	14	15	16	17+
95	10	12	15	14	15
75	5	7	9	10	10
50	3	4	6	7	7
25	1	2	3	4	4
5	0	0	0	1	0

and the number of seconds (to the nearest second) the subject maintains this position is the score that is recorded. Evaluative norms are presented in Table 10.10.

Push-ups Test

It doesn't get any easier for assessing upper body endurance – all you need is a mat. The goal of the test is to perform push-ups to exhaustion. The basic push-up position with hands under the shoulders and toes on the ground must be maintained throughout the test (no sagging or piking of the body) (Figure 10.12 A). The chest

Table 10.10 Norms (seconds) for the flexed arm hang, boys and girls 14-17 years old.

Percentile	Boys				Girls			
	14	15	16	17	14	15	16	17
95	80.8	84.0	92.0	80.8	58.0	53.0	52.0	55.0
90	72.5	72.5	80.5	73.1	46.5	45.3	46.1	47.5
85	66.9	67.3	74.3	69.5	41.8	40.5	41.4	43.0
80	63.1	64.2	68.8	66.7	36.3	36.0	39.2	40.1
75	61.1	62.4	65.8	65.2	31.9	31.3	35.8	37.1
70	59.6	60.9	63.0	63.9	29.4	28.8	32.8	34.1
65	56.8	59.7	61.8	62.5	26.5	25.1	30.2	32.5
60	54.0	57.1	60.8	60.9	24.2	23.4	27.1	30.8
55	51.6	53.8	59.8	58.3	22.6	21.5	24.6	28.7
50	48.7	51.6	57.0	56.0	20.3	20.0	21.4	25.4
45	45.8	50.1	53.7	52.3	18.5	18.5	19.2	24.0
40	42.7	47.4	51.0	49.8	16.6	15.8	16.7	21.3
35	39.9	44.8	48.7	46.7	14.1	14.2	15.1	19.1
30	36.3	42.3	45.3	43.7	12.0	12.4	12.8	16.9
25	33.8	38.3	42.0	41.5	10.2	10.6	10.6	14.8
20	31.0	34.5	39.8	38.9	8.8	8.6	9.0	12.0
15	26.8	29.1	35.1	34.8	6.9	7.1	7.8	9.1
10	21.8	24.1	29.8	30.7	5.2	5.8	5.8	6.2
5	12.5	15.5	18.3	24.5	3.5	3.3	3.9	4.5

Figure 10.12 The push-ups test. **A.** Standard push-up. **B.** Modified push-up.

must touch the mat on each repetition to count in the score. Women may perform modified push-ups with the knees bent and touching the mat rather than the toes (Figure 10.12 B). The score is simply the number of push-ups successfully completed. Evaluative norms are presented in Table 10.11.

Continuous Burpee Test

This test measures the participant's general muscular endurance. Appropriate for both males and females, all that is required for this test is a stopwatch, wrist watch, or clock with a second hand. A burpee is performed in the following sequence: from standing, (1) the subject squats and places the hands on the floor in front of the feet; (2) propels the legs backwards to a front-leaning rest position; (3) returns to the squat-rest position; and (4) rises back to a standing position (Figure 10.13). The test involves repeating this sequence as many times as possible after a "Go!" signal has been given. The subject's score is the total number of repetitions. Evaluative norms are presented in Table 10.12.

Table 10.11 Norms (number of repetitions) for the push-ups test.

Performance Level	No. of Push-ups	
	Males (15 – 29)	Females (15 – 29)
Excellent	50+	45+
Above Average	40 – 49	30 – 44
Average	30 – 39	20 – 29
Below Average	20 – 29	10 – 19
Needs Improvement	0 – 19	0 – 9

Table 10.12 Norms (total number of burpees) for the continuous burpee test.

Performance Level	No. of Burpees	
	Males	Females
Excellent	94+	46+
Above Average	70 – 93	38 – 45
Average	39 – 69	20 – 37
Below Average	22 – 38	12 – 19
Needs Improvement	0 – 21	0 – 11

Starting position   *Squat or crouch position*

Front-leaning rest position

Return to squat position   *Return to standing*

Figure 10.13 The sequence of a properly performed burpee.

Measuring Flexibility

Measuring **flexibility** or joint range of motion is an important measurement goal. Not only is flexibility important for performing physical skills, but it is also vital for performing daily tasks with comfort and ease. However, flexibility tends to be joint specific; therefore, a general test of flexibility really doesn't exist. Having flexible shoulders does not mean you will have flexible hamstrings. This creates a problem in measuring flexibility, unless the flexibility of a specific joint is being tested. Various laboratory methods exist that measure joint range of motion, including goniometry (manual, electric, and pendulum goniometers), radiography, photography, trigonometry, and linear measurements. While these methods are reliable and valid, many are not feasible for schools or average individuals. Other simple field tests exist that effectively measure flexibility.

Sit-and-Reach Test

This test assessing trunk and hamstring flexibility is satisfactory for both males and females from age five and above. Prior to testing, participants should warm up properly to stretch. These tests involve reaching as far forward as possible with the legs held straight. Some tests use a specially constructed box of specific dimensions with a measurement scale (Figure 10.14). However, the

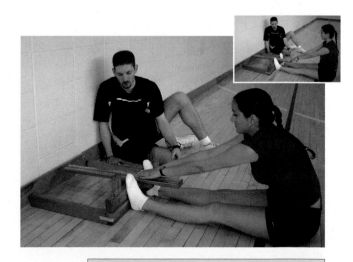

Figure 10.14 The sit-and-reach test.

Table 10.13 Norms (cm) for the modified sit-and-reach test.

Males			Females		
Percentile Rank	**Age Category**		**Percentile Rank**	**Age Category**	
	Under 18	**19 – 35**		**Under 18**	**19 – 35**
99	53	51	99	57	53
95	50	48	95	50	49
90	46	44	90	47	45
80	45	43	80	45	42
70	41	40	70	42	41
60	39	38	60	41	40
50	37	37	50	39	38
40	36	34	40	37	37
30	34	33	30	35	35
20	30	29	20	32	32
10	24	23	10	29	26
05	21	20	05	24	23
01	18	18	01	20	19

test may also be completed with a metre stick or measuring tape. For this modified test, the participant sits with one leg on either side of the metre stick or tape measure with the feet and arms outstretched and the hips, back, and head against the wall (see background image in Table 10.13). The tape measure on the floor should be lined up with the edge of the participant's outstretched fingers. The participant's head and back can now come off the wall and gradually reach forward along the metre stick three times. On the third attempt, the participant stretches forward as far as possible, and holds the final position for at least two seconds. The back of the participant's knees must remain flat on the floor. Each trial is scored to the nearest centimetre. Two trials are allowed and the final test score is calculated as the average of the two scores. Evaluative norms are presented in Table 10.13.

Bridge-up Test

Although little testing has been conducted on trunk extension, here is one test that is useful. It measures trunk extension, and is particularly useful for assessing flexibility for sports such as the butterfly (swimming), high jump, modern dance and ballet, and the balance beam and floor exercise events in gymnastics. It is appropriate for both males and females, and all that is needed is a mat and a yardstick. Subjects begin in a supine position (on their backs) with their feet against a wall. Each

Figure 10.15 The bridge-up test.

subject should tilt the head back, pushing upwards and arching the back. The subjects then walk their hands and feet as close together as possible. A partner then measures the highest point of the arched back from the floor (Figure 10.15). Record the best score of three trials; this score is then subtracted from the subject's standing height (floor to navel). The smaller the difference, the better the performance.

Hamstring Looseness Test

This test is designed to assess hamstring looseness. Prior to testing, participants should be properly warmed up to stretch. The participant stands with the feet approximately hip-width apart. Keeping the knees straight, the participant bends over at the waist and lets the arms drop towards the ground, pushing the hands as far towards the floor as the hamstrings will allow. Refer to Figure 10.16 A-D and Table 10.14 to determine your performance level.

Table 10.14 Performance levels for the hamstring looseness test.

Performance Level	Position Reached
Excellent	Palms touch the floor (Figure 10.16 A)
Above Average	Knuckles touch the floor (Figure 10.16 B)
Average	Fingertips touch the floor (Figure 10.16 C)
Below Average	Fingertips touch the feet
Needs Improvement	Fingertips touch the ankles or higher (Figure 10.16 D)

Figure 10.16 The hamstring looseness test. **A.** Palms touch the floor. **B.** Knuckles touch the floor. **C.** Fingertips touch the floor. **D.** Fingertips touch the ankles or higher.

Total Body Rotation Test

This simple test is designed to measure trunk flexibility. Begin by fastening a measuring tape on the wall at approximately shoulder height of the participant. At the 40-cm mark, draw a line with masking tape or chalk on the floor. Adjust the height of the measuring tape to each participant to ensure it is at shoulder height. Two stations are needed for testing both sides.

The participant should be properly warmed up to stretch. The participant stands sideways, an arm's length away from the wall. The toes must be lined up with the line on the floor with the feet parallel and shoulder-width apart, and the knees slightly bent. With the inside arm extended to the

Figure 10.17 The total body rotation test. **A.** Starting position. **B.** Right rotation.

wall and the outside arm stretched out parallel to the floor, the knuckles must face the ceiling (Figure 10.17 A). Now rotate the trunk, the outside arm stretching backwards until it touches the wall. Gradually slide the fist alongside the tape measure as far as possible. The final position must be held for a minimum of two seconds. The body must be kept as straight as possible and the feet should always be pointing straight forward (Figure 10.17 B).

The test is conducted on either the right or left side of the body. Each participant is allowed two trials on the selected side. Each trial is scored to the nearest centimetre at the knuckles, and held for at least two seconds. The average of two trials is used as the final test score. Evaluative norms are presented in Table 10.15.

Measuring Agility

Agility, the physical ability that enables rapid and precise change of body position and direction, is important for many activities and sports. Athletes who participate in sports such as judo, wrestling, or badminton, which require quick maneuverability and agile reactions, undoubtedly possess a high

Table 10.15 Percentile norms (cm) for the total body rotation test.

Percentile Rank	Left Rotation				Right Rotation			
	Under Age 18		Age 19 – 35		Under Age 18		Age 19 – 35	
	Male	Female	Male	Female	Male	Female	Male	Female
99	74	74	71	73	72	75	71	75
95	68	68	63	63	65	70	65	64
90	64	65	60	58	62	66	61	58
80	56	60	56	55	58	60	57	53
70	53	55	52	52	54	56	53	49
60	51	52	49	49	50	53	48	46
50	47	50	46	46	48	50	44	44
40	43	47	43	44	44	46	41	41
30	38	43	38	40	38	41	38	39
20	35	41	34	39	33	37	34	36
10	27	33	27	35	27	31	29	28
05	22	28	23	19	21	26	21	22

Performance Level	College Men	High School and College Females	High School Boys
Excellent	≥ 34	≥ 30	≥ 32
Above Average	29 – 33	26 – 29	28 – 31
Average	17 – 28	14 – 25	16 – 27
Below Average	12 – 16	10 – 13	12 – 15
Needs Improvement	≤ 11	≤ 9	≤ 11

Table 10.16 Raw score norms (number of parts completed) for the burpee test.

degree of agility. Testing for agility may be accomplished in many ways, but only a few simple tests will be presented here.

Burpee Test

This test, as described previously, can also be used for evaluating agility. It effectively measures how quickly participants can change their body position. The score represents simply the parts of the exercise sequence completed in 10 seconds. Squatting and placing the hands on the floor represents the first part (Figure 10.13 B); propelling the legs backwards is the second (Figure 10.13 C); returning to the squat position is the third (Figure 10.13 D); and rising back to standing is the fourth (Figure 10.13 E). Scores are only valid if all parts of the exercise are performed

properly as shown in Figure 10.13. Evaluative norms are presented in Table 10.16.

CAHPER Shuttle Run

Shuttle runs are often used to measure the agility of individuals in running and changing direction. Both males and females age nine and up can complete this test. Marking tape, a stopwatch, and three bean bags (or three of any small object, e.g., blocks of wood) are all the equipment needed for the test.

One bean bag is placed beside the participant on the starting line and two bean bags are placed on a line 10 metres away. The participant lies face down, hands at the sides of the chest and forehead behind the starting line (Figure 10.18 A). On the signal, the participant (1) jumps to his or her feet

Figure 10.18 The shuttle run. **A.** Start face down at the starting line. **B.** Pick up a bean bag before returning to the start line.

Table 10.17 Norms (sec) for the CAHPER shuttle run, boys and girls 14-17 years old.

Percentile	Boys				Girls			
	14	15	16	17	14	15	16	17
95	10.6	10.4	10.1	10.0	11.1	11.3	11.2	11.2
90	10.7	10.6	10.3	10.2	11.4	11.6	11.4	11.2
85	10.9	10.8	10.5	10.4	11.6	11.8	11.7	11.6
80	11.0	10.9	10.6	10.5	11.8	11.9	11.8	11.8
75	11.2	11.0	10.7	10.6	12.0	12.2	12.0	11.9
70	11.3	11.1	10.8	10.7	12.1	12.3	12.1	12.0
65	11.4	11.2	10.9	10.8	12.3	12.4	12.2	12.1
60	11.5	11.3	11.0	10.9	12.4	12.5	12.3	12.3
55	11.6	11.4	11.0	11.0	12.6	12.8	12.5	12.5
50	11.7	11.4	11.1	11.1	12.7	12.9	12.6	12.6
45	11.8	11.5	11.3	11.2	12.8	13.0	12.7	12.7
40	11.9	11.6	11.4	11.3	13.0	13.1	12.9	12.8
35	12.0	11.7	11.5	11.4	13.2	13.2	13.0	13.0
30	12.1	11.8	11.6	11.5	13.3	13.4	13.1	13.2
25	12.3	12.0	11.8	11.6	13.5	13.5	13.4	13.4
20	12.5	12.2	11.9	11.8	13.7	13.8	13.5	13.5
15	12.7	12.4	12.1	11.9	14.0	14.0	13.8	13.7
10	13.0	12.6	12.4	12.3	14.2	14.3	14.0	14.1
5	13.5	13.1	13.1	13.1	14.6	14.9	14.6	14.7

and runs 10 metres to the line; (2) picks up one bean bag (Figure 10.18 B); (3) returns to the start line; (4) sets the bean bag down across the line; (5) picks up another bean bag; (6) returns to the line 10 metres away; (7) exchanges the bean bag he or she is carrying for another; and (8) runs back across the finish line.

A "ready" warning signal should be given prior to the starting signal. Administer two trials with sufficient rest between them and record the better of the two to the nearest tenth of a second. Evaluative norms are shown in Table 10.17.

Hexagonal Obstacle Test

This test is designed to assess agility, coordination, and balance. Begin by drawing or taping a hexagon on the floor (66 cm per side). To simplify the task, first draw a large circle with a radius of approximately 66 cm; then insert the lines of the hexagon. Label the lines A to F (Figure 10.19 A).

Standing in the middle of the hexagon (Figure 10.19 B), the participant begins on signal to jump with both feet over side A and immediately back into the starting position within the hexagon. Then, without ever turning the body, the participant jumps over all sides to complete one round (Figure 10.19 C). The test continues until three full revolutions are completed. Time is recorded to the nearest tenth of a second. Time is stopped and recorded when the participant's feet enter the hexagon after jumping side F for the third time. The best time out of two trials is recorded (Table 10.18).

Figure 10.19 The hexagonal obstacle test. **A.** Schematic. **B.** Ready. **C.** Jump.

Table 10.18 Norms (sec) for the hexagonal obstacle test.

Performance Level	Males	Females
Excellent	≤ 10.0	≤ 10.5
Above Average	10.1 – 12.5	10.6 – 14.5
Average	12.6 – 15.5	14.6 – 18.5
Below Average	15.6 – 18.5	18.6 – 21.5
Needs Improvement	≥ 18.6	≥ 21.6

Summary

Physical fitness testing serves several important purposes, including diagnosis, placement, prediction, motivation, achievement, and program evaluation. When assessing physical fitness, it is important that reliable and valid fitness tests are selected. Reliability refers to the consistency of test scores, data, or observations, whereas validity refers to the extent to which a test measures what it proposes to measure. In addition, well-developed norms for all age categories help you compare and evaluate your personal test achievements relative to your peers.

Measures of physical fitness that are commonly assessed include aerobic capacity, body composition, muscular strength, muscular power, muscular endurance, flexibility, and agility. While more accurate test results can be obtained by using sophisticated laboratory equipment, many reliable and valid field tests (e.g., step tests, skinfold measurements, shuttle runs, and the sit-and-reach test) have proven to be useful in assessing the major components of fitness. However, you must realize that any assessment requires thorough preparation, practice trials, and attention to detail for sound measurement and evaluation of performance. Effective measurement and evaluation of your physical fitness should help you develop into a healthy and physically educated individual.

Key Words

Absolute strength
Achievement
Agility
Diagnosis
Field test
Flexibility
Grip dynamometer
Laboratory test

Maximal oxygen consumption
 ($\dot{V}O_2$max)
Motivation
Muscular endurance
Norms
One repetition maximum
 (1RM)
Placement

Power
Prediction
Program evaluation
Reliability
Skinfold measurement
Strength
Validity

Discussion Questions

1. List and briefly describe the six major purposes of testing and evaluation.

2. What are evaluative norms? Discuss their usefulness in interpreting test results.

3. Differentiate between the concepts of reliability and validity. Can a test have one without the other? Explain.

4. Discuss the advantages and disadvantages of laboratory versus field tests. Provide an example of each test.

5. List the most common sites used to measure skinfolds when estimating body composition. How do skinfold measurements differ from girth measurements?

6. Describe an alternative method of assessing maximal strength without performing a one repetition maximum (1RM) test.

7. Select one component of fitness and describe two field tests that can be used to assess it.

A Career in Teaching

NAME: Ross Murray
OCCUPATION: Health and Physical Education Teacher
EDUCATION: BPHE, University of Toronto (Physical and Health Education)
BEd, University of Toronto (Education)

What do you do?

I am the head of the Health and Physical Education Department of an independent boarding school 40 minutes outside of Toronto. My responsibilities include teaching grades 9 to 12 health and physical education, coordinating school-wide intramural programs, and coaching a variety of sports including soccer, ice hockey, and baseball. I also spend a lot of time writing curriculum, writing student reports, organizing department meetings, and monitoring the equipment and facilities.

What is unique about teaching?

A teacher's life is filled with wonderment and reward. A teacher has the ability to influence another life immeasurably, and teaching offers enormous possibilities for changing the lives of others for the betterment of society. Teaching is more than simply imparting subject matter to students. It is a complex profession that puts the greater needs of society before the content to be taught.

How have your studies in health and physical education benefited you as a teacher?

My years spent at the University of Toronto studying health and physical education have had a tremendous impact on my life, values, and motivations. I came to appreciate the pervasiveness and diversity of physical activity in human life. Physical activity is part of our nature. It is an important means by which we explore and discover our world, and it is a way for our uniqueness to be expressed. Not only did my knowledge of human anatomy, biomechanics, and nutrition increase, but so did my realization that something as vital to human life as physical activity deserves to be studied as seriously as other respected disciplines such as biology and history.

What do you enjoy most about teaching health and physical education?

It makes me feel great when students get to physical education class early and continually ask me, "What are we doing today, sir?" For many students, PE is the best part of their day and I really enjoy being able to provide positive experiences through physical activity and movement. Teaching and coaching allow for enormous social contact, from teaching classes and coaching after school, to just talking about the hockey game the night before with those students who just love being around the gym all day.

I also really enjoy teaching and interacting with students from all parts of the world. I often feel as though I am learning a lot more from them than they are from me. Teaching can be very draining and demanding; however it is very rewarding and I enjoy it tremendously.

What career advice would you give to those students thinking about teaching PHE?

Many students don't realize that to teach health and physical education in Ontario, students require two degrees. Both a four-year bachelor's degree in exercise sciences or kinesiology and a Bachelor of Education degree are needed. Therefore students have to maintain a high average in high school with a focus on the sciences.

Also, as a teacher you indirectly become a role model for many of your students. I feel that if you do want to teach physical education and promote health then you should practice what you preach, by living a balanced, active lifestyle and really enjoying playing.

In This Chapter:

The Digestive System   *263*

Nutritional Requirements: Types and Sources of Nutrients   *266*
Proteins   *267*
Fats   *268*
Carbohydrates   *270*
Fibre   *271*
Vitamins   *272*
Minerals   *274*
Water   *276*

Nutrition Guidelines and Recommendations   *277*
Canada's Food Guide to Healthy Eating   *278*

Nutrition Questions and Answers   *279*
How bad is fast food, really?   *282*
Why should I read food labels? What do they tell me?   *282*
How safe is the food supply?   *284*
Is vegetarianism a healthy alternative?   *285*
Do I need vitamin or mineral supplements?   *288*
What's the scoop on sugar?   *288*
How do nutritional needs change as we grow older?   *289*
Can diet improve athletic performance?   *289*

Summary   *292*

CHAPTER 11

The Nutritional Connection

After completing this chapter you should be able to:

- describe the anatomy and physiology of the digestive system;

- identify the nutritional requirements and components of a healthy diet;

- outline the official nutritional advice provided for Canadians;

- explain the unique nutritional needs of various populations;

- describe the effects of nutrition on athletic performance.

Not all the factors associated with health can be controlled, but your attitude and habits related to diet can influence your health in a positive way. The role of diet in overall health is significant and has profound effects on general well-being. Poor diets are often associated with disease and illness, but healthy diets can be sources of energy and vigor. Choosing foods that provide the necessary nutrients, while limiting those associated with disease, can therefore significantly affect the course your life and health will take. Furthermore, proper nutrition is essential to getting the competitive edge that athletes require to win, since it allows the body to perform at its best.

An understanding of what constitutes a healthy diet will allow you to make informed decisions about your nutrition-related concerns. While you should enjoy eating well and staying active, you must not assume that a healthy diet needs to be restricted to fat-free, low-sugar, and high-fibre foods all the time; in fact, the basics of a healthy diet are variety, balance, and moderation. Following these basic rules will effectively guide you to eating sensibly.

It is also important to understand that all foods are good – with one distinction: that some are good to have more often than others. There is nothing wrong with eating ice cream or a chocolate bar on occasion, just as long as it is *on occasion*. Labeling foods as good or bad sends a negative message about eating that should be avoided. An overall pattern of healthy eating should be your practical nutritional goal. We must not take for granted the remarkable ability of our bodies to deal with foods and substances over time, because it may catch up with us in the long run.

Students, for example, are faced with nutritional concerns on a daily basis over a simple matter such as what to eat for lunch. Bringing a lunch from home is always an option, but what kind of selection is there in school cafeterias (e.g., nutrition-wise, vegetarian dishes, etc.)? Many students settle for what is available to them, and fast foods (which fill school cafeterias and are conveniently located near schools) would not be considered ideal foods to eat on a daily basis.

A similar concern arises for the regular party-goer whose selection of food and snacks is often limited to potato chips, cookies, and pop (or alcohol) – all low nutritional choices. It is up to the hosts of these parties, as well as those attending, to ensure that a variety of food is available for those who would prefer to eat on the lighter side. Providing different options helps make everyone feel at ease and keeps the occasion enjoyable for all.

Clearly, many issues are related to your nutritional habits, and their impact on your daily life is considerable. This chapter will attempt to outline the dietary recommendations made for Canadians, helping you attain the tools necessary to incorporate a healthy diet in your own life.

World of convenien takes its t

Continued from A1

ventable. In this, the first of an eight part series, we examine a key factor that affects all of us.

It is the way we live. And – whether you're thick or thin – it will likely affect when you die.

The late 20th century swept us, via moving sidewalks, into a world of complex simplicity. Fast food, online banking, ride-on...

theoretically in save 21,340 live each year deaths among Through the on fitness th nificant asse obesity - ' ers have t derstand those can

---

Germs lurking in unexpected foods

WASHINGTON (AP) — Alfalfa sprouts contaminated by E. coli. Hepatitis-tainted strawberries in school lunches. Children sick from unpasteurized apple juice and 140 people struck by bacteria-laden raw oysters.

The recent recall of 11 million kilograms of hamburger is merely the latest scare about dangerous germs contaminating food. Keeping hamburger safe mostly requires thorough cooking. But consumer advocates say a larger threat may come from germs lurking in unexpected places, such as raspberries or fresh basil.

"Almost monthly, we are seeing new causes for concern based on food problems," said Caroline Smith De-Waal of the advocacy group Centre for Science in the Public Inte... don't have a gove... has climb...

The Food and Drug Administration is considering putting warning labels on unpasteurized apple juices and ciders after dozens of children were sickened by E. coli that got into one trendy brand. Pasteurization kills potentially deadly E. coli bacteria.

Scientists are investigating whether irradiating beef could kill E. coli and other disease-causing microorganisms and whether irradiating fresh berries would kill cyclospora, a parasite that sickened about 1,400 Americans who ate Guatemalan raspberries this spring.

The latest scare comes as rado residents hamburger

meat from one day in the next day's production, potentially causing a chain

---

Calcium needs upped

More a must for healthy bones, scientists say

...TON (Reuter-AP-...

en," said Dr. Connie Weaver, a Purdue University nutrition expert on the panel.

The level for ages 19 to 50 is 1,000 milligrams of milk or its equivalent in cheese and yogurt, as well as one helping each of turnip greens, broccoli and green...

posed daily guidelines with three cups of milk or its equivalent in cheese and yogurt, as well as one helping each of turnip greens, broccoli and green nip greens, broccoli and green beans, for instance.

Where the old system set only the recommended daily allowance – the minimum level of a nutrient needed to decrease the risk of chronic disease – the...

ple over 50 the board recommended levels of 1,200 milligrams daily.

For pregnant and lactating ...mens 1,300...

New calcium guidelines

Babies need less, while over 50 need more ca... day for good health.

Current daily intake:
New goal (men and...

Infants (1-3 yrs.)

500

Youths (9-18...

Double your fibre intake, says new food guide

BY PETER CALAMAI
SCIENCE REPORTER

OTTAWA — Canadians can look forward to greater flexibility in tailoring a daily diet that appeals to them but also fits a healthy lifestyle, according to a major North American nutrition study released yesterday.

The two-volume report by 50 Canadian and U.S. scientists recommends wide ranges rather than exact figures for healthy levels of carbohydrates, fat and protein to provide the necessary daily calories for normal eating. For adults, these ranges are:

■ Between 45 and 65 per cent of necessary calories from carbohydrates, the sugars and starches in bread, pasta and fruit.

■ 20 to 35 per cent from the fat in meat, dairy products and oils.

■ 10 to 35 per cent from the protein in meat, eggs, dairy products and vegetables like beans.

But the report emphasized that no more than a quarter of daily calories should come from the added sugars found in soft drinks, pastries and sweets. Nutrition surveys have found that people whose diets are high in these added sugars often get low amounts of essential nutrients.

The experts also recommend daily intakes of fibre that would double what the average Canadian now eats and urge everyone to keep their consumption of saturated fats and trans fatty acids as low as possible.

Mediterranean diet holds key to heal

Mediterranean people figured out long ago that good food, garnished with little more than fresh herbs, garlic and olive oil and enjoyed in a relaxing meal, not only tasted good but was good for their health.

Now the Mediterranean diet has been deemed by experts to be the most effective model for dining your way to good health.

HOMEGROWN VEGETABLES

People who consume a traditional Mediterranean diet live longer and have a lower incidence of heart disease and some cancers compared to people living in North America or Northern Europe.

The traditional Mediterranean diet includes whole wheat

Eat Write
LYNN ROBLIN

bread, an abundance of home-grown vegetables, legumes (such as beans and chickpeas) and seasonal fruit.

Fish and poultry are eaten in small quantities a few times a week. Yogurt and cheese are the preferred daily choice.

Meat is used less frequently and in small quantities, as a garnish more than as a main ingredient.

Olive oil is the major source of fat and most foods are eaten fresh rather than processed.

Red wine often accompanies meals (the grapes and grape

75 per cent — Cop...

skins are high in antioxidants). While the amount of fat eaten in the Mediterranean diet is similar to that of the North American diet, its components are quite different. The typical North American diet is very low in fruits and vegetables but rich in saturated fat from fast foods, processed foods, meat and dairy products.

No single factor is responsible for the good health associated with Mediterranean diets. The fact that the diet is high in monounsaturated fat and low in both saturated and polyunsaturated fat is one factor.

Olive oil is rich in mono-unsaturated fat which appears to raise HDL (good) cholesterol levels in our bodies. Olive oil

also contains vitamin E, a powerful antioxidant.

The high content of natural antioxidants and phytochemicals from vegetables, legumes, fruits, nuts, red wine and olive oil is an important feature of the Mediterranean diet.

Both antioxidants and phyto-chemicals play a role in reducing risk of cancer and heart disease.

HEALTH BENEFITS

But the potential health benefits derived from the Mediterranean diet are linked to its combination of high carbohydrates and fibre foods, antioxidant vitamins (vitamins C, E and beta carotene) and mono-unsaturated fats which work together to

decreasing the risk of disease.

Other lifestyle factors so contribute to the b hancing effect of the t Mediterranean diet. O lar importance is the preparation and leis sumption of meals w or friends.

The typical Me meal provides relie creased risk of h factor associat This eating patter different from our which might be e with eastern or w dine-and-dash m ence as we run e erywhere but to ner table.

The Digestive System

You have probably wondered at one time or another how your body uses the food you eat to produce energy, and how energy-rich nutrients, water, and electrolytes are transferred into your body's internal environment. It is largely the role of the **digestive system**, composed of numerous structures and organs that work together, to accomplish this vital task. Although the components of the digestive tract are often discussed as separate structures according to the specialized functions they perform, the tract is actually continuous.

The **gastrointestinal tract** (digestive tract) portion of the system includes the mouth, pharynx, esophagus, stomach, small and large intestines, rectum, and anus; the **glandular organs** involved in the process include the salivary glands, liver, gallbladder, and pancreas (Figure 11.1). This effective organization allows food to be ingested and processed into forms that can be absorbed and used by the body. Keep in mind that the contents of the digestive tract actually remain part of the external environment until they have been absorbed across the gastrointestinal wall into the body.

The digestive system performs four basic digestive processes: digestion, secretion, absorption, and motility (Figure 11.2). Because the foods we eat contain nutrients that cannot cross the gastrointestinal wall (such as carbohydrates, proteins, and fats), the process of **digestion** is required to dissolve and break down these foods into molecules that can be absorbed by the body. Digestion works very closely with the **secretion** of numerous substances, including hydrochloric acid by the stomach, bile from the liver, and numerous other digestive enzymes. The **absorption** of the molecules produced by digestion occurs across a layer of epithelial cells lining the gastrointestinal wall to enter blood or lymph, where the circulatory system is able to distribute them to body cells. While foods are being digested, enzymes secreted, and digested molecules absorbed, the digestive tract is exercising **motility** – the muscular contrac-

tions that move the contents of the digestive tract forward. This process is important not only to propel the contents forward, but also to mix food with digestive juices that promote digestion.

The Digestive Processes

The digestive system allows food to be ingested and processed into molecules that can be absorbed and used by the body by performing four basic digestive processes: *digestion, secretion, absorption,* and *motility*.

Although the purpose of the digestive system is to absorb nutrients, some material is obviously excreted via the gastrointestinal tract as waste. This material is **feces**, consisting mainly of bacteria and ingested material that was not digested and absorbed (including fibre). Therefore, this system effectively allows us to absorb what we need, and excrete what we don't need.

Functional Overview of the Gastrointestinal Organs

Thus far, we have discussed the functions and processes involved with the digestive system as a whole; but each portion of the system actually performs a specialized role. Digestion begins in the mouth, as chewing breaks food up into smaller pieces (bolus) that can be swallowed without choking. Further, **saliva** produced by three salivary glands in the head contains important mucus that moistens and lubricates food, as well as the enzyme **amylase**, which begins the digestion of carbohydrates.

The voluntary act of swallowing, initiated in the posterior mouth or **oropharynx**, results in movement of the food bolus into the **pharynx** and **esophagus**, where involuntary muscular contractions (**peristalsis**) take over and move the food down into the stomach. The **stomach** (a sac-like organ) serves as a storage site, dissolves

Mouth
Chewing (mechanical digestion); initiation of swallowing

Salivary Glands
Moistens food; mucus lubrication; amylase initiates digestion of carbohydrates

Liver
Secretion of bile; bile salts solubilize water-insoluble fats; bicarbonate neutralizes hydrochloric acid (HCl) entering small intestine from stomach

Gallbladder
Stores and concentrates bile between meals

Large Intestine
Storage and concentration of undigested matter; mixing and propulsion of contents; mucus lubrication

Rectum
Defecation

Pharynx
Initiation of swallowing

Esophagus
Moves food into stomach through peristalsis action; mucus lubrication

Stomach
Stores, mixes, dissolves, and begins digestion of food; regulates emptying of dissolved food into small intestine; hydrochloric acid (HCl) kills microbes; pepsin begins protein digestion

Pancreas
Secretion of enzymes and bicarbonate; digests carbohydrates, fats, and protein; bicarbonate neutralizes HCl entering small intestine from stomach

Small Intestine
Digestion and absorption of most substances; mixing and propulsion of contents; mucus lubrication

Anus
Defecation

Figure 11.1 An overview of the anatomy and physiology of the digestive system.

Figure 11.2 Schematic of the basic digestive processes: digestion, secretion, absorption, and motility.

and partially digests food, and prepares food for optimal digestion and absorption in the small intestine. Glands in the stomach's lining secrete a strong **hydrochloric acid** which serves to dissolve the particulate matter in food (except fat), and also kills bacteria that may have entered along with the food (though some do survive to flourish in the intestines). An enzyme called **pepsin** is also formed from the secreted precursor called **pepsinogen**. Pepsin begins protein digestion, and amylase (from the salivary glands) continues to break down carbohydrates into smaller fragments. However, despite the digestive actions that occur in the stomach, little absorption occurs across the stomach wall.

The next segment of the tract is the **small intestine**, where digestion is completed and most absorption occurs. The small intestine is approximately nine feet in length and consists of three segments: the **duodenum**, **jejunum**, and **ileum**. Most absorption occurs in the duodenum and jejunum, including the absorption of vitamins, minerals, and water, which do not

require enzymes to be digested. The existing molecules of carbohydrates, proteins, and fats are further broken down by hydrolytic enzymes into monosaccharides, amino acids, and fatty acids (absorbable units) respectively. While some of the necessary enzymes are located on the surface of the intestinal wall, others are provided by the pancreas and liver, which enter the duodenum of the small intestine via ducts.

The **pancreas** secretes both digestive enzymes, for each type of organic molecule, and an alkaline fluid consisting mainly of bicarbonate ions. The latter secretion serves to neutralize the acidic contents coming from the stomach to prevent damage to the small intestine wall, and to provide an optimal pH for enzymes to function.

The **liver** also provides an important secretory product – **bile**. While the liver performs a myriad of functions, its exocrine functions related to the secretion of bile will be the focus here. Bile from the liver contains cholesterol, bicarbonate ions (like those from the pancreas), and **bile salts**. Bile salts are essential to the digestion and absorption of dietary fats, as they solubilize fats that are otherwise insoluble in water, and convert large fat globules into smaller fat droplets. The **gallbladder** serves as a storage site for bile secreted from the liver; during a meal, the walls of the gallbladder contract to move the concentrated bile into the duodenum via ducts to exert its actions (mainly on fat).

In the small intestine, the molecules and ions are absorbed in a variety of ways, including diffusion (fatty acids), osmosis (water), active transport (mineral ions), and carrier-mediated transport (monosaccharides and amino acids). As the motility of the small intestine moves and mixes its contents, the material slowly moves toward the large intestine. By the time the contents reach the **large intestine**, very little water, salts, and undigested material are left. It is the role of the large intestine to temporarily store these materials and concentrate them by reabsorbing salt and water. Once this is complete, the material (now feces) is moved to the **rectum** to be eliminated from the body through contractile activities, including associated sphincter muscles (the process is called **defecation**). This completes the long road that food must travel when providing us with the essential nutrients we need to lead a healthy life. The following sections will present the components of a healthy diet, what it means to eat well, and the importance of proper nutrition to healthy living.

Nutritional Requirements: Types and Sources of Nutrients

Nutrition, the science of food and how the body uses it in health and disease, encompasses a wide variety of topics and issues. When you consider what your diet is composed of, you probably think about the foods you eat. Really, what is important is what nutrients are contained in the foods you eat. Your body requires six categories of **essential nutrients**, namely: proteins, fats, carbohydrates, vitamins, minerals, and water. The term "essential" refers to the fact that the body is unable to manufacture these substances (or not in adequate amounts to meet body needs), so they must be obtained from outside the body in the form of food or supplements. We rely on food to provide the nutrients we need to ensure proper growth and development (Figure 11.3). These nutrients are obtained when the foods we eat are digested (broken down) into compounds that can be absorbed and used by the body. It is vital to have a diet containing adequate amounts of all essential nutrients since they provide energy, as well as the ability to help build and maintain tissues and regulate body functions.

Figure 11.3 A balanced diet that includes all the essential nutrients is necessary to promote optimal growth and development.

There are three nutrients that provide your body with energy, expressed as **kilocalories**: proteins, fats, and carbohydrates. One kilocalorie represents the amount of heat it takes to raise the temperature of 1 kg of water 1 degree Celsius. An average person needs approximately 2,000 kilocalories per day to meet his or her energy needs. The term **calorie** will be used here to represent the larger energy unit or kilocalorie.

Of the three classes of nutrients that supply energy, fats are the most calorie dense, providing nine calories per gram. In contrast, proteins and carbohydrates each provide four calories per

Kilocalories Versus Calories

In common usage, you will find that kilocalories are often referred to simply as calories, i.e., one kilocalorie contains 1,000 calories.

gram. This difference is one reason why fats are recommended to be eaten in smaller amounts (excess calories are stored as fat). Another source of energy (though not an essential nutrient) is alcohol, which provides seven calories per gram. Alcohol has no nutritional value, but its high caloric content creates a problem with excess calories being consumed (which often replace calories from nutritional sources).

Calorie Densities of Various Energy Sources

Fats	9 calories per gram
Alcohol	7 calories per gram
Carbohydrates	4 calories per gram
Proteins	4 calories per gram

Energy needs are not our only concern. We also need a balanced intake of all the essential nutrients to achieve optimal growth and development. Just as the human body is largely composed of water (about 60 percent), the major component in foods is also water. Most foods, however, are composed of a mixture of nutrients, including vitamins and minerals, which perform special functions, and fill unique roles. We take a closer look at each class of nutrient in the following section.

Proteins

Proteins may be found in every living cell, and represent the basis of our body structure. Proteins not only provide important structural components

or parts for muscles, bones, blood, enzymes, some hormones, and cell membranes, but also function as an energy source. Proteins themselves are composed of chains of amino acids, the building blocks of life. There are 20 commonly recognized, naturally occurring amino acids; of these, the body can synthesize all but 9 – the so-called essential amino acids (*histidine, isoleucine, leucine, lysine, methionine, phenylalanine, threonine, tryptophan,* and *valine*).

Because the amino acids are the building blocks of proteins, they are essential to our existence. But some sources of proteins are better than others in providing these essential amino acids. Individual protein sources are "complete" if they supply all 9 essential amino acids. Such complete protein sources are animal products, such as meat, fish, poultry, eggs, milk, and cheese. Sources of food that do not contain all the essential amino acids are called incomplete protein foods. These usually come from plant sources such as grains, beans, peas, and nuts. Although these sources are usually low in 1 or 2 amino acids, they are still good sources of essential amino acids.

Although incomplete protein sources on their own will not provide the appropriate complement of amino acids, various sources may be combined to achieve the full range to make a meal complete (Figure 11.4). This can be particularly important for vegetarians who must prepare meals consisting of plant foods, combining foods that account for the essential amino acids missing in some foods. Some common combinations include peanut butter and bread, rice and

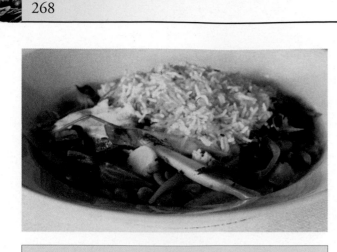

Figure 11.4 Rice and beans are examples of complementary protein sources.

beans, milk and cereal, and macaroni and cheese.

Protein is essential for promoting growth and the maintenance of body tissues; but eaten in excess, protein can pose a problem. Any protein consumed beyond the body's needs is synthesized into fat for storage or used as a source of energy. Nutritionists recommend that the amount of protein you eat should not exceed 10-15 percent of your total daily caloric intake. On the other end of the spectrum, a drop in caloric intake leads to protein being selectively broken down to provide glucose for the body, which can hamper the growth and repair of body tissues. In *extreme* situations where your diet lacks an adequate amount of proteins and carbohydrates, the body turns to its own proteins, which causes damaging muscle wasting. Thus, an intermediate range of calories must be consumed for optimal development.

Fats

Negative associations around the word "fat" would appear to be general and widespread. Anything in excess can be detrimental to your health, but fat in moderation is essential.

Fat (also known as **lipids**) is a very important nutrient in our diets for many reasons. It represents a source of usable energy, serves to insulate our bodies, cushions our organs, is involved in the synthesis of many hormones, and aids in the absorption of the fat-soluble vitamins (which would otherwise pass through our bodies). Further,

the presence of fats in foods adds important flavour and texture (palatability), which is one reason why many people find it difficult to cut down on some of their favourite foods (which happen to contain fat). Still, being the most concentrated source of energy, the consumption of fat should be closely monitored.

The fats in food are mostly in the form of **triglycerides**, composed of groupings of a glycerol (an alcohol) and three fatty acid molecules. Fats can be classified as saturated, monounsaturated, and polyunsaturated, based on the degree of saturation (the number of double bonds contained between the carbon atoms) of the fatty acid molecules. If no double bonds exist, these are **saturated fats**. When one double bond exists, the fatty acids are called **monounsaturated fats**, while those with two or more double bonds are called **polyunsaturated fats**.

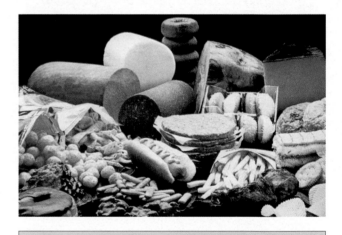

Figure 11.5 Foods containing high levels of saturated fat have been linked to heart disease.

While most foods contain some combination of these fats, the dominant type of fatty acid determines the characteristics of the fat. Foods that contain an abundance of saturated fat are usually solid at room temperature – commonly found in animal products such as meats, dairy products, eggs, and many baked products. This is the type of fat most closely associated with numerous cardiovascular diseases such as heart disease and should be eaten less often (Figure 11.5).

Those foods that contain large amounts of

Figure 11.6 Percentages of saturated, monounsaturated, and polyunsaturated fats in common oils.

unsaturated fats usually come from plant sources, and are liquid at room temperature (so-called "oils"). These unsaturated fats come in two forms, mono- and polyunsaturated fats. These fats are deemed more desirable, as they are not linked to cardiovascular disease as are saturated fats; in fact, monounsaturated and polyunsaturated fats may lower blood cholesterol levels and reduce the risk of heart disease. Monounsaturated fats are found in large amounts in olive, canola, sesame, and peanut oils. Sunflower, safflower, and corn oils contain mostly polyunsaturated fats (Figure 11.6).

Unfortunately, not all fats from plant sources are low in saturated fats. Palm oil and coconut oil (tropical oils often used in processed foods) contain a high quantity of saturated fat. Also, the process of **hydrogenation** turns what were double bonds in unsaturated fats to single bonds, yielding a more solid fat from an oil. This process is often used to extend the shelf life of fats (preventing its breakdown or its turning rancid), as well as to add the desired texture of pastry and cake

products. Hydrogenated oils and fats should be used sparingly, and it is important to read labels in order to identify those products that use the process of hydrogenation.

The issue of serum (blood) cholesterol levels as it relates to the intake of dietary cholesterol and saturated fats is an important issue to consider in attempting to control your blood cholesterol levels. While **cholesterol** is synthesized by our own bodies and is an important constituent of all animal tissue, high levels of cholesterol and triglycerides have also been implicated with the development of cardiovascular disease. There is evidence to show that an elevated intake of saturated fats may increase the levels of cholesterol in the blood. However, the relationship between the intake of dietary cholesterol (from sources such as egg yolk and animal fat) and blood cholesterol levels is uncertain. The process of hydrogenation mentioned earlier has another downside – it produces **trans fatty acids**, which are thought to increase blood cholesterol levels as well.

"Good" vs. "Bad" Cholesterol

Excess amounts of cholesterol in the body can accumulate on the inner walls of arteries, leading to a host of health implications, including atherosclerosis and heart disease.

The actual amount of circulating cholesterol itself, however, appears not to be as important as the ratio of total cholesterol to a group of compounds called **lipoproteins**.

Lipoproteins serve as transport facilitators for cholesterol in the blood and come in two basic forms: **high-density lipoproteins (HDLs)** (so-called "good" cholesterol) and **low-density** **lipoproteins (LDLs)** (so-called "bad" cholesterol). HDLs transport circulating cholesterol to the liver for metabolism and elimination, while LDLs transport cholesterol to the body's cells. Therefore, individuals with higher levels of HDLs have been shown to be at lower risk for developing plaque in the arteries and subsequent heart disease.

Participation in regular vigorous physical activity and consumption of monounsaturated fats such as olive oil appear to play a role in reducing cholesterol levels by increasing levels of HDLs.

Carbohydrates

When we are looking for food to give us a boost of energy, the foods containing high amounts of carbohydrates should be the ones we reach for (Figure 11.7). **Carbohydrates** are the primary source of energy in our diet, and should comprise approximately 60 percent of our daily calories. They are themselves composed of a number of sugar units, or saccharides, and can be divided into three groups based on the number of saccharides that form the molecule: monosaccharides contain one, disaccharides two, and polysaccharides more than two sugar units respectively. As a group, the mono- and disaccharides are considered sugars, while polysaccharides are commonly called starches.

Monosaccharides

Monosaccharides are the simplest of sugars. These would include glucose (also known as dextrose), fructose (also called levulose), and galactose. Because glucose makes up the blood sugar as the body's primary source of energy, it is the most important monosaccharide; in fact, the brain and nervous system use glucose for fuel almost exclusively. Glucose tends to be found in foods such as vegetables, fruit, and honey, whereas fructose is often found in fruits and berries.

Disaccharides

When you think of sugar you probably think of table sugar. Table sugar, as it is commonly known, is actually a disaccharide – sucrose (a combination of glucose and fructose). As stated earlier, **disaccharides** are made up of two monosaccharides, of which one is always a glucose molecule. Other familiar examples of disaccharides include lactose (found in milk) and

Figure 11.7 Pasta is an example of a food high in carbohydrates.

maltose (derived from germinating cereals). Along with the monosaccharides, the disaccharides provide much of the sweetness in the foods we eat. Sugar is abundant in our diets, although it is often hidden. We do not associate foods such as ketchup, salad dressings, or canned fruits and vegetables as containing significant amounts of sugar, but they do. The primary concern related to sugar consumption is dental caries (cavities) which can be combated by regular brushing.

Polysaccharides

Polysaccharides are commonly found in vegetables, fruits, and grains (e.g., pasta, bread, and rice). These are complex carbohydrates composed of extended chains of many sugar units (better known as *starches*). Aside from their role in providing a source of energy, starches often contain numerous vitamins, minerals, water, and protein. Dietary fibre is also a very important complex carbohydrate (see next section).

Before starches and double sugars can be taken up and used for energy, your body must digest them (break them down) into single sugar molecules (such as glucose) for absorption. Once in the bloodstream, glucose is able to provide cells with an energy source. The liver and muscles also store glucose in the form of **glycogen**. When such glycogen stores are full, any carbohydrates consumed above body needs are synthesized into fat and stored. Consuming large amounts of complex carbohydrates is beneficial to athletes since it enhances the amount of stored energy in the liver and muscles, providing an extended source of fuel for events of long duration.

Recommended Percentage of Total Daily Calories Supplied by the Three Major Nutrients

Proteins	10 – 15 percent
Fats	< 30 percent (< 10 percent saturated)
Carbohydrates	55 – 60 percent

Fibre

Fibre is not a nutrient by definition, but is still a very important element in our diets. For the most part, fibre includes plant substances that cannot be digested by humans; as a result, they pass through the digestive tract relatively unchanged, adding bulk for feces to facilitate elimination. Because some fibre can be metabolized by bacteria in the large intestine (producing acids and gases as by-products), a large intake of fibre can lead to intestinal gas.

Fibre can be classified as soluble or insoluble, and each has significant physiological effects on your body. **Soluble fibre** has the ability to bind cholesterol-containing compounds in the intestines, thus lowering blood cholesterol levels by clearing cholesterol from the intestinal tract. Soluble fibre has also been known to slow your body's absorption of glucose, having potential implications for the treatment of diabetes.

Fibre that is classified as insoluble also offers important benefits for good health. Its main function is to absorb water from the intestinal tract, thereby aiding in making feces softer and bulkier to improve elimination. A diet with adequate amounts of **insoluble fibre** can effectively prevent a variety of health concerns such as constipation and some forms of cancer of the lower intestinal tract.

It is important to note that all plant foods contain some dietary fibre, though some more than others. Some rich sources of soluble fibre include fruits, legumes (e.g., beans, peas, lentils), oats, and barley. Other sources of dietary fibre such as wheat, grains, vegetables, and cereals are classified as insoluble sources. It is always a good idea to eat fresh fruits and vegetables and whole grain foods, since the processing of foods can remove some of their valuable fibre content. Try eating a variety of fibre-rich foods, but do so gradually so as to avoid upsetting your digestive system. Also, make an attempt to choose alternatives – try whole wheat bread instead of white, or oranges in the place of orange juice. These types of habits can offer benefits that last a lifetime.

Types of Fibre

Fibre can be classified generally as soluble or insoluble. While sources of *soluble fibre* (such as fruit, legumes, oats, and barley) have been shown to help reduce blood cholesterol levels and maintain glucose balance, sources of *insoluble fibre* (such as vegetables, wheat, grains, and cereals) assist in bulking and softening feces, improving elimination, and preventing colorectal cancer.

Vitamins

Unlike the nutrients discussed thus far, vitamins do not provide calories; instead, they serve as **coenzymes**, facilitating the action of enzymes in a variety of responses and chemical reactions. **Vitamins** are organic (carbon-containing) substances that are required in small amounts for normal growth, reproduction, and maintenance of health.

A distinction can be made between two broad classifications of vitamins: **water-soluble** (able to dissolve in water) and **fat-soluble** (able to dissolve in fat or lipid tissue). The water-soluble vitamins are not readily stored, so any excess is usually eliminated from the body during urination. These would include vitamin C and the B-complex vitamins (Table 11.1). On the other hand, the fat-soluble vitamins (A, D, E, and K), taken in excess, are able to be stored in fat (adipose) tissue in the body (Table 11.2). As a result there is a concern, for consuming and retaining too many of these particular vitamins (especially A and D) may lead to toxicity. Obviously, a diet lacking a

particular vitamin (adequate amounts) will lead to characteristic symptoms of a deficiency (Tables 11.1 and 11.2).

Another fact to consider when dealing with water-soluble vitamins is that they will dissolve fairly quickly in water. It is therefore important not to overcook fresh fruits and vegetables, because the longer they remain cooking, the more vitamins will be lost (unless you also plan to use the water in which the food was cooked). Steaming vegetables rather than boiling them is the best way to retain their nutritional content.

Some vitamins form substances that act as **antioxidants**. These aid in preserving healthy cells in the body and decrease the breakdown of foodstuffs. As the body breaks down fats or uses oxygen, compounds called **free radicals** are formed. These free radicals require electrons, so they react with fats, proteins, and DNA, damaging cell membranes and mutating genes along the way. Antioxidants serve to react with these free radicals (donating electrons) making them harmless to you. Such antioxidants in our diet include vitamins E, C, and beta-carotene (the

Table 11.1 The major water-soluble vitamins.

Vitamin	Physiological Functions	Vitamin Food Sources	Deficiency Effects
Thiamin (B$_1$)	Glucose metabolism; nervous system synaptic functioning	Enriched breads and cereals; pork, kidney; peas; pecans	Constipation; nausea; depression, fatigue, irritability; loss of hand-eye coordination; gait changes; often seen with anorexics
Riboflavin (B$_2$)	Red blood cell formation; glycogen synthesis; energy release from glucose and fatty acids; growth; adrenal cortex activity	Beef, liver, heart; yogurt, milk, cheese; almonds, broccoli, asparagus; produced by intestinal flora	Personality shifts, depression; cracked mouth and lips; purplish-red tongue; dry skin; fetal development effects
Niacin (B$_3$)	Protein and fat synthesis; energy release from all nutrient forms	Meat, poultry, liver; peanut butter	Diarrhea; depression, irritability, headaches; sleeplessness; personality disorientation; pellagra-dermatitis; death
Pyridoxine (B$_6$)	Protein, lipid, and carbohydrate metabolism; neurotransmitter synthesis; hemoglobin synthesis; antibody production; fetal nervous system function; synthesis/breakdown of amino acids	Chicken, fish; egg yolk; bananas, avocados; whole-grain cereal	No known deficiency in adults; poor growth; anemia; skin lesions; decreased niacin production, convulsions; decreased antibody production
Cobalamin (B$_{12}$)	Red blood cell formation; metabolism of folacin; growth and function of nervous system	Meat, liver, kidney; eggs; dairy products	Pernicious anemia in adults; however, not caused by lack of B$_{12}$, but a lack of intrinsic factor influencing absorption
Folacin (folic acid)	Red blood cell formation; fetal development; DNA synthesis required for rapid cell division	Bread; oranges and orange juice; meat, poultry, fish, eggs; broccoli, lima beans, asparagus, spinach	Infections; rheumatoid arthritis; chronic alcohol use leads to inadequate absorption; toxemia of pregnancy
Ascorbic acid (vitamin C)	Tooth development; maintenance of scar tissue; folic acid formation; absorption of iron and calcium; neurotransmitter synthesis	Peppers, broccoli, kale, cauliflower, strawberries, lemons, papayas, spinach, asparagus; liver	Scurvy; fatigue, shortness of breath, muscle cramps, skeletal pain; dry skin; anorexia; bleeding gums; depressed glucose tolerance; personality disorders

Table 11.2 The major fat-soluble vitamins.

Vitamin	Physiological Functions	Vitamin Food Sources	Deficiency Effects
A	Bone growth; night vision; sperm production; growth of epithelial cells; estrogen synthesis; mucus gland secretion	Eggs, cheese, liver, milk; yellow, orange, and dark green vegetables; broccoli, carrots, cantaloupe, spinach	Night blindness, corneal deterioration; skin changes; enamel alteration; diarrhea; respiratory infections
D	Bone growth; calcium and phosphorus absorption; kidney resorption of calcium and phosphorus; neuromuscular activity	Egg yolk; fortified milk; fish-liver oil, tuna; sunlight stimulates the body's production of the vitamin	Osteomalacia; osteoporosis; tooth malformation; rickets
E	Vitamin A absorption; antioxidation of unsaturated fatty acids and tissue lipids; heme synthesis for red blood cell function	Wheat germ, whole-grain cereal; vegetable oils; liver; leafy green vegetables	Deficiency rarely seen in humans; destruction of red blood cell membrane
K	Synthesis of clotting factors in the liver	Dark green leafy vegetables, cabbage, cauliflower, tomatoes; eggs; liver; produced by intestinal flora	Prolonged coagulation time, bleeding, bruising

vitamin A derivative). A regular intake of these nutrients goes a long way in maintaining a healthy body over time.

Minerals

Minerals are inorganic (non-carbon-containing) materials which are needed in small amounts to perform numerous functions in the body. Minerals function as structural elements (e.g., in teeth, muscles, hormones), regulate body functions (e.g., muscle contraction, blood clotting, heart function), aid in the growth and maintenance of body tissues, and act as catalysts in the release of energy. There are approximately 17-21 identified essential minerals for human health; the major minerals (**macronutrients**) found in relatively large amounts in our bodies include calcium,

phosphorus, magnesium, sulfur, sodium, and potassium (Table 11.3). Other **micronutrients** (also known as **trace elements**) that are needed in relatively small amounts include zinc, iron, copper, fluoride, iodine, and selenium (Table 11.4).

Although needed only in small quantities, trace elements are nonetheless essential to good health. Mineral intake is like the intake of vitamins. Any essential mineral taken in an amount that is either too small or too large can lead to deleterious symptoms.

Calcium and iron are two minerals that are commonly lacking in our diets, leading to the potential conditions of **osteoporosis** and iron-deficiency **anemia**, respectively. The best way to ensure that you consume adequate amounts of essential minerals is by eating a balanced diet with variety.

Table 11.3 Macronutrient minerals and their roles.

Mineral	Physiological Functions	Mineral Food Sources	Deficiency Effects
Calcium	Bone ossification; tooth formation; general body growth; cell membrane maintenance; neuromuscular function	Milk and milk products; turnip greens, collards; broccoli; shellfish; soy products; molasses	Osteoporosis (not due to deficiency, but caused by calcium reabsorption); osteomalacia; tetany
Phosphorus	Tooth and bone development; energy release (ADP/ATP); fat transport; acid–base balance; synthesis of proteins, enzymes, and DNA/RNA	Meat, poultry, fish; eggs; cereal products; peanuts; cheddar cheese; carbonated soft drinks	Fatigue; demineralization of bone occurs in people taking high doses of antacids; often seen with anorexics
Potassium	Protein synthesis; fluid balance; acid–base balance; nerve transmission; energy release	Potatoes; bananas; liver; milk; apricots, cantaloupe, avocados; lima beans	Abdominal bloating; muscle weakness; heart abnormalities; respiratory distress; most often seen in infants with vomiting and diarrhea
Sulfur	Metabolism; blood clotting; collagen synthesis; detoxification of body fluids	Protein foods	Not clearly established
Sodium	Nerve transmission; acid–base balance; formation of digestive secretions	Bacon; olives; table salt; processed cheese; sauerkraut	Unlikely to occur; vomiting or extreme sweating in children could reduce sodium
Chloride	Acid–base balance; carbon dioxide transport; acidity of stomach	Table salt	Unlikely to occur; may be lost as a result of vomiting
Magnesium	Protein, lipid, and carbohydrate metabolism; energy production; protein synthesis; nerve transmission; tooth enamel stability	Nuts; soy beans; whole grains; spinach; green leafy vegetables; clams; cocoa	Uncertain effects; nervousness, irritability, convulsions; skin changes; vasodilation; related to vomiting

Table 11.4 Micronutrient minerals and their roles.

Mineral	Physiological Functions	Mineral Food Sources	Deficiency Effects
Iron	Oxygen and carbon dioxide transport; red blood cell formation; vitamin A synthesis; antibody production; collagen synthesis; removal of lipids from the blood	Spinach, peas, greens, asparagus; liver; enriched breads and cereals; clams; beans	Anemia and fatigue
Zinc	DNA/RNA synthesis; enzyme formation; acid–base balance; collagen production; fetal development; wound healing; HCl production; enhanced appetite and taste	Meats, seafood; whole-grain bread, whole wheat; cashew nuts	N/A
Copper	Hemoglobin, protein, and cholesterol synthesis; energy release; enzyme formation; myelin sheath development	Liver; oysters; cherries; mushrooms; whole-grain cereal; nuts; cocoa	N/A
Iodine	Protein, thyroxine, cholesterol, and vitamin A synthesis; cell metabolism	Water supply (depending on location); seafood; dairy products; iodized salt; spinach	Goiter (mainly in developing nations)
Fluoride	Skeletal stability; prevention of osteoporosis, dental caries, and periodontal disease	Water supply; tea; rice; spinach; soy beans; mackerel, salmon	N/A
Selenium	Antioxidation; energy release; heart muscle function	Meats, organ meats; cereal; milk and dairy products; fruits; plant sources depend on soil concentrations	N/A

Water

Why do athletes consistently drink water before, during, and after periods of exercise? Water is a vital nutrient that is often ignored but it is perhaps the most essential nutrient to life. Water composes such a large percentage of our bodies and the food we eat that its importance cannot be overstated. How can we overlook a substance that provides the medium for nutrient and waste transport, aids digestion and absorption, helps regulate our body temperature, forms the base of fluids that serve as

lubricants (e.g., synovial fluid within joints), and plays a key role in the majority of the chemical reactions that take place within our bodies?

Water is an essential part of our diet. You can live without food for several weeks (up to 50 days), but only a few days without water. Yet many of us still underestimate the importance of an adequate daily intake of water. Each day, you experience a loss of body fluids through urine, feces, sweat, and evaporation in your lungs. In order to maintain a balance between the water you consume and the water that is lost each day, you need to consume about 1 ml of water for each calorie you burn – this turns out to be approximately eight cups (one cup = 250 ml) or 2 litres in total of fluid per day (more if you are more active or live in a warmer climate). Of course, those who choose to drink fluids that tend to dehydrate the body, such as tea and coffee, would be advised to increase their water intake.

Dehydration is more of a problem than many acknowledge. Although thirst alerts us to consume more water, it is not always a reliable indicator of dehydration. For example, during an illness or during intense exercise, you may not feel the urge to drink, but that does not mean that your body is fully hydrated. On days that we feel uncharacteristically weak or fatigued, it just may be that we are slightly dehydrated and need to take in more fluids. An extreme bout of dehydration can cause severe weakness and land you in the hospital, or even lead to death.

Nutrition Guidelines and Recommendations

Most of us know what kinds of foods are good for us, and which we should perhaps eat less often, but where do we get this information? Various groups have established sets of nutrition guidelines that help us plan a diet that is healthy and balanced. Based on current research, these authorities on nutrition recommend nutrient requirements according to age, sex, body size, and activity level. These **Recommended Nutrient Intakes (RNIs)** are designed to meet the needs of virtually the entire healthy population; as a result, the recommended intake of any nutrient will exceed the requirements of most people. RNIs allow for a margin of safety, taking into account the vast individual variation that exists. An easy way to understand the concept of RNIs is to think of them as doorways. If all doorways were made the height of the average person, that would leave all those above the average height hitting their heads. But if the doorways were made higher than average height, this would allow just about every individual to pass safely. It is important to note that although RNIs are expressed on a daily basis, they should be regarded as an average recommended intake over a period of time (days, or even weeks).

A similar idea to the RNIs is **Recommended Daily Intakes (RDIs)**, which serve as a reference standard for nutrition labeling purposes only. Based on the RNIs, RDIs represent the highest RNI that exists for a nutrient for that age group, and is expressed as the percentage of RDI of the nutrient on labels (not mg, etc.). Two sets of RDI's exist – one for infants (< 2 years) and one for children (> 2 years) and adults. More details will be discussed later when food labels are presented.

The established RNIs form the basis of eight recommendations presented by Health and Welfare Canada, defining the desirable characteristics of the Canadian diet based on a review of the scientific literature. These recommendations provide a technical look at nutrition, targeting mainly educators and health professionals (see box *Nutrition Recommendations for Canadians*). The nutrition recommendations are reviewed regularly, and act as the foundation for all healthy eating and nutrition programs in the country.

The nutrition recommendations are made more user-friendly in a report called *Action Towards Healthy Eating*, which outlines five general statements to keep in mind when choosing what foods to eat. These constitute *Canada's Guidelines for Healthy Eating*. The language used is simple, easy to understand, and is aimed at all Canadians. The guidelines are as follows:

- *Enjoy a variety of foods.*

- *Emphasize cereals, breads, other grain products, vegetables, and fruits.*

- *Choose lower-fat dairy products, leaner meats, and foods prepared with little or no fat.*

- *Achieve and maintain a healthy body weight by enjoying regular physical activity and healthy eating.*

- *Limit salt, alcohol, and caffeine.*

Canada's Food Guide to Healthy Eating

Of course, we do not consume RNIs or nutrients alone. **Canada's Food Guide to Healthy Eating** effectively translates nutrient recommendations or RNIs into a food group plan that provides a guide to ensuring a balanced intake of essential nutrients. *Canada's Food Guide to Healthy Eating* (Figure 11.8) takes Canada's Guidelines for Healthy Eating one step further by helping you plan healthy meals through a daily selection of food, and allowing you to evaluate your eating habits in a general way. It meets the needs of all Canadians four years of age and over, being designed for the general public at a reading level of grade seven.

Just as no two people are exactly alike in appearance, personality, or interests, the same holds true when it comes to food and nutritional needs – different people need different amounts

---

Nutrition Recommendations for Canadians

The Canadian diet should:

- provide energy consistent with the maintenance of body weight within the recommended range.

- include essential nutrients in amounts recommended.

- include no more than 30 percent of energy as fat (33 g/1,000 kcal or 39 g/5,000 kJ) and no more than 10 percent as saturated fat (11 g/1,000 kcal or 13 g/5,000 kJ).

- provide 55 percent of energy as carbohydrate (138 g/1,000 kcal or 165 g/5,000 kJ) from a variety of sources.

- have a reduced sodium content.

- include no more than 5 percent of total energy as alcohol, or two drinks daily, whichever is less.

- contain no more caffeine than the equivalent of four regular cups of coffee per day.

Health & Welfare Canada, 1990

---

and types of food. The amount of food you need each day from the various food groups differs according to your age (e.g., teenagers have higher energy needs), body size (e.g., nutrient and energy needs are greater for those with a larger body size), sex (e.g., men generally have higher nutrient and energy needs), activity level (e.g., the greater the activity the higher the energy and nutrient needs), and if you are pregnant or breast-feeding. The Food Guide accounts for these differences and makes daily planning easier for all individuals by including a lower and higher number of servings from each food group.

The Food Groups

Most of us have heard and learned about **food groups**. These groups are created to help us choose foods that will lead to a healthy diet, emphasizing the ideas of balance, variety, and moderation. Choosing foods from each group in appropriate amounts will improve your chances of having a healthy diet. The Guide presents a recommended number of servings from five food groups: grain products; vegetables and fruit; milk products; meat and alternatives; and other foods. Choosing foods from the last group should be done with caution and in moderation, since some of the foods are higher in fat or calories.

You will notice that Canada's Food Guide to Healthy Eating has two major components. First, although all food groups are vital to a healthy diet, the amounts required from each group vary – the rainbow design depicting the food groups provides a visual representation of this idea. Notice also, the directional statements that offer key points to choosing appropriate foods.

- *Enjoy a variety of foods from each group every day.* This is a message that should be emphasized for any healthy diet.

- *Choose lower-fat foods more often.* This statement applies to each of the food groups (including the Other Foods group), highlighting the importance of watching your fat intake according to the nutrition recommendations for Canadians described earlier (i.e., only 30 percent of energy should come from fat, and 10 percent from saturated fat).

- *Choose whole grain and enriched products more often.* This statement is found under the Grain Products arc, signifying the importance of grain foods for the B-complex vitamins, zinc, iron, and energy (in the form of calories) in our diet. Whole grains are also an important source of dietary fibre.

- *Choose dark green and orange vegetables and orange fruit more often.* Located under the Vegetables and Fruit arc, this statement highlights the need for adequate intakes of vitamins A and C, and folacin (one of the B vitamins). Foods in this group also provide complex carbohydrates and fibre in our diets.

- *Choose lower-fat milk products more often.* This key statement under the Milk Products arc points to choosing lower-fat milk products as a way of lowering total dietary fat (saturated fat in particular).

- *Choose leaner meats, poultry, and fish, as well as dried peas, beans, and lentils more often.* The last statement, under the Meat and Alternatives arc, encourages the choice of lower-fat alternatives. This protein-rich group provides us with needed protein, iron, and the B vitamins.

The second major component of the Guide is the side bar which indicates the number of servings recommended for each food group. It is important to recall, however, that the Food Guide was designed to provide guidance for a diversity of people; therefore, a range is given for each group. This means that a woman with lower energy needs will aim for the lower end of the range, whereas an active teenage girl may choose towards the upper end of the range for the food groups. This adaptability makes using the Guide easy and effective for most people.

The inclusion of the Other Foods category accounts for the foods that do not fit into any of the four recognized food groups. Obviously, foods such as potato chips, colas, butter, candy, and cookies are not essential components to health, but they do add enjoyment and a little taste to eating. Such foods should be considered treats. Accordingly, all foods can be a part of a healthy eating pattern.

Nutrition Questions and Answers

There are several issues in choosing which diet to follow and in making decisions that apply to your own nutritional needs. This section will attempt to highlight some of these issues, now that you understand the basis of good nutrition and a healthy diet.

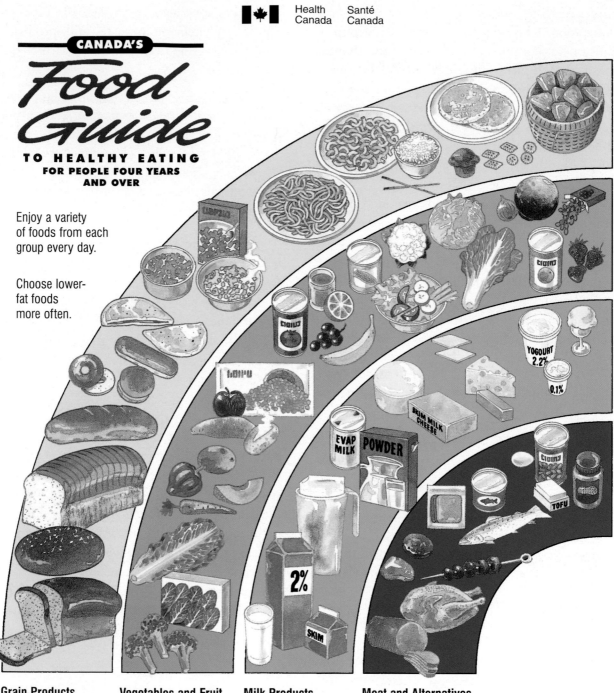

Health Canada Santé Canada

CANADA'S
Food Guide

TO HEALTHY EATING
FOR PEOPLE FOUR YEARS AND OVER

Enjoy a variety of foods from each group every day.

Choose lower-fat foods more often.

Grain Products
Choose whole grain and enriched products more often.

Vegetables and Fruit
Choose dark green and orange vegetables and orange fruit more often.

Milk Products
Choose lower-fat milk products more often.

Meat and Alternatives
Choose leaner meats, poultry and fish, as well as dried peas, beans and lentils more often.

Canada

Different People Need Different Amounts of Food

The amount of food you need every day from the 4 food groups and other foods depends on your age, body size, activity level, whether you are male or female and if you are pregnant or breast-feeding. That's why the Food Guide gives a lower and higher number of servings for each food group. For example, young children can choose the lower number of servings, while male teenagers can go to the higher number. Most other people can choose servings somewhere in between.

Consult *Canada's Physical Activity Guide to Healthy Active Living* to help you build physical activity into your daily life.

Enjoy eating well, being active and feeling good about yourself. That's VITALIT

Figure 11.8 Canada's Food Guide to Healthy Eating.

How bad is fast food, really?

The term "fast food" is synonymous with greasy, high-fat foods that have little or no nutritional value. But unlike junk foods, the nutritional value of fast foods prepared in walk-in or drive-through restaurants can vary immensely (Table 11.5). Still, the amount of fat (particularly saturated fat) and cholesterol found in most fast foods (especially those that are fried) makes consumption of these foods a poor nutritional choice. The limited variety of foods containing sources of dietary fibre available at most fast food establishments also represents a concern.

The picture is not all bad, however. Fast food restaurants have recently made an attempt to offer a wider variety of foods to meet the nutritional needs of the population. Menus have been extended to include salad bars, lower-fat meats, whole wheat breads, and lower-fat milk products. Nutritional information is also provided by the larger restaurants, and some fast foods can offer some real nutritional value. Although an excess of fast food consumption as a primary source of nutrition is undoubtedly unwise (and expensive), it can offer variety in a meal, which is the key to preventing most nutrient deficiencies. Still, fast foods are high in calories, fat, and salt, so you must be cautious when it comes to eating out. Your body will thank you for it.

Why should I read food labels? What do they tell me?

If you are to make intelligent choices about what you eat, it is important to know how to read and understand food labels. Establishing healthy eating patterns begins at the grocery store where you choose your food. Increasingly, food labels are providing more information relevant to nutrition, even though Canada's nutrition labeling program is voluntary.

Nutrition labels are standardized presentations of the nutrient content of food, designed to aid your choices as a consumer (Figure 11.9). Each label consists of a heading, a serving size, and values for energy, protein, fat, and carbohydrate based on the serving size. Some labels may also include the breakdown of fat into fatty acids (i.e., saturated, monounsaturated, and polyunsaturated) and cholesterol; the breakdown of carbohydrates into sugars, starch, and dietary fibre; as well as the sodium and potassium, and vitamins and minerals contained. The vitamins and minerals are expressed as a percentage of RDI (used for food labels only). Therefore, if a product contains 28 percent of iron RDI, this would mean that you are guaranteed at least 28 percent of your RNI in the serving size indicated on the label. Always check the serving size carefully, as all subsequent values on the label are calculated based on this amount of the product.

Not only do food labels make comparing products easier, but they also enable you to choose foods for healthy eating that reflect the nutrition recommendations. You must be careful about reading nutrition claims, however. These claims (often appearing in a clear, bold format) highlight a specific nutritional feature of a product, trying to influence your buying habits (see box *Nutrition Claims and What They Mean*). Because the words used in claims are government-defined (e.g., *low*, *less*, *light*), their meaning is standardized. The term "less" for example, is used to compare one product with another. A package of bacon that claims to have "50 percent less salt" may have half the amount of salt found in the product to which it is

Table 11.5 Selected fast food facts.

Food	Calories	Protein (g)	Carbohydrate (g)	Fat (g)	Calories from Fat (%)	Cholesterol (mg)	Sodium (mg)
Hamburgers							
McDonald's hamburger	263	12.4	28.3	11.3	38.6	29.1	506
McDonald's Big Mac	570	24.6	39.2	35	55.2	83	979
Dairy Queen single hamburger with cheese	410	24	33	20	43.9	50	790
Wendy's double hamburger (white bun)	560	41	24	34	54.6	125	575
Burger King Whopper	640	27	42	41	57.6	94	842
Chicken							
Arby's chicken breast sandwich	592	28	56	27	41	57	1340
Burger King chicken sandwich	688	26	56	40	52.3	82	1423
Dairy Queen chicken sandwich	670	29	46	41	55	75	870
KFC Nuggets (one)	46	2.82	2.2	2.9	56.7	11.9	140
Others							
McDonald's Filet-O-Fish	435	14.7	35.9	25.7	53.1	45.2	799
Arby's roast beef sandwich	350	22	32	15	38.5	39	590
McDonald's french fries (regular)	220	3	26.1	11.5	47	8.6	109
Wendy's french fries (regular)	280	4	35	14	45	15	95
Drinks							
Dairy Queen shake	710	14	120	19	24	50	260
McDonald's vanilla shake	352	9.3	59.6	8.4	21.4	30.6	201
Coca-Cola	154	—	40	—	—	—	6
Diet Coke	0.9	—	0.3	—	—	—	16
Sprite	142	—	36	—	—	—	45
Diet Sprite	3	—	0	—	—	—	9

Serving Size

Are you eating the serving size indicated on the label? If not, you must adjust the nutrient and calorie values accordingly.

Protein

Where are you getting your protein? Animal proteins are usually higher in fat and cholesterol. Emphasize low-fat milk, yogurt, and cheeses, and try vegetable proteins such as beans and cereals, as well as nuts and seeds.

Total Carbohydrate

Need a boost of energy? Carbohydrates provide a major source of energy and are found in foods such as breads, cereals, and fruit. But watch out for foods high in simple sugars.

Sodium

You know it better as salt. High sodium consumption is associated with high blood pressure in some individuals, so keep your intake low.

Energy

Are you watching your weight? This value tells you how many calories are contained in a single serving of the product.

Total Fat

It's a good idea to cut back on fat for heart health and general well-being. Look for products with low-fat alternatives.

Dietary Fibre

Soluble and insoluble sources of fibre help prevent heart disease and cancer, as well as keep you regular.

Vitamins and Minerals

Eat a variety of foods daily to ensure an adequate intake of vitamins and minerals needed for vital body functions.

Daily Intake

What percentage of your RNI does a serving of this product give you? Use these numbers as a guide.

NUTRITION INFORMATION
INFORMATION NUTRITIONNELLE

per 30 g serving (3/4 cup) • par portion de 30 g (3/4 tasse)

	CEREAL ALONE CÉRÉALES	CEREAL PLUS 125 mL P.S. MILK* CÉRÉALES PLUS 125 mL DE LAIT P.É.*	
ENERGY	118 Cal 490 kJ	183 Cal 770 kJ	ÉNERGIE
PROTEIN	4.9 g	9.4 g	PROTÉINES
FAT	1.5 g	4.0 g	MATIÈRES GRASSES
CARBOHYDRATE	21 g	27 g	GLUCIDES
SUGARS	6.3 g	12 g	SUCRES
STARCH	12 g	13 g	AMIDON
DIETARY FIBRE	2.4 g	2.4 g	FIBRES ALIMENTAIRES
SODIUM	180 mg	244 mg	SODIUM
POTASSIUM	173 mg	372 mg	POTASSIUM

PERCENTAGE OF RECOMMENDED DAILY INTAKE
POURCENTAGE DE L'APPORT QUOTIDIEN RECOMMANDÉ

VITAMIN D	0 %	26 %	VITAMINE D
THIAMINE	46 %	50 %	THIAMINE
RIBOFLAVIN	2 %	16 %	RIBOFLAVINE
NIACIN	6 %	11 %	NIACINE
VITAMIN B_6	10 %	13 %	VITAMINE B_6
FOLACIN	8 %	11 %	FOLACINE
VITAMIN B_{12}	0 %	23 %	VITAMINE B_{12}
PANTOTHENIC ACID	7 %	13 %	ACIDE PANTOTHÉNIQUE
CALCIUM	2 %	16 %	CALCIUM
PHOSPHORUS	14 %	25 %	PHOSPHORE
MAGNESIUM	16 %	23 %	MAGNÉSIUM
IRON	28 %	29 %	FER
ZINC	10 %	15 %	ZINC

* PARTLY SKIMMED MILK (2% M.F.) /*LAIT PARTIELLEMENT ÉCRÉMÉ À 2 % M.G.

CANADIAN DIABETES ASSOCIATION FOOD CHOICE VALUE/
VALEUR DE CHOIX D'ALIMENTS DE L'ASSOCIATION CANADIENNE DU DIABÈTE :
30 g SERVING (3/4 CUP) / PORTION DE 30 g (3/4 TASSE)
= 1 ■ + ½ ✱ + ½ ⊘

Figure 11.9 Sample nutrition label.

being compared, but it does not necessarily mean the product is itself low in salt (half the amount may still be a lot of salt) – you should check the label for more information.

How safe is the food supply?

We rarely inquire about what is actually in the food we eat especially if it is already prepared. But the quality and safety of the food we eat are important factors. There are in fact many concerns pertaining to environmental contaminants present in foods (e.g., pesticides), the presence of potentially dangerous additives, and the threat of bacteria and microorganisms that cause food-borne illness. Unfortunately, the occurrence of various food-borne illnesses are fairly prevalent; in fact, the last time you thought you had the flu, you may have actually been suffering from the effects of a food-borne illness. This mistake can be made because the symptoms are so similar – diarrhea, vomiting, weakness, and fever. Although the effects of most food-borne illnesses are usually not serious, elderly people and children are at higher risk.

The source of most food-borne illnesses is bacteria and the toxins they produce; they are caused by a variety of factors and can largely be prevented. Food can become contaminated by

Nutrition Claims and What They Mean

Often presented in a bold, banner format on the product package, nutrition claims highlight a nutritional feature of a product. Since these claims must always be backed up by detailed facts relating to the claim, look for more information on the label.

- **Low** is always associated with a very small amount.

- **Less** is used to compare one product with another. A bag of chips claiming to contain "50 percent less salt" means it has half the salt of the food to which it was compared.

- **Light** or **Lite** may refer to anything about the product including taste, texture, colour, or fat content. Look further to find out which feature of the product is "light."

- **Low in Saturated Fat** or **Cholesterol** may lead you to believe the product is low in fat. Not necessarily so. Vegetable oils may be low in saturated fat and contain no cholesterol, but may still be high in total fat.

- **Fat Free** indicates the product contains less than 0.5 g of fat per serving.

- **Low Fat** indicates the product contains 3 g of fat or less per serving and no more than 15 percent fat on a dry basis.

- **Fat-reduced** indicates at least 25 percent less fat than the original product.

- **% M.F.** or **% B.F.** listed on most dairy products indicates percentage of milk fat or butter fat, respectively. This information can be used to choose lower fat dairy products.

bacteria if it is not prepared or stored properly. This is especially true of eggs, meat, milk, and poultry (which can lead to **Salmonella** poisoning, the most common type of food-borne illness). Another type of bacteria is **Staphylococcus aureus**, which lives primarily in nasal passages and skin sores; it manages to spread to food when you handle food, or sneeze or cough over it. Ham,

cheese, eggs, and seafood are common sources of this bacteria. More dangerous types of bacteria (although rare) also exist including **Clostridium botulinum** (causing botulism) and **Escherichia coli** (*E. coli* for short), which arise mainly from improperly canned foods (particularly meats and vegetables), and are found in the intestinal tract of humans and other animals respectively. Therefore, it is important to handle food with extreme care, and be vigilant about what you eat in restaurants when you eat out (Table 11.6).

The multitude of substances added to processed foods can also be an issue of concern. While most are added for good reason (e.g., to improve nutritional quality, taste, and appearance, or to maintain freshness), additives can lead to allergic reactions in some individuals. Sulfites, for example, that protect vegetables from turning brown, have been known to cause wheezing, hives, diarrhea, vomiting, and dizziness in some individuals. The use of colouring agents (e.g., yellow No. 5) and flavour enhancers (such as MSG) can also lead to reactions – another reason to pay attention to labels. Yellow No. 5 can cause hives, itching, a runny nose, and even asthma in some, while monosodium glutamate (MSG) may lead to bouts of high blood pressure and sweating in those who are sensitive. Therefore, if you are sensitive to any substance or are concerned about what is in the food you eat, check the labels carefully to avoid any potential reaction or illness.

Is vegetarianism a healthy alternative?

Some people choose to eliminate or restrict meat and other animal-derived foods from their diets for various reasons (philosophical, health, environmental, etc.). A **vegetarian** diet can provide the necessary nutrients required by the body if a few rules are followed (children and pregnant women require special individual guidance). In fact, a well-planned vegetarian diet can offer immense benefits to adults and can lead to better health.

Vegetarians are often placed under one

Table 11.6 Tips on food safety.

Food can become contaminated by bacteria if it is not handled, prepared, or stored properly. Keep the following tips in mind to avoid the potentially serious effects of food-borne illnesses.

- Thoroughly clean dishes, cutting boards, counters, and other utensils before and after use, particularly if used with raw foods such as meat, fish, or eggs.

- Wash hands thoroughly with hot water and soap before and after handling all foods.

- Pesticide residues tend to concentrate in animal fat; therefore, trim excess fat from meats or remove skin which contains most of the fat. Also remove fats and oils from soups and pan drippings.

- When handling food, cover any cuts on your hands, and avoid sneezing or coughing over the food.

- When preparing foods to be eaten raw (such as vegetables), use a different cutting board than one used for meats. The relative worth of plastic over wooden cutting boards remains contentious.

- Do not leave groceries in the car for extended periods of time – bacteria thrive in warm temperatures. Also, purchase products that require refrigeration last to keep them fresh.

- When cooking with poultry, cook stuffing separately, or wash poultry well and stuff immediately before cooking and transfer to a separate dish immediately after cooking.

- Wash produce under running water to help loosen any trapped dirt.

- Cook all foods thoroughly (especially meats and eggs) which will kill most microorganisms. Avoid eating raw animal products.

- To avoid the deadly botulism toxin, do not buy prepackaged foods in containers that leak, are dented, or bulge.

- The outer leaves of leafy vegetables should be removed. Wash and scrub other fruits and vegetables well (with a brush if possible) or peel them if necessary (even though some nutrients may be lost).

- Use only pasteurized milk and juices.

- Avoid leaving cooked or refrigerated foods at room temperature for more than two hours. Foods should be stored below 4 degrees Celsius.

- When fishing, throw back the big ones – smaller fish tend to have lower concentrations of pesticides and other harmful residues.

- Do not barbecue more than three times per week to avoid ingestion of cancer-causing compounds. Also avoid overcooking (burning) foods for the same reason.

- Do not eat eggs with runny yolks or batter made with raw eggs; over 80 percent of Salmonella outbreaks can be linked to eggs.

Vegetarian Styles

Although they are often categorized as one large, homogeneous group, vegetarians are actually quite a diverse population. Here are the various vegetarian diets, ranging from strict to lax:

- **Sproutarianism:** A diet based around sprouted seeds, such as bean sprouts, wheat sprouts, and broccoli sprouts. Usually supplemented with additional raw foods.

- **Fruitarianism:** A diet consisting of raw or dried fruits, as well as grains, nuts, seeds, legumes, honey, and vegetable or olive oil. Basically, includes any part a plant can easily replace.

- **Raw Foodism:** A diet built primarily on raw foods, excluding anything cooked past 48 degrees Fahrenheit. This is the temperature at which enzymes begin to be destroyed.

- **Veganism:** An all-vegetable diet, excluding meat, milk products, eggs, and any other animal products – including honey.

- **Ovo-vegetarianism:** A diet including vegetables as well as eggs.

- **Lacto-vegetarianism:** An all-vegetable diet plus dairy products – no eggs.

- **Ovo-lacto-vegetarianism:** An all-vegetable diet plus dairy products and eggs.

- **Pesco-, Pollo-, and Semi-vegetarianism:** A diet including vegetables plus some group(s) of animal products such as fish (pesco) or chicken (pollo). Semi-vegetarians who frequently, but not systematically, avoid meat and dairy products, are not true vegetarians.

---

broad heading, but there are several types. **Vegans** restrict their diet to plant foods; **lacto-vegetarians** also eat plant foods, but include dairy products; **lacto-ovo-vegetarians** choose to eat plant foods, dairy products, as well as eggs; finally, **semi-vegetarians** eat plant foods, dairy products, eggs, and usually a small selection of poultry, fish, or other seafood (see box *Vegetarian Styles* for a complete summary of all the various vegetarian diets). Those vegetarian diets that offer a wider variety make it easier to meet nutritional requirements. While there is relatively little risk associated with the others, a vegan diet requires a higher degree of nutritional understanding to avoid malnourishment.

One potential concern is whether a vegan diet includes sources of all the essential amino acids because no single plant source contains all of them. However, a careful combination of non-meat, high-quality **complementary proteins** (proteins that supply the essential amino acids missing in each other), can prevent amino acid deficiencies. Some examples include black beans and rice, peanut butter and wheat bread, and tofu and stir-fried vegetables with rice. Other potential difficulties include maintaining adequate intakes of vitamin B_{12}, calcium, iron, and zinc, as well as a concern with satiation (satisfaction of hunger). Early satiation as a result of large amounts of fibre in the diet may lead to a decrease in carbohydrate intake.

It takes planning and common sense to put together a vegetarian diet that works. Thus, if you are a vegetarian or are considering becoming one, think carefully about eating a variety of foods, and plan ahead to ensure that your nutritional needs are adequately met.

Do I need vitamin or mineral supplements?

You may wonder whether you could benefit from taking a vitamin or mineral supplement. Promotional tactics often try to convince consumers that supplements are essential to health. The question you need to ask yourself is whether you are following Canada's Food Guide to Healthy Eating. If you enjoy a balanced diet that has adequate variety, most nutritionists would agree that the need for supplements is low or non-existent; in fact, megadoses may even lead to toxicity. Many people use supplements as nutritional insurance, making sure they get all the nutrients they need, but there is no reason why most people can't obtain the vitamins and minerals they need from a healthy, balanced diet.

That being said, there are several special cases where vitamin and mineral supplementation should be considered (Figure 11.10):

- women with excessive bleeding during menstruation may need iron;

- pregnant or breast-feeding mothers may require iron, folate (also known as folic acid or folacin), and calcium (inadequate amounts of folate during pregnancy have been linked to birth defects called neural tube defects);

- individuals with low nutritional caloric intakes (e.g., single eaters, elderly, heavy drinkers);

- some vegetarians may need calcium, iron, zinc, and vitamin B_{12};

- exclusively breast-fed infants and shut-in elderly may need vitamin D (lacking in human milk and in an environment lacking sunlight); and

- people with certain illnesses or on medication may need supplements.

Although most of us can rely on a healthy diet to provide us with the nutrients we need, if you choose to use nutrient supplements, do so only after consulting with a public health nutritionist, dietitian, or doctor. The special nutritional

Figure 11.10 Vitamin and mineral supplementation may be necessary for some individuals.

requirements of athletes may necessitate supplementing vitamins and minerals to ensure their bodies receive adequate amounts of the essential nutrients.

What's the scoop on sugar?

Many of us crave sugar but believe it is detrimental to good health. Sugar is often linked with fatness, despite research showing that fat people do not consume more sugar than thin people. However, sugar can create a unique dilemma – while sugar itself does not make you fat, sugary foods in our diets also tend to be high in fat and calories, which *can* make you fat. And any calories consumed beyond body needs, which are not burned off during activity, are inevitably stored as fat.

How about the effects of sugar on kids' behaviour? Does sugar consumption increase hyperactivity, delinquency, or learning disorders in children? Although these are popular beliefs held by many, there is no evidence that clearly validates these claims.

The primary health problem linked to sugar is tooth decay (dental caries). For many years, sugar has been known to cause tooth decay (leading to fluoridated drinking water) – a problem that can be effectively combated by regular brushing and dental checkups. It is also worth noting that eating *sweets* with other foods is less damaging to your teeth, as a result of increased saliva and foods that buffer the acid effect in your mouth.

Sugar has also been linked to **diabetes,** a disease of the pancreas affecting normal metabolism. When we eat food, our blood sugar rises; diabetic individuals fail to produce enough insulin (from the pancreas) in response to this increase, leading to an elevated blood sugar level. While high sugar consumption will not cause diabetes, those who are genetically susceptible to the condition may want to limit the amount of sugar they eat. The indirect link still remains, however. A high sugar diet can lead to obesity, which is a risk factor in developing diabetes.

How do nutritional needs change as we grow older?

It should come as no surprise that nutritional needs change as we age (Figure 11.11). The main factors that account for this are the physiological changes that accompany the aging process, diseases that may develop affecting nutrition (directly or indirectly), as well as psychosocial factors. We will now look at these individually.

Aging leads to a drop in activity and a lower metabolic rate and to lower total energy requirement. This in turn often leads to less food intake among the elderly. Still, while the need for calories declines, the need for vitamins and minerals still remains vital. Not only do many elderly people sense the need for less food, but changes in teeth, salivary glands, taste buds, oral muscles, gastric acid production, and peristalsis make it harder to chew, and make eating less pleasurable. Other changes, such as an increased occurrence of constipation, further add to a declining interest in food.

Also, a variety of diseases and disorders can affect the nutrition of the older adult significantly. Dental problems, swallowing disorders, mood disorders (e.g., depression), and gastrointestinal disorders are commonplace. But elderly individuals also suffer from chronic infections more regularly, and many must deal with musculoskeletal problems such as osteoporosis and arthritis, which indirectly affect nutrition (for example, eating with arthritic hands can be a real challenge).

Perhaps psychological factors are the most overlooked influence on nutrition in the older adult. Social isolation, poverty, transportation limitations, and institutionalization (nursing homes) are all factors that figure into the lifestyle of the elderly. These factors may change the enjoyment and ease with which foods may be prepared and consumed, affecting nutrition greatly.

Can diet improve athletic performance?

Athletes are always searching for the formula for success in maximizing their potential; sound nutrition is certainly part of it. Eating particular types of foods before participating in athletic events can be more beneficial than others. But what specific nutritional concerns do athletes face? How can an athlete prepare a diet that will maximize performance?

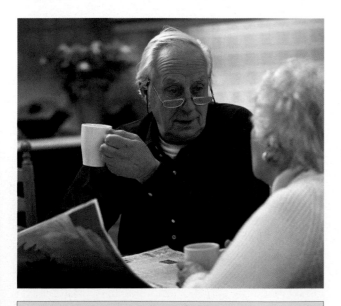

Figure 11.11 Age-related physiological changes alter the nutritional needs of older adults.

Ergogenic Aids and Supplements

Research and experience have shown that athletes have a greater need for energy, proteins, and amino acids than moderately active or inactive people (see box *Training and Competition Make a Difference*). However, the Canadian diet seems to be adequate to meet the protein needs of most individuals, including athletes, as long as energy requirements are met. Further, amino acid supplementation cannot be scientifically justified. Because all athletes have higher energy needs in general, a diet that aims to provide 15 percent of total energy intake as protein should be adequate for athletes as well. Even in the presence of extra protein, the body can only build muscle so fast, and excess protein is broken down to be eliminated as waste. So athletes should focus on maintaining a balanced diet with adequate calories, rather than looking to supplements.

There is widespread interest in the effects of carbohydrates on endurance performance. Carbohydrates are recognized as the major fuel for most athletic performance, and its depletion from muscle stores (as glycogen) is associated with fatigue in endurance exercise. The practice of **carbohydrate loading** (see Chapter 13) can increase muscle glycogen stores by gradually reducing the duration of training sessions during the week before an important competition, and progressively increasing the consumption of dietary carbohydrates. This technique has been shown to be effective before endurance-type competition (over 60 minutes), although some drawbacks can be identified. Some individuals feel gastrointestinal discomfort and sluggishness as a result of increased carbohydrates. Training is compromised in the days that precede competition. It is not recommended for athletes with diabetes or heart irregularities, and the long-term effects of this practice on muscles have not been studied yet. Any such program should be done under the supervision of a qualified coach or trainer.

What Are Ergogenic Aids?

Ergogenic (*work producing*) refers to the application of a nutritional, physical, mechanical, psychological, or pharmacological procedure or aid to improve physical work capacity, athletic performance, and responsiveness to exercise training.

Other substances such as caffeine, sodium bicarbonate, and various vitamins and minerals have been shown to have an effect on athletic performance. Caffeine, for example, has been

Training and Competition Make a Difference

Individuals who are engaged in intense physical activity experience increased daily energy needs to match their higher level of daily energy expenditure. Their daily food intake contains the essential and many non-essential nutrients in amounts that are two or more times greater than the amounts eaten by non-athletes. Furthermore, depending on the activity, energy needs of athletes can range from a low of 1,700 to a high of 8,000 calories (or higher) to meet the special requirements of an athlete. Energy requirements vary according to age, activity, and metabolism. For example, average daily nutrient intake of a 14-year-old 50-kg gymnast is drastically different from the nutrient requirement of a 28-year-old 75-kg road cyclist.

The practice of eating specific amounts of protein, carbohydrates, and fats is essential for the enhancement of athletic performance. Additionally, meal timing and frequency are important. While non-athletes can maintain their health by consuming three moderately sized, well-balanced meals per day, athletes must utilize a diet that is much more complex. For example, to facilitate muscle recovery athletes need to consume high-quality protein several times a day. To ensure an adequate supply of energy, athletes must consume specific amounts of high-quality carbohydrates several times a day.

identified as a possible **ergogenic aid**, found in coffee, tea, and colas (see Chapter 13). It is believed to enhance the release and use of free fatty acids, conserving glycogen and prolonging endurance when taken before exercising. Although some studies have shown positive results, some individuals react negatively to caffeine. It's use should be controlled and introduced on a trial basis only.

Pre-event Meals

Before an athlete is fully ready to compete, there are certain nutritional guidelines that should be followed. First, meals before a competition should be high in carbohydrates, and low in fat, because carbohydrate-containing foods leave the stomach more quickly than other foods (fats are slowest) (Figure 11.12). Food in the digestive system makes a demand on the circulatory system, so it

Figure 11.13 Although often taken for granted, water is perhaps the most essential nutrient.

Figure 11.12 Packed with an assortment of vitamins and minerals, bananas make a great snack to boost energy before, during, and after a bout of exercise.

is beneficial to have food move quickly through the system to allow needed oxygen to be supplied to the working muscles. In stressful competitive conditions, muscle damage can occur if muscles are deprived of energy-yielding oxygen. Second, only familiar foods should be eaten before an event to avoid any strange or surprising reactions.

Hydration

We have already stressed the importance of water as a nutrient. The need for water is increased during exercise because of increased losses through the lungs and sweat losses. Fluid losses can be dramatic, especially in warm and humid environments, so keeping hydrated by drinking fluids is essential (Figure 11.13). It is important to drink early (prior to exercise), often (during exercise), and also after exercise. Cool drinks also make your performance more effective by cooling your body. Waiting until you "feel" thirsty is not recommended because your body may not feel the need for fluids even when it is there. An adequate supply of water is therefore a key to performing your best.

Food for Thought

You can make your eating experience nutritious and fun. Remember, what pleases the eye pleases the palate.

Summary

Nutrition is an important science concerned with food, and how our bodies use it in health and disease. Our attitude to nutrition and diet can influence our health in a positive way. Because some diets are associated with disease, while others protect us from them, we must choose foods that provide us with the essential nutrients. This means understanding the essential nutrients (carbohydrates, proteins, fats, vitamins, minerals, and water), and what foods contain them. This is where Canada's Food Guide to Healthy Eating and related recommendations and guidelines can help you establish sound eating patterns and vitality. While all foods are good to eat, some are good to eat more often than others.

Of course, individuals have different needs, and these needs change as we age. Understanding the nutritional needs of various populations (e.g., children, the elderly, athletes, diabetics) is important if we are to assist those around us, as well as helping us to adapt our own nutritional habits as we change over the years. Then, there's always the issue of weight and maintaining a healthy body image, which all comes down to balancing your caloric intake, and following a lifestyle that includes regular exercise (see Chapter 12). Other relevant information concerning food labels, nutrient supplements, the safety of the food supply, or the risks associated with vegetarianism are important in formulating a nutritional program that is right for you. Any way you put it, nutrition has profound effects on your general health and well-being.

Key Words

Absorption	Free radicals	Peristalsis
Amino acid	Gallbladder	Polysaccharide
Amylase	Gastrointestinal tract	Polyunsaturated fat
Antioxidant	Glycogen	Protein
Bile	Hydrochloric acid	Recommended Daily Intake
Bile salts	Hydrogenation	(RDI)
Calorie	Incomplete protein	Recommended Nutrient Intake
Carbohydrate	Insoluble fibre	(RNI)
Carbohydrate loading	Kilocalorie	Saliva
Cholesterol	Large intestine	Saturated fat
Complementary proteins	Lipid	Secretion
Complete protein	Liver	Small intestine
Digestion	Macronutrients	Soluble fibre
Digestive system	Micronutrients	Stomach
Disaccharide	Minerals	Trans fatty acid
Ergogenic aids	Monosaccharide	Triglyceride
Esophagus	Monounsaturated fat	Vegetarian
Essential amino acids	Motility	Vitamins
Essential nutrients	Nutrition	Water-soluble vitamins
Fat-soluble vitamins	Pepsin	

Discussion Questions

1. List the four basic digestive functions. What is the role of the small intestine?

2. What is a nutrient? Identify the six essential nutrients and explain their contribution to growth and development.

3. List the calorie densities of the three classes of nutrients that supply energy. Which nutrient is the most calorie dense?

4. Identify the two major classifications of dietary fibre and provide two examples of each type.

5. Distinguish between RNIs and RDIs. What are RDIs used for?

6. How many food groups are included in Canada's Food Guide to Healthy Eating? Give an example of three foods and sample serving sizes from each group.

7. Describe the different vegetarian diets. Which type puts you at the most risk for nutrient deficiencies?

8. Are vitamin and mineral supplements necessary for health? Explain.

9. What factors affect the nutrition of the older adult?

10. What is carbohydrate loading? Can all athletes benefit from it?

In This Chapter:

Energy Balance Equation *296*
    Energy Needs of the Body *298*
    Exercise and Weight Management *298*

Body Composition *300*
    Lean Body Mass *301*
    Fat Body Mass *301*
    Measuring Body Fat *301*
    Body Mass Index *302*
    Misleading Norms *304*
    Somatotyping *304*

Obesity *306*
    Creeping Obesity *306*
    Weight-loss Industry *307*

Consequences of Dieting *308*
    Eating Disorders *309*

Summary *314*

Weight Management: Finding a Healthy Balance

After completing this chapter you should be able to:

- discuss the differences between overweight and obese and implications for health;

- explain the concept of caloric balance in weight control;

- describe the role of exercise and lifestyle modification in maintaining a healthy weight;

- discuss the consequences of dieting and eating disorders;

- set and evaluate personal goals for maintaining a healthy weight.

Weight is an issue for all of us. Many people feel obliged to buy diet books, try fad diets and supplements, attempt special programs, and even consider medical procedures, all in the pursuit of attaining an "ideal" weight. The key to weight management lies not in some vague ideal or perfection but in sensible dietary practices and adequate levels of physical activity.

Despite the efforts of many people, Canadians are clearly in a state of nutritional crisis and in need of sound remedies. The statistics are sobering. Collectively, we have grown fatter over the years. Today, more than 35 percent of adults and 30 percent of children are considered overweight or obese. Too many children and young adults are facing an epidemic of numerous obesity-related diseases that were unheard of just a generation ago.

We live in an environment where physical activity has been engineered out of day-to-day life, and the food environment has become more "toxic" by the day (Figure 12.1). Eating disorders have also emerged in greater numbers as the social pressure to be thin has increased, especially among adolescents and young adults.

Energy Balance Equation

Human beings come into the world well equipped to regulate what scientists call the **energy balance equation** (Figure 12.2). On one side of the equation are the calories we burn through exercise and other bodily processes. Calories consumed beyond the body's needs are stored as fat. In short, one gains weight when energy input exceeds energy output (Figure 12.2 B), and loses weight when the opposite occurs (Figure 12.2 C). One's weight will remain constant if caloric input and output are the same, and one's body is said to be in **caloric balance** (Figure 12.2 A).

Although it is more common to hear about people who want to lose weight, there are those who have the desire to put on a few pounds to look better, or to "bulk up" for athletic events, etc. Just as weight loss is based on your balance of calories, so is weight gain. This can be achieved by increasing your food intake while participating in an activity program aimed at developing muscular strength. This increase in mass is due to an increase in functional muscle tissue, not fat.

Figure 12.1 Modern conveniences, lower levels of activity, and poor nutritional choices contribute to a myriad of weight and health issues.

Figure 12.2 The energy balance equation. **A.** Caloric input equals caloric output. **B.** Caloric input exceeds caloric output. **C.** Caloric output exceeds caloric input.

Energy Needs of the Body

Of the total calories you require on a daily basis, the highest proportion is used for basal metabolism. Your basal metabolism or **basal metabolic rate (BMR)** is defined as the minimum amount of energy the body requires to carry on all vital functions (including blood circulation, respiration, brain activity, etc.). Thus, your basal metabolism will vary throughout your life. As a general rule, your BMR is relatively high at birth and continues to increase until the age of two, after which it will gradually decline as your life progresses (except for a rise at puberty). Other variables also affect your BMR, such as body composition (muscular bodies have higher BMRs), physical fitness (fit people have higher BMRs), sex (the BMRs of men are 5 percent higher than those of women), sleep (BMRs are 10 percent lower during sleep), pregnancy (a 20 percent increase in BMR), and body temperature (a one degree rise in body temperature increases BMR about 7 percent). Among all these factors, age is probably the most significant because many people fail to recognize their changing metabolic needs, and do not adjust their food intake to reflect these changes. Many people put on extra pounds as they grow older for this very reason.

To calculate your BMR, use the formula presented in the box below (*Calculate Your Basal Metabolic Rate*).

Exercise and Weight Management

When you exercise, the body's needs for energy increase significantly beyond basal metabolic needs. The amount of extra energy or calories required depends upon the volume of exercise (how long you exercise or the quantity of exercise performed), the intensity of exercise (the rate of exercise per unit of time), and the type of exercise performed (Table 12.1). However, it must be stressed that exercise on its own can be a slow way to lose weight. For example, if you are a woman weighing 55 kg, you would have to walk over two hours or cross-country ski for over one hour to burn off the calories consumed in a single vanilla milkshake (Figure 12.3, Table 12.1). But combined with controlled eating patterns involving calorie reduction, your chances for success are greatly enhanced.

If you doubt the importance of exercise to such a program geared at weight loss, consider this. Not only does regular exercise (especially endurance type) strengthen the heart, improve endurance, provide a means of managing stress, and help prevent osteoporosis, it also burns calories and keeps your metabolism using food for energy rather than storing calories.

As described earlier, a higher amount of fat-free mass (muscle) and a higher level of physical fitness are associated with higher metabolism. These can both be achieved by engaging in regular

---

Calculate Your Basal Metabolic Rate

Your basal metabolic rate (BMR) reflects the amount of energy in calories (C) needed to maintain basic body functions such as breathing and blood circulation. Use the simple equation below to help you determine your approximate BMR. NOTE: a woman's BMR is approximately 5 percent lower than that of a man the same age.

> **BMR per day = 1 C x body weight (kg) x 24**

Example: 70-kg man

BMR per day = 1 C x 70 x 24
= 1,680 C

This individual needs approximately 1,680 calories to maintain his body at rest. Of course, any additional activity above this level raises calorie requirements accordingly.

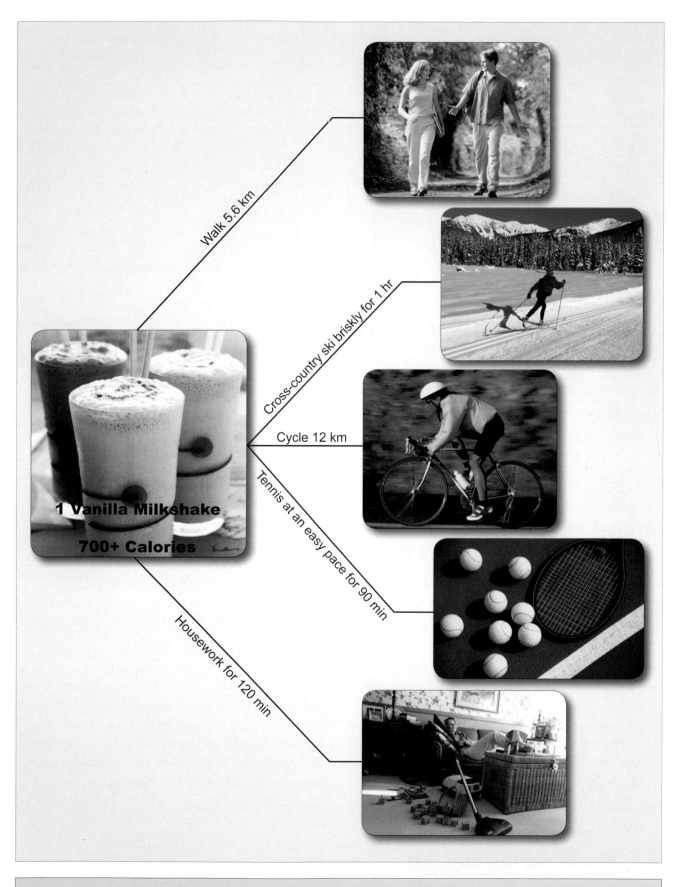

Figure 12.3 Using food energy. How much activity would it take to burn off the calories from a single shake?

Table 12.1 Approximate calories expended for male (70 kg) and female (55 kg) participants in sporting and recreational activities lasting an hour.

Activity	Male (70 kg)	Female (55 kg)	Calories/hour/kg
Sporting Activity			
Basketball	581.0	456.5	8.3
Cycling (racing)	714.0	561.0	10.2
Ice hockey	875.0	687.5	12.5
Running 8 min/mile	868.0	682.0	12.4
7 min/mile	959.0	753.5	13.7
6 min/mile	1050.0	825.0	15.0
Cross-country skiing	679.0	533.5	9.7
Soccer	546.0	429.0	7.8
Squash	889.0	698.5	12.7
Swimming breaststroke	686.0	539.0	9.8
Tennis (singles)	462.0	363.0	6.6
Weight training	294.0	231.0	4.2
Leisure Activity			
Cycling 10 km/hour	266.0	209.0	3.8
15 km/hour	413.0	324.5	5.9
Canoeing	182.0	143.0	2.6
Dancing	350.0	275.0	5.0
Golfing	357.0	280.5	5.1
Hiking	385.0	302.5	5.5
Jogging (11 min/mile)	553.0	434.5	7.9
Rowing ergometer	735.0	577.5	10.5
Walking	329.0	258.5	4.7

physical exercise. Individuals with elevated or normal metabolic rates are less likely to become overweight. When your metabolism is more active, you can eat more without necessarily gaining weight, and your body will burn more calories even when you are not exercising. Weight management becomes much easier with a lifestyle that includes regular exercise.

Body Composition

The human physique includes three interrelated aspects of the body: size, structure, and composition. **Size** refers to the volume, mass, length, and surface area of the body, while body **structure** refers to how certain aspects such as the skeleton, muscle, and fat are arranged or distributed throughout the body. **Body composition** refers to the amounts of body constituents, such as fat, muscle, bone, and other organs, and is regarded as one of the major components of physical fitness.

The composition of the human body can be divided into many components. However, a two-component model dividing the body into lean body mass (LBM) and fat body mass or total body fat (TBF) is the most common.

Lean Body Mass

Perhaps the most important component of the body is **lean body mass (LBM)**. It refers to the "non-fat" or "fat-free" component of the human body, and generally consists of skeletal muscle, bone, and water. LBM can be calculated by using the following simple formula:

$$LBM = TBM - TBF$$

By subtracting the **total body fat (TBF)** from **total body mass (TBM)** we arrive at lean body mass. TBF is calculated by multiplying TBM or weight by percent body fat (see calculation in next section) divided by 100. For example, if a subject weighs 70 kg and has 10 percent body fat, he or she has 7 kg (70 kg x 10/100 = 7 kg) of TBF. If TBF is known, LBM can be calculated. In our example, this works out to an LBM of 63 kg (70 kg – 7 kg). Individuals with high amounts of lean body mass normally have higher rates of metabolism.

Lean body mass may represent a biological lower limit beyond which a person's body mass cannot be reduced without impairing health. In women, excessive leanness may increase the chances of developing amenorrhea (absent menstruation). Amenorrhea should be viewed as a red flag and women with amenorrhea should discuss their condition with a knowledgeable sports physician.

The reproductive system can be compromised in situations where an athlete does not eat enough calories to support her body's metabolism and exercise needs, leading to a decrease in estrogen production. The body will try to conserve calories and shift metabolism down, which in turn shuts down the reproductive system's production of estrogen. Estrogen plays an important role in maintaining bone health, and thus females with low levels of estrogen are at a greater risk of developing osteoporosis.

Fat Body Mass

Fat body mass or **total body fat** can be divided further into two types of fat. **Storage fat (SF)** is fat that accumulates as adipose tissue (fat cells). This fat serves as an energy reserve (should the body be subjected to starvation) and also serves to protect internal organs by cushioning them. The main storage site for SF is beneath the skin surface; this fat is thus often referred to as subcutaneous fat. The average man has about 12 percent of body weight as SF, while the average woman has about 15 percent of body weight as SF. Individuals require some fat to exist; however, excess fat is associated with numerous health problems.

The second type of fat is **essential fat (EF)** which is the fat that is required for normal physiological functioning. Some of this fat is present in the bone marrow, heart, lungs, liver, spleen, kidneys, intestines, muscle, and the lipid-rich tissues of the central nervous system. EF comprises about 3 percent of body weight for the average man and 12 percent for the average woman. Not surprisingly then, this sex-specific essential fat is located in the mammary glands and pelvic region and is involved in hormone-related functions, pregnancy, etc.

Measuring Body Fat

There are many ways to assess total body fat and most involve an *indirect* method. The *direct* method is simply to grind tissue and measure the amount of fat through **chemical analysis**. Obviously, this is impractical for living organisms and this method is generally used only on cadavers.

The most common indirect method involves measuring skinfold thickness with **skinfold calipers**. This indirect method requires some technical expertise but is relatively inexpensive (see Chapter 10). The measurements obtained can be used to predict or estimate total body fat based on the assumption that subcutaneous fat is directly related to total body fat. To perform this technique the skin is pulled away from muscle and pinched between two flattened prongs of

Figure 12.4 Research methods for establishing percent body fat. **A.** Hydrostatic weighing. **B.** Dual energy x-ray absorptiometry (DEXA).

the fat calipers that exert a constant tension. The accuracy of skinfold measurement is about ±3.98 percent when performed correctly by an experienced individual. By measuring skinfolds at a number of sites and comparing to tables or using mathematical formulas, a percentage of body fat can be predicted.

A second indirect method of determining percent body fat is to use **hydrostatic weighing** or underwater weighing (Figure 12.4 A). This is a more accurate means of measuring body composition and the standard for other indirect techniques. It is based on Archimedes' principle of water displacement. According to this principle, when an object is submerged in water, there is a buoyant force equal to the weight of the water displaced. Since bone and muscle have a greater density than water, an individual with a high percentage of fat-free mass will weigh more in the water than an individual with a high percentage of body fat. To use hydrostatic weighing, one must first determine body density by measuring (a) body weight on land, (b) underwater body weight, (c) water density at the temperature used for the test, and (d) residual lung volume. Once body density has been determined, equations can be used to calculate **percent body fat**.

Another method of measuring body fat is the **Bod-Pod**, a very expensive but accurate method that does not require underwater submersion and may facilitate measuring very heavy or large individuals. **Bioelectrical impedance analysis (BIA)** is yet another method based on differences in electrical conductivity between fat-free mass and fat mass. By passing an electrical current through the body, a change in voltage is detected, which allows body density, and hence percent body fat, to be calculated. One disadvantage of BIA is the extent to which measurements are influenced by the hydration level of the subject. Other indirect methods of measuring body fat are also available such as **dual energy x-ray absorptiometry (DEXA)**, which is also used to determine bone mineral content (Figure 12.4 B).

Body Mass Index

Except for skinfold calipers, the measurement of body mass can be expensive and/or time consuming. It is largely limited to research labs and hospitals. Therefore, the **body mass index (BMI)** can be used as an easy alternative to assess healthy body weight using an individual's weight (kg) and height (m) measurements. BMI is calculated by dividing total body weight (kg) by body height (metres squared):

$$\text{BMI} = \text{weight (kg) / height (m)}^2$$

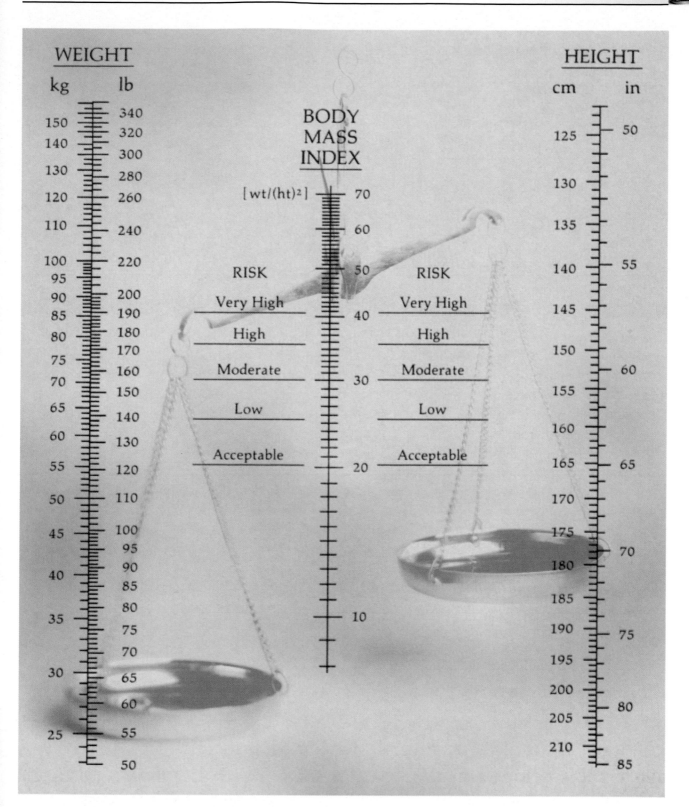

Figure 12.5 Use the nomogram above to determine your BMI. First, find and mark your body weight (kg or lbs) on the scale to the left and your height (cm or in) on the scale to the right. Then simply place a straight edge connecting the two values. Your BMI (metric units) is read where the line intersects the scale in the centre. The degree of risk associated with your BMI is also indicated to the left or right of the scale.

Table 12.2 **A.** BMI values in relation to sex. **B.** Desirable BMIs in relation to age.

A

Weight Status	Men	Women
Underweight	< 20.7	< 19.1
Acceptable weight	20.7 – 27.8	19.1 – 27.3
Overweight	27.8	27.3
Severely overweight	31.1	32.3
Morbid obesity	45.4	44.8

B

Age Group (years)	BMI (kg/m²)
19 – 24	19 – 24
25 – 34	20 – 25
35 – 44	21 – 26
45 – 54	22 – 27
55 – 65	23 – 28
> 65	24 – 29

For example, a person that is 167 cm tall and weighs 70 kg would have a BMI of 25.0 kg/m² [70 kg/(1.676)² = 70/2.80 = 25.0 kg/m²]. Once the BMI has been obtained, its relationship to desirable body mass indexes can be determined using Table 12.2 A and B.

The BMI has three general ranges: an underweight range, a healthy or acceptable weight range, and an overweight range. The overweight range may be further subdivided. BMI scores above 30 are classified as obese and scores in this range or above increase one's risk of developing health problems. Use of the BMI is generally intended for men and women aged 20-65 and is not useful for babies, children, teenagers, pregnant women, or very muscular people, such as athletes.

An easy and quick way of determining your BMI is to use the nomogram in Figure 12.5.

Misleading Norms

Weight norms must be interpreted with caution. Being overweight according to norms does not necessarily mean that one is obese. Consider two individuals that are both 180 cm tall and weigh approximately the same weight. One 70-kg person might be very fit and have only 7 percent (4.9 kg) body fat, while another 70-kg person might have 30 percent (21 kg) body fat. Clearly, both individuals have the same mass, but their body composition differs drastically. Thus, although

an excess of muscle and other lean body mass can render an individual overweight by normative standards, it does not render him or her obese, since he or she may not have an excess of body fat.

Somatotyping

The human body is composed of **roundness**, **muscularity**, and **linearity**. Based on these three components, individuals can be classified into three major body types. **Endomorphs** exhibit a predominance of the gut and visceral organs, giving them a round appearance. **Mesomorphs** exhibit a predominance of muscle, while **ectomorphs** exhibit a predominance of linearity, tending to be tall and thin.

Typically, various sporting activities require sport-specific body types for achieving optimal performance. Therefore, it is not surprising that athletes from different sports demonstrate different somatotypes (Figure 12.6).

An example of a predominantly endomorphic individual would be an obese person or athlete participating in sports like sumo wrestling (Figure 12.6 A). A bodybuilder, a gymnast, and a running back in football (Figure 12.6 B) are examples of mainly mesomorphic individuals. An example of a predominantly ectomorphic individual would be a basketball player, a long-distance runner, or a high jumper (Figure 12.6 C).

Figure 12.6 Typical body types across a variety of sporting activities. **A.** Endomorphs. **B.** Mesomorphs. **C.** Ectomorphs.

Putting the "Pop" in Popularity

After water, carbonated beverages are the most popular drinks in North America. And there is no shortage of choices. From Cherry or Vanilla Coke to Pepsi Twist or Blue, new flavours, colours, and labels are constantly being developed to entice consumers – especially young consumers (12- to 24-year-olds) who comprise the majority of high-consumption pop drinkers.

According to Statistics Canada, Canadians drank nearly 113 litres of carbonated soft drinks per capita in 2000, exceeding values for coffee (102 litres), milk (88 litres), tea (73 litres), and beer (67 litres). Americans guzzled even more of the stuff at almost 187 litres per person.

Our love for these carbonated beverages, which often come full of empty calories, has contributed to the overweight epidemic facing Canadians both young and old. Next time you consider reaching for a can of pop, consider the impact on your health.

Obesity

Obesity is defined as having an excess of body fat beyond some particular standard that is usually based on age and sex (i.e., norms derived from a large number of people). To be classified as obese, men and women between the ages of 17 and 50 require a body fat percentage of greater than 20 and 30 percent, respectively. Older individuals are granted more leeway, although it is not clear why body fat should increase with age.

Obesity has become an epidemic in the Western world and 30 percent of all adults in Western countries can be considered obese. In Canada, approximately 15 percent of adults are considered obese. Unfortunately these numbers seem to be getting worse, not better.

Obesity is a complex condition that may involve environmental, social, psychological, and genetic factors, although only a small percentage of people are genetically predisposed to be obese (Figure 12.8). Research has shown that obesity poses serious health problems, increasing the risk of coronary heart disease, stroke, hypertension, diabetes, osteoarthritis, some forms of cancer, and other diseases. On the bright side, obesity can be prevented and by itself is perhaps less harmful than the many health complications that are associated with the condition.

Creeping Obesity

Although obese individuals are often viewed as gluttonous, they generally do not consume large amounts of calories. In fact, physically active

Figure 12.7 Sumo wrestlers represent an extreme example of endomorphy.

individuals have been shown to consume more calories than obese individuals. Thus, obesity is often the result of too little activity rather than overeating, bringing about **creeping obesity**: a slight change in the energy balance occurring over a period of time causes a gradual increase in fat mass each year. As people age, their metabolic rate and physical activity patterns decline. If their caloric intake is not reduced to re-balance with energy expenditure (according to the energy balance equation in Figure 12.2), then body mass will increase due to excess calories stored as fat.

Creeping obesity is often experienced by individuals that were active in their teens and twenties but for various reasons (work, family, etc.) reduced their physical activity levels later in life, only to realize years later that they have an excess amount of body fat.

Consider This

If you consume only one potato chip per day (roughly 10 calories) in excess of caloric expenditure, then over a year (365 days) you will have accumulated 3,650 extra calories, equivalent to approximately 0.5 kg of body fat. In view of this, it is easy to understand how one can gradually become obese.

Weight-loss Industry

There are a variety of fad diets that people use in an attempt to achieve weight loss. Weight-loss industry has become a billion-dollar industry as more and more people suffering from obesity seek help from food-industry experts and nutritionists. High-protein, low-carbohydrate diets; high-carbohydrate, low-protein diets; fasting–starvation

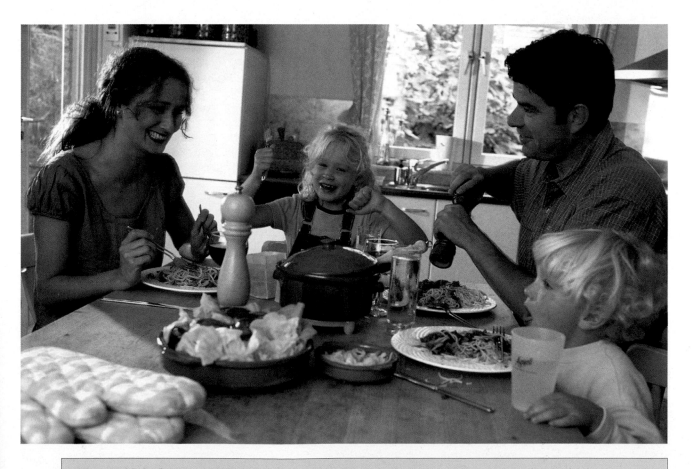

Figure 12.8 Good eating habits are developed early and may help prevent obesity in the long run.

Figure 12.9 It is your choice when it comes to making sensible dieting decisions.

diets; high-fibre, low-calorie diets; and limited food choice diets are just a few of the many possibilities available. In most cases, these approaches are ineffective and potentially harmful. Following Canada's Food Guide presented in Chapter 11 coupled with an active lifestyle that includes regular exercise seems to be the best approach to weight management (Figure 12.9 B).

Consequences of Dieting

Dieting for the purposes of improving health, working capacity, or athletic performance can be positive if you follow the recommended

guidelines for healthy eating. Unfortunately, cultural pressures to be thin (especially among girls and young women) and the stigma of being overweight have pushed many weight-conscious youths to dieting and abnormal eating patterns lacking nutritional balance. Dieting for these reasons is not only distressing, but sets you up for failure in the long run. Although obesity can be a real health concern, managing your weight needs to be done in an atmosphere that is both positive and realistic – not under conditions in which eating itself seems like a crime.

Should we be preoccupied with the issue of weight if it does not pose a major health risk? This is a question young people especially should

Knowledge Check

For each of the following statements below, indicate whether it applies to *anorexia nervosa* (**AN**), *bulimia nervosa* (**BN**), or both (**AB**) eating disorders. After you have finished reading this chapter, take the test again.

1. Need or desire for perfection. (   )

2. Recurrent episodes of binge eating. (   )

3. Low self-esteem and sense of self-worth. (   )

4. Extreme concern about appearance. (   )

5. Evidence of purging (through vomiting or use of laxatives or diuretics). (   )

6. Amenorrhea (loss of menstrual periods). (   )

7. Signs of starvation (thinning of hair, yellow appearance of palms or soles). (   )

8. Refusal to maintain body weight at or above normal weight for age and height. (   )

9. Frequent, unusual dental problems. (   )

10. Frequent weight fluctuations. (   )

(Answers: 1. AB; 2. BN; 3. AB; 4. AB; 5. BN; 6. AN; 7. AN; 8. AN; 9. BN; 10. BN)

---

ask themselves. At one time or another you have probably questioned your weight or the way you look because of cultural pressures to be "thin and attractive." But chronic dieting, especially among teenagers, can be a serious concern because it can lead to retardation of physical growth, menstrual irregularities in women, a lowering of metabolic rate, and the development of eating disorders.

· Self-esteem and Body Image

Basing self-esteem more on outward appearance and body shape than on other assets – such as musical, artistic, creative, scholastic, nurturing, or other abilities – many of today's adolescent girls have an appallingly low sense of self-worth, poor views of their value to society, and often less confidence than boys of similar age. One Canadian survey found that while 60 percent of girls aged eight to nine report they are "happy with the way they are," by the time they reach age 16, only 29 percent of girls are content and confident about themselves, compared to 48 percent of boys of similar age.

The Complete Canadian Health Guide,
University of Toronto, 1993

Eating Disorders

The term "eating disorders" does not reveal the true seriousness of these conditions. Problems with weight control are not just problems of avoiding excess body fat. In fact, these disorders have increased in frequency and pose specific public health risks among athletes, dancers, models, and others who become preoccupied with body weight and shape. Disorders of this nature also put women at risk of developing the female athlete triad (FAT), a deadly combination of eating disorders, amenorrhea, and osteoporosis.

The two major eating disorders characterized by abnormal eating behaviours are *anorexia nervosa* and *bulimia nervosa*. These disorders develop as a result of many factors, including dissatisfaction with body image, which stems from distorted thinking, unrealistic expectations, and excessive self-criticism. A fear of being overweight, excessive dieting, and a preoccupation with food become obsessive. Related issues are *binge eating* and *subclinical eating disorders* among athletes. Another problem is *cognitive restraint*, a psychological means to intentionally restrain intake to lower dietary intake.

Anorexia Nervosa

Individuals suffering from **anorexia nervosa** fail to eat an adequate amount of food to maintain a reasonable body weight – to the point of starvation. Anorexics have an intense fear of gaining weight or becoming fat, so they often avoid eating and may use compulsive exercise to reduce body weight. They begin by restricting their intake of high-calorie foods, which eventually leads to a restriction of virtually all foods from their diet. Typically, anorexics weigh less than 85 percent of normal weight for their age and height (Figure 12.10). Some of the physical symptoms include dry skin, amenorrhea, reduced bone mass, brittle nails, and carotene pigmentation (yellowish appearance of the palms and soles of the feet).

The psychological problems associated with anorexia such as depression and other clinical disorders can be even more serious than the physical ones. It has been reported that between 5 and 18 percent of anorexics commit suicide or develop serious, irreversible medical problems.

Bulimia Nervosa

Bulimia nervosa is characterized by continual episodes of binge eating (large amounts of food consumed in a discrete period) followed by purging. Bulimics feel a lack of control when they binge, unable to stop what and how much they eat. After a binge, bulimics compensate by vomiting or using laxatives or diuretics to rid the body of the food they just ate. Frequent vomiting often leads to dental problems, as the acid reflux from the stomach damages the teeth and gums in the mouth. Bulimics may also engage in vigorous exercise to compensate for the increased calories consumed during a binge.

Bulimics are more difficult to identify because their body weight is often normal, and they usually conceal their eating habits well (Figure 12.11). However, look for warning signs such as secretive eating patterns, repeated isolation soon after a meal, disappearance of large amounts of food, nervous or agitated behaviour immediately after eating, or the loss or gain of extreme amounts of weight. Bulimics may experience weight fluctuations exceeding 4.5 kg during periods of binge eating.

Bulimia is generally considered to be less serious than anorexia, since treatment is effective in the majority of cases and most individuals experience a full and lasting recovery. However, all eating disorders should be taken seriously and dealt with promptly.

Hair loss

Depression

Brittle fingernails

Carotene pigmentation

- Low blood pressure
- Low heart rate

Amenorrhea

Dry skin

Weight loss

Reduced bone mass (osteoporosis)

Swelling around ankles and hands

Cold extremities

Figure 12.10 The effects of anorexia nervosa.

Recognizing Binge Eating Disorder

Presented below are a few signs and symptoms characteristic of *binge eating disorder (BED)*.

1. Recurrent episodes of binge eating. An episode of binge eating is characterized by both:

- eating an amount of food during a discrete period that is larger than most people would eat during the same time and in similar circumstances; and

- a sense of lack of control over eating (what or how much) during the episode.

2. During most binge episodes, *at least* three of the following behavioural indicators of loss of control are present:

- eating much more rapidly than usual;

- eating until feeling uncomfortably full;

- eating large amounts of food even when not feeling physically hungry;

- eating alone because of being embarrassed by how much one is eating; or

- feeling disgusted with oneself, depressed, or very guilty after overeating.

3. The binge eating causes episodes of considerable distress.

4. Binge eating occurs, on average, at least two days a week over a six-month period.

Figure 12.11 Distorted thinking and excessive self-criticism lead many bulimics to constantly monitor their weight and appearance in the pursuit of an ideal figure.

Binge Eating

A syndrome related to eating disorders and obesity in particular is **binge eating disorder (BED)**, which involves ingesting large amounts of food, without the purging behaviour characteristic of bulimia nervosa. Although this is considered to be a hazardous health behaviour, it is actually encouraged in such sports as sumo wrestling and football (linemen), where gaining greater mass is an asset. However, it is worth noting that binge eating leads to obesity in most cases.

Female Athlete Triad

Modern society and the media place enormous pressure on individuals, and especially on young women, to maintain a thin body image (also see Chapter 1). Such goals are unrealistic, but many athletes pursue them through extreme dieting and overtraining. They thereby risk developing a medical syndrome known as the **female athlete triad (FAT)**. Although athletes from all types of sports run this risk, those who participate in gymnastics, dance, figure skating, ballet, and cross-country running are the most susceptible because these sports demand an unrealistic stereotypical body shape.

Figure 12.12 The female athlete triad (FAT) represents a series of three progressive conditions that should be taken seriously.

Three distinct interrelated problems form the FAT condition: disordered eating, amenorrhea, and osteoporosis (Figure 12.12).

Disordered Eating The term **disordered eating** refers to a spectrum of poor and unhealthy nutritional behaviours that can be as extreme as anorexia nervosa and bulimia nervosa or as subtle as consciously restricting food intake.

Amenorrhea The occurrence of irregular or absent menstrual periods for at least three months is referred to as **amenorrhea**. When an athlete stops having a menstrual period or menstrual periods become irregular, it should not be viewed as a normal adaptation to exercise training. It is actually a classic sign of the triad and medical intervention should be initiated.

Osteoporosis If amenorrhea persists over long periods, it leads into **osteoporosis**, or a weakening of the bones, which unfortunately is not entirely reversible. Osteoporosis refers to low bone mass; bones become weak and brittle, which in turn increases the risk of fracture. An athlete who suffers from a stress fracture may be also struggling with the FAT: in fact, a stress fracture should be considered by coaches and athletes as a possible indicator of an unhealthy approach to training.

Take FAT Seriously

The *female athlete triad* is a serious medical condition that can be fatal in some cases. An athlete who is suffering from any symptoms of the triad should seek medical counsel. Early intervention is more likely to result in successful treatment.

How to Prevent FAT The single best strategy to prevent the FAT is to eat more calories, especially during intense or increased exercise training. Eating a healthy and balanced diet is very important to maintaining bone and muscle

Case Study

Anthropometric Data:

Height: 174 cm
Weight: 54 kg
LBW: 46.5 kg
Her goal was to be 49-50 kg.
She had amenorrhea.

Present Dietary Pattern:

Breakfast: Nil
On the way to dance class a power bar, various flavours

Lunch: Nil
Diet Coke during the day

Dinner: Steamed vegetables and fruit

An intelligent 16-year-old dancer wanted to reduce her weight prior to her final examination to help her make the national junior squad, which was to travel abroad to compete at an international tournament (see data on the left).

After following this pattern for some time, the problem began: binge eating on anything that was in the house (bread – dry or with peanut butter or jam, biscuits and cheese, breakfast cereal, ice cream, etc.), followed by discomfort and guilt and finally induced vomiting before bedtime. The pattern would be repeated the next day.

Solution

The instructor, with the professional help of a dietitian, was able to explain to the dancer the negative effects of her nutrition practice on performance. Furthermore, the instructor suggested nutrition counseling. The dietitian was able to persuade the dancer that it is possible to eat normally and still lose weight. A low-calorie diet was planned with emphasis on a high percentage of carbohydrate intake. A multivitamin/mineral was recommended to supplement the low-calorie diet.

Result

At the review visit six weeks later, the dancer's weight had decreased by 1.5 kg. She felt well, was able to follow the nutritional regimen, and had achieved her goals. She continued to lose weight and was selected to the squad.

mass. Female athletes should also ensure they get enough calcium in their diets. Young women require 300 mg of calcium a day to maintain strong and healthy bones, since the years before and after puberty are the most important bone building years.

Eating Disorders Among Athletes

While eating disorders are an issue faced predominantly by girls and women concerned with body image, many athletes rely on extreme (although temporary) dieting measures to achieve or maintain a desired body weight. Many athletes competing in sports with weight classes often strive to make weight in lower weight classes (e.g., wrestling, boxing, weightlifting) or maintain the minimum weight allowed (e.g., jockey in horse racing, coxswain in rowing) to gain a competitive advantage. For these athletes, the issue of body weight is secondary to the objective of performing well. Dieting issues are only temporary in most cases for these individuals. Contrast this with the more prolonged issues faced by individuals suffering from the eating disorders described previously, which stem from issues of self-esteem, self-evaluation, and self-identity.

Summary

The human body is made up of components that are arranged and distributed in different ways. Individuals may exhibit different amounts of roundness (endomorphs), linearity (ectomorphs), or muscle (mesomorphs) and thus have different body types. Various sporting activities require sport-specific body types for achieving optimal performance.

Basal metabolic rate (BMR) is defined as the minimum amount of energy the body requires to carry out all vital functions. Energy requirements increase with any additional activity above this level. Weight management is a matter of balancing the calories consumed with the calories expended; body weight will remain constant if caloric input and output are the same.

Lean body mass (LBM) refers to the "non-fat" components of the human body (i.e., muscle, bone, and water). LBM can be calculated by subtracting total body fat from total body mass. One way of indirectly measuring body fat is through skinfold measurements. This method uses calipers to measure skinfold thicknesses at various sites on the body, and the results are then used to predict total body fat. An easy way of assessing healthy weight is to divide body weight (kg) by body height (metres squared) to arrive at a measure known as body mass index (BMI).

Obesity is defined as having excess body fat beyond some particular standard, usually based on age and sex. The proportion of muscle and fat you have greatly influences your risk of disease, and obesity poses serious health problems including coronary heart disease, stroke, hypertension, and diabetes. At the other extreme, cultural pressures to be thin and the stigma of being overweight have led some individuals along the dangerous path of extreme dieting and abnormal eating patterns. Examples of common eating disorders include anorexia, bulimia, binge eating, and female athlete triad.

Fortunately, weight is one body component that we do have control over. By coupling an awareness of sufficient caloric intake with adequate amounts of physical activity, a healthy body weight can usually be achieved.

Key Words

Amenorrhea	Bioelectrical impedance	Body mass index (BMI)
Anorexia nervosa	analysis (BIA)	Bulimia nervosa
Basal metabolic rate (BMR)	Bod-Pod	Caloric balance
Binge eating disorder (BED)	Body composition	Creeping obesity

Disordered eating
Dual energy x-ray
  absorptiometry (DEXA)
Ectomorph
Endomorph
Energy balance equation

Essential fat (EF)
Female athlete triad (FAT)
Hydrostatic weighing
Lean body mass (LBM)
Mesomorph
Obesity

Osteoporosis
Percent body fat
Skinfold calipers
Storage fat (SF)
Total body fat (TBF)
Total body mass (TBM)

Discussion Questions

1. Briefly describe the energy balance equation. What situation would need to exist for someone to lose weight? To gain weight?

2. What is a basal metabolic rate? How does exercise influence it?

3. What is the two-component model? Discuss each component of the model and how it relates to overall body composition.

4. Identify and define the two major types of body fat. How do levels of each type differ in males and females?

5. List four indirect methods used to measure body fat. Which methods are most accurate? Least accurate?

6. What does BMI stand for? How is it used to assess body weight? What is a healthy BMI value?

7. Individuals can be classified into three main body types. List them and briefly describe each one.

8. Define creeping obesity.

9. Body weight norms can be misleading. Discuss the implications of this statement.

10. Distinguish between the two major types of eating disorders. How do these differ from binge eating disorder and eating disorders among athletes?

In This Chapter:

Drugs Versus Dietary Supplements *318*
    Drugs *318*
    Dietary Supplements *318*

Drugs and Exercise *318*
    Everyday Drugs *318*
    Illegal Drugs *323*

Ergogenic Aids and Exercise *323*
    How Do Ergogenic Aids Work? *324*
    Vitamins and Minerals *324*
    Carbohydrate Loading *324*
    Creatine *326*
    Banned Ergogenic Aids and Exercise *326*

Summary *333*

CHAPTER 13

Performance-enhancing Substances and Methods: Substance Use and Abuse

After completing this chapter you should be able to:

- explain the differences between drugs and dietary supplements;

- evaluate the effects of drugs and supplements on performance;

- describe various ergogenic aids and how they work;

- explain the impact of substance use and abuse on health status.

Body image strongly affects how young men and women feel about themselves. Our society places value on a slender female body and a muscular male body. Athletic prowess, traditionally important for males, is now appealing to females as well. These pressures along with the many financial and extrinsic rewards of becoming a professional athlete can lead to an unhealthy obsession with a particular body image or the pursuit of athletic excellence, leading to dangerous habits such as taking steroids.

Experts suspect that a large number of high school students use dietary supplements. Claims of instant energy, increased quality and quantity of training, washboard abdominals, huge gains in strength and performance, and overnight weight loss, all without side effects, make taking supplements seem very attractive. This attraction is made stronger by peer pressure and the constant bombardment of ideal body images in the media (see Chapter 1), which take advantage of the insecurities of consumers.

A high proportion of youth experiments with drugs. What effects do these substances have on the human body, and why do people continue to pursue their desired effects? These are some of the questions that will be explored in this chapter, helping you make the decisions necessary to prevent injury, compete ethically, and maintain a healthy body.

Drugs Versus Dietary Supplements

Drugs and dietary supplements help keep us healthy, and they restore our health when we are sick. Drugs have given many people a new lease on life, helping them cope with medical conditions such as hypertension, rheumatoid arthritis, pain from severe trauma, bacterial infection, diabetes mellitus, and osteoporosis. However, drugs also cause side effects, some more serious than others.

But what is the difference between drugs and dietary supplements? Are dietary supplements safer than drugs? This section answers these two questions.

Drugs

Drugs are defined in two different ways. According to the Food and Drug Act, **drugs** refer to substances used as medication or in the preparation of medication. Merriam-Webster's medical dictionary defines drugs as substances that cause addiction, habituation, or a marked change in consciousness. **Addiction** refers to the compulsive physiological need for and use of a habit-forming substance, such as heroin, nicotine, or alcohol. **Habituation** describes tolerance to the effects of a drug acquired through continued use. As a result it takes greater amounts of the substance to elicit the same effect.

Table 13.2 on page 330 presents a summary of drugs and dietary supplements, some permissible and some banned.

Dietary Supplements

Food sustains growth, repair, and vital processes in the body. The foods we eat consist of protein, carbohydrate, fat, minerals, and vitamins. **Dietary supplements** are ingredients found in food, but they have been processed to provide one or more vitamins, minerals, herbs, amino acids, or food constituents. Steak, for example, is considered food because it contains protein, fat, carbohydrates, minerals, vitamins, and creatine. However, creatine processed and consumed by itself is considered a dietary supplement.

Drugs and Exercise

Everyday Drugs

When most people think of drugs they think about medication or banned substances. However, many drugs are both legal and readily accessible. Nicotine, alcohol, and caffeine are perfect

Do You Want to Be a Guinea Pig?

Many dietary supplements do not have research backing their claims. When they do it is often by the companies producing the supplement, resulting in a serious conflict of interest. Even worse, many products sold do not contain the ingredients listed on the labels. This deception can occur because the dietary supplement industry is not regulated, unlike the drug industry. Without regulation consumers are at risk of serious side effects. In addition, numerous side effects are unknown because the research conducted was only short term (up to six weeks). This may lead to problems because most dietary supplements are cycled on and off for many years. For a dietary supplement to be considered safe, long-term side effects need to be determined.

Even when supplements are well researched, where the biochemical mechanism of action is established and the supplements have been tested through randomized clinical control trials, problems can still arise. Ephedra is a prime example of such a supplement. Health Canada has requested a recall of certain products containing ephedra from the market.

You must be aware of advertising hype that promotes alleged health and fitness benefits of certain products in order to make informed decisions!

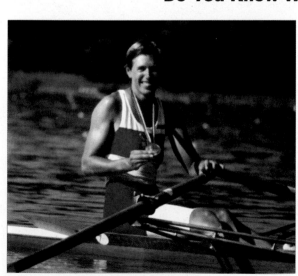

examples. Remember, to be classified as a drug the substance must cause addiction, habituation, or marked changes in consciousness. According to this definition nicotine, alcohol, and caffeine meet these criteria. The ergogenic effects of these everyday drugs are discussed in this section.

Caffeine

Commonly found in coffee beans, tea leaves, cocoa beans, cola nuts, chocolate, and energy drinks, **caffeine** is a stimulant of the central nervous system (Table 13.1). It is the most commonly taken drug to increase alertness and fat burning during endurance exercise. Studies have shown an

Do You Know What You're Taking?

Canadian hero Silken Laumann tested positive at the 1995 Pan Am Games for a banned drug after taking an over-the-counter cold medication. Laumann and her quad-sculls teammates were stripped of their gold medals.

Laumann did not simply compare the ingredients listed on the box with the manual given to all athletes by the Canadian Centre for Ethics in Sport (CCES). She sought medical expertise, but the team's physician thought she was referring to Benadryl *antihistamine* and not Benadryl *decongestant* and did not ask to see the product. The medication contained the banned substance pseudoephedrine, as well as substances that inhibit athletic performance. But, of course, no one tests for those substances.

Table 13.1 Caffeine content of various foods and beverages.

Product	Serving Size	Milligrams of Caffeine (approximate values)	Product	Serving Size	Milligrams of Caffeine (approximate values)
Coffee			**Cola Beverages**		
Brewed	237 ml (1 cup)	135	Cola beverage, regular	355 ml (1 can)	36 – 46
Roasted and ground, percolated	237 ml	118	Cola beverage, diet	355 ml (1 can)	39 – 50
Roasted and ground, filter drip	237 ml	179	**Cocoa Products**		
Roasted and ground, decaffeinated	237 ml	3	Chocolate milk	237 ml	8
Instant	237 ml	76 – 106	Candy, milk chocolate	28 g	7
Instant, decaffeinated	237 ml	5	Candy, sweet chocolate	28 g	19
Tea			Baking chocolate, unsweetened	28 g	25 – 58
Average blend	237 ml	43	Chocolate cake	80 g	6
Green	237 ml	30	Chocolate brownies	42 g	10
Instant	237 ml	15	Chocolate pudding	145 g	9
Leaf or bag	237 ml	50			
Decaffeinated	237 ml	0			

ergogenic effect in runners and swimmers after consuming caffeine-loaded foods and beverages. Strength training athletes take caffeine to prime their nervous systems in preparation for heavy lifting. Caffeine is also a diuretic.

Research has shown that people who normally avoid caffeine may experience side effects such as insomnia, headaches, irritability and nervousness, elevated heart rate, and high blood pressure after ingesting the drug. Health Canada currently states that for an average adult, moderate daily caffeine intake at levels of 400 to 450 mg per day is not associated with any adverse effects. Women of childbearing age and children may be at higher risk.

Caffeine Boost

The consumption of caffeine is not banned in international competition. However, the International Olympic Committee (IOC) has set urinary limits of caffeine concentration to 12 micrograms per ml. This amount would be present after approximately four to seven cups of coffee. Ingesting caffeine tablets can also trigger a positive doping infraction.

Alcohol

Alcohol is the most popular drug among most Canadians. Some athletes consume alcohol believing it helps them perform in competition. However, research has not shown any ergogenic effect on athletic performance. Nevertheless, some athletes use alcohol because of its psychological effects, which include reduced tension and anxiety before competition, enhanced self-confidence, and promotion of aggression. As a depressant, alcohol may also have an anti-tremor effect in activities that require steadiness and accuracy, such as archery and shooting.

On the negative side, alcohol may profoundly impair performance in activities that require motor coordination and balance, hand–eye coordination, reaction time, information processing, and decision making. These effects, for example, impair the ability to drive, causing drivers to take more risks, speed, and drive dangerously. Nearly half of all drivers killed in traffic accidents have been drinking.

Nicotine

Nicotine is perhaps the most widely used potent stimulant in our society. As the tobacco industry has recently acknowledged, it is one of the most addictive drugs known. Nicotine is a dangerous and harmful substance, especially for athletes. It negatively affects almost all levels of body functions, impairing performance in many ways.

Did You Know?

A standard serving of beer, wine, or liquor contains roughly the same amount of pure alcohol.

12 ounces   **5 ounces**   **1 ounce**

From the Statistics Files

Common toxic substances found in cigarettes cause cancer and other serious complications of long-term smoking that include chronic bronchitis or emphysema, ulcers, asthma, cold fingers and toes, dulled sense of smell and taste, cataracts, gum disease, tooth decay, ear infections, dry skin, early aging, and impotence. Each year 45,000 Canadians die because of smoking, and many more live with debilitating lung and heart problems. It has been estimated that the cost of smoking on the Canadian economy approaches more than 24 billion dollars annually.

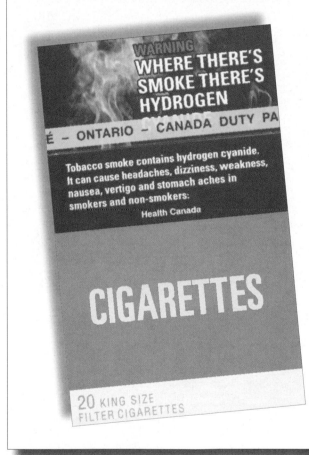

Common carcinogenic agents found in cigarettes. Is there any wonder why smoking is bad for your health?

Substance	Commonly Found In
Arsenic	Rat poisons
Acetic acid	Hair dye developer
Acetone	Nail polish remover
Ammonia	Household cleaners
Benzene	Rubber cement
Cadmium	Batteries
Carbon monoxide	Car fumes
Carbon tetrachloride	Dry cleaning fluid
Ethanol	Alcohol
Formaldehyde	Embalming fluid
Hydrazine	Rocket fuel
Hexamine	Barbeque lighters
Hydrogen cyanide	Poison gas chambers
Lead	Batteries
Methane	Swamp gas
Methanol	Rocket fuel
Naphthalenes	Explosives
Phenols	Disinfectants and plastics
Polonium	Radiation
Stearic acid	Candle wax
Tar	Roads
Toluene	Embalmer's glue

Research has shown no ergogenic effects related to smoking. Smoking decreases the oxygen-carrying capacity of blood, restricts oxygen supply to the heart while making the heart need more of it, increases heart rate and blood pressure, alters the blood and air flow in the lungs, and decreases temperature in the fingers and toes. For an athlete, who especially needs an adequate supply of oxygen, smoking is a deadly opponent to optimal performance.

The adverse effects of smoking are due to nicotine and the numerous (several thousand) other chemical substances contained in tobacco smoke. Many of these substances act as irritants and carcinogenic agents (see table in the box *From the Statistics Files*).

Illegal Drugs

Illegal drugs are classified into six basic categories – stimulants, depressants, hallucinogens, anabolic steroids, opiates, and cannabis. **Stimulants**, such as cocaine, crack, ecstasy, amphetamines, and methamphetamines, stimulate the central nervous system. In contrast, **depressants** have a sedating effect on the central nervous system. Common examples include barbiturates, rohypnol, anavar, and dianabol. **Hallucinogens** are natural or synthetic drugs that can produce hallucinations when taken. Examples include LSD, PCP, mushrooms, peyote, ecstasy, and special K. **Anabolic steroids**, drugs or hormones that resemble human testosterone, increase muscle growth. Winstrol, deca durabolin, and nandrolone are three common examples of a list of hundreds of anabolic steroids. **Opiates**, such as heroin, morphine, and codeine, are narcotics that have a depressant effect on the user, helping to induce sleep and to alleviate pain. **Cannabis** describes hemp plants that are smoked and ingested to produce various psychophysical changes. Examples include marijuana, hash, and hash oil.

Tables 13.2 and 13.3 at the end of the chapter present a summary of the most commonly used drugs and their harmful side effects on health.

Cannabis

The four types of cannabis are **marijuana, hashish, hash oil,** and **tetrahydrocannabinol (THC)**. The effects of cannabis vary from person to person and depend on the method of consumption and amount. Cannabis commonly creates feelings of calm and relaxation and encourages a person to be more talkative. It impairs concentration and short-term memory, causing some people to feel drowsy. Sensory perception of colours and sounds becomes more vibrant and intense, which alters the sense of time and space. Physical effects of cannabis include impaired coordination and balance, increased appetite, rapid heartbeat, red eyes, and dry mouth and throat.

Drug Bust

At the 1998 Winter Games in Nagano, Canadian snowboarder Ross Rebagliati became the first Olympian to lose a gold medal for testing positive for marijuana. The medal was later reinstated when an arbitration panel ruled that the IOC failed to follow proper testing procedures.

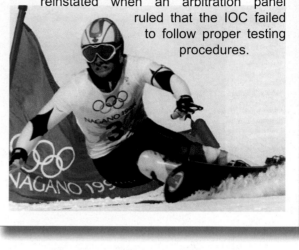

Ergogenic Aids and Exercise

Synthetically derived substances, manufactured for medical purposes, are becoming extremely popular among athletes. Many drugs improve athletic performance, albeit at great expense to health. Likewise, dietary supplements can improve athletic performance, improve immune function, and treat or control medical conditions. Drugs and dietary supplements are therefore considered ergogenic aids. **Ergogenic aids** are substances that enhance work output, particularly as it relates to athletic performance.

What the Professionals Think

Many professionals believe that a well-balanced nutritious diet offers the greatest ergogenic effect, especially when blended with good genetics and proper training.

How Do Ergogenic Aids Work?

There are four basic mechanisms by which ergogenic aids work to enhance performance:

(1) act as a stimulant to the central nervous system (e.g., caffeine, nicotine);

(2) increase the storage of limiting substrate needed for exercise (e.g., carbohydrate, creatine);

(3) act as a supplemental energy source (e.g., glucose); and

(4) facilitate recovery from training (ephedra, carbohydrate, water).

Vitamins and Minerals

It is no secret that competitive athletes in most sports consume vitamin and mineral supplements on a regular basis. There are two reasons for this. First, vitamin–mineral supplements are designed to ensure adequate micronutrient intake. Second, athletes believe that ingesting excess vitamins and minerals elevates their performance and training responsiveness. Research generally does not support these beliefs. Various studies have shown that vitamin–mineral intake neither improves exercise performance nor necessarily increases the blood levels of these micronutrients.

There are, however, exceptions to this. Vegetarian athletes and athletes with low energy intake such as female gymnasts, dancers, and competitors in weight-class sports may be vitamin–mineral deficient. For them, vitamin–mineral supplements may be prescribed to augment their daily diet.

As discussed in Chapter 11, individuals who eat well-balanced meals do not require vitamin or mineral supplementation of their diet. The common practice of "su-

percharging" or consuming more than 10 times the recommended daily allowance may be harmful to heath.

Carbohydrate Loading

Using the muscle biopsy technique (Chapter 3), exercise physiologists studied the relationship between the amount of stored glycogen in the muscle and the ability to do work. They found that sustained work of two to three hours fully depleted glycogen supplies and led to an inability to work further. Thus the amount of glycogen present in the muscle cells before the start of exercise was exceedingly important. The scientists then tried to determine how long it took to replenish glycogen supplies in the muscle (one day or more) and to see if a "super" load of glycogen could be stored by manipulating the diet. They determined that **carbohydrate loading** could be accomplished by first depleting the carbohydrate in the cells with two to three hours of exhaustive exercise, by then starving the muscles of carbohydrate for two days (eating high-protein meals with some fat and little carbohydrate), and finally by eating enormous amounts of carbohydrate. Under these conditions, the muscle cells over-compensated in their demand for carbohydrate and developed muscle glycogen levels significantly higher than normal.

Carbohydrate loading offers potential benefits for endurance athletes (distance runners, road cyclists, cross-country skiers) and others who risk depleting glycogen stores. For example, in rowing races of up to eight minutes a well-stocked muscle will probably possess enough glycogen to meet metabolic demands. But if intensive training occurs in the days prior to the race, if several races are rowed on successive days, or if recovery time and diet are inadequate, then the athlete may have low levels of carbohydrate to start with and the muscle may not have sufficient quantities of glycogen to perform at full potential.

Figure 13.1 shows how diet and work influence the amount of glycogen in the muscles. If a normal mixed diet (fat, protein, carbohydrate) is eaten, additional carbohydrate increases muscle

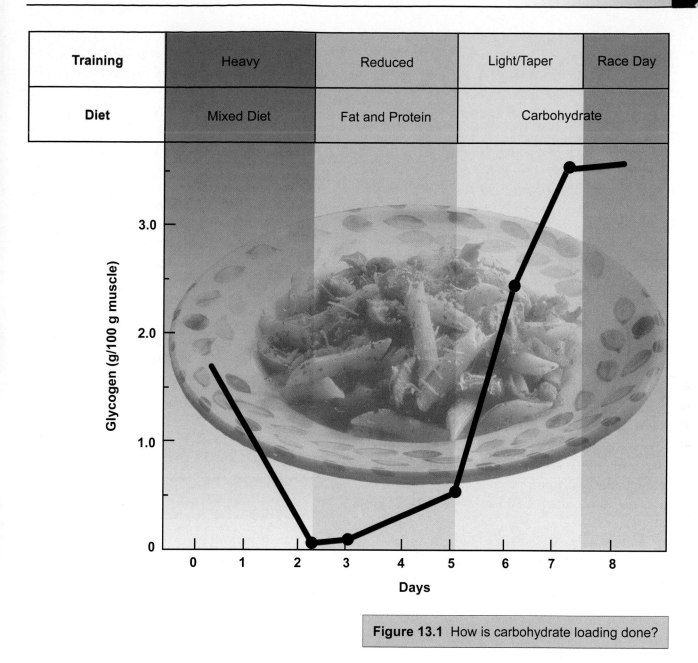

Training	Heavy	Reduced	Light/Taper	Race Day
Diet	Mixed Diet	Fat and Protein	Carbohydrate	

Figure 13.1 How is carbohydrate loading done?

glycogen. Adding carbohydrate to the depleted muscle (i.e., after work) loads the muscle to a level higher than possible on the normal mixed diet. Depleting the muscle, eating fat and protein for two days, then adding carbohydrate provides even more glycogen – about 20 percent higher than a mixed diet.

Negative aspects of carbohydrate loading include some gastrointestinal discomfort and sluggishness as a result of increased carbohydrates. It can add body weight that might actually negate the potential benefits of the increased

glycogen storage. Before trying to achieve a super-compensation effect before a race, long-distance athletes are advised to first experiment with carbohydrate loading.

Modified Carbohydrate Loading

Many of the negative aspects of carbohydrate loading can be eliminated by following a less stringent loading protocol. This protocol does not require prior exercise to exhaustion. During the first two days the athlete trains at about 75 percent of $\dot{V}O_2$max for about 1.5 hours. Training duration and intensity are then gradually reduced, leading into an exercise taper before the day of the race. During the first three days, the carbohydrate content in the diet should represent about 50 percent of total calories consumed. An increased carbohydrate content, about 65-75 percent of total energy intake, then follows during the three days prior to competition. Research has shown that this modified approach to carbohydrate loading enhances glycogen concentration in the muscle without requiring the dramatic glycogen depletion–loading protocol outlined earlier.

Creatine

Creatine is a natural compound created from three amino acids. It is found in red meats, poultry, and fish, and is also produced in the body by the liver and kidneys. The muscles use creatine during explosive, powerful movements such as jumping, sprinting, and lifting heavy weights.

One of the most popular nutritional supplements on the market today, creatine is sold in its supplemental form (creatine monohydrate, or CrH_2O) and comes in powder, tablet, capsule, and liquid form.

Studies have shown that creatine significantly increases lean muscle mass in just two weeks, improves performance in high-intensity exercise, and speeds up recovery rates. Side effects associated with creatine may include dehydration, diarrhea, stomach cramps, and muscle and ligament tears. Creatine supplements are not banned by any professional or amateur sports governing bodies, including the IOC.

Power athletes in particular believe that creatine consumption generates great benefits. These benefits include better performance in strength and power activities, greater muscular overload in training (see Chapter 9), and increased muscular endurance.

Up to 75 percent of NFL players and 90 percent of bodybuilders and weightlifters use some form of creatine supplement. Creatine is also used by the U.S. Navy SEALs, and a survey in England showed that more than 57 percent of elite British athletes use creatine regularly. Creatine has established itself around the world as a form of "soft doping" that has been accepted by the IOC.

Banned Ergogenic Aids and Exercise

Steroids

Anabolic steroids are a group of powerful drugs or compounds that duplicate the function of the male sex hormone testosterone. They are used medically to treat certain kinds of anemia, severe burns, endocrine problems, and some types of breast cancer.

Bodybuilders and professional and amateur athletes use steroids to give them a competitive advantage. Research has shown that anabolic steroids increase lean muscle mass, strength, and the ability to train longer and harder. However, research also indicates that steroid use comes at a huge cost to health because it generates numerous harmful side effects as shown in Figure 13.2. For adolescents using steroids, growth may be stunted through premature skeletal maturation and accelerated puberty changes. The consequences certainly outweigh any potential performance benefits.

Is It Worth It?

Many athletes will go to great lengths to train hard, eat well, and receive medical attention for various injuries to maximize their performance. It's ironic that these same athletes are willing to ingest synthetic agents such as anabolic steroids, which put them at risk for potential side effects such as sterility, abnormal liver function, hair loss, acne, and heart disease.

Anabolic steroids are either taken orally or injected in cycles of weeks or months, rather than continuously. Multiple types of steroids are often combined to maximize their effectiveness while minimizing negative effects, a process known as **stacking**.

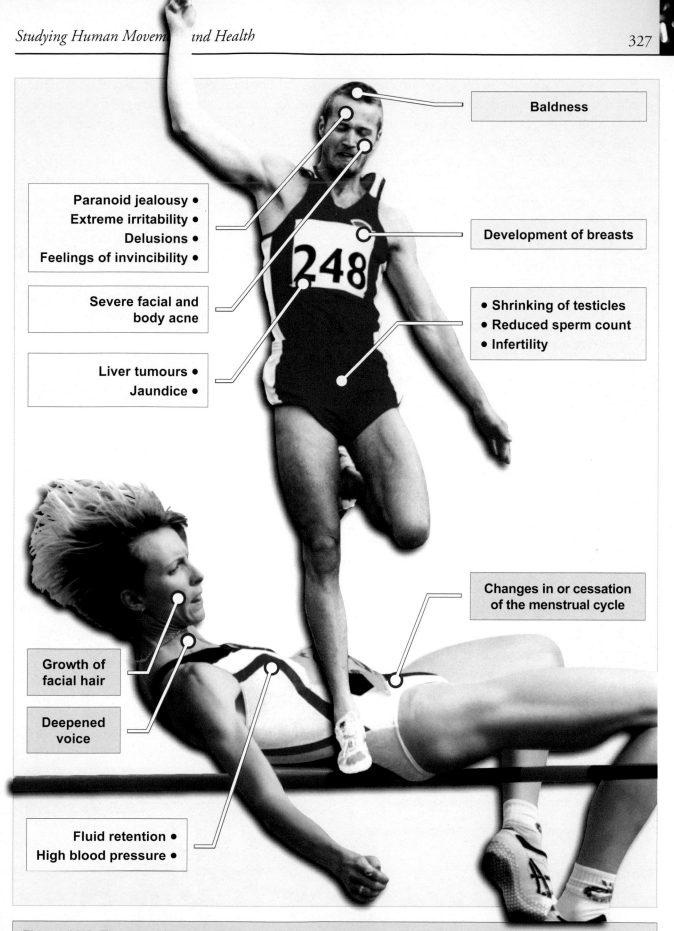

Baldness

Paranoid jealousy •
Extreme irritability •
Delusions •
Feelings of invincibility •

**Severe facial and
body acne**

Liver tumours •
Jaundice •

Development of breasts

• **Shrinking of testicles**
• **Reduced sperm count**
• **Infertility**

**Changes in or cessation
of the menstrual cycle**

**Growth of
facial hair**

**Deepened
voice**

Fluid retention •
High blood pressure •

Figure 13.2 The major health-related harmful side effects of anabolic steroid use to men (indicated in blue), women (indicated in purple), and users in general (indicated in yellow).

The use of anabolic steroids by athletes is contrary to the rules and ethical principles of athletic competition as set by the IOC and all international and national sports governing bodies. See Chapter 19 for more on cheating among athletes.

Ephedra

Ephedra is an extract of the Chinese plant Ma Huang that stimulates the cardiovascular and central nervous systems. It is found in numerous weight-loss, energy-boosting, and body-building products, including Stacker 2 and Metabolife 356.

Known risks associated with ephedra are elevated blood pressure, cardiac arrhythmia, heart palpitations, heart attacks, psychosis, seizures, stroke, and death. In 2001, Health Canada requested a recall of certain products containing ephedra from the market because of the serious health risks. Several promising high school athletes and professional players have recently died after taking ephedra to lose weight. This prompted Major League Baseball to ban the use of ephedra. It had already been banned by the National Football League (NFL), National Collegiate Athletic Association (NCAA), and World Anti-Doping Agency which oversees Olympic drug testing.

What Could Happen?

Taken in overdose quantities, ephedra stimulates the cardiovascular and nervous systems to a high level, causing acute myocardial infarction. The athlete's heart pumps at a much higher than normal rate, eventually resulting in death.

Blood Doping

Red blood cells carry oxygen to all cells in the body. During endurance events, such as long-distance swimming, running, rowing, and cycling, oxygen is delivered to the working muscles by the cardiovascular system. It is critical that these muscles receive oxygen. Raising the number of red blood cells can increase oxygen delivery and improve performance.

A process used by endurance athletes to enhance performance is **blood doping**. It involves artificially increasing red blood cell mass by withdrawing blood, removing its plasma, and freezing the packed red cells. After the athlete's body re-establishes the blood cells lost during the withdrawal, normally in about five to six weeks, the stored red blood cells are then reinfused one to seven days before an endurance event.

Blood doping may elevate an athlete's red blood cell count and hemoglobin level by up to 20 percent, thus increasing the athlete's aerobic capacity. Research has shown that blood doping is equally potent for male and female athletes.

Erythropoietin The cumbersome method of blood doping – removing, storing, and reinfusing blood over many weeks during an athlete's training – has recently been replaced by administering **erythropoietin (EPO)**, a genetically engineered version of a natural hormone that stimulates bone marrow to make red blood cells. EPO is used medically to treat patients with anemia, a condition where the oxygen-carrying capacity of

Cross-country Doping

A recent sport medicine study concluded that blood doping is prevalent and effective in cross-country ski racing and current testing programs for blood doping are ineffective.

What Is the World Anti-Doping Agency?

From 1965 to 2000, athlete testing in international competition was conducted by the International Olympic Committee (IOC). The **World Anti-Doping Agency (WADA)** was formed in 2000 to achieve a more effective anti-doping system. The agency's new World Anti-Doping Code sets uniform drug-testing codes and sanctions across all sports and countries and serves to harmonize and accelerate the fight against doping in sport. The agency, funded by and working together with the IOC, is charged with (1) conducting an effective in-competition and out-of-competition testing program for all sports and (2) sponsoring research into new tests to combat the use of currently undetectable substances, such as human growth hormone and erythropoietin.

How Are Athletes Tested for Drugs?

The testing of athletes for drugs is controlled on several levels. Olympic sports must follow the WADA drug code. Each international governing body sets its own controls and so does each country's governing body and/or country's Olympic committee. In Canada, drug testing is entrusted to the Canadian Centre for Ethics in Sport (CCES). The athletes are tested on a regular out-of-competition and in-competition basis. Any athlete selected for an out-of-competition test who does not make himself available for that test is ineligible to compete at the Olympic or World Championship level for two years starting from the date of the test.

Drug Testing at the Olympic Games for Rowers Each competitor is given a number. Several athletes from all countries are randomly chosen and tested before competition commences and during preliminary races leading to the finals. Immediately after the final race, members of medal-winning crews (gold, silver, and bronze) and one or two crews finishing 4th to 6th and 7th to 12th (small finals) are also randomly selected for testing. In large boat classes (eights and fours) only one or two members are randomly selected for testing. The testing involves several steps.

Step 1

Accompanied by a race official, athletes go to the Testing Control Centre where they declare any medication used.

Step 2

Under strict supervision athletes produce a urine sample.

Step 3

The urine sample is split and stored in two separate sealed containers, Sample A and Sample B. The procedure is supervised by the athlete.

Step 4

The containers are sent to the IOC-sanctioned Drug Testing Laboratory.

Step 5

Sample A is tested. If negative results are found no further action is required. Sample B is destroyed. The governing body and the athlete are told of the results.

Step 6

If results are positive (drugs are identified) the governing body is told of the results. The athlete is suspended from further competition or the crew's results are voided (i.e., medals are returned).

Step 7

The international and country's sport governing bodies arrange a hearing where the athlete's case is presented. If requested, Sample B may be tested.

Step 8

If found guilty the athlete is banned from competition for up to four years. In certain cases a life ban from all competition may be imposed. The athlete can appeal the ban.

Table 13.2 A summary of common drugs and dietary supplements used as ergogenic aids to improve athletic performance and physical appearance.

Drug or Dietary Supplement	Description	Action	Side Effects
Drugs			
Erythropoietin	Synthetic hormone that helps increase red blood cell production	Increases red blood cell production	Can cause thickening of blood with risk of heart attack or stroke
Human growth hormone	Hormone secreted by the anterior pituitary gland that regulates tissue growth, cellular repair, energy levels, fat loss, and muscle growth	Promotes muscle growth and fat loss	Stimulates excessive bone growth causing big hands and feet, bulging forehead, jutting jaw
Insulin	Hormone that helps glucose enter cells	Promotes entry of glucose and amino acids into muscle	Hypoglycemia, coma, seizures
Dietary Supplements			
Androstenedione (Andro)	Direct precursor of the hormone testosterone	Boosts testosterone levels for about three hours	Same side effects as testosterone: acne, mood swings, liver damage, heart attacks, stunted growth
Beta-hydroxy beta-methylbutyrate (HMB)	Metabolite of leucine, one of the body's essential amino acids	Improves the body's ability to burn fat and build muscle consistently in response to exercise Appears to decrease muscle atrophy or tear down that occurs with intense training	No known side effects
Creatine	Natural compound created from three amino acids commonly consumed when eating red meat	Increases lean muscle mass in just two weeks Improves performance in high-intensity exercise Speeds recovery rates	Liver or kidney problems in high doses Bloating
Ephedra	Extract of the Chinese plant Ma Huang that stimulates the cardiovascular and central nervous systems	Promotes weight loss and boosts energy	Elevated blood pressure, cardiac arrhythmia, heart palpitations, heart attacks, psychosis, seizures, stroke, death
Methyl-sulfonylmethane (MSM)	Found in the fluid and tissues of all living organisms. Most important constituent of MSM is sulfur	Provides raw materials the body uses to make cartilage Has antioxidant and anti-inflammatory properties	No known side effects

Table 13.2 contd.

Dietary Supplement	Description	Action	Side Effects
Glutamine	Amino acid found in protein powders, beans, meats, fish, poultry, and dairy products	Enhances gut and immune system function Plays an important role in protein metabolism Helps volumize cells Increases growth-hormone release	No known side effects
Nitric oxide	Free form gas produced in the body and used for communication between cells. To produce this gas, enzymes in the body break down the amino acid arginine	Transmits messages between nerve cells; associated with learning, memory, sleeping, feeling pain, and probably depression Increases blood flow to deliver more nutrients to muscles, thus helping muscles become larger when subject to stress Affects the release of gonadotropin releasing hormone and the release of adrenaline from the adrenal medulla	Dosing guidelines have not been established and there are no known side effects
Tribulus terrestris	Plant that grows in many tropical and moderate areas of the world. Many different cultures have used it for a number of conditions (e.g., the Greeks used it as a diuretic and a mood enhancer)	Enhances testosterone Increases libido and improves sperm count	Gastrointestinal upset
Whey protein	Type of protein that comes from milk. During the process of turning milk into cheese, whey protein is separated out	Provides the body with the necessary building blocks to produce amino acids used for building muscle tissue Enhances immune system function	Diarrhea Liver and kidney failure (extreme cases)
ZMA	All-natural, scientifically designed anabolic mineral formula. Contains zinc monomethionine aspartate plus magnesium aspartate and vitamin B6	Increases anabolic hormone levels Increases muscle strength in trained athletes Improves sleep	No known side effects

Table 13.3 A summary of selected harmful illegal drugs and their side effects.

Drug Class and Examples	Side Effects	Important Facts
Stimulants		
Amphetamines (speed, uppers, ups, hearts, black beauties, pep pills, copilots, bumble bees, benzedrine, dexedrine, footballs, bephetamine)	**Physical:** irritability, increased blood pressure, aggression, convulsions, dilated pupils and blurred vision, dizziness, sleeplessness, loss of appetite, malnutrition, increased body temperature, increased risk of exposure to HIV, hepatitis, and other infectious diseases if injected **Psychological:** addiction, anxiety, paranoia/psychosis, depression	Chronic use can induce psychosis with symptoms similar to schizophrenia such as paranoia, visual and auditory hallucinations
Ecstasy (XTC, love drug, X) Mind-altering drug with hallucinogenic and amphetamine properties	**Physical:** rapid eye movement, blurred vision, teeth clenching/muscle tension, faintness, chills/sweating **Psychological:** paranoia, nervousness, insomnia, drug craving, heightened sense of touch	Popular at all-night underground dance parties (called "raves"). The most common "designer drug"
Cocaine (coke, snow, nose candy, flake, blow, big C, lady, white, snowbirds) Snorted or dissolved in water and injected	**Physical:** dilated pupils, elevated blood pressure and heart rate, seizures, heart attack, respiratory failure, constricted peripheral blood vessels, restlessness, irritability, loss of appetite, insomnia, increased body temperature, death from overdose, increased risk of exposure to HIV, hepatitis, and other infectious diseases if injected **Psychological:** tactile hallucinations, addiction, paranoia, anxiety	A powerfully addictive drug. Heavy use may produce hallucinations, paranoia, aggression, insomnia, depression
Crack cocaine (rock, cookies) Freebase form of cocaine that is broken up into pebble-like rocks	**Physical:** dilated pupils, loss of appetite/weight, increased respiratory rate, severe perspiration **Psychological:** tactile hallucinations, addiction, loss of interest in family, paranoia, depression, need for money	A cheaper form of cocaine that may be more addictive
Depressants		
Rohypnol (roofies, the forget pill) Powerful depressant and sedative often sold in pill form	**Physical:** blackouts with loss of memory, violent outbursts of temper, nausea, speaking/motor difficulty, intoxication **Psychological:** complete/partial amnesia, aggression, loss of memory, lack of inhibitions, prolonged blackouts	Referred to as the "date-rape" drug. Creates a drunk feeling that lasts two to eight hours

Table 13.3 contd.

Opiates		
Heroin (smack, dope, junk) A narcotic drug, ranging from a white to dark brown powder, synthesized from morphine	**Physical:** "nodding off" (at high doses), itchy and dry skin, constricted pupils/droopy eyelids, constipation **Psychological:** addiction, restlessness, insomnia, depression	Users quickly develop a tolerance to the drug and need more and more of it to get the same effects, or even to feel well
Hallucinogens		
LSD (acid, microdot, tabs, doses, trips, hits, sugar cubes) Tabs taken orally or gelatin/liquid put in eyes	**Physical:** elevated body temperature and blood pressure, suppressed appetite, sleeplessness, tremors **Psychological:** chronic recurring hallucinations	The most common hallucinogen. LSD tabs are often decorated with colourful designs or cartoon characters
Ketamine (K, special K) A vet anaesthetic that is sold as a liquid but usually converted to a powder	**Physical:** hallucinations, blurred vision, dizziness, numbness, drunken appearance **Psychological:** out-of-body experiences, visual "flashbacks," paranoid/delusional thinking, aggressive behaviour, amnesia	Popular at raves. Used as an anaesthetic for animals
Inhalants (whippets, boppers) Any substance that gives off fumes or vapors for a high	**Physical:** nosebleeds, headaches, muscle weakness, body parts/clothing with paint or stains on them, intoxicated appearance **Psychological:** fatigue, lack of coordination, violent behaviour, mood swings, irrationality	Hundreds of legal household products can be sniffed or "huffed" to get high. All inhalants can be toxic

blood is reduced.

EPO provides advantages to endurance athletes roughly comparable to the advantages conferred to power athletes by anabolic steroids. By increasing the amount of red blood cells in the bodies of endurance athletes, EPO provides a truly unfair advantage to those who use it. Although it is a banned practice, many endurance athletes use blood doping to increase performance. The newer versions of EPO drugs are exactly the same as human EPO and almost impossible to detect.

Blood doping has serious side effects. It increases blood viscosity, which places a large load on the heart. The heart is not designed to pump thickened blood throughout the body, especially during maximal aerobic activity, so blood doping may lead to varying degrees of permanent heart damage.

Summary

Ergogenic aids such as drugs and dietary supplements can have many beneficial effects on the human body. They improve athletic performance, improve immune function, and treat and cure many medical conditions. However, when these substances are abused, health-related physiological and psychological side effects occur.

Drugs come in a variety of forms, from everyday drugs such as caffeine, nicotine, and alcohol to illegal drugs such as cocaine, LSD, and heroine. Illegal drugs can be divided into six basic categories: stimulants, depressants, hallucinogens, anabolic steroids, opiates, and cannabis. Unfortunately, many athletes resort to dangerous banned practices (e.g., blood doping and steroid use) to gain an athletic advantage.

With so many harmful substances readily accessible today, the best defense is knowledge and appreciation of the power and potential of ergogenic aids. This chapter is just an introduction to the many effects drugs and dietary supplements can have on the human body. It is hoped that after reading this chapter that knowledge will turn to practice.

Key Words

Addiction
Alcohol
Anabolic steroids
Blood doping
Caffeine
Cannabis
Carbohydrate loading
Creatine

Depressants
Dietary supplements
Drugs
Ephedra
Ergogenic aids
Erythropoietin
Habituation
Hallucinogens

Nicotine
Opiates
Stacking
Stimulants
World Anti-Doping Agency
 (WADA)

Discussion Questions

1. What is the definition of a drug versus a dietary supplement? Provide three examples of each.

2. Explain how alcohol can be theoretically used as an ergogenic aid.

3. What are the six categories of illegal drugs? Provide two examples of each type of illegal drug.

4. Creatine is a substance found in what foods?

5. What are the medical purposes of taking anabolic steroids?

6. What substance was requested by Health Canada to be recalled from the market in 2001?

7. Describe the short-term effects of cannabis use.

8. How does blood doping increase performance?

A Career in Policing

NAME: Robert Mooney
OCCUPATION: Police Officer, Peel Regional Police
EDUCATION: BPHE, University of Toronto
Police Foundations, Algonquin College

What do you do?

I currently work as a general patrol officer. My duties include traffic patrol, neighbourhood policing, and call response. I am also responsible for general investigations, arrests, and court preparation. As a coach officer, I assist in the training of new officers for their career in policing.

What is unique about your job?

Every day is different. When I wake up in the morning, I have no idea what I will be doing at work that day. The nature of policing means that I constantly come into contact with different people and situations requiring different responses and solutions. I also work shift work, meaning sometimes I work during the day, evening, or over night, on a rotating basis. Each shift brings with it different types of calls for service and different types of people. Policing is a mixture of action and paperwork, responding to calls and following up with general investigations, arrests, and court appearances.

Why did you choose a career in policing?

When I was a student at the University of Toronto, I thought I was going to be working in the fitness industry. On graduation I began working at a club as a fitness consultant, but the job did not provide enough variety to keep me motivated. I went back to school and became a police officer because it provided me with the daily variety I was looking for while still allowing me to work with and within the community.

How competitive is the field?

Policing is a very competitive field. Each year thousands of people apply to our force and only a few hundred are chosen. Nowadays, Police Services is looking for candidates with post-secondary education, life skills, and experience. In order to become an officer a candidate must pass a series of written tests, physical tests, a base interview, a comprehensive interview, a psychological test, background checks, and finally a board interview. After all that is completed, there is a six- to nine-month period of training before the candidate becomes a police officer. Each point along the way sees candidates not meeting standards and being eliminated from the process.

What career advice would you give to students interested in entering this field?

Anyone interested in becoming a police officer should continue his or her studies beyond high school. It does not really matter what post-secondary degree you obtain because Police Services today is trying to select candidates from a wide variety of backgrounds, so college and university are both beneficial. Today's "new recruits" are usually more mature (24+ years of age) and bring a wide variety of life skills and experiences. It is important to demonstrate a desire to continue learning by taking courses beyond high school or college/university. Police services also likes to see volunteer work, demonstrating a willingness to give back to your community. Be sure to be physically fit – individuals who demonstrate a lifelong pattern of healthy living are more likely to be hired.

What are the future job prospects in the field? Where is it heading?

There will always be job opportunities in policing. As our communities expand they require more officers to efficiently patrol them, thus always creating new job openings. Within policing there is a multitude of different job opportunities. You can work as a general patrol officer, youth education officer, tactical officer, or K9 officer, or in forensic identification, training, recruiting, and many other fields. What career you have in policing is up to you. Policing is always evolving, having to change with the community and government legislation. Policing today is heading toward a working partnership with the community to detect and prevent crime rather than just being a response to crime.

In This Chapter:

Personality and the Athlete *338*
    Comparing the Personalities of Athletes and
      Non-athletes *340*
    Comparing Personality Profiles of Athletes Differing
      in Skill Level *340*
    Developmental Effects of Sport on Personality *341*

Anxiety and Athletic Performance *343*
    Arousal, Stress, and Anxiety *343*
    The Relationship Between Anxiety and Athletic
      Performance *345*
    Relaxation Interventions to Lower Cognitive State Anxiety *347*

Motivation and Sport *348*
    Achievement Motivation *348*
    Self-confidence, Self-efficacy, and Motivation in Sport *349*
    Causal Attribution in Sport *351*
    Affective Responses Associated With Causal Attributions *353*
    Causal Attributions, Future Expectations, and Motivation *353*

Audience Effects in Sport *355*
    Implications of Early Social Facilitation Research *355*
    The Relationship Between Audience Characteristics and
      Team Performance *356*

Summary *358*

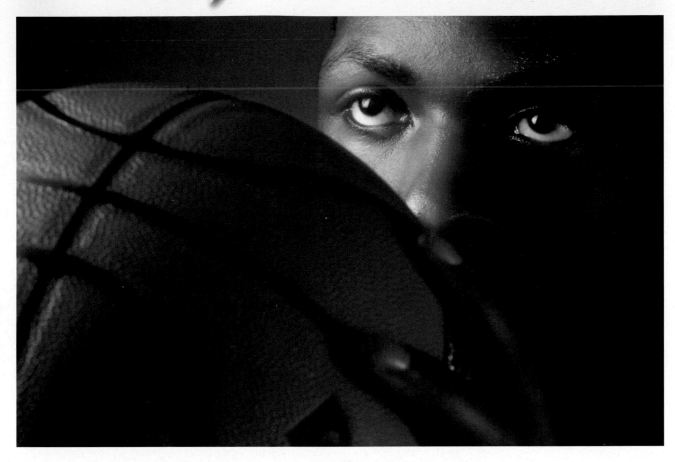

The Mental Side of Human Performance

After completing this chapter you should be able to:

- define the topic of sport psychology;

- discuss the influence of personality on performance;

- describe the effect of sport on personality;

- explain the relationship between anxiety and performance;

- describe the effect of motivation on sport performance;

- explain the effects of the audience on athletic accomplishments.

337

The idea of a healthy mind in a healthy body dates back to ancient China and Greece. It is only in recent years, however, that the discipline known as **sport psychology** has become recognized as a major factor in the study of sport performance. This is somewhat surprising when one considers that research in this area actually dates back to the late 1800s, when a study showed that cyclists performed better in the presence of an audience than when they competed alone.

The growth of sport psychology over the past 30 years has occurred for two major reasons. First, the scientific body of knowledge relating to the area has expanded so greatly that different branches of the subject have begun to emerge as well. For example, sport psychology textbooks traditionally cover topical areas such as techniques for improved sport performance, social and psychological considerations, as well as theoretical issues. A second reason for the increased interest in sport psychology can be attributed to popular coverage of the discipline. Many professional and amateur athletes now seek advice from sport psychologists, and this is reported frequently in the media.

The value of the discipline remains contentious. Goran Ivanisevic, a professional tennis player, was once quoted as saying, "You lie on a couch, they take your money, and you walk out more bananas than when you walk in." Others do not share this scepticism: research indicates that the majority of Olympic athletes believe that working with a sport psychologist has improved their performance. Champion athletes and gold medal winners who have spoken publicly of the value of sport psychology have done much to dispel any doubts that remain.

Consider the following scenarios:

- The best basketball player in history retires in the prime of his career, stating that he no longer feels motivated to compete.

- A high school volleyball player performs perfectly in practice, but poorly in competition.

- Because of one bad call from the referee, an athlete loses his cool, and vows to quit soccer forever.

- The varsity basketball team wins almost all home games, but loses most of the away games.

- A top-ranked tennis player drops out of the world rankings for over a year, then returns to peak form.

All these examples share several common characteristics. First, they are all recent real life examples from the world of sport; second, they all have psychological explanations; and finally, they pose the question whether their outcomes would have been different with the intervention of sport psychology. This chapter provides the necessary tools that can help prevent the occurrence of similar behavioural problems.

In this chapter, you will be introduced to the discipline of sport psychology and learn firsthand of its value in promoting both improved performance and satisfaction in the participant. Perhaps the best place to start is by examining the relationship between personality and performance.

Personality and the Athlete

Personality is best defined as "that pattern of characteristic thoughts, feelings, and behaviours that distinguishes one person from another and that persists over time and situations." The study of personality and the role it can play in successful athletic performance has interested sport psychologists for decades. But the interest is not only academic. Almost everyone, amateur and professional alike, would be interested in discovering the answers to the following questions:

- Does personality determine sport preference, or does a particular sport mold our personality?

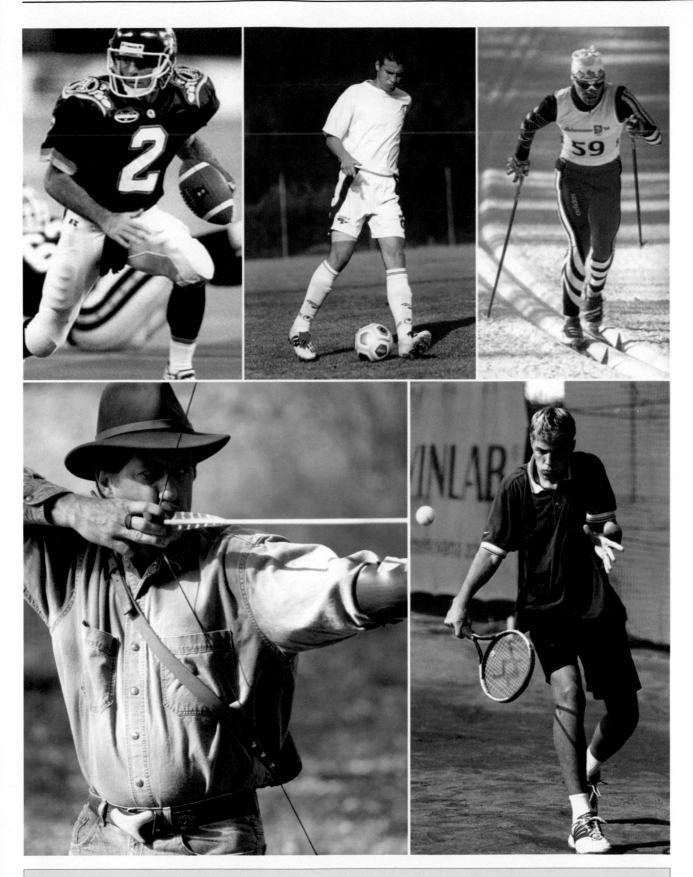

Figure 14.1 For decades, sport psychologists have attempted to identify psychological differences among participants across a variety of sports.

- Do athletes possess different personality characteristics than non-athletes?

- Do winners possess different personality profiles than losers?

- Can personality be changed, or does it remain relatively fixed throughout involvement in sport?

The search for answers to these and similar questions has resulted in a deluge of personality studies in the sport environment (Figure 14.1). Over 1,000 studies were conducted during the 1960s and 1970s at the height of academic research into personality. In spite of all this research, we still have only limited knowledge about the relationship between personality and sport performance. In this section, we will highlight the major findings to date.

Comparing the Personalities of Athletes and Non-athletes

One of the most common sport personality research themes concerns the extent to which athletes and non-athletes differ in their personality profiles. Early research suggested that athletes were more stable and extroverted. These early studies also reported that athletes were more competitive, dominant, self-confident, and achievement-oriented. Athletes have also been found to be more psychologically well-adjusted and often display higher levels of self-esteem than non-athletes. Research has also revealed that, compared with non-athletes, athletes hold more conservative political views, are more authoritarian, and demonstrate higher levels of persistence.

Comparing Personality Profiles of Athletes Differing in Skill Level

Sufficient evidence now exists to suggest that elite athletes can be distinguished from lesser skilled athletes when psychological states are considered. The **Profile of Mood States (POMS)** has identified

an "iceberg" profile in elite athletes, illustrated in Figure 14.2.

Careful examination of Figure 14.2 indicates that successful athletes are well below unsuccessful athletes in tension, depression, anger, fatigue, and confusion. They are markedly higher, however, in the mood state of vigor. This elevated vigor score causes the elite profile to resemble an iceberg. In the case of lesser skilled individuals, the profile can be described as rather flat.

Although it is possible to distinguish between the successful athlete and the unsuccessful athlete in terms of mood *states*, it is not yet possible to distinguish between successful and unsuccessful athletes in any particular sport using personality *traits*. For this reason, it is important to understand the difference between personality traits and personality states. **Personality traits** refer to psychological characteristics of the athlete which remain relatively stable over time. **Personality states**, on the other hand, represent

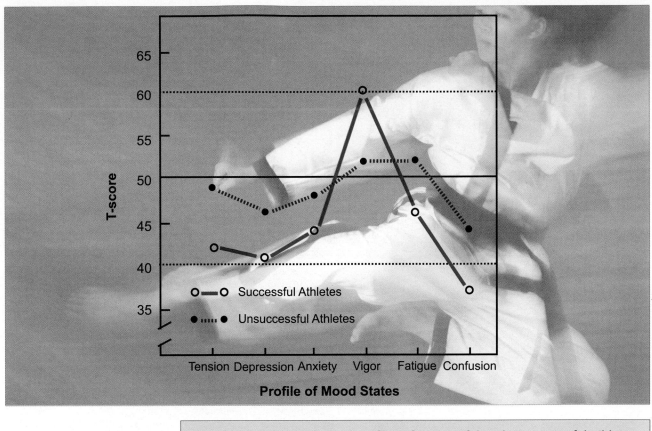

Figure 14.2 Psychological profiles of successful and unsuccessful athletes.

"right now kinds of feelings" which are situation-specific. Although a long-standing disagreement known as the state–trait controversy has argued the relative merits of studying states versus traits, the best approach appears to be one that considers personality traits, personality states, and situation-specific factors. This compromise is called the **interactional theory**, and is the prevalent way of currently conducting sport personality research.

Developmental Effects of Sport on Personality

Earlier in this chapter, you learned that athletes and non-athletes have been shown to differ in certain personality dimensions such as extroversion, independence, self-confidence, and anxiety. This has led many researchers to question whether these differences are due to the athletic experience, or whether certain personality traits bring about an involvement in sports. Although a definitive

response would appear impossible, available evidence tends to support the latter position. This **gravitational hypothesis** suggests that individuals who possess stable, extroverted personalities tend to gravitate toward the sporting environment. It is important to remember, however, that research has shown that participation in physical activity can enhance personality development as well.

For example, it is easy to agree that athletes continue to learn while they participate in sports. But it also makes sense that what is learned can be transferred to other interests in life. For example, while children play, they are laying the foundations for future behaviour, and maybe even developing personality traits as well. After all, playing is also a vehicle for learning. Moreover, skills learned in one sport might easily be transferred to another sport. This is why many NHL players are also excellent golfers. Learning that takes place in the sporting environment can also have an impact on other interests in life. Many athletes often go on to

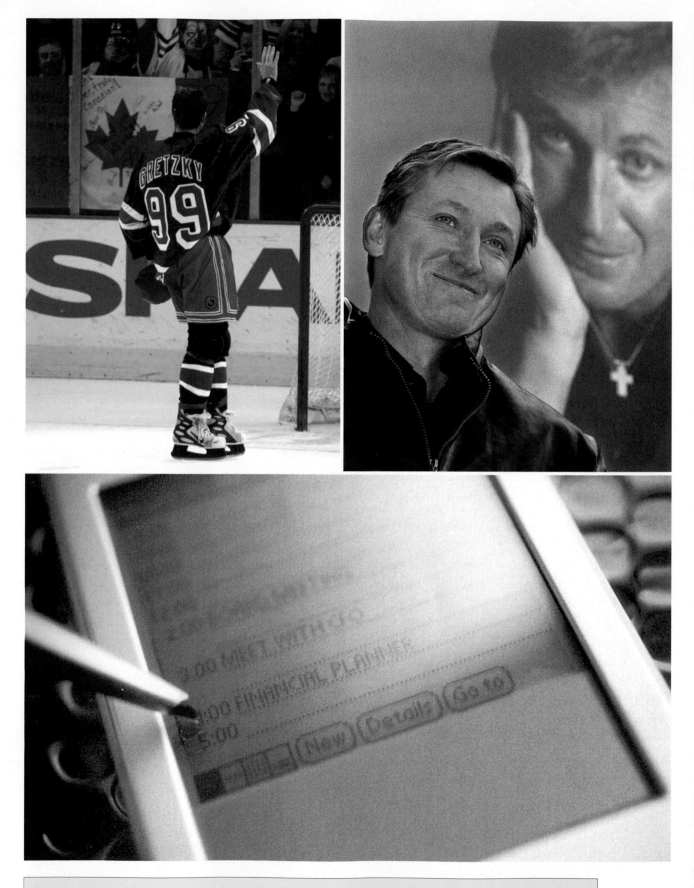

Figure 14.3 A sporting background can transfer positively to a successful career in business.

become leaders in their future vocations because of the skills they developed in their sporting backgrounds (Figure 14.3).

In summary, research in sport psychology shows that:

- Athletes tend to be more extroverted, independent, and self-confident than non-athletes; they also tend to be less anxious.

- Elite athletes can be distinguished from lesser skilled athletes by means of the iceberg profile; it is not possible, however, to distinguish between winners and losers.

- Individuals with certain personality traits tend to gravitate toward sports; sport also has the potential to enhance certain personality traits.

What effect do you feel sport has played in your life?

Anxiety and Athletic Performance

Before examining this experimental evidence, it is important to address the following questions:

- What is the difference between arousal, stress, and anxiety?

- Is all stress and anxiety bad for an athlete?

- What causes some athletes to "choke?"

- What can be done to help an athlete deal with stress and anxiety?

Arousal, Stress, and Anxiety

An interesting story is told about an African hunter who loses his weapon while being pursued by a lion. Running as fast as he can, with the lion in close pursuit, the hunter spots a tree limb almost 3 metres off the ground. At the last second, he jumps with all his strength, hoping to reach safety. He misses the limb by jumping too high, but catches it on the way down! This anecdote illustrates very well the phenomenon of arousal which can sometimes produce amazing feats of strength, power, and endurance.

Arousal

Arousal can be described as a physiological state of readiness and psychological activation. The neurophysiology of arousal involves the autonomic nervous system. A good example of this function is the feeling you get when you are frightened by a loud noise, or confronted by a growling dog. This is really the body's way of preparing you for **fight or flight**.

Stress

Stress has been best described as the "non-specific response of the body to any demand made upon it." Stress, like arousal, is an unemotional bodily response to some type of stressor. The stressor could be in the form of physical exercise, joyful excitement, or fear of bodily harm. Stress, then, can be either positive or negative. Positive or good stress is called **eustress**. An example of eustress would be winning a lottery. Bad stress, on the other hand, is referred to as **distress**. Receiving a failing grade on a midterm test would reflect distress. It is very important to remember that whether stress is seen as good or bad depends upon the individual's personal interpretation of the situation.

Anxiety

Anxiety can be described as the tension and worry that results from distress. Anxiety is a negatively charged emotional state characterized by discomfort and nervousness. Generally speaking, there are two forms of anxiety. **Trait anxiety** is a personality characteristic that is relatively stable over time, predisposing the individual to be anxious across a wide variety of situations. **State anxiety**, on the other hand, refers to a "right now" kind of anxiety that is situation-specific. Research has revealed that state anxiety is made up of two distinct components. **Cognitive state anxiety** is the psychological component of state anxiety, and is caused by fear of failure or fear of negative social

Competitive State Anxiety Inventory–II (CSAI–II) – Mini-version

Date:

Name:

Sex: M   F

Directions: A number of statements that athletes have used to describe their feelings before competition are given below. Read each statement and then circle the appropriate number to the right of the statement to indicate how you feel right now – at this moment. There are no right or wrong answers. Do not spend too much time on any one statement, but choose the answer which describes your feelings right now.

		1	2	3	4
1.	I am concerned about this competition.	1	2	3	4
2.	I feel nervous.	1	2	3	4
3.	I feel at ease.	1	2	3	4
4.	I have self-doubts.	1	2	3	4
5.	I am concerned that I may not do as well in this competition as I could.	1	2	3	4
6.	My body feels tense.	1	2	3	4
7.	I feel self-confident.	1	2	3	4
8.	I am concerned about choking under pressure.	1	2	3	4
9.	My heart is racing.	1	2	3	4
10.	I'm confident about performing well.	1	2	3	4
11.	I feel my stomach sinking.	1	2	3	4
12.	I feel mentally relaxed.	1	2	3	4
13.	I'm concerned that others will be disappointed with my performance.	1	2	3	4
14.	My hands are clammy.	1	2	3	4
15.	I'm confident about coming through under pressure.	1	2	3	4

Figure 14.4 The CSAI–II mini-version.

evaluation. Worrying is often the result of cognitive state anxiety. **Somatic state anxiety** represents the physical component of anxiety, and reflects the perception of such physiological responses as muscular tension, increased heart rate, and bodily activation. When an athlete says, "I feel nervous before a major contest," this is a perfect example of somatic state anxiety. Conversely, the comment "I'm afraid I am going to lose" illustrates cognitive state anxiety. A psychometric instrument known as the **Competitive State Anxiety Inventory–II (CSAI–II)** has been developed and it allows us to obtain valid measures of these two types of anxiety. A mini-version is provided (Figure 14.4) to help you assess your own level of cognitive and somatic anxiety.

Now that we have provided a description of these important terms, let's look at their relationship to athletic performance.

The Relationship Between Anxiety and Athletic Performance

One of the factors that is believed to have a significant effect on athletic performance is the level of state anxiety experienced prior to an athletic contest. This is referred to in the literature as **pre-competitive anxiety**. Current research provides a good picture of the temporal changes in anxiety that occur before a competition, as well as immediately following the start of the contest. This relationship is shown in Figure 14.5.

The graph shows that pre-competitive cognitive anxiety starts relatively high and remains high and stable as competition approaches. Conversely, somatic anxiety remains relatively low until about one day before the event, then increases rapidly until the contest starts. Once the performance begins, somatic anxiety decreases rapidly, while

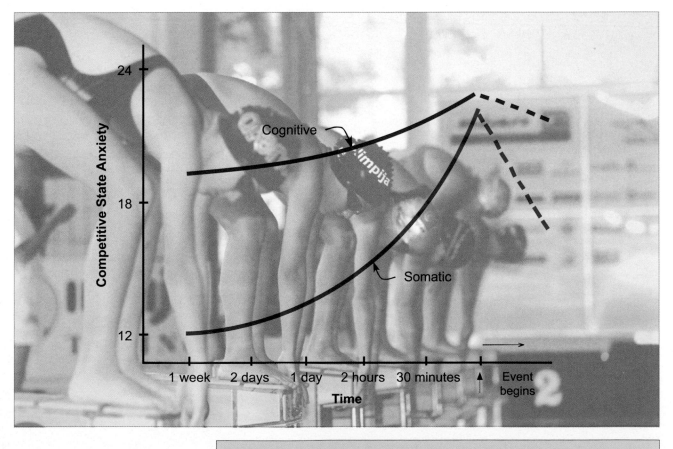

Figure 14.5 Cognitive and somatic anxiety as competition approaches.

cognitive state anxiety fluctuates as the probability of winning or losing changes.

Now that researchers are able to obtain independent measures of cognitive and somatic anxiety, we have been able to increase our knowledge about the relationship between anxiety and athletic performance. It now appears that the relationship between somatic anxiety and performance takes the form of an **inverted U**. On the other hand, the relationship between cognitive state anxiety and athletic performance has been shown to be linear and negative. These trends are illustrated in Figure 14.6.

Figure 14.6 provides us with some very important information. First, it shows how increases in somatic anxiety are associated with improved athletic performance up to a certain optimal level. After this optimal point has been reached, performance begins to drop off with further increases in somatic anxiety. This suggests that athletes should attempt to increase their somatic anxiety up to an optimal level, by "psyching up." With practice, an athlete is usually able to identify the optimal level of somatic anxiety. Second, Figure 14.6 indicates how the worry associated with increased cognitive state anxiety creates a major hindrance to sports performance. The lower the level of cognitive state anxiety, the better an athlete's performance. It is probably these increases in cognitive state anxiety that cause athletes to "choke," or perform worse than expected. Knowing this, coaches must help athletes learn how to deal with the symptoms of cognitive state anxiety. The **symptoms of distress checklist** (see box *The Symptoms of Distress Checklist*) can help you identify when you are becoming stressed-out, and need to use one or more of the strategies described in the following section.

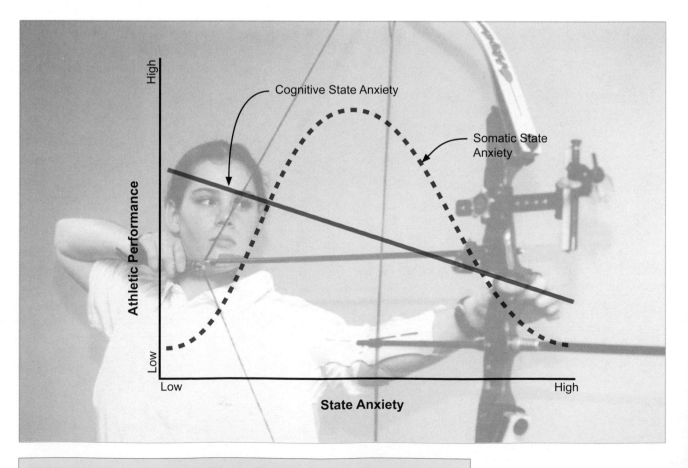

Figure 14.6 The effect of cognitive and somatic anxiety on performance.

The Symptoms of Distress Checklist

Cold, clammy hands	_____	Desire to urinate often	_____
Increased heart rate	_____	Tense muscles	_____
Cotton mouth	_____	Diarrhea	_____
Faster breathing	_____	Nausea	_____
Unable to concentrate	_____	Feeling of fatigue	_____
Trembling hands	_____	Voice distortion	_____

Relaxation Interventions to Lower Cognitive State Anxiety

There are several active strategies athletes can use to manage their cognitive state anxiety although they should be prepared to try each technique to discover which one works best for any one individual.

Progressive Muscular Relaxation

Progressive muscular relaxation (PMR) is one of the most popular coping techniques. In this procedure, the athlete is asked to lie or sit in a comfortable position. The room is kept peaceful, quiet, and free of distractions. The athlete is then asked to inhale and tense a specific muscle group for approximately five seconds, then exhale and release the tension from the muscles, concentrating on the feeling of relaxation. This procedure is repeated for a number of muscle groups. Many athletes prefer to start with the lower legs, then work their way systematically up to the face muscles to complete the exercise. This technique initially takes quite a bit of time to complete, but with practice, an athlete can learn to perform the exercise on several muscle groups at once, thereby reducing the time to a matter of minutes. PMR is especially valuable the night before a major competition.

Positive Imagery

A second popular technique for handling cognitive state anxiety is called **positive imagery**. Imagery can best be explained as "seeing a picture through your mind's eye." With this approach, an athlete is asked to close his or her eyes, and then imagine performing well in precisely the performance environment that is the source of the anxiety. The athlete is also encouraged to imagine the positive feelings associated with this successful performance. Like any physical skill, the use of imagery requires practice to be effective.

Positive Self-talk

A third related intervention is called **positive self-talk**. This technique involves reassuring oneself with positive thoughts and statements. For example, consider the basketball player at the free-throw line at a crucial spot in the game. When faced with a situation like this, athletes often think negative and self-defeating thoughts such as "what will the coach or my team think of me if I blow this shot?" This in turn increases cognitive state anxiety and thereby increases the possibility of a missed free throw. For this reason, an athlete should be trained to think positive thoughts, such as "I'm a good free throw shooter," or "all of my training has made me ready to make this free throw." In a related study, the effect of positive and negative self-talk on dart throwing performance was measured. Results indicated that subjects who used positive self-talk missed the bull's-eye by an average of 70 cm, while a control group missed by an average of 85 cm. Not surprisingly, the group that used negative self-talk missed the bull's-eye by an average of 93 cm. This study highlights the importance of positive self-talk in crucial situations.

Motivation and Sport

On October 6, 1993, Michael Jordan announced his retirement from professional basketball. The sporting world reacted with disbelief, disappointment, and confusion. But why did Jordan, at the peak of an illustrious career, and at a fairly young age, decide to retire? And why did he decide a year later to return?

Figure 14.7 Michael Jordan, the best basketball player of the nineties, announced relatively early retirement from pro basketball.

The answer, not surprisingly, has to do with motivation (Figure 14.7). **Motivation** is defined as the direction, energy, and intensity of behaviour. The term has been used synonymously to mean inspiration, enthusiasm, or the will to win. The importance of motivation in sport is undisputed, but several important questions remain. For example: How does motivation develop? What factors modify its impact in the sporting environment? How can motivation be changed, or improved? Why are some athletes more motivated to succeed than others? The following section attempts to answer these very important questions.

Achievement Motivation

Achievement motivation can be defined as the athlete's predisposition to approach or avoid a competitive situation. In a broader sense, it includes the concept of desire, or desire to excel. The desire to achieve success in sport is not an innate drive, such as hunger or thirst, but is likely one that is developed or learned in the sporting environment.

The box *Johnny's Experience* illustrates a classic approach–avoidance conflict situation for the athlete. The best explanation of this situation is provided by the **McClelland–Atkinson model of achievement motivation**. In its simplest form, it suggests that **achievement motivation (AM)** is a function of two constructs. These two constructs are (a) the motive to achieve success, and (b) the fear of failure. The **motive to achieve success** is believed to represent an athlete's **intrinsic motivation (IM)** to engage in an exciting activity. The **fear of failure** is a psychological construct associated with **cognitive state anxiety (CSA)**.

According to this theory, a person's desire to enter an achievement situation is a function of the relative strengths of these two constructs – the motive to achieve success and the fear of failure. If an individual's desire to participate in the activity is greater than the fear of failure, then it is likely that the person will perform the activity. This is probably what happened in the case of Johnny.

Johnny's Experience

Johnny is a 14-year-old boy who recently moved from a little town called Dutton, Ontario (population: 1,400) to metropolitan Toronto (population: 2+ million). While in Dutton, Johnny learned to play hockey, and was a member of his high school hockey team. Upon arriving in Toronto, he was encouraged by his father to try out for the hockey team at his new school. At his first practice, Johnny quickly realized that the other boys were much bigger and stronger than he. As such, he was worried whether or not he could make the team. By the same token, he felt his skill level was every bit as good. As well, he didn't want to give up his favourite sport just because he had moved to a new city. After several days of agonizing, he decided to try out for the team.

This process is best represented by the following equation:

$$AM = IM - CSA$$

In the early years of testing the McClelland–Atkinson model, research was not able consistently to demonstrate that individuals with high achievement motivation perform better than those low in achievement motivation. Sport psychologists therefore concluded that it seems unlikely that athletic performance can be predicted solely on the basis of achievement motivation. This is consistent with earlier research suggesting that the real value of measuring achievement motivation is in predicting long-term patterns of motivation, not in predicting athletic success.

Because the original model did not consistently predict behaviour, a modified version was developed. The newer version was able to improve the predictive ability of the model by introducing an additional factor: extrinsic motivation. Since some individuals who possess low intrinsic motivation but experience high fear of failure nonetheless still enter competitive situations, extrinsic motivation must make the difference. Examples of extrinsic motivation include praise, money, trophies, and other forms of reward. The inclusion of extrinsic motivation in the modified model acknowledges that factors external to the athlete may influence that individual's overall motivation. In other words, the prospect of receiving a badge or trophy might prove to be the top priority for the would-be participant (Figure 14.8).

Self-confidence, Self-efficacy, and Motivation in Sport

Researchers have long recognized that a distinguishing feature between individuals showing high and low achievement motivation is **self-confidence**. Athletes who are self-confident and expect to win are generally the athletes who do win. Since the late 1970s, research has focused more upon self-confidence, and less upon achievement motivation. Even so, the construct of self-confidence is similar to the motive to achieve success. The confident athlete has a high motive to succeed and a high expectation for success.

One of the most popular models of self-confidence is **Bandura's Theory of Self-Efficacy**. The concept of **self-efficacy** can be defined as an individual's belief that he or she is capable of succeeding at a particular task. In other words, self-efficacy is really a form of situation-specific self-confidence, which, by contrast, represents a more global personality trait. A self-confident person feels self-confident across a wide variety of situations. An individual with high self-efficacy, on the other hand, feels confident about succeeding at a particular task. Because the sporting environment represents a very specific situation, researchers have focused almost exclusively on the concept of self-efficacy.

Self-efficacy is enhanced by four factors: (a) successful performance; (b) vicarious experience; (c) verbal persuasion; and (d) emotional arousal. Let's look at the major implications of this model for the coach and athlete.

Figure 14.8 Athletes celebrating their great performances.

Successful Performance

This represents the most important factor in improving self-efficacy. **Successful performance** raises expectations for future successes; failure lowers these expectations. By developing strong feelings of self-efficacy through repeated success, the occasional failure will not negatively affect the athlete. Ways of developing self-efficacy through successful performance include the following:

- break down skill learning into small steps to ensure early success (Figure 14.9);

- practice, practice, practice before entering a competition; and

- coaches should highlight successes and downplay setbacks.

Vicarious Experience

Another very important way to develop self-efficacy is by demonstrating repeated success through **vicarious experience** or **participatory modeling**.

In this technique, the subject first observes a model perform a task. The model is highly competent at the skill being demonstrated. In this manner, the athlete sees the skill done properly before trying it on his/her own. Then the model assists the subject in successfully performing the task. The subject is not allowed to fail. As a result of these repeated successes, a strong feeling of self-efficacy develops. When using this technique, best results occur if you observe the following guidelines:

- introduce participatory modeling before the athlete attempts the skill on his/her own;

- use only models who are technically correct in their execution; and

- ensure successful execution by the athlete in the early stages of learning.

Verbal Persuasion

The teacher or coach constantly must provide encouragement, as well as specific skill instructions

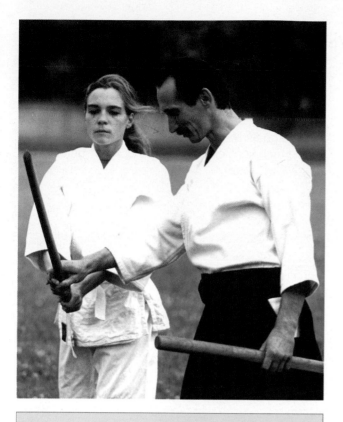

Figure 14.9 Breaking down the skill into smaller parts is a proven coaching strategy.

Figure 14.10 The coach's positive feedback to the athlete is key to effective instructions.

(Figure 14.10). Athletes learn by hearing, just as they do by watching. When providing **verbal persuasion** through feedback, the best results will occur if coaches remember to:

- provide specific rather than general feedback;

- have an athlete repeat back the instructions before proceeding; and

- focus on the positive aspects of the athlete's performance.

Emotional Arousal

In the last section of this chapter, you learned about the importance of arousal in athletic performance. Evidence was provided to suggest that athletes need an optimal level of **emotional arousal** to perform their best. Similarly, an optimal level of arousal is required to develop self-efficacy. Too much or too little arousal will impact negatively on the athlete's development of self-efficacy. For this reason, coaches and teachers should take care to observe the following guidelines:

- in the early stages of learning, keep things as relaxed as possible;

- get to know your students and athletes one-on-one (some will need more arousal, while others will need to be taught to relax); and

- help your students and athletes learn how to recognize when they need to "psych up or calm down."

One last way to improve athlete or participant motivation is to employ effective **goal-setting strategies** (see box *Goal-setting Strategies for Maximum Motivation*).

Causal Attribution in Sport

In the last section, we discussed several important elements of motivation in the sporting environment. **Attribution theory** is a cognitive approach to motivation. It assumes that people strive to explain, understand, and predict events based on their own perceptions. When young

Goal-setting Strategies for Maximum Motivation

1. Set goals that are observable, measurable, and achievable.

2. Set realistic but challenging goals.

3. Set positive goals, not negative goals (such as play defensively).

4. Coaches and teachers should negotiate goals for their athletes or students, not mandate them.

5. Set short-term as well as long-term goals.

6. Set goals for your practices, as well as your actual competitions.

7. Set goals related to an athlete's performance or technical execution, not contest outcome (win vs. lose).

athletes are asked "Why were you successful today?" they are being asked for their perceptions. Whether these perceptions are correct or incorrect is beside the point. What the athlete believes to be true is more important for future motivation than what is actually true. For this reason, it is important to seek a thorough understanding of the process of causal attribution.

The Development of Causal Attribution Theory

Outcomes can be attributed **internally** to the person (personal force) or **externally** to the environment (environmental force). **Personal force** is composed of the **attributional factors** of ability and effort, while **environmental force** is composed of the attributional factors of task difficulty and luck. Expanding upon these terms, a classification scheme for causal attribution has been developed. This classification is illustrated in Figure 14.11.

As can be seen in Figure 14.11, the original four main factors have been restructured into two main causal dimensions. These two dimensions are labeled stability and locus of control. **Stability** is shown to be composed of stable and unstable attributes. This dimension differentiates between attributes that are relatively unchanging from one day to the next (stable), from those that vary markedly from time to time (unstable). **Locus of control** includes internal and external attributes. Internal locus of control involves those attributes an athlete perceives as controllable, while external

locus of control is perceived to be outside an athlete's control.

The elements of effort, ability, task difficulty, and luck were then included in the classification scheme. This schematic illustrates how ability and task difficulty are considered stable attributes, while effort and luck are shown to be unstable attributes. Similarly, both ability and effort are seen as internal locus of control, while task difficulty and luck are viewed as external locus of control. Let's take a moment to clarify these distinctions with some practical examples.

A basketball player's ability won't change much from game to game, but the effort expended may fluctuate a great deal. Although the athlete is personally in control (internal locus of control) of both ability and effort, ability is relatively stable while effort is unstable. The athlete should therefore be encouraged to focus on effort, since

Figure 14.11 The original causal attribution scheme.

this is within the individual's control. Conversely, task difficulty and luck are external in terms of locus of control. Task difficulty (an opposing team's skill level, for example) is relatively stable, while luck is unstable. Coaches should therefore ensure that their athletes view luck as an external attribute beyond anyone's control. Focus should therefore be on preparing strategies that will be effective against an opposing team.

Affective Responses Associated With Causal Attributions

It has been suggested that in decreasing order, the greatest emotion or **affect** (pride with success, shame with failure) is associated with effort, ability, task difficulty, and luck. Intuitively, this also makes a great deal of sense. After a victory, an athlete is going to feel more pride if he or she believes that the win was a result of an internal attribute such as effort or ability rather than an external attribute such as an opponent's poor ability or a lucky call from the referee.

Research has also shown that an internal attribution generally results in greater affect than an external attribution. Imagine a professional golfer who has just posted an early score of 65 in tournament play. At this point, the golfer probably feels he or she has played the round of a lifetime. Over the next several hours, however, 10 other players post similar scores, with almost all competitors shooting under 70 for the round. Faced with this observation, the golfer can no longer attribute his success internally, because the consistent low scores by most players indicate that the course is playing easy on this given day.

This suggests that there may be certain cause-and-effect relations among attributions, outcome, and affective response. These affective response relationships are illustrated in Figure 14.12.

Figure 14.12 points to several important conclusions. In terms of locus of control, the expected pattern of emotional responses is clear. When people attribute success to internal causes, they typically respond with pride, confidence, and

Figure 14.12 Different emotions experienced with different causal attributions.

satisfaction. Conversely, if after a success they attribute the success externally, they will likely feel gratitude and thankfulness. It is also interesting to note that after a success, regardless of attribution, the affective response tends to be positive and enthusiastic. On the other hand, the affect for failure usually is negative and possibly subdued.

Causal Attributions, Future Expectations, and Motivation

It is important to remember that the attribution endorsed has an important impact on the athlete's **expectancy** for future performance. Imagine what happens when an athlete with a history of success is unexpectedly defeated. Conversely, suppose an athlete who consistently loses suddenly experiences a victory. How would these individuals explain their unexpected outcomes? Whenever an outcome is different from what was expected based on past experience, an athlete tends to endorse an unstable attribution (e.g., effort or luck). When an outcome is as expected, based on past performances, a stable attribution (e.g., ability or task difficulty) is endorsed.

Given these findings, it follows that we should be able to predict future expectations about athletic performance based on the types of attributions

The Open-ended Measurement System for Causal Attributions

Ask yourself, or your athlete, to consider a recent unsuccessful outcome. Try to recall the event in as much detail as possible, and then list any factors that you believe were responsible for the unsuccessful outcome. Circle the number that best represents how important that factor was in contributing to the outcome.

		Not Important		Somewhat Important		Very Important	
Factor # 1	_____	1	2	3	4	5	6	7
Factor # 2	_____	1	2	3	4	5	6	7
Factor # 3	_____	1	2	3	4	5	6	7

they indicate for their present performance. For example, an athlete who attributes a loss to a lack of ability is in fact saying that the result will be the same the next time. However, an athlete who attributes a loss to bad luck is declaring that things may be different next time. This observation points out the benefit of ascribing failures to unstable causes, since it does not imply repeated failure. Young athletes should therefore be encouraged to attribute a failure to a lack of effort. This suggests that more effort can change the next outcome from failure to success. The athlete should therefore be encouraged to endorse an internal attribution in this situation. This teaches the child or athlete to accept responsibility for the results.

The teacher or coach should also attempt to promote feelings of self-efficacy and self-confidence by encouraging the young athlete to attribute successes and failures to appropriate causes. Children who succeed should be encouraged to attribute the success to both stable and internal factors. A stable attribution will improve the child's expectancy for future success, while an internal attribution will enhance self-confidence (Figure 14.13).

In conclusion, coaches and teachers are encouraged to utilize attributional training strategies. These training strategies are designed to help an athlete adopt an attribution pattern that will lead to increased self-confidence and higher expectancy for future performance.

Figure 14.13 Promotion of self-efficacy and self-confidence must be started early in an athlete's career.

Recommended guidelines include the following:

- record and classify attributions that athletes and students make after successful and unsuccessful performances;

- after each outcome, help the athlete ascribe attributions that will lead to greater expectancy of success and increased effort;

- provide an attributional training program for athletes who consistently utilize attributions that lead to lowered expectancy; and

- for best results, combine planned goal-setting with attributional training.

The open-ended measurement system (see box on previous page) should enable athletes to interpret success or failure effectively.

Audience Effects in Sport

Perhaps no other social–psychological effect is more important to athletic performance than the effect of an audience or of spectators. Two separate social factors operating in competitive situations have been identified: social facilitation and rivalry.

Social facilitation can be defined as the enhancement of performance by others doing the same thing. The case example outlined below provides a good example of social facilitation. **Rivalry**, on the other hand, represents a desire to win or beat the other opponent.

This has been taken one step further, suggesting that social facilitation be broken down into two components: audience and coaction effects. An audience condition can be described as a situation involving the mere presence of other individuals in the same room or area who are there as spectators. This differs markedly from coaction, where other people are present, but are performing the same task. It has further been suggested that audience or coaction conditions could serve to increase drive level, leading to improved performance on simple, well-learned tasks, or impede performance on complex tasks, or skills in the early stages of being mastered.

The finishing touches on the conceptual development of this model indicated that a distinction must be made between whether or not the audience is perceived as important, relevant, or referent for the individual. This addition is termed the **evaluation component**. If the athlete perceives the audience to be important and/or knowledgeable, then drive level is increased. If the audience is perceived to be unimportant and/or not knowledgeable, then drive level is decreased. This whole process can be summarized in model form in Figure 14.14.

Implications of Early Social Facilitation Research

Several guidelines useful to both coaches and teachers can be gleaned from Figure 14.14. Perhaps the most important concerns the relationship between an athlete's drive level and performance. Coaches need to determine when an audience may be present at a practice or competition, since the audience effect can turn out to be either positive or negative. Based on a review of current research, the following recommendations can be made:

Social Facilitation at Work

A high school boy arrives at the gymnasium earlier than his classmates, and begins shooting some baskets. He works comfortably and effectively, making several of his shots. Then a second boy enters the gym and also starts practicing his shots. The two boys do not speak, but the presence of the second person has a profound effect on the first one. He begins to try harder, concentrates more, and pays more attention to his shooting technique. Merely having someone else in the gymnasium has changed his shooting effectiveness.

Legend:

1. If **drive level** is *lowered*, performance on simple, well-learned tasks is likely to be lowered, while performance on complex tasks, or those in initial stages of learning, is likely to be helped.

2. If **drive level** is *heightened*, performance of simple tasks is likely to be improved, while that of difficult tasks, or those in early stages of learning, is likely to be impeded.

Figure 14.14 Audience effects on physical performance.

- devote an initial, prolonged period to **over learning**. This ensures that the skill is well learned and less susceptible to performance drop-off in the presence of an audience;

- in the early stages of learning, incorporate the arousal adjustment strategies outlined earlier to lower arousal. This will lead to quicker skill learning;

- allow audiences access to your practices only after the skills have been learned. At this point, skill learning won't be hindered. In fact, once the skills are well learned, an audience should improve the quality of your practices; and

- once the skills have been well learned, use the arousal adjustment strategies to increase arousal in your athletes. This will lead to performance improvements.

The Relationship Between Audience Characteristics and Team Performance

One of the most widely discussed topics associated with audience effects on performance is "home advantage." The fact that a home advantage exists in such sports as baseball, basketball, ice hockey, football, and soccer is well documented in the research (Figure 14.15).

Early researchers collected data on 1,880 major league baseball (MLB) games, 1,092 professional and collegiate football games, 542 National Hockey League (NHL) games, and 1,485 college basketball games. Their results clearly supported the home advantage hypothesis, revealing that the home team won 53 percent of the time in baseball, 60 percent of the time in football, and 64 percent of the time in both basketball and ice hockey.

Home advantage has also been shown to extend to the Olympic Games, where the host country wins more medals during the Olympics they host than either the Olympics before or after. And finally, it has also been documented that 63 percent of no-hitters in baseball were pitched at home, and that 78 percent of the perfect games were also pitched in front of the home crowd.

A number of theories have been proposed to explain the home advantage, each with varying persuasive force. For example, travel considerations are not predictive of whether the home or visiting team will win the competition. The travel variables that were studied included visitor travel, home team travel, length of visitor's road trip, length of homestand, series game number, and season game number. It is also well known that when the effect of the crowd is removed by having both teams play on a neutral field, the home team advantage completely disappears. These two facts, taken together, support the conclusion that it is the crowd effect that is responsible for home advantage, not tangential factors such as travel considerations.

The value of a supportive audience is obvious but the explanation of home advantage remains elusive. Do certain audience characteristics lead to a greater home advantage? This has been answered by an examination of audience characteristics such as size, density, and intimacy. Results revealed

Figure 14.15 A home crowd can often have a positive effect on the home team players.

that basketball and ice hockey enjoy a greater home advantage than football and baseball. Since basketball and ice hockey normally accommodate fewer numbers of fans, a logical conclusion is that factors such as audience density and audience intimacy may be more important than size for creating the home advantage. This being said, the best possible advantage is gained by developing an audience base that is large, supportive, and close to the playing area (density and intimacy). Filling the stands and creating an intimate environment represents a good strategy, even if it requires lower ticket prices.

Consider for a moment how the presence of an audience affects you personally, either in a game situation, a practice, or even in a classroom learning environment. Take a moment to answer the questions in the box *How Does the Audience Affect You Personally?*

How Does the Audience Affect You Personally?

Read through the following audience characteristics and circle the ones you feel would improve or impede your performance. Remember, there are no right or wrong answers, so answer honestly.

Factor	Improve (I)	Hinder (H)
Large audience	I	H
Small audience	I	H
Supportive audience	I	H
Non-supportive audience	I	H
Friends present in the audience	I	H
Parents present in the audience	I	H
Opposite sex members present	I	H

Summary

In this chapter, we examined the relationship between personality and athletic participation. We compared personality characteristics of athletes and non-athletes (athletes tend to be more competitive, dominant, self-confident, and achievement-oriented), as well as athletes of differing skill levels (elite athletes demonstrate a markedly higher level of vigor). We also considered the developmental effects of sport on personality.

The relationship between anxiety and athletic performance was an important topic in our discussion. State anxiety, which is of special concern for students and athletes, refers to a "right now" kind of anxiety that is situation-specific. Interventions to lower state anxiety include progressive muscular relaxation, positive imagery, and positive self-talk. The development of self-efficacy, or how to improve your situation-specific self-confidence,

remains a key to achievement in sport or life in general.

Motivation – the direction, energy, and intensity of behaviour – also represents an important issue in sport psychology. Achievement motivation is basically a function of two constructs: the motive to achieve success and the fear of failure. Another motivational theory, causal attribution, examines the effects of how we interpret successes and failures on our future motivation. This theory helps explain how our interpretation is closely related to our future expectations of participation and how much motivation we take to the setting.

Lastly, we looked at how an audience can affect our sporting performances. Social facilitation and rivalry are two separate social factors that operate in competitive situations. This section concluded with suggestions for incorporating audience effects research in the teaching and learning environment, as well as in the sport context.

Key Words

Achievement motivation	Intrinsic motivation	Progressive muscular
Anxiety	Inverted U	relaxation (PMR)
Arousal	Locus of control	Rivalry
Attribution theory	Motivation	Self-efficacy
Cognitive state anxiety	Motive to achieve success	Social facilitation
Competitive State Anxiety	Participatory modeling	Somatic state anxiety
Inventory–II (CSAI–II)	Personality	Stability
Distress	Personality states	Stress
Emotional arousal	Personality traits	Successful performance
Eustress	Positive imagery	Trait anxiety
Fear of failure	Positive self-talk	Verbal persuasion
Fight or flight	Pre-competitive anxiety	Vicarious experience
Gravitational hypothesis	Profile of Mood States (POMS)	

Discussion Questions

1. What are some important topics you have heard about on the radio, seen on television, read about in the newspaper, or heard your classmates discuss lately that relate specifically to sport psychology?

2. From your personal experience, what do you feel is the relationship between personality and sport? Do you think sport changes personality, or that certain personalities choose certain sports? Explain.

3. When you get really stressed-out, what do you do to relax? Which suggestions offered in this chapter do you think would be worth trying? Which ones would work best the night before a big test or exam?

4. What do you feel are some of the most important motivators in your life? Feel free to include not only your sporting involvement, but also aspects of your personal life inside and outside school.

5. Can you think of times when you have attributed success or failure to the wrong reasons?

What effect did these interpretations have on your motivation for future efforts? Having read this chapter, how would you change these initial perceptions?

6. What features about an audience do you feel would affect you most? Explain why you feel this way.

7. How have you personally used imagery and positive self-talk in your sporting experiences? What effect do you feel they had on your performance? Explain.

8. What factors do you feel contribute most to your sporting self-confidence and self-efficacy? Why do you feel these factors are so important? Can you think of anything you might do differently to feel even better about yourself?

9. Would you rather think that your sporting success was the result of hard work or personal ability? Why do you feel this way? Would you feel the same way about your academic success?

Motor Development

- **Growth and Development**

- **Movement Intelligence: A Vast Store of Motor Skills**

- **Information Processing in Motor Learning**

- **Motor Learning in Practice: Skill Acquisition Processes**

In This Chapter:

Early Stimulation *365*
    Introduction *365*
    Early Exposure to Physical Activities *365*
    Critical Periods *366*
    Readiness *367*

Stages of Growth and Development – Infancy to Adolescence *367*
    Infancy *367*
    Childhood *369*
    Adolescence *371*

Factors Affecting Growth and Development *371*
    Heredity *371*
    Nutrition *371*
    Socioeconomic Class *372*
    Exercise *372*

Perceptual Motor Development Across the Growth and Development Cycle *373*

Gender Body Structure Differences Across the Growth and Development Cycle *374*
    Stature *374*
    Weight *374*

Gender Fitness Differences Across the Growth and Development Cycle *377*
    Cardiorespiratory Fitness *377*
    Body Composition *377*
    Flexibility *379*
    Muscular Strength *380*

Social and Psychological Factors Across the Growth and Development Cycle *381*
    Self-esteem and Self-concept *381*
    Social Influences *383*

Youth Sports *384*
    Why Children Participate in Sports *384*
    Why Children Drop Out of Sports *384*
    Youth Sport Coaching *385*

Summary *388*

CHAPTER 15

Growth and Development

After completing this chapter you should be able to:

- explain the importance of early exposure to physical activity;

- outline the stages of growth and development;

- describe the factors affecting optimal growth and development across the life cycle;

- explain the necessity of physical activity for optimal growth and development;

- demonstrate an understanding of the differences between the sexes across the life cycle;

- demonstrate an understanding of individual differences in performance, growth, and development.

When we are born, our capabilities and experiences are minimal. With time and maturation, we soon develop into proficient beings, with an almost limitless capacity to perform movements and skills of varying complexity. But the process of growth and development does not simply follow a predetermined genetic blueprint; rather, it is altered by various social and cultural factors, and influenced by family and peers. As we grow and develop, factors such as nutrition, heredity, social interaction, and experience shape our physical and psychological skills. This can explain why individuals begin to walk at different ages, learn some activities more easily than others, possess variable levels of self-esteem, and grow to be of different height or weight. Just imagine what it would be like to live in a world with people who resembled each other in every way (Figure 15.1).

Individual differences are a natural part of the world in which we live, so each person deserves to be treated as an individual. Still, several stages of development can be identified that describe the general changes that occur as we grow and mature. Throughout life, as our motor capacities increase and our repertoire of skills is enhanced, these general changes significantly affect human movement. Some factors facilitate optimal development, while others tend to inhibit it. Focusing on the positive factors may effectively allow you and those around you to get the most out of life.

Determining the most appropriate physical activities at the various stages is important to optimal physical development. Certainly, some activities are more suitable for infants than children, and others for adolescents and adults. You will not find aggressive sports such as rugby and lacrosse being introduced to children, while these same sports may be of interest to the stronger and more mature adolescent. Understanding these important differences is significant in providing the ideal environment for each life stage. Adapting sports and activities to facilitate the progression of skills, and valuing the additional motor learning challenges facing some individuals, are important issues to consider: each individual faces different

challenges, and has unique strengths.

Obviously, the stages of development until maturation have a direct impact on our acquisition of physical skills and capabilities. Why do some children excel at some activities while others struggle to perform the same skills?

Figure 15.1 We all come in different shapes and sizes – even professional basketball players.

Gym Class – Love It or Hate It?

Amanda stood by the gym door waiting for her teacher to arrive. She listened to the laughter and loud chatter coming from the change-rooms. For an instant, she almost wished she had the guts to join her friends in getting ready for the volleyball lesson. But she suddenly became terrified as she imagined herself standing on the court, missing the ball each time it came towards her. Her teammates would get frustrated and the humiliation would be unbearable. She glanced at

her watch and skimmed over the note her mother wrote for her that morning: "Please excuse Amanda from gym class today because she is not feeling well." She wondered if her teacher would once again try to persuade her to join the class anyway. Perhaps she should have asked her mom to write something about a dentist appointment instead? After all, she just could not imagine how someone as clumsy and uncoordinated as herself could be an asset to this class. As a child, her parents always discouraged her from participating in sports and physical activities, explaining to her that it was not lady-like to run around getting sweaty and dirty. So Amanda never got involved in any type of athletics, and she now despised the fact that grade nine gym was still a mandatory subject. Suddenly, the gym door opened and her teacher appeared. As Amanda stood there, once again not changed for class, the disappointment on Mrs. Spencer's face was obvious. But as Amanda handed her the note, she did not care what her teacher thought. All she knew was that she had managed to avoid gym class again.

What factors allow smooth, continuous growth and development? The exact progression through the life stages is different for each individual. Understanding these differences and the unique changes that accompany various stages of growth is of great importance to physical and health education.

Early Stimulation

Introduction

You can probably think of someone you know, or knew, who showed considerable aversion for gym class. Unfortunately, the example presented in the box above is not unusual. On the other hand, for many others, the high school gymnasium is a place to let loose, have fun, and improve on many skills needed to lead a healthy, active lifestyle. When you consider that physical education may also enhance academic achievement, the benefits of

early participation in physical activity often seem clear. Why is it, then, that by the time they get to high school, some young people enjoy physical activity while others dread it?

Early Exposure to Physical Activities

A positive attitude towards physical activity from childhood is a key factor affecting future athletic participation and the enjoyment of sports. Although some children seem to be naturally inclined to sports, having inherited many advantageous traits from their parents, the environment in which children grow and develop has a large impact on their future success in athletics.

Children who grow up in homes that encourage participation in physical activity will eventually develop some degree of balance, coordination, strength, flexibility, and endurance. These characteristics will enable them to learn new and more complex skills with greater ease than if their exposure to physical activity did not occur until they entered high school (Figure 15.2).

Although high school years are marked by increased growth and development, early involvement in physical activities that lead to positive experiences simply makes it easier, and often less threatening, for young people to learn and improve their physical skills (see box *From the Research Files*).

Since early exposure to physical activity is likely to be beneficial, parents are increasingly enrolling their children in early educational programs for swimming, gymnastics, and many other sports. Stimulating motor development in young children may allow them fully to reach their genetic potential. Two concepts related to the issue of early stimulation are particularly important.

Critical Periods

Critical periods in the growth of a child, also known as **sensitive periods**, are times of particular sensitivity to environmental stimuli. If a child is exposed to the appropriate stimuli during this period, a particular human behaviour is likely to emerge, or at least be facilitated. If the appropriate stimuli are not present at this time, the potential for optimal development is lost. It is of course still

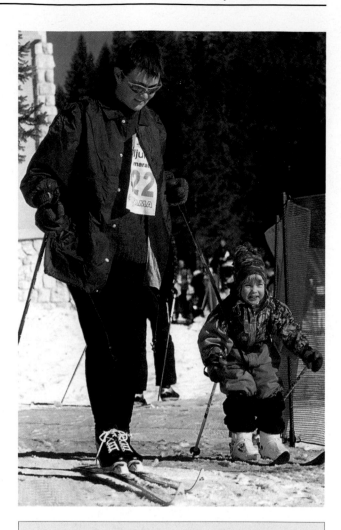

Figure 15.2 Exposing children to multiple activities helps develop important perceptual motor abilities such as balance, coordination, timing, and anticipation.

From the Research Files

The dramatic findings of a ground-breaking study of 120 immensely talented individuals reveal astonishing new information on

Developing Talent In Young People

BENJAMIN S. BLOOM, Editor

A study by Benjamin Bloom on the development of talent in young children examined the process by which individuals who have reached the highest levels of accomplishment in their respective fields developed their capabilities so fully.

The study provided strong evidence suggesting that no matter what the initial characteristics of the individuals,

unless there is a long and intensive process of encouragement, nurturing, education, and training, they will not attain extraordinary levels of capability. Many of the tennis champions studied, for example, began playing tennis between the ages of 3 and 11. An important conclusion to be drawn from this study is that tennis players who reached the highest levels of achievement typically came from families that valued athletics highly. It can then be said with some confidence that "what any person in the world can learn, *almost* all persons can learn *if* provided with appropriate prior and current conditions of learning."

possible to master a given skill at a later time, but the possibility for *optimal* development may have been lost. The critical period for the acquisition of many psychomotor and cognitive skills appears to be very early in a child's life.

The difficulty, however, is determining just how early the child should be introduced to physical activity. This is where early introduction to quality physical education programs in school may be helpful. Early experience and learning will give children a strong foundation and allow them to develop a repertoire of skills for the future.

Readiness

Readiness implies that the individual is prepared to acquire a particular behaviour or skill. In other words, sufficient information must be accumulated and the necessary physical abilities and characteristics must be attained for certain movements or skills to be performed (Figure 15.3). Readiness requires that the child wants to perform the task; without such internal motivation readiness has no foundation. Indeed, instruction in a particular physical activity that does not take into account readiness may even prove detrimental.

Stages of Growth and Development – Infancy to Adolescence

The stages of the life cycle, from infancy to adulthood, are marked by numerous physical and psychological changes. Although the general sequence of growth and development tends to be the same, there is considerable variation among individuals during each growth period. We all pass from infancy through childhood and adolescence to adulthood. But not everyone grows as fast, as much, or in the same way as others. Some may mature early, while others may take a little longer to "bloom." So as you read the following section on periods of growth, keep in mind the central importance of individual variability.

Infancy

Infancy begins at birth and ends at the age of 1 (Figure 15.4). This period is marked by extremely rapid growth: a child may triple in birth weight (for example, from 3.3 kg to 10 kg) and may increase in length by as much as 50 percent (for example, from 50 cm to 75 cm). Although there are

---

Knowledge Check

True or False?

1. At birth, boys are significantly heavier and longer than girls. ☐ True ☐ False

2. The adolescent growth spurt occurs approximately two years earlier in girls than in boys. ☐ True ☐ False

3. There is a significant difference between female and male physique prior to puberty. ☐ True ☐ False

4. Within each of the life stages, there is variability in growth and development among individuals. ☐ True ☐ False

5. Boys achieve world-class status in swimming and gymnastics earlier than girls. ☐ True ☐ False

(Answers: 1. F; 2. T; 3. F; 4. T; 5. F)

Joe Montana
Football's all-time greatest quarterback

"I got Joe started in sports," said his father, Joseph Sr. "I put a ball in his hands when the kid was big enough to walk and told him to throw it. Once he got started, he was always waiting at the door with a ball when I came home from work. What I really wanted to do was to make it fun for him. And I wanted to make sure he got the right fundamentals. I read books... we worked on techniques, sprint out, run right, run left, pivot, and throw the ball."

Wayne Gretzky
Hockey's all-time greatest player

If Wayne wasn't born to be a star, he was certainly raised in this direction. His father, Walter, iced down the backyard of their home for three-year-old Wayne. He strung lights so young Wayne could practice longer through the cold evenings. All through Wayne's childhood, the rink was a passion for both of them. In the daytime, the boy would skate on it and play hockey with the sticks Walter used to shave down for him. In the evenings, they would work together on the drills Walter had worked out. The father placed tin cans, then pylons on the ice for the son to swirl between. He dropped sticks for the boy to hop over as he received passes; he made targets smaller so Wayne's shots became more and more accurate.

Tiger Woods
The world's greatest golfer

From the start, Tiger Woods' life was dotted with feats of genius. At 10 months of age, having spent his infancy watching his dad hit golf balls in the family garage, Tiger picked up one of Earl's clubs and smacked a ball into the practice net left-handed. Father Earl taught one-year-old Tiger to putt; he won a putting contest at two; by three he had developed a fearsome swing; and by six Tiger was playing and beating 18-year-olds.

Figure 15.3 There are many well-known child prodigies who developed their skills very early in life.

not many obvious differences between male and female babies, males are usually slightly heavier and longer than females at birth.

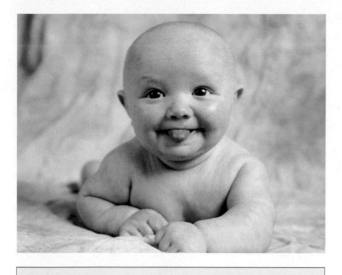

Figure 15.4 Infancy starts at birth and ends at age one.

Childhood

The **childhood** period begins when an infant is 1 year old and lasts until age 13. During **early childhood**, which lasts until age 6, there is a gradual loss of baby fat. Girls lose less body fat than boys, so in the first year after early childhood girls tend to be fatter than boys of similar age. Early childhood is a time of rapid growth, although the rate of growth is slower than it is during infancy. If you have ever watched young children play, you may have noticed that they are quite flexible. Since they usually cannot sit still for any extended periods of time, their muscles develop readily as they run around and enjoy life.

Children between the ages of 6 and 10 are said to be in their **mid-childhood.** Growth tends to be slower and more constant during this time so the body has a chance to improve in coordination and motor functioning. But during **late childhood**, 10 through 13 years, the rate of growth increases once again. Many children put on excess fat just before the adolescent growth spurt, which begins between the age of 9 and 10 in girls and between 11 and 12 in boys. As a result of the earlier onset

of the growth spurt, 10- and 11-year-old girls are usually taller and heavier than boys for about two years, until the boys catch up. Puberty is marked by rapid physical changes and occurs at different times for different individuals. Along with the height spurt, puberty involves the maturation of the reproductive system, the appearance of secondary sex characteristics such as breasts and pubic hair, and the redistribution of body weight. While boys show an increase in muscle tissue and a decrease in body fat, girls show a slight increase in body fat during this period.

Although the rate of growth and development is quite variable, the average range for boys is between 13 and 14, while for girls it is between 12 and 13 years of age. Perhaps the earlier onset of maturation in females accounts for the fact that young girls are able to achieve world-class status across many sports (such as swimming, diving, gymnastics, and figure skating), while males usually begin to succeed in sports at a somewhat older age (Figure 15.5).

An example of this difference can be seen in figure skating, where Tara Lipinski recently became the youngest ever U.S. ladies' figure skating champion at 14. She proceeded to capture the World Figure Skating Championship a few short months later and the gold medal at the 1998 Olympic Games in Nagano. Males, on the other hand, rarely excel at sports at such a young age, must anticipate the emergence of their athletic potential for many years.

Tara Lipinski

Age: 16

Martina Hingis became the youngest number one player in the world at 16.

Age: 14

With seven perfect scores (10s), 14-year-old Nadia Comaneci was a multiple gold-medal winner at the 1976 Montréal Olympics.

Age: 13

Thirteen-year-old Fu Mingxia captured gold for China in the 10-metre platform diving competition at the 1992 Barcelona Olympics.

Age: 12

Nine days before her 13th birthday, Morgan Pressel became the youngest player in LPGA history to earn a berth at the U.S. Women's Open Championships.

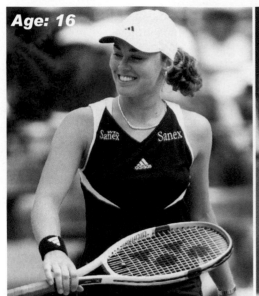

Figure 15.5 The earlier onset of maturation among women is reflected in their achievement of a high level of performance across various sports.

Adolescence

Adolescence is the period following puberty. It begins at about age 14 and ends around age 20. During adolescence, the various body types (**somatotypes**) become more evident: **ectomorph**, **mesomorph**, and **endomorph**. For more on somatotyping, see Chapter 12.

In general, the ectomorph has a linear shape with a delicate bone structure, little fat, and long limbs in relation to the body. The mesomorph is well-muscled, has little fat, and tends to have broad shoulders with a narrow waist. The endomorph has a rounded appearance, heavy bone structure, with little bone and muscle definition. While most of us are a combination of the different body types, we are all aware of the pressures placed on us by a variety of sources to obtain the body shape deemed as *ideal* in our society (see Chapter 1).

The eating disorders which are so common in young women and men are frequently associated with the tremendous pressure to "look good" (see Chapter 12). Undoubtedly, the many physical, hormonal, and psychological changes that accompany adolescence make this life stage a challenging and often frustrating period for many young people. Adolescence ends with the onset of adulthood. Although we continue to develop in different ways into our late adulthood, obvious differences in physical growth cease once adolescence ends.

Factors Affecting Growth and Development

Although just about everyone grows and develops in the same sequence, how fast one grows, and the final size reached, varies tremendously. Some develop early, while others mature later. Also, people come in different shapes and sizes, and variations in appearances can exist even within the same family. A number of factors – such as heredity, nutrition, socioeconomic status, and exercise – affect growth and development.

Heredity

Whether we are short, tall, large, or small is largely determined by the genes we possess at birth. Of course, the environment in which we develop can have a great impact on the degree to which our genetic potential is expressed. For example, chronic malnutrition can prevent a child from reaching his or her maximum size as an adult, regardless of the genes inherited. On the other hand, obesity is often the result of improper dietary practices.

Nutrition

The saying "you are what you eat" has some truth to it. The nutrients derived from food are critical for the body's growth and development (Figure 15.6). Carbohydrates and fats are processed for energy while proteins are used mostly to build

Figure 15.6 Nutritional habits are established early and may significantly affect a child's growth and development.

body tissues such as muscle. Vitamins, minerals, and water are also essential components of a daily diet since they allow various reactions and functions to take place within the body. Although malnutrition in childhood may delay growth, most children can still grow to their genetically predetermined size, provided the lack of nutrients is not prolonged. Unfortunately, even in countries with an abundant food supply, there are many children who remain chronically undernourished.

Overeating also remains a problem. Studies have shown that the number of fat cells in the body is definitely established during puberty. Thus, a constant overeating without exercise causes the number of fat cells in the body to increase. These fat-storing cells remain in the body for life, waiting to be filled, and consequently start a continual battle with body weight. The child who overeats will have trouble keeping weight down as an adult. The role of nutrition and related concepts are covered in more detail in Chapter 11.

Socioeconomic Class

Children from higher socioeconomic classes tend to have larger average body sizes at all ages than children from lower socioeconomic classes. One reason for this finding is related to nutrition; higher socioeconomic classes tend to have higher incomes, and thus have more money to spend on healthy food. Other factors such as lower levels of stress, better sleeping patterns, and regular exercise – all easier to ensure if basic needs are met – may also be responsible for the identified differences.

Exercise

Regular exercise is important for optimal growth and development. Although moderate exercise does not affect an individual's rate of growth, it does have an impact on bone development. Regular exercise tends to increase the diameter and density of bones so that they become stronger and more durable, and has an impact on increasing the length of the non-weight-bearing bones, such as those in the arms. Body composition is

Exercise Caution

Exercise is not always beneficial for growth and development, especially when it is over-done at a young age. While some stress on the bones is needed for optimal development, too much strain on a bone during a period of growth can lead to *osteochondrosis* – a de-arrangement of the normal process of bone growth. **little league elbow** is one type of osteochondrosis caused by the strain produced by repetitive throwing motions (see Chapter 8).

Overuse injuries are becoming more prevalent among young North American athletes. This should come as no surprise in light of the fact that young athletes are specializing in sports at increasingly earlier ages. Specialization generally entails intense year-round involvement. In fact, it is not uncommon for young athletes to attend sport camps that require them to train anywhere from four to six hours per day. Perhaps even more discouraging are reports that runners as young as four and six years of age are successfully completing marathons.

also affected by regular exercise. Active children and teenagers show an increased lean body mass and decreased percentage of body fat. Increased physical fitness increases and an enlargement (hypertrophy) of muscle tissues are directly related to regular physical exercise. Exercise may also help children and teens develop socially, since many take part in team sports that stress positive interaction and cooperation with other members.

Fun and Enjoyment

The goal of physical activity among growing children should be enjoyment. Children who feel pressured by parents and coaches to perform are often pushed to the limit and lose interest in pursuing an active lifestyle. Instead of developing skills for lifelong enjoyment and health, they may dislike a sport or physical activity because of the stress it causes. So even though regular exercise during childhood and adolescence may be beneficial, excessive exercise or physical activity may be counter-productive. Refer to Chapter 9 on training and fitness development for more detailed information on exercise and training.

Perceptual Motor Development Across the Growth and Development Cycle

The importance of physical education as an integral part of the school curriculum is often overlooked. Arguing that the amount of time spent on physical education in schools should be kept to a minimum, some parents discourage their children from participating in after-school sports because they fear that their grades may suffer. Others support their children's desires to pursue athletic interests by sending them to camps or enrolling them in clubs and other activity programs. But the reality is that many families just cannot afford the time or money required to take advantage of such programs.

However, one place that all children must attend during their critical years of development is school. Physical education in schools affords all children the opportunity of making important strides in their development (Figure 15.7). Such programs also highlight the importance of long-term perceptual motor development among children.

Although some parents still maintain that physical education compromises their children's cognitive development, others believe quite the

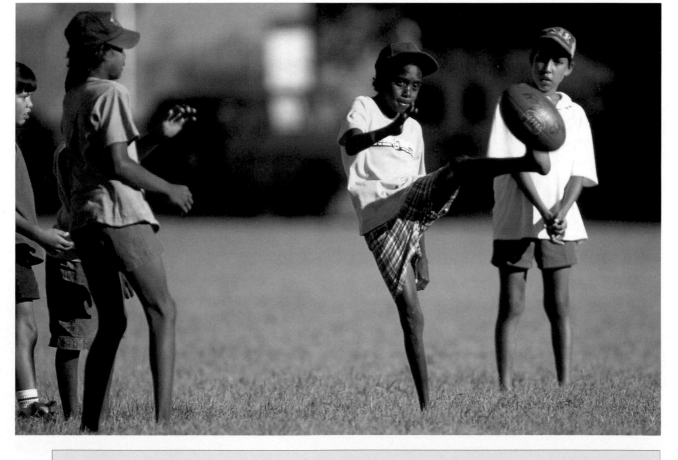

Figure 15.7 Physical activity promotes the development of physical fitness and positive social skills.

opposite is true. Indeed, research shows that students' academic performance can be enhanced through physical activity, exercise, and team sports.

Perceptual motor development activities, in particular, can be used to enhance academic or intellectual performance. One of the leading theorists of perceptual motor development was Kephart. Kephart argued that learning deficiencies resulted from the inability to integrate present stimuli properly with the stored information about past stimuli. As a result, Kephart theorized that participation in basic forms of movement could help correct this problem and improve the ability to learn such skills as reading and writing.

Other research has supported this general conclusion. A six-year study of 546 elementary-level students conducted by Roy Shephard at the University of Toronto concluded that those students who were engaged in five extra hours of physical activity a week actually did somewhat better academically than did the less physically active students, despite having spent 14 percent less time in academic classes. One reason for the findings may be that physical activity helps students "let off some steam" so they can focus better and be more alert. Thus, in addition to the benefits of daily physical activity to general health – a reduced risk of developing heart disease, osteoporosis, and certain types of cancers later in life – there is evidence that it reaps academic benefits as well.

Gender Body Structure Differences Across the Growth and Development Cycle

Stature

Stature refers to a person's standing height, which is the distance between the floor and the highest point on the skull. Since infants are unable to stand without assistance, the body length is initially measured while the child is supine.

Males and females do not differ much in average length at birth; boys are usually 50.5 cm long and girls generally measure about 49.9 cm long. But by the end of the first year of life, boys are generally 75 cm long while the average length of girls is 73.1 cm (Table 15.1).

After a child has reached the age of 2, stature increases at a slower rate than before, until the onset of the adolescent growth spurt. Usually around the age of 10 or 11 in girls and 12 or 13 in boys, hormonal changes cause the body to grow taller more rapidly. However, since not all children mature at the same rate, the time of onset of the adolescent growth spurt can vary by three or more years. During this period, the height of boys increases by about 10 cm per year and that of girls by a slower rate of 8 cm per year. Almost 100 percent of adult height is reached by the age of 16 among girls and 18 among boys.

There is usually no change in stature for a while after age 30. But some time after age 45, height begins to decrease slowly. The decrease in height is caused by a dehydration and degeneration of the disks that are located between the vertebrae in the back.

Seasons of the Year

It is noted that large gains in weight are evident during the Fall season, in September, October, and November. Exactly the reverse appears to occur with respect to increments in height. Maximum growth seems to occur during the Spring season, in March, April, and May. Although the reasons for seasonal variations in growth rates are unknown, it is probable that variations in hormone secretions are involved.

Weight

The average birth weights of boys and girls are 3.27 kg and 3.23 kg, respectively. During the first six months after birth, the infant gains about 20

Table 15.1 Important growth changes in body length and stature.	
Age	**Selected Growth Information**
Conception	0.14 mm in diameter
Birth (median length)	Boys: 50.5 cm Girls: 49.9 cm
6 months (median length)	Boys: 67.8 cm Girls: 65.9 cm
1 year (median length)	Boys: 75 cm Girls: 73.1 cm Length increases approximately 50% during the first year
2 years	Length increases about 11.8 cm
3 – 5 years	Decelerated growth rate to about 6.7 cm/yr
6 years to adolescence	Decelerated growth rate to about 5.5 cm/yr
Adolescence	20% of adult stature is attained during this 2 ½- to 3-year period Approximately 10 cm/yr growth for boys and 8 cm/yr for girls
16 years	Females attain 98% of adult stature
18 years	Males attain 98% of adult stature Females attain final 2% growth in stature
20 years	Males attain final 2% growth in stature
20 – 30 years	Growth of vertebral column may add another 3 – 4 cm to stature
30 – 45 years	Stature is stable
Above 45 years	Possible decrease in stature from disc dehydration and degeneration

Table 15.2 Important growth changes in body weight.

Age	Selected Growth Information
Conception	Ovum weighs roughly 0.005 mg
Birth (median weight)	Boys: 3.27 kg Girls: 3.23 kg Small mothers tend to have smaller babies Later-borns are heavier than firstborns Twins are approximately 0.6 kg lighter than singletons
First 6 months	Gains of about 20 g/day Birth weight generally doubles at 5 months
1 year (median weight)	Boys: 10.15 kg Girls: 9.53 kg Birth weight triples during first year
2 years	Gains of about 2.5 kg
3 – 5 years	Gains of about 2 kg/yr
6 years to adolescence	Slight increase in rate of weight gain to 3 kg/yr
Adolescence	Boys add about 20 kg of body weight and girls about 16 kg of body weight during this 2 ½- to 3-year period
18 years (median weight)	Men: 68.88 kg Women: 56.5 kg
Above 19 years	Weight becomes a matter of nutritional and exercise status

grams per day, so that by the fifth month, an infant has doubled in weight. By the age of 1, boys weigh about 10.15 kg and girls weigh about 9.53 kg.

During the second year of life, the rate of weight gain decelerates. Although the child continues to gain weight for the next three years, only approximately 2 kg per year are gained. Then, from the age of 6 until the onset of adolescence, there is a slight increase in the rate of weight gain to 3 kg per year.

Adolescence brings a sharp increase in body weight. Boys usually add 20 kg (44 lbs) to their body weight and girls about 16 kg (35 lbs). Much of the weight gain is caused by increases in height and changes in body composition (Table 15.2).

Diet and exercise have an obvious impact on weight. Regular consumption of calories in excess of daily requirements will result in weight gain. Conversely more calories burned than the number consumed will result in weight loss (see Chapter 12).

What Do You Think?

Ideal weight should not be dictated by societal norms, but is the weight at which an individual is healthy, feels well, and is reasonably happy with his or her personal appearance.

Gender Fitness Differences Across the Growth and Development Cycle

Do you consider yourself fit? Many assume that a lean individual must be a fit individual. But there is more to fitness than meets the eye. The components that make up fitness include cardiorespiratory endurance, body composition, flexibility, muscular strength and endurance, and psychomotor ability (see Chapter 9). Let's briefly examine four of these components to see how they differ between the sexes.

Cardiorespiratory Fitness

Cardiorespiratory fitness is the efficiency of the heart, lungs, and vascular system in delivering oxygen to the working muscles so that prolonged physical work can be maintained. Muscles need oxygen to carry out prolonged work, and the body's ability to deliver oxygen to these muscles is affected by such factors as heart rate, stroke volume, and cardiac output (see Chapter 6).

Heart rate is the number of times the heart beats each minute. At rest, a child's heart rate is much higher than that of an adult. For example, children under six years of age have an average heart rate greater than 100 beats per minute. Also, heart rates among boys are approximately 10 percent lower than those of girls. By the time people reach their twenties, males usually have a heart rate of 75 beats per minute. During physical activity, the heart rate increases in response to the increased oxygen and energy demands of the body.

Stroke volume refers to the amount of blood that is ejected from the heart each time it contracts. Unlike heart rate, stroke volume is much lower in children than in adults. The most likely reason for the difference is the fact that children have smaller hearts, and since they are unable to pump much blood with each beat, their hearts are forced to beat more frequently. At rest, the typical untrained adult male has a stroke volume of 70-80 ml per beat. In contrast, an athlete who regularly performs aerobic exercise has a stroke volume of 100-110 ml per beat at rest. During exercise, an untrained male usually has a stroke volume of 110-120 ml per beat, while a highly trained male can obtain values as high as 200 ml per beat. Females generally have a lower stroke volume than males both at rest and during exercise.

Cardiac output is the amount of blood that can be pumped from the heart in one minute, and is the product of heart rate and stroke volume. Cardiac output is lower in children than in adults, and is lower in untrained than in trained individuals. At rest, adults have a cardiac output of approximately 5 L/min. However, during exercise, it increases to anywhere from 20-25 L/min in untrained individuals and 30-35 L/min in trained athletes.

An individual who is able to pump out a large volume of blood from the heart in each minute is better able to deliver needed oxygen to the working muscles during exercise. The beneficial effects of endurance training on cardiovascular fitness in adults are well documented. Thus, it is wise for adolescents and young adults to get into the habit of performing large-muscle activities such as jogging, swimming, and cross-country skiing three to five days per week, for 20-30 minutes, at an intensity that causes breathing to become heavier than normal.

Body Composition

Body composition refers to how much of the body is made up of fat, and how much is composed of lean body tissue such as muscle or bone. It is estimated that the amount of fat present at birth is approximately 13 percent in boys and 15 percent in girls. Fat is stored in fat cells called **adipocytes** and the number of these cells increases during childhood. During the first year of life there is a large increase in the amount of fat tissue in the body; then, during puberty, there is once again a growth spurt in the number of fat cells.

Table 15.3 Body composition of elite male and female endurance runners.

Group	N	Height (cm)	Mass (kg)	LBM* (kg)	Body Fat %
Runners					
Male	19	176.4	62.6	59.6	3.0
Female	11	169.4	57.2	48.1	15.2
Untrained					
Male	54	176.4	71.4	60.5	15.3
Female	69	160.4	59.0	43.5	26.2

*Lean body mass

After puberty, girls tend to end up with a greater percentage of fat than do boys.

Although some fat is necessary in the body for insulation and protection of the internal organs, as well as a possible energy reserve for the body, it is unhealthy to have a fat content that is too high. A body fat content around 15 percent for men and 25 percent for women is recommended. Generally, a healthy body fat content is 10-22 percent in men and 20-32 percent in women. Athletes, especially endurance athletes who burn a lot of fat during training, tend to have bodies composed of less fat tissue and more lean tissue such as muscle (Table 15.3). But, just as it is unhealthy to have a high

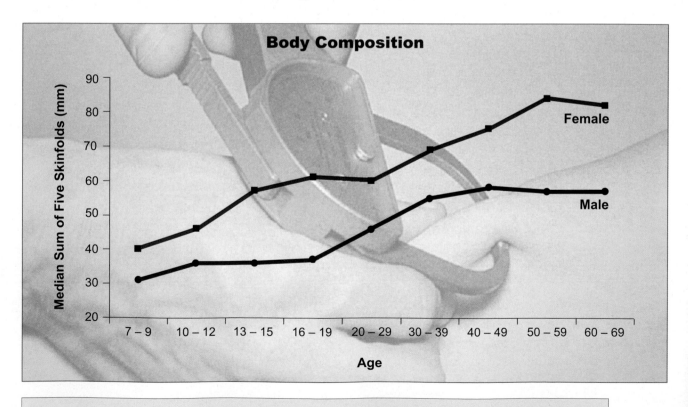

Figure 15.8 Comparison of body composition (fatness) between the sexes and at various ages.

body fat composition, it is also important not to fall to the other extreme. A minimal fat content of 3-7 percent in men and 10-20 percent in women should be maintained. For more on body composition and how to measure it, see Chapter 12.

Figure 15.8 shows differences between men and women in terms of total body fat. Calipers are the instruments used to measure the thickness of skinfolds in various parts of the body to determine the percentage of body fat. For both men and women, there is a gradual increase in the amount of body fat with age. Women generally accumulate more fat than men and it is distributed more evenly over the entire body. In contrast, men tend to collect more fat on the trunk and less on the extremities in comparison to women.

Did You Know?

It is important to note that muscle tissue weighs more than fat. Thus, you may be surprised to see an actual gain on the scale from frequent exercise due to the increased percentage of lean body mass.

Flexibility

Flexibility is defined as the range of motion about a joint or series of joints. Many factors affect this component of physical fitness, and individuals vary widely in the degree of flexibility they possess.

The anatomical structure of the joint itself is one factor that affects flexibility. For example, the bony structure of the joint, the bulk of the muscles close to the joint, and the structure of the ligaments and tendons all influence the degree of flexibility at a particular joint. In addition, lack of exercise and stretching lead to poor flexibility and make daily tasks such as bending over to pick up an object or tying shoes quite difficult. Flexibility decreases with age and, on average, is better in women than in men. However, a regular exercise program that includes proper stretching can improve flexibility substantially in any age group.

Muscles have a built-in mechanism that helps to protect them from injury. When a muscle is stretched, the "spindles" inside the muscle signal an increase in length and a stretch reflex is invoked, causing the muscle to contract in order to prevent overstretching and potential injury. If slow and gentle movements are used in stretching, the stretch reflex will not be invoked and the muscle can relax and lengthen. However, if fast, bouncy, or jerky movements are used, the stretch reflex will be activated, causing the muscle to contract and shorten in an attempt to prevent injury.

Inside tendons are Golgi tendon organs that act in opposition to the stretch reflex. When tension in the tendon is high, it sends a signal to the muscle to relax. However, this only comes into play if the muscle is stretched and held so it cannot shorten due to the stretch reflex. Thus, if the stretch is gentle and slow, the signal for the muscle to relax is activated and the stretched muscle can adapt to its new length.

It is important to remember that stretching should reach the point of tightness but not of pain, which can result in damage to the muscle. Holding the stretched position for 15-20 seconds is usually adequate for any stretch.

Warm Up for a Better Stretch

Just like an elastic band that stretches better once it has been warmed up by a few tugs, it is also better to stretch warm muscles than cold ones. Always begin with a light jog or other light aerobic activity to warm up your muscles. Warm up to stretch, not the other way around.

Figure 15.9 shows the results of a Canadian flexibility test. A score of 24-25 cm is equivalent to being able to touch one's toes – a task the average female subject in any age group can accomplish with ease. The graph clearly shows that in any age group, females are more flexible than males, and that flexibility declined with age across the sexes. Since good flexibility is important, particularly as we grow older, there is no better time than now to get into the habit of stretching properly and regularly. Stretching is discussed in more detail in Chapter 9.

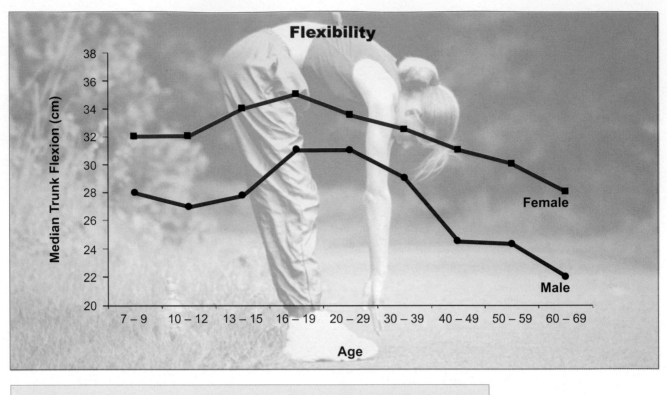

Figure 15.9 Comparison of flexibility between the sexes and at various ages.

Muscular Strength

Muscular strength is defined as the maximum tension or force a muscle can exert in a single contraction. Muscular strength is important because it is the contraction of skeletal muscle that allows human movement to occur. Older children and adults whose freedom of movement is restricted by inadequate levels of muscular strength usually lead a sedentary lifestyle. Thus it is important to develop and maintain some degree of muscular strength throughout the life cycle.

The most common measurement used to determine muscular strength is grip strength. An instrument is used to measure the force exerted when a hand squeezes this instrument as hard as possible. The rate and pattern of strength development can be seen in Figure 15.10. Adolescence marks significant strength gains for both sexes. Among females, muscular strength begins to peak by the late teens, and among males, during the twenties. However, in boys the strength spurt occurs about a year after their height spurt,

which may explain why some boys experience a brief period of clumsiness during puberty. Their bodies suddenly grow larger but they do not yet possess the required strength. In girls, on the other hand, the spurts in height and strength tend to occur synchronously.

The difference in muscular strength between the sexes becomes most apparent after puberty. During puberty, the male sex hormones are responsible for the increase in muscularity in boys. Since girls have a much smaller amount of male sex hormones, they develop less musculature and more body fat. Thus, women are about 70 percent as strong as men on measures of dynamic strength. This value can range from 60-84 percent, depending on the specific muscle groups tested. Strength peaks between the ages of 20-30 and then slowly declines with age in both sexes.

Resistance training with weights is a well-known method of increasing muscular strength. However, the age at which it is deemed healthy and beneficial to start such a training program remains a question. Recent studies have shown

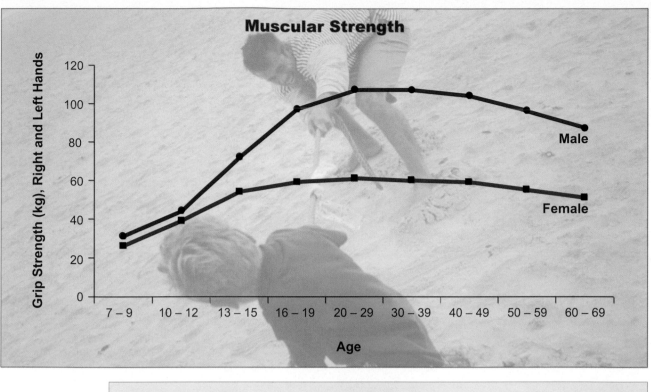

Figure 15.10 Comparison of muscular strength between the sexes and at various ages.

that prepubescent children are capable of making significant gains in muscular strength with resistance training, but the potential risk for injury makes weight training programs highly unsuitable and possibly dangerous to young children. Weight training by young children should only be attempted under strict supervision.

Body weight exercises and calisthenics are more appropriate means of developing strength fitness in the early through late childhood years.

The use of resistance training among adolescents is less controversial. However, a properly designed progressive strengthening program is essential and can minimize the chances of injury.

The strength of adults who train regularly and continue to do so into late adulthood does decline, but this decline is less significant than if they had stopped training altogether. Those who continue their strength training regimen have a much easier time accomplishing everyday tasks and are able to lead more active, healthier lives. More on this topic is presented in Chapter 9.

Social and Psychological Factors Across the Growth and Development Cycle

When discussing the factors affecting growth and development, psychological and social factors are often underemphasized. These factors, however, play an integral role in our development throughout the life cycle. What happens to us on a daily basis does not occur in a vacuum; internal and external forces are continually molding us as individuals. For a more detailed discussion on this topic, refer to the chapter on health and wellness (Chapter 1).

Self-esteem and Self-concept

Many experts agree that both self-esteem and self-concept are influenced by physical activity. Self-esteem refers to the value we place on

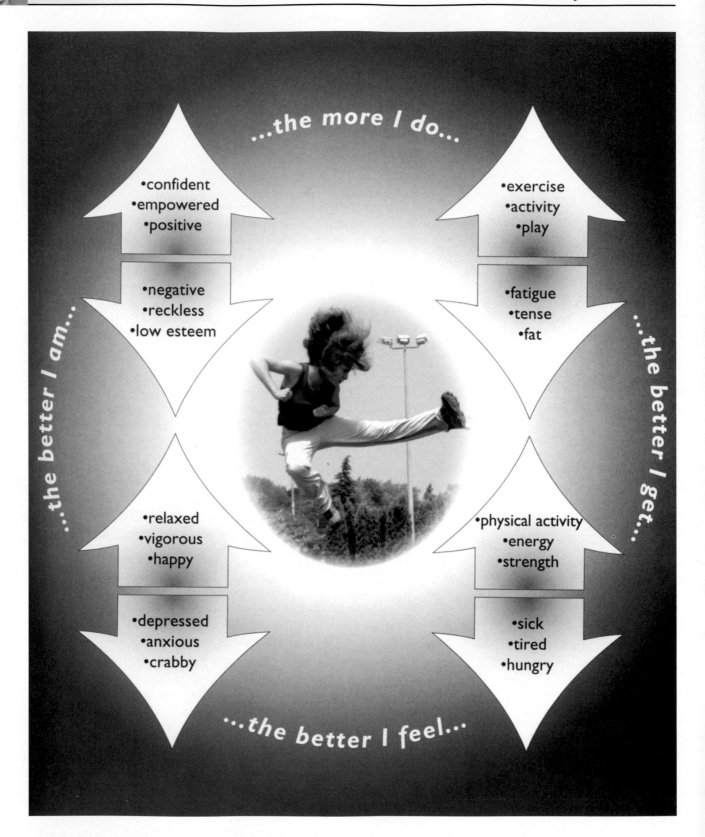

Figure 15.11 The self-confidence cycle.

ourselves as persons, while self-concept is the perception we have of ourselves. Although it is not clear why, studies show that involvement in physical activities by children can enhance their self-esteem and self-concept. It is possible that the diversion physical activity provides is enough to alter a child's mood and influence self-image. Or, perhaps the physiological changes in hormones that occur during physical activity somehow play a role. Nevertheless, it is important to recognize that physical activity is different from "athletic competence," which implies a perceived level of success in competitive sporting activities. Obviously, how competent you feel at a sport can have a very different effect on your self-esteem than involvement in an enjoyable physical activity for its own sake.

Self-confidence Cycle

Regular participation in physical exercise has an impact on all the fitness components presented in Chapter 9. Improved strength, flexibility, endurance, and agility, as well as enhanced coordination and other perceptual motor abilities in turn promote self-confidence, which provides an important foundation for overall well-being.

Engaging in physical exercise will initiate a cycle that will help you control your weight, protect yourself against various diseases, boost your energy level, manage stress and anxiety, and improve your self-esteem. It may also be the diversion you need to develop self-discipline and mental toughness. As you continue to participate in these activities, you will gradually experience increased fitness, positive shifts in your nutritional habits, increased vigor, and a strong sense of self-empowerment – all of which feed the **self-confidence cycle** presented in Figure 15.11.

Social Influences

Family

The choice to participate in physical activities and the success attained by a child in sports is largely influenced by the family environment. Family

Getting an Early Start

Andre Agassi's father, Mike, had been directing Andre's tennis career since birth. "As soon as Andre could open his eyes," he told an interviewer, "I got a tennis racquet, attached it to the ceiling, and tied a ball to it with a string so that it hung down above his crib. Then whenever I walked by, I would just give the ball a little tap and it would swing back and forth over him. That was to develop his eyes and get him to follow the ball. When he could sit in a high chair, I took a ping pong paddle and split it down the middle so it was very thin and light, and taped it into his little hand. Then I'd take a balloon and put a little bit of water in it and toss the balloon at him until he learned to meet it with the paddle. That teaches timing."

All in the Family

A strict family upbringing on a farm in Viking, Alberta, and many years of disciplined skill development at the local hockey rink, propelled six of seven Sutter brothers into the world of professional hockey and the National Hockey League (NHL).

The influence of the family on sport participation was clearly evident in the Sutter household. Positive views regarding physical activity were established early and paved the road for successful careers in the NHL.

Can you think of any other examples in the world of sport where more than one individual in the same family has excelled in the same sport?

views concerning physical activity are often instilled in a child at an early age. Studies show that strong parental interest in physical activity likely produces an increased level of participation among children. In addition, parental approval or disapproval of physical activity has an impact on a child's future involvement in sports (see box *Getting an Early Start* and Figure 15.3).

Peers

As a child approaches adolescence, the family's influence begins to diminish and the need for peer approval becomes greater. Dress and speech, no less than decisions concerning participation in sport, are strongly influenced by peers. If a group of peers considers participation in physical activities an accepted norm for their group, they pressure each other to be active and involved in this pursuit. However, if many of the group members do not value the importance of physical activity, the individual who is physically active may find it difficult to pursue his or her athletic interests without peer support, and may instead conform to group norms. Thus, the peer group often guides the individual into, or away from, participation in physical activities.

Take a look at the people you associate with on a regular basis. Have they helped or hindered you in your sport involvement?

Youth Sports

Why Children Participate in Sports

Children participate in sports for various reasons. Some of these reasons include: improving skills, having fun, being with friends, being part of a team, experiencing excitement, receiving awards, winning, and becoming more physically fit. Of all these reasons, the most common one is to have fun (Figure 15.12).

Researchers in this area stress that the emphasis should be placed on involvement and participation, skill development, and enjoyment of the skill since these are the factors valued most by children. Winning and receiving awards are not as important to children. Unfortunately, too often parents and coaches place enormous pressure on children to win.

Why Children Drop Out of Sports

One of the reasons normally given for withdrawing from sports programs is excessive stress. However, contrary to popular belief, most children do not drop out of sports because of high stress levels,

Figure 15.12 We participate in physical activities and sports for many different reasons: to have fun with friends and to improve skills while being part of a team.

but because of interpersonal problems (such as disliking the coach) or to pursue other leisure activity interests. The good news is that many of the youngsters that drop out of a specific sport only do so to become involved in another, different sport activity.

Teams, Teams, and More Teams!

Whereas young children are content to play alone or in small groups, the emphasis changes as children approach adolescence. Team or club participation tends to become increasingly important as we get older. Playing on a team encourages responsibility, division of labour, and working together towards a common goal. These are valuable lessons to learn at a young age and to remember throughout one's life. However, the emphasis placed on competition and winning should not overshadow the benefits of participation for its own sake.

Youth Sport Coaching

Youth sport programs led by competent coaches can do much to reduce the number of children who drop out of sports permanently. Many youth sport coaches are volunteers who have a child involved in the league. Although most have good intentions, very few have any training; so, anyone considering becoming a coach would be wise to become certified first through the National Coaching Certification Program (NCCP) (Figure 15.13).

Instructing according to well-established coaching principles (see Chapter 9) and learning how to analyze skills, how to break them down into parts that can be easily assimilated, and how to work with children is very important. After all, if children are to develop the attitudes, skills, and capacities that can help them lead healthy, active lives, their first encounters with organized sport should be positive.

Long-term Development of Athletes

Elite athletes are not created overnight. Top performances are the result of long-term development and training that spans over many years, from early childhood to adulthood. Researchers in developmental and training methodology from the National Coaching Institute in British Columbia have developed a model of long-term athlete development and the training requirements across different sporting activities.

According to this model, athletes progress through four major stages of development that span over two decades. Future top athletes go through a long process to reach their maximum potential. The beginning of the fundamental (first) stage of development depends on the activity chosen. **Early specialization** sports, such as gymnastics, figure skating, diving, and dancing, commence structured activities earlier than **late specialization** sports, such as rowing, track and field, cycling, and weightlifting, which require strength and endurance. The model for long-term athlete development is based on the **biological age** of the child. An example of the late specialization sports model follows.

How Old Are You?

Chronological age: how old the calendar says you are.

Biological age: how old your physical development says you are.

Puberty usually causes biological age to be older or younger than chronological age. Biological age changes as you progress towards maturity, and is therefore a variable age that corresponds only roughly with chronological age.

Stage 1: FUNdamental
Biological age: Females, 6-9; Males, 6-10

The first stage emphasizes development of basic movement intelligence (see Chapter 16 for more on this topic) through structured programs based on fun participation in as many sports activities as possible. The fundamental movement skills to be developed in this early stage range from **ABCs** (Agility, Balance, Coordination, and Speed), **RJTs** (Running, Jumping, Throwing, and Skipping), and **KGBs** (Kinesthetics, Gliding, Buoyancy, and Striking with the body) to **CKs** (Catching, Kicking, and Striking with an implement).

Speed, power, and endurance are developed through fun games and play. In addition, children are introduced to the simple rules and ethics of sports within a well-structured and properly monitored program. A minimum of 6-7 hours a week is required to assist children in their early movement intelligence development.

Stage 2: Training to Train
Biological age: Females, 10-13; Males, 11-14

During this stage emphasis is placed on training rather than on competition. The focus is the development of aerobic and physical conditioning and individual sport-specific skills (see Chapters 6 and 9). The time commitment for organized training is increased significantly to 10-14 hours a week as the volume of work becomes more demanding. A high volume of work is accomplished at low intensity levels. Some competition is introduced with no specific performance target. The emphasis is technical, tactical, and mental preparation of the young athletes over one or two periodization phases per year (for the periodization concept, see Chapter 9).

Athletes develop strength through medicine ball and Swiss ball exercises, as well as by using their own bodies as resistance. Later in the stage, the participants are introduced to correct techniques for weightlifting, warming up and cooling down, and stretching. Furthermore, the athletes learn about nutrition and hydration, mental preparation, and regeneration. Foundations for pre-competition, competition, and post-competition routines are also established. Further development and refinement of general movement intelligence continues in this stage.

Stage 3: Training to Compete
Biological age: Females, 14-17; Males, 15-18

The emphasis during this stage is on physical conditioning, with particular focus on maintaining a high volume of workloads but with increased intensity. Competition gradually increases throughout the stage. Individual strengths are developed and weaknesses are identified through simulation of sport-specific technical and tactical skills (modeling).

Training also focuses on developing maximal strength through the use of free weights. This work is coupled with further sport-specific technical refinements and further development of movement intelligence. The time commitment for organized training increases to more than 20 hours a week

and can go as high as 30 per week.

Stage 4: Training to Win
Biological age: Females, 18+; Males, 19+

In this final stage in the development of elite athletes, the focus shifts to sport-specific specialization and achievement of high-level performance. All of the athletes' physical, technical, tactical, and mental capacities are now fully established. Athletes are trained to peak for specific competitions and major events, such as the playoffs. Depending on the sport, athletes follow single, double, or multiple periodization. During this stage, training continues to develop general and sport-specific strength and endurance. The time dedicated to training varies depending on the activity, and ranges from 20-30 hours per week.

From a competitive point of view it is important to realize that future champions will be created only if they follow each and every step of the presented four-stage long-term athlete development model. However, in addition to sport performance development, an important aspect of the model is the suggestion of opportunities to study and prepare for a future career beyond competitive years.

Figure 15.13 The National Coaching Certification Program (NCCP) is an excellent way for volunteer coaches to become effective instructors. Ask your teacher about how to get involved in this program.

Criticism Sandwich

The best way to offer constructive criticism to athletes is by serving up a "criticism sandwich." This sandwich has three simple ingredients. It starts with a slice of praise; this gets the athletes' attention and builds trust. Next comes a healthy spread of constructive criticism; this should be specific to the movement or activity and should be given in a positive way. Finally, it is best to finish with another slice of praise. The athletes should be made to realize that they are capable of improving the skill. This effective technique improves the athletes' performances and leaves them feeling good about themselves.

Summary

Early exposure to physical activity makes it easier and less threatening to acquire new physical skills. However, it is not beneficial – and can actually be harmful – to expect individuals to acquire skills before they are physically and psychologically ready to do so. This notion of readiness is also related to the various stages of growth and development throughout a person's life. However, individual needs and abilities are different. A number of factors – such as heredity, nutrition, socioeconomic status, and exercise – affect growth and development and account, at least in part, for the differences.

Exercise has always been known to have many positive effects on health. But now it is increasingly recognized that exercise can have a positive impact on academic work. Regular participation in physical activities has also been found to have a positive impact on self-esteem and self-concept. In addition, much recent research focuses on the differences between the sexes in terms of height, weight, and fitness levels. Rather than focusing on these differences, it is more important to concentrate on your individual health and fitness.

In essence, there are many advantages that come with being active throughout one's life. So, whether you have been involved in sports from the time you were a child, or if you are just starting to be physically active, remember that it is never too late to develop good habits that last a lifetime.

Key Words

Biological age	Ectomorph	Mesomorph
Cardiac output	Endomorph	Mid-childhood
Childhood	Heart rate	Readiness
Chronological age	Infancy	Self-confidence cycle
Critical (sensitive) periods	Late childhood	Somatotype
Early childhood	Late specialization	Stroke volume
Early specialization	Little league elbow	

Discussion Questions

1. Why is early exposure to physical activity recommended?

2. Define what is meant by critical periods and readiness. Why do you think it is best to learn a skill when these two concepts are present?

3. Why are very young women generally more successful at world-class levels of sport than very young men?

4. Describe any two characteristics that are associated with each of the following stages of growth and development: infancy, childhood, and adolescence.

5. Briefly describe four factors that have an effect on growth and development.

6. Define the term cardiorespiratory fitness. What are the components that we can measure to see if a person is fit?

7. How do the sexes generally differ in terms of body composition, flexibility, and muscular strength? What do you suppose accounts for these differences?

8. Can you think of any reasons, besides the ones stated in the text, why participation in physical activity may enhance a person's self-esteem and self-concept?

9. List eight reasons why children participate in sports and two reasons why they drop out.

10. Briefly describe an effective method for providing critical feedback to athletes.

In This Chapter:

Movement Intelligence *393*
    Unlocking Your Potential *393*
    Motor Programs *393*
    Factors Affecting Movement Intelligence *396*
    Movement Abilities *396*
    Human Abilities Questions and Answers *397*

Understanding Skills *401*
    Skill as a Task *401*
    Skill as Quality of Performance *401*

Characteristics of Skills *402*
    Hierarchical Organization *402*
    Serial Nature of Skills *404*
    Temporal Patterning *405*
    Classification of Skills *405*

Enhancing Your Learning Potential *411*

Summary *412*

CHAPTER 16

Movement Intelligence: A Vast Store of Motor Skills

After completing this chapter you should be able to:

- explain the concept of movement intelligence in motor skill development;

- describe the rationale for and characteristics of motor programs and movement abilities, and give examples of each;

- discuss the relationship between motor abilities, motor programs, and skills;

- define motor skills and describe their characteristics;

- apply knowledge of the characteristics of a skill to analyze movement;

- explain classification of skills and demonstrate an ability to design learning progression for an open skill.

391

Whatever activity we may be engaged in, the ability to perform certain skills will always have a bearing on how the activity eventually turns out. Watching others perform skills, and doing so ourselves in various contexts, is a significant part of our lives. During the NHL playoffs, the Winter and Summer Olympic Games, and other sporting spectacles, our eyes are glued to the television as we watch, in awe, players and athletes demonstrate an unbelievable level and range of skill. We watch them believing that perhaps we might attain a fraction of their skill, but also so we can share their experiences, if only for a moment.

While Olympic and professional athletes have attained a level of achievement in athletics that most of us will probably never reach, we are all capable of performing the same motor skills they do to one degree or another (Figure 16.1). But many factors will have a significant impact on our ability to execute these skills. All skills share some common characteristics, but also possess some unique differences that influence learning and performance.

It is no mystery that human skills take many forms. Indeed, the remarkable number of skills we perform is an integral part of not only physical activity and sport but also our daily lives. But the term "skill" is open to several interpretations. We see swimmers execute flip turns at the wall, track athletes clear hurdles with remarkable precision, basketball players shoot jump shots from various positions on the floor, and soccer players head the ball with amazing control. But what are the elements common to these skills? How are skills classified? And what factors affect the learning and execution of these skills? These questions will now be considered in greater detail.

Figure 16.1 In order to attain a high level of achievement in physical activity and sport later in life, it is important to develop a vast repertoire of movement experiences early in life.

Movement Intelligence

Movement intelligence is an aggregate or vast repertoire of movement experiences developed since birth.

We possess the capacity to produce a seemingly endless variety of skills that are inextricably woven into the fabric of our lives. Numerous skills enable us to complete the daily tasks involved with work and school, as well as to participate in many physical activities, all of which offer different and unique challenges. The skills we possess are by no means static elements of our lives; they are continually being enhanced, revised, and adapted through experiences. The ability to learn new skills allows us to improve the way we live in striking ways.

Unlocking Your Potential

Today, we often hear about the many benefits to be had from active living, regular exercise, and a healthy lifestyle. But the advantages of any physical activity depend on some degree of movement intelligence. Participating in activities at an intensity and duration that have a positive impact on our health is greatly enhanced by having a developed skill level. While the advantages offered by physical exercise seem obvious, many individuals may feel uninspired to follow an active lifestyle because they believe their options are limited. Activities such as walking, running, and cycling are undoubtedly effective for improving one's level of fitness, but how attractive are they to the average person? Some might prefer to take part in other non-physical activities that arouse their interest and that are more fun and enjoyable.

The development of diverse skills can help greatly in this respect. A grasp of the certain skills involved in the activities you would like to pursue will broaden your options and the possibilities will begin to seem endless. Rather than using the excuse that walking and running are dull and monotonous, you can get out onto the tennis court or take part in a beach volleyball game (or whatever activity you enjoy), displaying your enhanced level of skill with renewed interest and confidence. Being skillful means getting out of physical activity all there is to gain – health, fun, and vitality.

Motor Programs

When learning new skills, we develop movement plans that are eventually stored in memory, known as **motor programs (MPs)**. It is hypothesized that repetitive practice encourages the formation of specialized nerve circuits in the central nervous system that work together when developing a plan for an activity or skill (for more on this topic see Chapter 17). Thus, motor programs emerge as a result of learning.

Motor programs are a set of pre-structured muscle commands that, when well developed, allow the performer to carry out the skill automatically. Many skills and movement patterns that must be carried out quickly, almost reflexively, serve as strong evidence for the concept of motor programs. Motor programs also help explain the performances of figure skaters, gymnasts, dancers, and pianists who must quickly combine together a series of discrete movements into a lengthy program.

Generalized Motor Programs

It is quite possible that developing and storing motor programs for every conceivable movement would place too great a demand on memory. How then do we explain the ability of a performer to meet the ever-changing demands of environmental conditions? In sports, the situations that arise during training and competition and the appropriate actions (motor programs) that must be taken are never exactly the same. In table tennis, for example, every forehand the player hits differs from the one that preceded it. How many motor programs, then, are really needed for the great variety of strokes a table tennis player makes during a rally?

Motor learning scientists have suggested a **generalized** or **dynamic motor program (GMP)**, an alternative to the simple motor program just discussed. The generalized motor program still consists of a stored pattern of movements, but its actual structure is conceived as more abstract. Central to this more general concept is the existence of **parameters**. Some of these parameters are stable and others are more unstable, or changing, depending on the situation in the environment. Parameters specify such things as the order of events or subroutines (see Figures 16.7 and 16.8 for examples of skill hierarchies), the overall duration of the movement, the overall force needed to accomplish the movement, the temporal patterning (explained later in this chapter), and the spatial and temporal order in which the components of the movement are to be executed (explained later in this chapter). An example of a generalized motor program's characteristics and its actions is provided in the box *Table Tennis Forehand in Action*.

When generalized motor programs become well established, they form the basis for automatic and spontaneous movements in sports. They ensure that the athlete's movements, even under different conditions, become supple and adaptable. Well-established generalized motor programs require little or no attention or mental effort, and with experience, their execution becomes fully automatic (see learning stages in Chapter 18). A theoretical discussion of this topic is beyond the scope of this textbook.

Movement Intelligence and Motor Programs

Movement intelligence does not refer to any specific ability an individual may inherit. Rather, it is a term that can be used to explain proficiency in performing various skills. Movement intelligence is viewed simply as a vast store or library of motor programs. Like a store or library holding thousands of CDs, each containing numerous tracks, our movement intelligence store is a collection of numerous motor programs, some simple or

---

Table Tennis Forehand in Action

The order of events in a table tennis player's forehand serves as an example of a **stable parameter** in the generalized motor program underpinning the stroke. Relative time and relative force to be applied in each stroke are considered stable parameters as well. Both, however, may also have **unstable characteristics** that are easily changed from one stroke to another. These characteristics can be readily adapted to the particular requirements of the rally. To hit one forehand harder than another, the overall force applied must be greater and

the overall time taken to carry out the stroke must be faster. Speeding up the sequence of the movements (or subroutines) and increasing the overall force can seemingly be done without altering the stable characteristics of the generalized motor program controlling the player's forehand strokes. The parameters are applied to the generalized motor program in order to specify how a particular forehand is to be expressed.

A generalized motor program responsible for the table tennis player's forehand can then be used to perform a large number of similar and yet slightly different forehands by simply adding the appropriate set of movement parameters to the abstract plan of action stored in memory. Armed with a well-developed generalized motor program, the player is ready for the challenges that await him or her during a rally. The execution of forehand strokes becomes fluid and effective under most varied external conditions generated by an opponent.

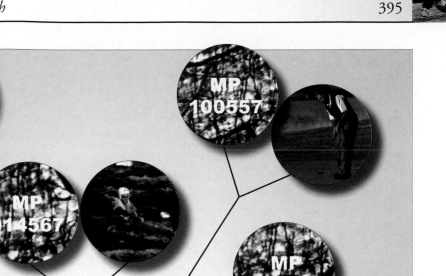

Figure 16.2 Hypothetical example of coded motor programs (MPs) assembled in an individual's motor memory, movement intelligence. Will we ever know how the human brain codes and stores MPs, the blueprints of skills?

complex, others fundamental or specialized.

Just as you cannot distinguish individual tracks on a CD until it is placed in a CD player, the motor programs stored in our memory through learning cannot be observed directly. But motor programs can be inferred by observing the skills and movement patterns we are capable of performing. In this sense, motor programs can be regarded as the blueprints of the skills we perform. They represent one side of a coin; skills represent the other. Skills are the observable side of the coin; they represent the movements we perform at the swimming pool, ice-hockey rink, or soccer field (Figure 16.2).

Obviously, the number of CDs matters as well. Greater selection usually makes a larger collection better than a smaller one. Similarly, the degree of motor intelligence you possess has a direct bearing on participation in sports. The larger and more sophisticated your movement intelligence, the more proficient you will be in playing sports at recreational or competitive levels.

It follows that movement intelligence is an active and ongoing process which, through practice, helps individuals develop new specialized movement patterns that will help them adapt to ever more demanding situations in any athletic or recreational environment. Many factors affect the development of movement intelligence.

Factors Affecting Movement Intelligence

The development of movement intelligence depends upon many factors, some of which are discussed in Chapters 15 and 18. They include adequate stimulation starting at an early age, opportunities for practice and continuous encouragement, expert instruction throughout educational programs, opportunities for practice in community clubs, the use of quality equipment, etc.

However, one factor remains vital for the development of movement intelligence: the inheritance of abilities. In the next section we will look briefly at the question of abilities and their implications for developing movement intelligence.

Movement Abilities

In previous sections we established that motor programs, the blueprints of skills, are active nervous circuits entrenched in the brain and stored in memory. The quality and the effectiveness of these motor programs depend on the presence of underlying motor abilities. In this context **motor or movement abilities** are considered inherited, relatively enduring, and stable traits that serve as the foundation for the development of motor programs. They are the "hardware" that learners bring with them to the learning environment.

For example, balance, speed of reaction, and finger and wrist dexterity are examples of abilities that are important for the development of a variety of motor programs that are outwardly manifested in a badminton smash, a sculling stroke, or a hockey slap shot (Figure 16.3).

A workbench analogy may help in understanding the relationship between motor abilities

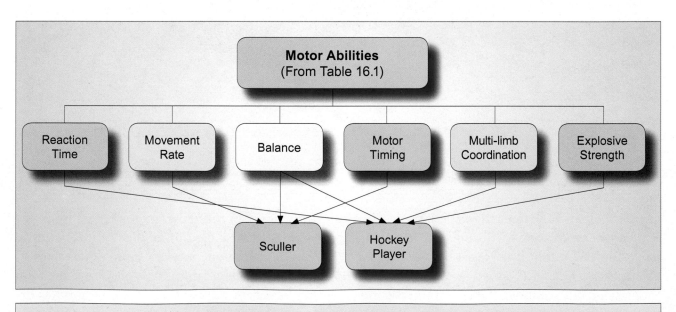

Figure 16.3 Hypothetical model of links indicating abilities underlying performance in two skills, rowing and hockey.

and skills. Motor abilities can be regarded as tools of various kinds used by the carpenter. To build a particular item, such as a table, the carpenter uses several different sets of tools that are highly specialized for cutting, filing, holding in place, drilling, etc. However, several different sets of tools are used for building a shelf. Similarly, the inherited movement abilities are the "tools" used in a variety of combinations to develop and perform skills (Figure 16.3).

Human Abilities Questions and Answers

How many abilities are there?

Relatively limited motor learning research has revealed 26 abilities that have been classified into three major categories as shown in Table 16.1. The first category of abilities deals with perceptual motor abilities, such as reaction time, dexterity, speed of movement, and coordination. The second category of abilities is related to human physical proficiency, such as flexibility, strength, endurance, and balance. The abilities in the third category deal with control of timing, rate of movement, and control of muscle force.

The search for human abilities is far from over. Practice has shown that there may be more abilities than have been identified by laboratory research to date, ranging from visual skills and kinesthetic sensitivity to body configuration. It is expected that future research will identify new abilities that could better explain sport performances of various kinds.

How many abilities do we have?

It is assumed that all individuals possess all of the abilities listed in Table 16.1, albeit to varying degrees. In other words, people differ in the amount or the strength of each ability. For this reason, abilities (or lack thereof) impose limits that influence an individual's potential for success in performing certain skills.

Furthermore, no two individuals have exactly the same pattern of motor abilities. This also explains individual differences in the quality of performance on movement tasks.

Why do people excel at some activities and do poorly in others?

This depends upon the strengths and weaknesses of one's inherited motor abilities (Figure 16.4). A champion sculler, for example, would possess inherited strengths in the particular abilities relevant to sculling (balance, movement rate, motor timing). If the abilities required to play hockey (explosive strength, multi-limb coordination) were relatively weak, the same individual would not necessarily excel in hockey and may therefore exhibit less skill as a hockey player (Figure 16.3).

Who are the all around athletes?

From experience we know there are individuals who perform well in several sports. Because many fundamental abilities are likely common across a variety of sports (balance in Figure 16.3), it is reasonable to assume that **all-around athletes** possess strong abilities that underlie the many sports in which they excel. These athletes differ from the average individuals in the number of abilities in which they are superior. As a result, there are more activities (ball sports, racquet sports, contact sports) in which these individuals can achieve success.

Can practice improve motor abilities?

We have stated that human abilities are genetically determined and relatively stable. However, many teachers and coaches believe, based on long-term experience, that intensive ability-specific practice may potentially improve motor abilities. For example, hockey coaches use countless speed drills to enhance the reaction time and agility in goalies; circus performers practice diligently on various types of swaying equipment to develop better balance; gymnasts improve their dynamic and extent flexibility through range-of-motion-specific practice.

Table 16.1 Human abilities as identified by motor learning research.

A. Perceptual Motor Abilities	Examples of Skill
Control Precision: Requires fine, highly controlled muscular adjustments, primarily in situations in which large muscle groups are involved. This ability extends to arm–hand as well as to leg movements.	• Forklift operators who are required to maneuver with careful positioning of the arms and feet.
Multi-limb Coordination: The ability to coordinate a number of limb movements simultaneously.	• Batting in baseball, shooting in hockey, or hitting in volleyball.
Response Orientation: Involves quick choices among numerous alternative movements, more-or-less as in choice reaction time.	• Task facing a goalie in soccer, where the type and direction of a shot on goal is uncertain.
Reaction Time: The speed with which a person is able to respond to a stimulus when it appears.	• Starting off the mark quickly in swimming, sprinting, or speedskating.
Speed of Arm Movement: The speed with which a person can make large, discrete arm movements in which accuracy is not the requirement.	• Throwing a shot for maximum distance.
Rate Control: Involves making continuous anticipatory motor adjustments relative to changes in speed and direction of a continuous moving target or object.	• Skiing, snowboarding, or white-water canoeing.
Manual Dexterity: Demonstrated by skillful, well-directed arm–hand movements in manipulating fairly large objects at various speeds.	• Dribbling a basketball or setting in volleyball.
Finger Dexterity: Involves making still-controlled manipulations of small objects involving, primarily, the fingers.	• Threading a needle or assembling parts of a small object.
Arm–Hand Steadiness: The ability to make precise arm–hand positioning movements where strength and speed are minimized.	• Archery and pistol shooting.
Wrist–Finger Speed: Involves the rapid movement of the wrist and fingers with little or no demand for accuracy.	• Playing the bongo drums and a quick snap of the wrist during a badminton smash.
Aiming: Requires the production of accurate hand movements towards targets at various speeds.	• Throwing a horseshoe or hitting a target with the rapid throw of a dart.

B. Physical Proficiency Abilities	Examples of Skill
Explosive Strength: The ability to expend maximum energy in one or a series of explosive acts.	• Performing maximum vertical jumps in volleyball, basketball, or high jump.
Static Strength: The maximum force a person can exert for a brief period.	• Maximum lifts in weightlifting or moving a large object such as a refrigerator.

Continued on next page....

Dynamic Strength: The ability to exert muscular force repeatedly or continuously over time.	• Rock climbing or performing on the still rings in gymnastics.
Trunk Strength: A more dynamic strength factor, specific to the abdominal muscles.	• Performing abdominal curls or crunches, leg raises, or holding a position on the parallel bars in gymnastics.
Extent Flexibility: The ability to flex or stretch the trunk and back muscles as far as possible in either a forward, lateral, or backward direction.	• Holding a pose in rhythmic gymnastics or yoga.
Dynamic Flexibility: The ability to make repeated rapid, flexing movements in which the resiliency of the muscles in recovery from stretch or distortion is critical.	• Performing dance or gymnastics routines.
Body Equilibrium: Involves maintaining equilibrium while blindfolded.	• Blindfolded tightrope walking.
Balance with Visual Cues: The ability to maintain total body balance when visual cues are available.	• Performing skills on the balance beam in gymnastics.
Speed of Limb Movement: Underlies tasks in which the arm(s) or leg(s) must be moved quickly, but without a reaction-time stimulus, to minimize movement time.	• Pitching in baseball, shooting in water polo, kicking in soccer, and tap dancing.
Large Body Coordination: The ability to coordinate the simultaneous actions of different parts of the body while making large-body movements.	• Stick handling in hockey while skating and coordinating the arms and legs while cross-country skiing.
Stamina: The ability to continue maximum effort requiring prolonged exertion over time.	• All endurance events including marathons, cycling, and rowing.

C. General Coordination Abilities	**Examples of Skill**
Movement Rate: Applies more to situations in which a series of movements must be made at a maximum speed.	• Playing the piano, typing, or keyboarding.
Motor Timing: Important for the performance of tasks in which accurately timed movements are essential.	• Most open skill activities, including throwing and receiving a pass in basketball, soccer, or football.
Perceptual Timing: Underlies tasks in which accurate judgements about the course of perceptual events are required.	• Judging the speed and direction of a bounce of the ball in tennis, basketball, or lacrosse.
Force Control: Important for tasks in which force of varying degrees is needed to achieve the desired outcome.	• Playing pool and dancing, figure skating, and gymnastics routines.

Recent research at the University of Toronto has indicated that intensive practice by athletes on the Dynavision board significantly improves a variety of psychomotor abilities at all levels of performance (Figure 16.5).

Figure 16.4 A student who has a low skill level in one activity should not be assumed to have a low skill level in another activity: it all depends upon the pattern of inherited abilities.

Figure 16.5 Practice on the Dynavision board.

Understanding Skills

Now that we have established the roots of skills, we turn to questions about what skills are, how they may be characterized, and their various types of classification.

The term **skill** can be used in many ways and applied to different scenarios. We will look at skills as tasks and as quality of performance.

Skill as a Task

The use of the term **skill as a task** is quite straightforward and simply denotes "an action or task that requires voluntary body and/or limb movement to achieve a goal." In this context, a skill must be learned, have a purpose, and be performed voluntarily. Serving in table tennis, catching a baseball, jogging, and throwing a Frisbee are all examples of skills defined as tasks.

Skill as Quality of Performance

Skill as quality of performance can be defined as the ability to bring about some end result with maximum certainty and minimum outlay of energy, or of time and energy.

Maximum Certainty

An important feature of this definition is that being skilled involves attaining the performance goal with maximum certainty. Therefore, sinking a long putt in golf on one occasion, and missing on all other attempts at the same distance, does not constitute a skilled action because the element of luck may have been involved; in other words, making one successful shot does not demonstrate that the shot can be made on other occasions with any certainty.

If your team was down by three points with only three seconds left to play in the game, who would you want to take the final shot of the game – the player who once hit a shot from half court in practice, or the player who hits three-point shots consistently? Obviously, the player who can consistently hit the shot is your pick because he or she has demonstrated the ability to generate the skill reliably over time.

Minimization of Energy

The second element in understanding skill as quality of performance is the minimization of energy. If energy is conserved, this allows skilled individuals the opportunity to use their energy at times when it is most needed, or to pace themselves for longer periods of time. Consider the player who expends most of his or her energy early on in the game, only to "run out of gas" in the clutch. Executing skills with minimum energy puts less of a burden on physiological and psychological processes, and allows a player to direct more attention to other aspects of the activity, such as creativity and tactical advantages.

Minimum Time

Finally, skilled performers should be able to accomplish their goals in minimum time. Although this may not be true for all activities, some skills are judged almost entirely on the ability to complete a skill in minimum time, such as a 100-metre race, where the person with the fastest time is deemed victorious. Other skills may also be performed successfully if executed rapidly, such as a slap shot in hockey or a punch thrown in boxing; but minimizing time is not the strict goal of all movements. For example, increasing the speed of some skills (e.g., shooting) may lead to less accurate or precise movements. Further, the rapid execution of some movements may affect energy costs by using muscles differently. Therefore, many aspects of skills must be considered when attempting to optimize performance under different conditions.

Characteristics of Skills

Organization and sequence are essential in developing the ability to perform skilled movements. Just try to find an individual who ran before he or she walked, or dunked a basketball before he or she could jump. Obviously some movements precede others, and the specific sequencing of these movements is important to the overall execution of the intended goal.

Hierarchical Organization

A skilled act may be thought of as following a **hierarchical organization pattern**, whereas an unskilled act lacks such organization.

One way to visualize such a hierarchy is by comparison to an organizational chart in which the president is at the top, with lower ranked members located at lower levels. In such an arrangement, the president and the executives direct responsibilities to the lower level members. In a similar way, skills may be characterized by a hierarchy consisting of different levels. The top of a **skill hierarchy** is occupied by the **executive program** (Figure 16.6), the overall purpose of the act, with **subroutines** (components or units of movement) located at lower levels of organization. To put it in simple terms, a skill is directed by an executive program and specific subroutines at various levels of command, which are responsible for carrying out the executive plan.

Executive programs act as a goal, aim, or objective; give direction to skilled acts; order the execution of certain subroutines; and make

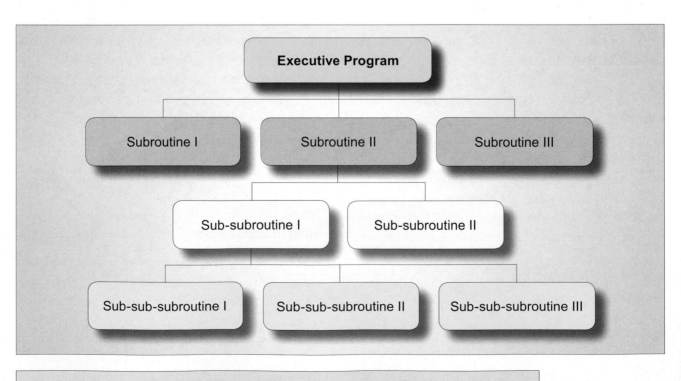

Figure 16.6 A theoretical skill hierarchy showing the executive program and subroutines.

Figure 16.7 A rowing stroke skill hierarchy.

decisions and adaptations that are flexible. However, the executive program, or plan, is dependent upon the sequential execution of subroutines. These subroutines are isolated units of the total executive program, but no less significant. Subroutines on the lowest level of a skill hierarchy are characteristically fixed and will run automatically once the sequence is established. These stereotyped movements are capable of being repeated over and over again unless interrupted or changed by the executive program.

Serial Nature of Skills

Still, a skilled act is serial in nature, meaning the subroutines must follow a particular sequence in order for the executive program to be effectively carried out. A skilled pitcher realizes what sequence produces a good pitch: the motions of the leg kick, hips, shoulders, arms, wrist, and fingers must follow one another during delivery. A coordinated, sequential movement is more productive, and often easily distinguished from awkward, uncoordinated movement that is clearly less effective.

A rowing stroke (executive program) consists of four main subroutines – the catch, the pull, the finish, and the recovery – that are further broken down into finer movements of the wrists and fingers, arms, shoulders, torso, and legs (Figure 16.7).

Similarly, most swimming strokes consist of several subroutines such as the kick, arm strokes, and breathing. It is the executive plan that directs the ordering of these units so that the final skilled act may be performed smoothly (Figure 16.8).

Figure 16.8 Breast stroke skill hierarchy.

Temporal Patterning

The preceding discussion may have painted a simple picture of how skilled acts are executed. In reality, integrating several movement units or components to produce a single movement pattern is more complicated than simply chaining together several separate activities. Anyone who is just learning how to swim can appreciate the difficulty in coordinating all the movements involved with a particular stroke – until the kick, the breathing, and the arm strokes (subroutines) can be well established and correctly organized in the proper coordination pattern, the stroke will not be effective.

The ability to perform a skilled act is closely related to **temporal patterning**, the capacity of the performer to integrate the sequential organization of a movement pattern. This would include the ability to connect successive subroutines smoothly so that a skill may be executed in a flowing, coordinated fashion. A gymnast performing on an apparatus should not string individual exercise components together in an isolated fashion but rather must combine them into a fluid routine or series of elements. A boxer will be more efficient in action when he stops chopping away with straight lefts then rights followed by a left hook. Only when he combines these individual actions together will he be successful.

The inexperienced performer will execute movements in a jerky manner because the timing between related subroutines has not been well established. On the other hand, a skilled individual will most often produce movements in which the transition between each subroutine is shorter as well as smoother, leading to a more successful performance. Once an effective rhythm has been achieved for any movement, the executive program may be carried out with optimal efficiency.

Classification of Skills

Thus far, we have placed skills under one broad heading and discussed them as a single entity. Now, we will consider the various ways that skills

may be classified. **Classification systems** allow for a deeper level of understanding of skills, and can directly affect the structuring of the learning environment. Certain training methods and learning strategies may be more appropriate for some skills than others; therefore, methods of instruction can be molded to meet the specific requirements that different activities demand.

Traditional classification systems have focused on classification of activities rather than skill. A common distinction is made between individual, dual, and team sports, but this classification serves really only to provide a description of the number of participants involved. Other classifications of skills include distinctions between summer and winter sports, water and land activities, and contact and non-contact sports. Although such classifications may enable you to differentiate among many activities, a more recent taxonomy provides a more comprehensive and useful way to classify motor skills.

An effective way to classify motor skills is based on the environment in which the skill is to be performed. A skill for which the environment remains stable and predictable is called a *closed skill*. At the opposite end of the continuum are skills for which the environment is variable and unpredictable, called *open skills*. Skills in this case are classified according to the effects of the environment on learning and executing skills, and thus include the performer's need to respond to many changes in the environment.

Closed Skills

Closed environments are relatively stable: the surroundings do not change moment to moment. **Closed skills** are correspondingly performed under constant, relatively unchanging conditions, so the movement itself is often the goal of the skill (Figure 16.9). Performers of closed skills will almost certainly benefit from learning to repeat a particular movement pattern with minimal variation involved.

For example, gymnastics routines are performed under controlled conditions, and judged by high standards as a result of the

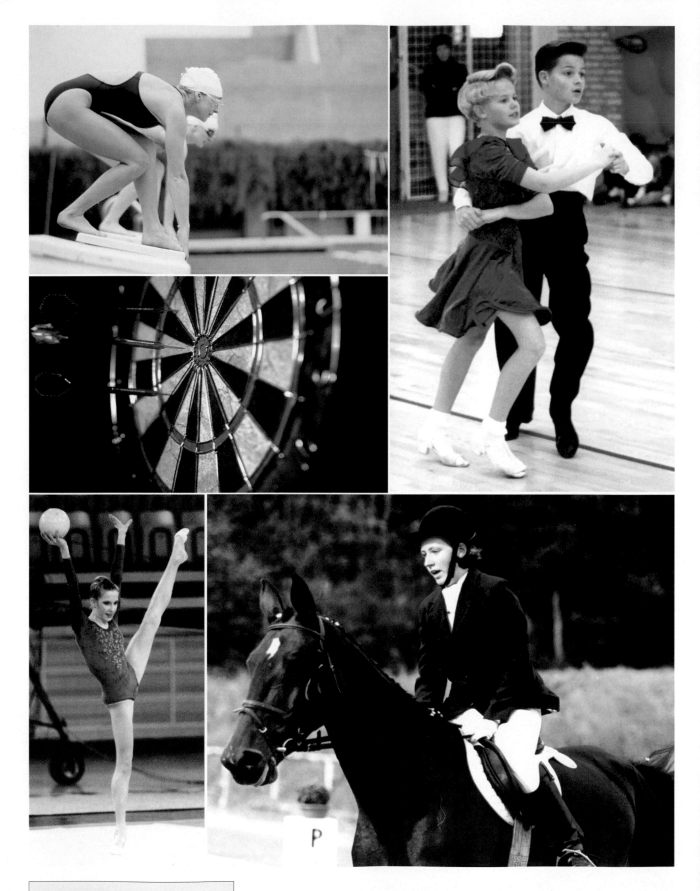

Figure 16.9 Closed motor skills.

predictable environment in which the athletes perform. A similar situation exists in sports such as figure skating, diving, and dance, where precise movements and execution are required for success. Another clear example of a closed skill is bowling. The lanes remain in relatively the same condition from frame to frame, and the pins only move as a result of individual movements in the environment.

Teaching Strategies for Closed Skills In order to develop movements that consistently produce the desired response, it is essential that the learning environment be conducive and that teachers select the proper subroutines. Students should be encouraged to repeat the selected movement pattern consistently without allowing external influences to affect the performance.

Since repetition of specific movement patterns is necessary for success in closed skills, students must learn to block out external distractions. For example, a student must learn to filter out noise when shooting a free throw, or to concentrate on the next shot in bowling regardless of how well a partner is doing.

The learning environment should allow the learner to refine movements more precisely, since the demands on sensation and perception are not as significant to the execution of closed skills. Proprioceptive feedback (also known as muscle sense; see Chapter 18) can be especially effective for learning closed skills by allowing a student to become more in tune with his or her own body position in space and relative balance. However, this is difficult for the beginner to develop, so the role of a teacher or coach is important in providing early feedback (described in more detail later in the chapter).

Open Skills

Executing **open skills** involves some very different considerations. Open environments are continually changing and require performers to adjust and respond to the environment around them. Because the conditions of the environment tend to be unpredictable from moment to

moment, responses cannot be made effectively far in advance (Figure 16.10).

Examples of open motor skills include hockey, basketball, rugby, volleyball, and wrestling, where movements by the performer reflect the changing nature of the environment. Whereas the diver can practice her dives the same way each time, the basketball player is forced to take what is given to him, reacting to the movement of other players and the ball. The ability to anticipate certain events before they actually occur (including scouting reports on players) would certainly make performing open motor skills an easier task. Therefore open skills demand that performers adapt, anticipate, and remain flexible in their responses.

Uncertainties in Open Skills Open skills harbor many uncertainties that make a performer's job very challenging. Team players and those involved in combat sports, for example, may have to deal directly with one or more opponents, their own teammates, and such things as the speed of the ball, the playing surface, and the weather. For the performer, this creates response, spatial, temporal, and tactical uncertainties.

Responding to an opponent's intentions rarely permits the use of the same movement response (or motor program) on two successive attempts. This creates **response uncertainty**. Therefore, it is important that the performer be able to execute many subtle variations of the skill by using a well-developed generalized motor program responsible for the task at hand.

Open skills take place in a temporally and spatially changing environment. In hockey, players must effectively overcome **spatial uncertainty**. To be successful, hockey players must continually move around the ice surface and act in accordance with the puck's spatial location and its speed characteristics, both to a great extent dictated by the opposing team.

In closed environments, skills are mostly self-paced whereas open skills are externally paced. Again in hockey, players' actions are typically externally paced – they can not stand in one

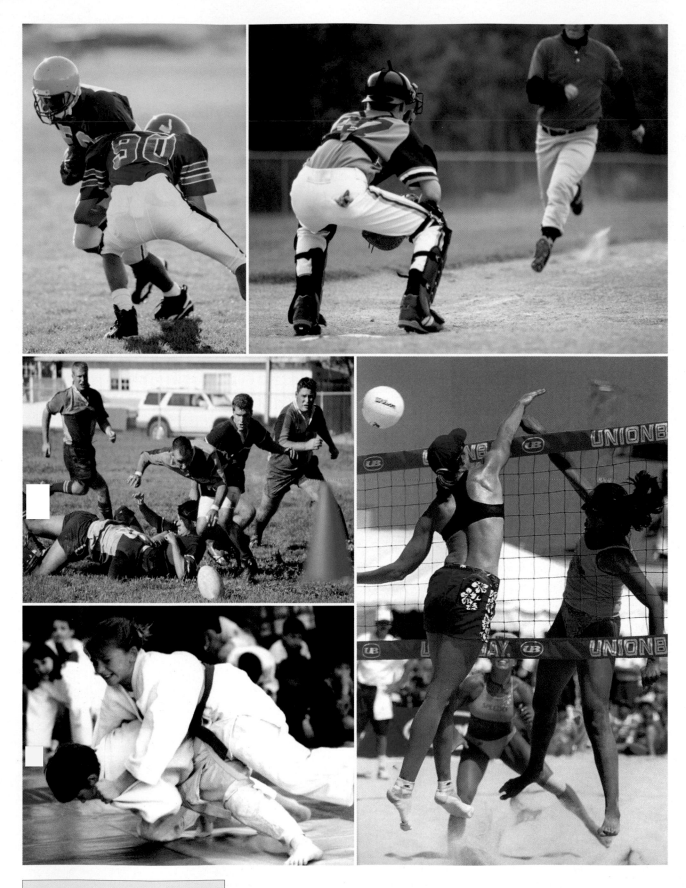

Figure 16.10 Open motor skills.

spot and decide when they will respond to the puck – because they must continuously adjust to the action dictated by the general pace of the game, which is partially influenced by the opposing team's intentions. This creates **temporal uncertainty**.

And finally, all team members must deal with **tactical uncertainty**. For example, a player's actions – losing the puck or unsuccessful coverage of the opponent – might bring about a tactical problem that threatens the interaction between teammates when they are carrying out tactical moves previously rehearsed. Unknown tactical maneuvers by the opponent further increase tactical uncertainties in open skill environments.

Teaching Strategies for Open Skills In order to make the learning of such skills effective, the learning environment should closely approximate the environment in which the skill will take place. In other words, learners should be encouraged to exercise variability and adaptability that more closely approximates the actual environment.

For example, a receiver is not likely to catch the ball in the same area on the football field, just as the quarterback will not throw to the same spot each time. An attempt should be made to incorporate various situations that may arise during the execution of open skills as they unfold. This is not to say that early development of such skills cannot benefit from practicing similar movements over and over again. This may help to establish proper movement patterns early, and help to avoid the development of bad habits (which may be difficult to eradicate).

Opponents will often deliberately try to create uncertainty and unpredictability in the environment to gain an advantage. Consider the tennis player who hits a drop shot in the middle of a point, which is returned by the opponent on the other side of the net, but the next shot is a lob that lands just inside the base line. This makes it more difficult to respond than if the player was only able to hit simple forehands and backhands to an opponent. The player who practices in an environment that provides this kind of uncertainty

and variation will benefit from the experience of adjusting to a changing environment. Players should also try to identify patterns in the movement of objects and other players. If you are able to recognize that your opponent's serve (tennis) is slicing out wide, or that the rebound (basketball) is coming off the front of the rim, you can better position yourself to return the serve or to get the rebound even though the outcome of the movement may initially be in doubt.

Open–Closed Continuum

While many skills can be placed in one of these two categories, there are certainly others that do not fall specifically under either of them. Some tasks are neither completely open nor closed, so this classification must be considered on a continuum of varying degrees of environmental predictability (Figure 16.11). At first glance, golf might appear to be a clear example of a closed skill – the environment does not change much, and your swing stays fundamentally the same on each type of shot. But what about the effects of the wind or rain on performance? Still other sport tasks may be closed in one situation and open in another. Skiing, for example, may be a closed skill when you are alone on a slope of even grade where your skills may be executed quite routinely. This same task can become an open skill when others arrive on the scene, and the slope becomes a little less predictable and has more curves and angles – not to mention changing snow conditions.

Learning Progression Along the Open– Closed Continuum Many sports and activities characteristically change as the context or level of experience changes. What is the advantage of utilizing batting cages and pitching machines for teaching baseball fundamentals in hitting? Obviously, these may help to simplify open skills by performing them initially in a closed environment (e.g., playing tee-ball). Once a certain level of competence has been achieved, the learner may advance to practice with live pitching, and so on, until open skills have been effectively established. Adapting a skill from a closed to an

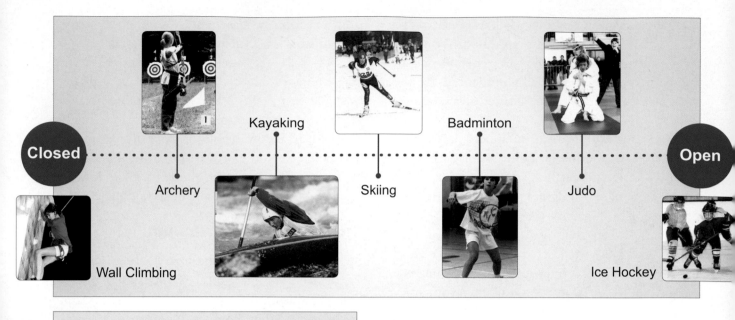

Figure 16.11 Closed and open skills continuum.

open environment provides a good progression for skill development (Figure 16.12).

Reducing the demands of certain task components may serve to reduce the complexity of the skill and various environmental and response uncertainties. Beginning tennis players may utilize ball machines and other devices to practice their ground strokes (see box *Learning Progression in*

Tennis); young children may begin their baseball experience by playing tee-ball; and all of us can probably remember the training wheels that accompanied our first bicycles. All these tactics remove a component of uncertainty that serves to simplify a skill until its overall execution becomes more proficient.

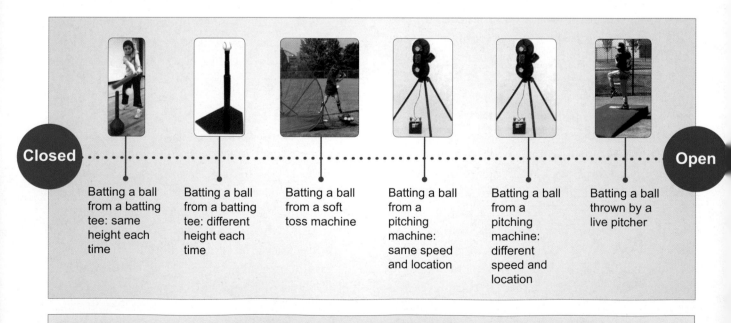

Figure 16.12 Learning progression along the closed and open learning continuum for an open skill: baseball batting.

Learning Progression in Tennis

An effective learning progression for a beginning tennis player may involve several stages:

1. hitting a stationary ball attached to a rubber string or the end of the instructor's stick;

2. hitting balls dropped strategically by a partner or instructor;

3. hitting balls gently thrown by a partner or instructor;

4. playing against a ball-throwing machine: same speed and location each time;

5. playing against a wall;

6. playing against a ball-throwing machine: different speed and location each time;

7. playing with the instructor or partner.

Helping the learner find the correct body or arm position – muscle feeling or kinesthetic sense – is an effective teaching method instructors can use at any stage of a player's development.

Enhancing Your Learning Potential

Many factors affect skill development. Understanding them and their positive and negative effects is essential for optimal achievement and performance.

The structure of our bodies allows us to perform a range of activities and tasks, both simple and complex. The intricate human nervous system and the diverse system of muscles and levers of the human body allow it to perform skills with extreme precision, accuracy, and speed. It is this precise anatomical structure that determines the limits of the human body's vast capabilities. But how the body moves in order to execute skills is another question. A clear understanding of how the body moves most efficiently is a considerable

asset when learning and performing skills effectively. Understanding how our bodies grow and develop over time, where our energy comes from, and how the foods we eat affect our health and fitness all positively aid the human body in learning motor skills.

Unfortunately, the human body does not always perform as expected. The occurrence of injuries can greatly affect our ability to execute skills as we would like to, so a healthy body is important to maintaining our level of skill. The ever-increasing occurrence of substance abuse for improving performance in sport is an issue that continually arouses interest and controversy. Is it worth using performance-enhancing drugs to improve one's level of skill? And at what risk? These are examples of some of the issues that negatively affect skill development.

The remainder of the unit will attempt to highlight skill development, the factors associated with performing skills, and the general components that make the human body unique and remarkable in its complexity.

Summary

The ability to perform skills affects everything we do. Although some individuals are recognized as being more skilled than others at certain activities, we all have the capacity to perform the same motor skills to varying degrees. Understanding skills and their roots, motor programs, and why they are important to our daily lives is important to getting the most out of life. In order to enjoy the full benefits of active living (including health and enjoyment), a certain level of movement intelligence is necessary. A relatively well-developed movement intelligence allows you to perform a great variety of skills at the intensity and duration that is most beneficial to health, and also makes you confident in your physical pursuits.

Skills share common characteristics, but also have unique differences that influence learning and performance. The skills used in one activity differ from those used in another, just as individuals differ in their capabilities to perform these many skills. But some features remain the same. Skills are organized in a hierarchical pattern that defines the sequential actions that must be followed (subroutines) to execute a performance goal (executive program). This progression of movement units must be integrated to produce a single movement pattern that is smooth, flowing, and coordinated (temporal patterning). All skills may be developed more effectively with an understanding of how they are characterized.

Some skills are performed in open environments that are uncertain and unpredictable. A coach involved with hockey (an open activity), will face different challenges than a gymnastics coach, whose athletes do not face the same degree of variability in a relatively closed environment.

Skills undoubtedly affect most of what we do, and our anatomy, physiology, health, and other behaviours affect our skill development. Gaining an understanding of how our bodies are structured and organized can only enhance our ability to execute skills effectively.

Key Words

All-around athlete	Movement intelligence	Skill
Closed skill	Open skill	Skill as a task
Executive program	Parameter	Skill as quality of performance
General coordination abilities	Perceptual motor abilities	Subroutine
Generalized (dynamic) motor program (GMP)	Physical proficiency abilities	Tactical uncertainty
Motor program	Response uncertainty	Temporal patterning
	Spatial uncertainty	Temporal uncertainty

Discussion Questions

1. Define movement intelligence. How does this concept differ from motor programs and skills?

2. What role do motor abilities play in determining an individual's skill level and performance?

3. Design a four-level skill hierarchy for an activity of your choice.

4. List the three main classifications of human abilities. Then provide three examples of abilities that fall under each category.

5. Using specific examples of abilities, explain what makes someone an all-around athlete.

6. How are skills defined? Identify the main features of this definition.

7. Explain the importance of temporal patterning in performing skills.

8. How have skills traditionally been classified? What taxonomy has been used more recently?

9. Distinguish between closed and open skills. Give examples of each.

10. Why are open and closed skills considered to be a continuum?

In This Chapter:

Introduction to the Structure and Function of the Nervous System *417*
> The Neuron and Its Function *417*

Information Processing and Making Decisions *421*
> Information Processing Stages *423*

Feedback in Motor Control *423*
> Closed-loop Control System *425*
> Open-loop Control System *427*

Factors Affecting Information Processing *428*

Summary *428*

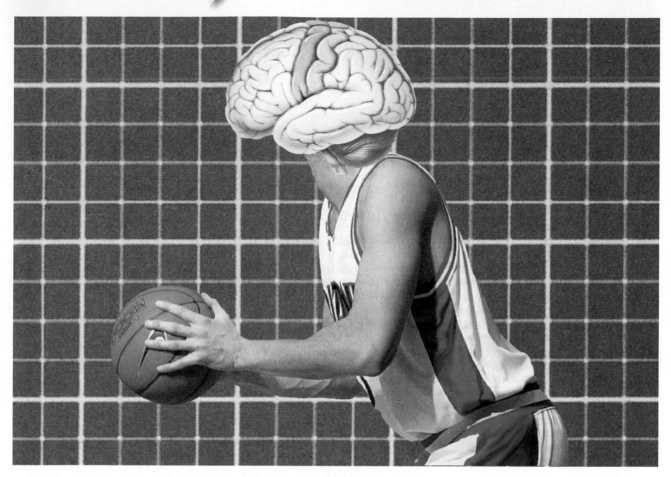

Information Processing in Motor Learning

After completing this chapter you should be able to:

- describe the structure and function of the human nervous system as it relates to information processing;

- explain the ways humans perceive and process information;

- demonstrate an understanding of the role of feedback in motor control;

- explain the advantages and disadvantages of closed- and open-loop control systems in motor control.

When we view the ease with which people move and execute most skills, it is difficult to appreciate the true complexities of human movement. At a glance, human actions appear simple and perhaps even trivial, but the intricate network and processes underlying motor skills are nothing short of extraordinary. The brain and spinal cord, comprising the **central nervous system (CNS)**, are accepted as the control centre for our powerful and far-reaching abilities whereas the nerve cells and fibres that lie outside the CNS, the **peripheral nervous system (PNS)**, connect the CNS with the rest of the body. The organization and vast capacity of the two systems are often oversimplified to the point that we rarely question how we are able to accomplish a range of movements with the precision we do. Not only are we able to perform relatively simple skills such as walking and jumping without much thought, but more complex skills such as those involved in gymnastics and advanced dance steps. Whatever the activity, the colossal network of neurons sending messages to one another from one part of the body to another is responsible in no small part for our ability to sense, respond, and react to the world around us (Figure 17.1).

In today's world of advanced technology, many people marvel at the considerable capabilities of the modern-day computers. Indeed, they are improving so quickly that they often become obsolete within years or even months of their creation. The human brain has often been compared to a computer with its immense capacity, striking speed, and pin-point precision. Yet, many consider the computer to be superior in many respects to the human nervous system.

It's a Draw!

Computers have demonstrated extraordinary success in playing chess. In fact, by the early 1990s only the world chess champion and a few others were able to beat the top computer programs like Deep Thought that were able to examine up to 450,000 positions a second. Going one step further in 1996 to showcase the computer's incredible abilities, a match was set up between Garry Kasparov (the world chess champion) and Deep Blue, an IBM supercomputer that took a five-person team six years to build – for the sole purpose of challenging Kasparov to a few games of chess. Deep Blue was able to consider an unbelievable 200 million moves in one second, more than any of its predecessors. The processing speed and efficiency of such supercomputers is mind-boggling, but who eventually came out victorious you might ask? Garry Kasparov, four games to two. Not bad for a *half-witted* human being, wouldn't you say?

In the rematch held a year later (1997) the computer was victorious, whereas in February, 2003, the match ended in a draw. Kasparov finally admitted that computers, indeed, are starting to show some "signs of intelligence."

Central Nervous System (CNS)

Peripheral Nervous System (PNS)

Figure 17.1 The central and peripheral nervous systems.

have many parts that cohesively work together to maintain control by sending messages to one another. What are the mechanisms that keep these messages flowing? How do humans process information? What effects do attention and memory have on human processing and performance? The answers to these and other questions to follow should shed light on the marvel of the human body, its capabilities, and its numerous abilities to perform an almost limitless number of motor skills.

Introduction to the Structure and Function of the Nervous System

How is it that a champion chess master is able to plan several moves ahead, or that a tennis player can plan many shots in advance during a point? What processes underlie an individual's ability to perceive, respond to, and execute certain movements and actions? The answer lies in the human brain. But nervous activity is not solely achieved by the brain; rather, in conjunction with the spinal cord and nerves, a complex system is set up whereby vast interconnecting pathways integrate and control the actions of the entire body from head to toe. How the nervous system accomplishes such a remarkable feat is the subject of the brief overview that follows.

While it is true that modern computers are capable of carrying out logical tasks (such as solving equations in higher mathematics) in a fraction of the time it would take most individuals to do so, we must not forget that it was the brilliance of the human mind that allowed for the creation of this splendid technology. The fact that any individual is able to claim victory against a machine with such speed and capacity only solidifies the astonishing competency of the human brain itself (see box *It's a Draw!*). So the next time you find yourself driving along the information superhighway, remind yourself how it came to be.

The human body and its nervous system

The Neuron and Its Function

Types of Neurons

Neurons (nerve cells) are the fundamental functional and structural units of the nervous system that allow information to travel throughout the body to various destinations. There are three general categories of neurons that carry neural information between the brain, spinal cord, and muscles. **Afferent neurons** carry signals *to* the brain or spinal cord and are also referred to as **sensory neurons**. **Efferent neurons**, or **motor neurons**, carry signals *from* the brain or spinal

A Giant on Maximum and Minimum Scales

The external appearance of the human brain conceals its true complexity. Approximately 15 billion neurons are concentrated within the 1,400 cubic cm of the brain, the largest number located in the cortex numbering 10 billion (a value over two and a half times the number of inhabitants on the globe).

At only 3 mm thick, the cortex may seem insignificant in size, but if all of its numerous folds and clefts were spread out, it would approximate the dimensions of a newspaper page bustling with neurons. Another staggering fact is that all the nerve fibres link to form a network four times greater than the distance between the earth and the moon. Now that's maximum use of space!

cord (Figure 17.2). A third category of neurons, the **interneurons**, originate or terminate in the brain or spinal cord.

Every neuron is composed of many parts, each of which serves a particular purpose. The **dendrites** extend from the **cell body** (which houses the cell nucleus) as branch-like fibres and serve as the centres for stimuli by receiving messages. The **axon** exists as a single extension from the cell body and functions to transmit and carry messages to its **terminal endings**, numbering in the thousands, along to the dendrites of other neurons (Figure 17.3).

Some axons also have a fatty covering that wraps around the axon, called a **myelin sheath**, that is separated by gaps called **nodes of Ranvier**. This specialized structure of some neurons, such as the motor neurons that innervate muscle fibres, offers an advantage because neural messages travel much faster as the impulse skips from one node to the next (Figure 17.3). Myelin acts as an insulator, similar to the rubber that surrounds electrical wire to prevent leakage of current. This rapid and efficient system allows the body to react quickly whenever and wherever required. Whether you are trying to avoid a hit in football, reacting to a spike in volleyball, or contemplating your next move during a hockey game, the central mechanisms involving neurons are essentially the same.

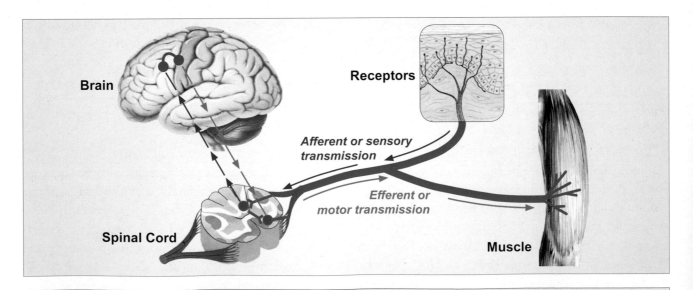

Figure 17.2 The receptors guide the stimulus across a sensory pathway (afferent) network to a specific sensory region of the cortex. Decisions are sent via a motor pathway (efferent) network to muscles and joints for execution.

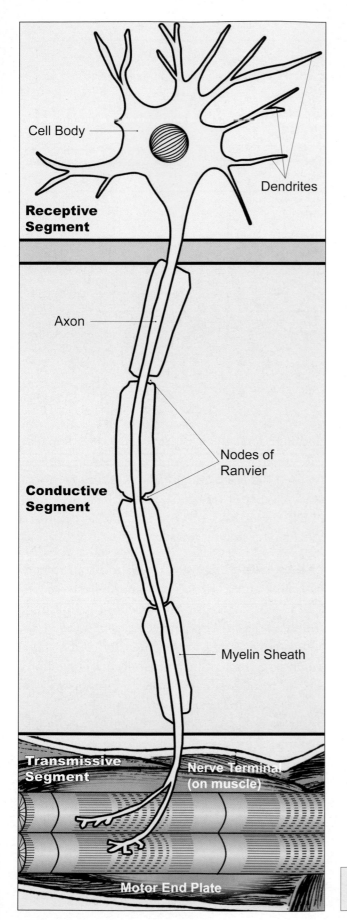

Figure 17.3 Functional organization of a typical neuron.

The Neuron's Function

Most neurons contain three functional regions (i.e., **receptive**, **conductive**, and **transmissive segments**), each responsible for a very specific information processing task (Figure 17.3).

Receptive Segment This segment receives a continuous bombardment of synaptic input from numerous other neurons on the receptor site. These inputs are processed and sent further to the conductive region of the neuron, the axon.

Conductive Segment The axon serves as the conductive segment of the neuron. It is specialized for the conduction of neural information in the form of nerve impulses.

Transmissive Segment The axon terminals convert the stimulation of the nerve impulse to release chemical neurotransmitters at its synapses. These chemicals give rise to effective reception of information by another neuron or muscle cell.

Neural Impulses

Our nervous systems can be likened to a railway complex and our brains to a signal tower, although along our sensory pathways, traffic is the law. Neural impulses may be thought of as trains that transport the information necessary for all the activities and actions we carry out, including reading the words in this sentence. They are the language of the nervous system, continually relaying information to the appropriate sensory cells and musculature. But how do these messages find their way along the axons, one neuron to another, without being derailed?

The secret lies with the distribution of ions (charged particles, e.g., sodium and potassium) that are located on both sides of each neuron's cell membrane. The inside of the neuron tends to be negative relative to the outside, while the outside tends to be positive relative to the inside – this

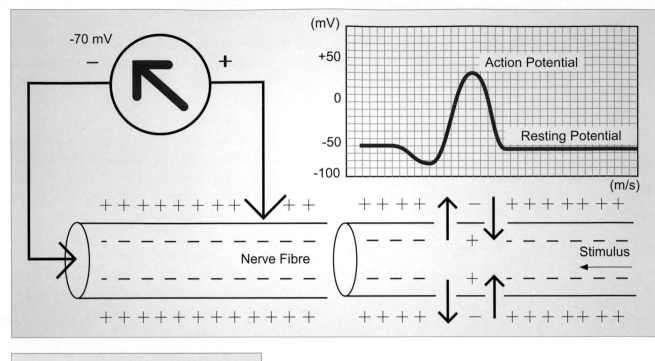

Figure 17.4 Action potential of a neuron.

creates an imbalance of charges, or an electrical potential difference across the cell membrane called a **membrane potential**. This idea may be compared to a battery that has a positive terminal (outside cell) and negative terminal (inside cell).

The situation just described reflects the neuron's resting potential, or state of **polarization** at approximately -70 millivolts (mV). When a stimulus reaches the nerve fibre, positive ions rush into a particular region of the membrane and are then quickly pumped back out to return the neuron to its resting state. This is called an **action potential**, or state of **depolarization** which reaches its peak at about 40 mV. In a domino effect, the same process is repeated in adjacent areas of the neural membrane until the action potential reaches the end of the cell membrane (Figure 17.4).

The Synapse and Synaptic Transmission

Each axon branches into terminals and at its end forms a junction with another neuron called a **synapse**. Synapses are small – a few billion could fit into a thimble – but their small size says

nothing about the very important role they play. Movement of a neural impulse across this junction is called **synaptic transmission**. Although several steps in synaptic transmission have been identified, much about the precise mechanics behind it remains shrouded in mystery.

"All-or-none" Law   A synaptic transmission will cause an action potential in the post-synaptic cell as long as its strength is above a minimum threshold level. This characteristic is called the **"all-or-none" law** and the intensity of the action potential remains constant along the nerve fibre's length. It follows that a stronger stimulus will not give rise to a stronger action potential.

It is useful to explain this phenomenon by making a comparison to the firing of a gun. In order for the gun to be fired successfully, there is a minimum degree to which the trigger must be pulled. Further, when the trigger is pulled past that critical point and the gun fires, it will fire at full force regardless of the force applied to the trigger.

In similar fashion, a neuron will either fire an action potential at full force or it will not fire at all. But while a stronger stimulus will not elicit a stronger action potential, it will cause it to fire at a faster rate. Thus, the rate at which neurons fire provides an indication of the strength of a stimulus.

For example, intense stimuli, those that might result from rapid, powerful movements in the muscles (e.g., golf swing, soccer ball kick, or football throw) or deep bending and stretching in the joints, trigger numerous simultaneous impulses; weaker stimuli, such as those during slow stretching movements, trigger fewer.

The firing rate of action potentials has a limit, just as a gun cannot be fired a second time until the first shot is complete. In other words, an **absolute refractory period** exists (about a millisecond) – a period in which a second action potential is not possible. After this period, neurons enter what is called a **relative refractory period** of several milliseconds, during which a neuron can only be fired by a very strong synaptic transmission (i.e., an elevated threshold level). Although this slight limit exists, rates remain amazingly fast, allowing a batter, for example, to swing at that pitch which seemed to be going outside but instead curved back over the plate.

All synaptic transmissions are not of the same strength nor do they exert the same effects. In fact, they differ in terms of the chemical transmitter located at the synapse as well as the general function they serve at that synapse. Some transmitters, like **acetylcholine (Ach)**, have a strong excitatory effect (usually to muscles) and result in a fast response. Others, however, respond more slowly, while still others exert an inhibitory effect. Depending on the particular location and intended function, a variety of transmitters exist serving to keep the system under precise control.

The preceding discussion has only touched the surface of the complex network that forms the nervous system. If anything, this brief overview was intended to open your eyes to the involved processes that control our every move and guide our perceptions. Without them, you would not be able to turn the pages in this book or even read the words before you.

Information Processing and Making Decisions

The goalie starts out of his net, preparing for the oncoming breakaway. As the player draws nearer, the goalie slowly backs in towards the net, following his adversary's every move. The goalie knows that the charging player likes to go to his backhand shot, so he prepares to react to such a move. Indeed, the offensive forward begins the motions of a backhand, but stops half way, pulls the puck back, and rifles a wrist shot that finds the corner of the net. What was going through the goalie's mind? How did he process the information used to make the decision to move the way he did? Similarly, how does the batter contend with pitches of varying speeds and spins? And what goes through the mind of the tennis player awaiting a powerful serve by her opponent? The ability to sense and respond quickly and with accuracy to such dynamic information in the environment is a crucial component of successful performances.

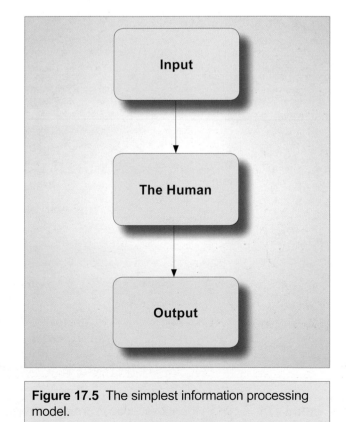

Figure 17.5 The simplest information processing model.

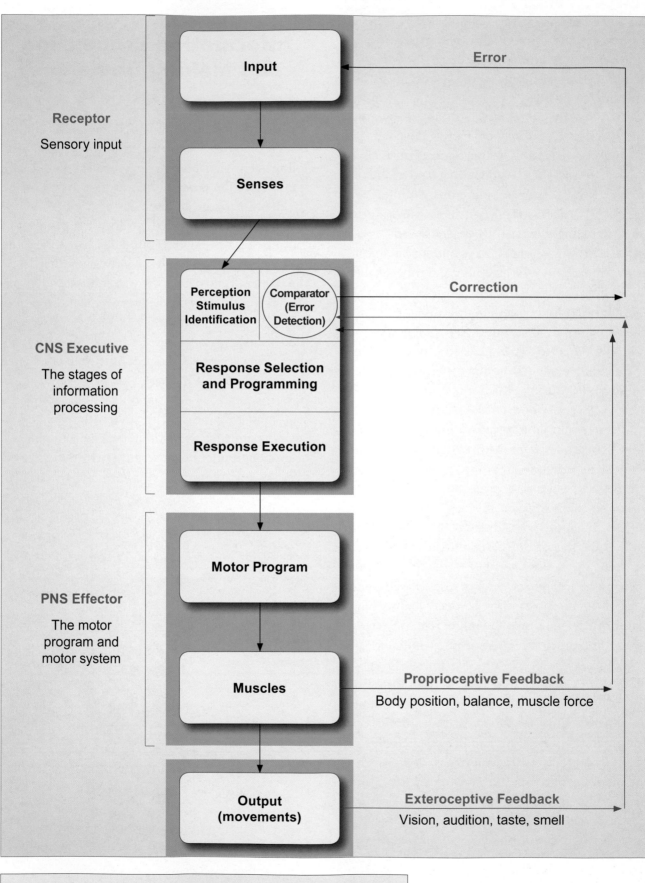

Figure 17.6 A conceptual closed-loop information processing model.

Human beings are often thought to process information in ways similar to a computer. Hence the label **information processing**. Information that is available in the environment provides the input which, after going through several stages of processing, leads to an output of some desired action or movement (Figures 17.5 and 17.6). But what happens at each stage, and what are the processes that allow players to react effectively in a situation that requires a swift decision and a rapid reaction? We will focus on three stages that underlie the processes by which players are able to respond effectively to the demands of their environment.

Information Processing Stages

Stimulus Identification Stage

Whether you are a goalie facing a breakaway or a batter awaiting a pitch, before any real decision can be made, a stimulus must be detected that warrants analysis. Therefore, this first stage is focused on sensing environmental information and determining what it is. Is the pitch a fastball? A curveball? These sensations come from diverse sources including the five classic senses (known as **exteroceptors**) of vision, audition, smell, touch, and taste, as well as a few others such as **proprioception** (the sense of joint movement, muscle tension, orientation, touch, and balance).

This stage is important for providing information about the nature of the environmental stimuli, including patterns of movement, direction, and speed of movement. For example, in order to catch a football successfully, you would need to identify the projection of the ball, its direction of motion, as well as its relative speed. With this information secured, you have a representation of the stimulus and the information is prepared so that it can be passed on to the next stage for further processing.

Response Selection Stage

Whereas the first stage deals with the nature of a stimulus and its recognition, this stage is required to generate a response to one's perception of the stimulus, which in turn serves as a stimulus to effector function (which calls upon specific muscles). In other words, there is a translation from perception to a movement or response in the form of a motor program (see discussion on motor programs in Chapter 16), based on the demands of the environment or the intentions of the performer.

An action, i.e., motor program, is selected from among several convenient options. Thus a basketball player may try to decide whether to make a no-look pass to a teammate on a fast break, or take off from the free-throw line for a slam dunk. For this reason, the response selection stage can be described as a translation mechanism between what is sensed and what movement is desired.

Response Programming and Execution Stage

This brings us to the final stage of processing, which organizes the selected movement from the prior stage. Of course, before a movement may be executed, many things must first occur: the system must prepare mechanisms in the brainstem and spinal cord, retrieve a motor program that will direct the action, and command the correct muscles to contract in the proper sequence, with the appropriate force, and with suitable timing. For example, it is not enough merely to decide to swing at a pitch; a batter must consider how fast the swing should be, the force that should be applied, and the most appropriate sequence to follow, depending on the pitch and the circumstances of the game.

Feedback in Motor Control

The efficiency of motor control by the human information processing system is based to a large extent on receiving various types of **feedback**

Understanding a Basketball Player as an Information Processor

Afferent Transmission

Efferent Transmission

Central Processing System Functions
- Perception
- Decision making
- Data storage and coding
- Translation to motor program

Sensory Receptors
- Ears
- Eyes
- Proprioceptors
- Vestibular system
- Etc.

Effector System
- Biceps
- Quadriceps
- Abdominals
- Latissimus dorsi
- Etc.

Coaching Instructions
- Watch the opponent
- Feel the ball
- Keep balanced
- Listen to teammates

Output
- Pivot
- Dribble
- Jump
- Shoot
- Pass

Exteroceptive Feedback
- Error Information
- Motivation
- Reinforcement

Coaches seldom realize that most coaching principles are based upon our knowledge of the athlete's limitations and capacities in receiving and processing information. After a poor performance it seems most coaches begin a long lecture about which bone does what and what muscles to use and at what particular time in the movement this or that muscle is to be activated. In essence, such coaches are observing and commenting only on the end result – the response of a whole series of interior processes that go on while the player is trying his or her best to execute the new skill. What are these various processes?

Psychomotor processes are part of the player's nervous system and are in most instances taken for granted. These mechanisms help the player to sense, perceive, attend to, store or memorize, decide, and organize an action in relationship to the demands placed on him or her by the coach and the environment. These mechanisms transmit information that is flowing between the coach and the athlete. However, these mechanisms are full of limitations that dictate correct coaching approaches and teaching strategies. By keeping these limitations in mind, the coach becomes more effective which in turn helps players to progress faster. Table 17.1 outlines some of the major limitations of the player's information processing systems and the main coaching strategies to overcome these limitations.

It is difficult to separate a player's sensory capacities and perceptual processes. What input the athlete actually processes is highly dependent upon the quality of both sensory and perceptual mechanisms

In practice an athlete is constantly bombarded with stimuli coming in through various senses. These stimuli are provided externally by the coach and internally by proprioceptors (receptors in the muscles, tendons, ligaments, and vestibular apparatus). However, a player's selective attention serves to filter out most of the available information presented. A coach who wants the player to perceive, i.e., hear or see, the right things would have to select and present instructions carefully so that they have a chance of getting through for interpretation and recognition.

Selective attention and short-term memory are limitations of a player's perceptual mechanism that every coach must consider for optimal learning results in practice.

(see discussion on feedback in Chapter 18). As we execute movements, the numerous receptors located throughout our bodies are continually updating the central nervous system about the nature of our actions. When figure skaters take off in attempting a triple axel, how does the feedback received from their senses affect the rest of the jump? Are they able to adjust their body position in the air in order to complete the rotations, or is the jump so routine that it is run off automatically? That is the question we will now consider.

Closed-loop Control System

The human senses perceive stimuli as images from the outside world and sensations from the body's internal environment. These stimuli are the first links in a long cause-and-effect chain of activities in the central nervous system and other interconnected mechanisms. Each sensory cell receives or is sensitive to a specific form of impinging stimuli or energy. The receptors then guide the stimuli across a sensory pathway network to a specific sensory region of the cortex for evaluation.

A process in which a specific reading is continuously compared with a standard value is referred to as a **closed-loop control** system. The system is based on the idea that movements may be planned and adjusted by feedback even during the movement. Therefore, the gymnast who senses a slight loss of balance on the balance beam can make an adjustment that will bring her body back to its desired state to salvage the performance (see box *Closed-loop Control System in Action*).

Several key elements form the basis for closed-loop control: error detection, error correction, and feedback. There is also a **reference of correctness** that specifies the desired value for the system. The resulting movement (output) is fed back and compared to the reference by a **comparator** for error detection and, if necessary, corrected.

A Thermostat Operates Like a Closed-loop Control System

This principle of a closed-loop control system, in which bits of information travel around a circuit from entry to exit, enabling the control reading to be approximated to its standard value, even has applications in technology. The automatic home furnace that has a thermostat set at the desired temperature may serve as an example. The current temperature is continually fed back to this reference, and any difference between the current and desired temperature leads to the furnace turning on or shutting off in order to maintain the desired temperature.

This general process is self-regulating and will continue to maintain the desired movement of the performer.

Advantages of the Closed-loop Control System

Clearly, closed-loop processes offer distinct advantages. Whenever we attempt new skills, we cannot be expected to master them immediately. But the closed-loop control system allows us to perform unpracticed actions, provided that we understand the difference between what we are doing and what is essentially desired (see comparator in Figure 17.6).

Also, the closed-loop control system offers flexibility and adaptability to movement, especially important in tracking skills. Just imagine the limitations to a hockey goalie if all of his or her actions had to be pre-planned in advance – reacting to shots and fakes would turn out to be a nightmare. By having the ability to execute a planned movement that may be adjusted according to the situation, we have a great deal more versatility in our movements.

Finally, closed-loop control systems come in really handy in activities requiring precision and accuracy. This may be clearly seen in the shooter who has a strict target to aim at, and that requires that movements be continually adjusted and adapted to suit the goal.

Disadvantages of the Closed-loop Control System

However, certain drawbacks do exist with closed-loop control systems. It is generally agreed that such systems do not effectively explain the control of rapid, discrete actions. Because the stages of information processing are an integral

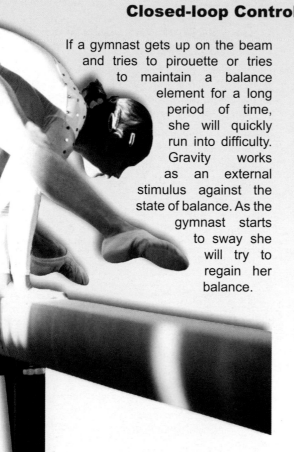

Closed-loop Control System in Action

If a gymnast gets up on the beam and tries to pirouette or tries to maintain a balance element for a long period of time, she will quickly run into difficulty. Gravity works as an external stimulus against the state of balance. As the gymnast starts to sway she will try to regain her balance.

If the gymnast sways significantly more than what is acceptable, the deviation difference is detected by a sensitive measuring instrument in the inner ear, the vestibular apparatus. The brain is continuously kept up to date on the actual state of things via a system of nerves leading from the vestibule (error detection). The incoming data are then compared with the standard values in the cerebellum of the hindbrain, and the difference between the two is determined. If the body movement is "off target," corrective orders that compensate for the swaying movement are sent to the motor cortex as well as to the motor units in the spinal cord that control the muscles in the arms and legs (error correction). These commands in the form of motor programs (discussed in Chapter 16) contain information that tells the muscles how much they must tense to reach the level where balance can be regained. In turn, the vestibule – as precise in its workings as a seismograph – quickly determines whether or not the order has been executed (ongoing feedback). The process may then begin all over again. Thus, the process is not a single correction, but a continuous updating throughout the duration of the movement, which is the essence of the closed-loop control system.

Intrinsic–Extrinsic Feedback Interaction

Luge riders who think they can negotiate the labyrinth of turns by relying solely on their eyes will find themselves at the bottom of the leader board. If they rely on external stimuli (especially visual stimuli) to guide their movements, the extrinsic (outer) regulatory circuit takes over. On the other hand, if luge riders are guided by the intrinsic or inner regulatory circuit, ideally when riding flat on their sleds, we say that their intrinsic (inner) regulatory circuit is at work. Both are important, however, and both play a role in the regulation of their movement down the track.

The intrinsic circuit has an advantage: movements and their corrections can be executed quicker and

with more precision (inner or red circuit in Figure 17.6). The muscle feeling or kinesthetic sense (discussed in more detail in Chapter 18) takes precedence, then, over the eyes (outer or blue circuit in Figure 17.6), and this is often the acknowledged goal in many sporting activities.

component of the closed-loop control system, they demand attention as well as time. In fact, each time a correction is deemed necessary, feedback must pass through several processing stages as shown in Figure 17.6. This presents a big limitation. Therefore, although closed-loop control systems may accurately describe relatively slow movements, faster discrete movements (e.g., golf swing, batting in baseball, a quad in skating) once initiated may not properly fall under such control.

Open-loop Control System

Have you ever wondered how figure skaters, gymnasts, and dancers are able to perform routines that run minutes in length without skipping a beat? How is a figure skater able to complete the four rotations required to execute the quad in competition (Figure 17.7 B, page 430)? How is it possible to complete certain skills automatically, without thinking about execution? **Open-loop control** attempts to provide answers to such questions.

The whole concept of the open-loop control system is based on the **motor program** concept,

discussed in chapter 16. A motor program is a centrally located structure that defines the essential details of skilled action, before a movement begins, and without the influence of peripheral feedback. This means that certain movements may be structured in advance, enabling automatic execution when initiated.

Whereas a typical closed-loop control system involves feedback and an associated comparator, an open-loop control system is made up of only two main parts – the *executive* and the *effector*. A stimulus (input) reaches the executive, which puts the system into action by choosing a response in the form of a specific motor program and relaying instructions to the effector (specific muscles). It is the job of the effector to carry out the specified instructions automatically. Unlike closed-loop control, the open-loop system will not respond again until the executive is activated anew.

Advantages of the Open-loop Control System

Upon analyzing the basic features of open-loop control and motor programs, certain advantages immediately stand out. First, many movements that are fast and forceful can be produced

Traffic Lights Operate Like an Open-loop Control System

Traffic signals that follow a defined sequence regardless of the conditions on the road are an example of an open-loop control system. Operations and sequencing are specified in advance, so once a motor program has been initiated, it will follow without modification. For this reason, it appears that open-loop control is particularly important in predictable environments, where changes will not require variations in movements once they have been initiated.

without the need for extensive conscious control. Therefore, we can throw, kick, and swing a golf club as established by a motor program.

Another benefit is the amount of attention that is able to be diverted to other processes. Because feedback does not require processing in the control of movements, a greater amount of attention may be directed to strategy and creativity to enhance performance.

Disadvantages of the Open-loop Control System

Not everything about open-loop control is advantageous, however. As mentioned earlier, open-loop control is not as effective in situations that are unstable and less predictable. In these situations, movements may not be determined effectively in advance, so many movements would suffer without feedback. It follows that the more precise and complex actions would be in need of more extensive well-developed motor programs.

Although practice can help develop motor programs so that they do become more elaborate, an open-loop control system is generally more accurate for describing rapid, discrete skills that occur in relatively predictable environments.

Factors Affecting Information Processing

The effectiveness of the learner's information processing depends upon many factors. The most important among them are: (1) the quality of sensory input information reaching the performer's senses; (2) the quality and effectiveness of sensory receptors in relaying information to the CNS; (3) the speed of processing stimulus information, known as reaction time; (4) the ability to anticipate; (5) the capacity to concentrate and attend to stimuli; and (6) the level of arousal and psychological readiness. An overview of characteristics of a learner's information processing mechanisms and appropriate instruction strategies is presented in Table 17.1. A more thorough discussion of these mechanisms is beyond the scope of this textbook.

Summary

It is difficult to appreciate the complexities of human movement, especially when we see the ease with which many actions are performed. The human nervous system, composed of the brain, spinal cord, and nerves, acts as the control centre that integrates all of our actions. The numerous parts of the nervous system work together by sending messages to one another with remarkable speed, precision, and capacity, allowing the movements we make to be efficient and accurate. From the dendrites and axons of neurons, to neural impulses that travel a complex route, we are able to sense, react, and respond to stimuli in the world around us – as well as if not better than modern-day computers.

Table 17.1 Summary characteristics of a learner's information processing mechanisms and effective instruction strategies.

Mechanism	Limitation	Instruction Strategy
Sensory mechanisms • Exteroceptors • Proprioceptors	• Poor visual skills, such as dynamic visual acuity	• Detect vision problems early
	• Learner does not hear instruction	• Limit the noise in the gym; speak clearly and loudly
	• Learner does not feel the correct position required	• Move the learner's body into the correct position
Perceptual mechanisms	• Limited attention span; can attend to only one major novel point	• Provide only one critical component of a skill at a time
Short-term memory	• Limited capacity	• Provide only limited amount of information; do not overload athlete
	• Significant rate of loss	• Minimize time between demonstration and rehearsal of skill, i.e., practice skill immediately after it has been presented
	• Subject to easy interference	• Avoid unrelated activities in the gym, such as workers in the background, spectators yelling and commenting, other teams practicing, etc.
Long-term or permanent memory	• Must rehearse/practice to encode and retain information	• Provide continuing rehearsal of skill until it is learned properly
Learner's psychological state	• Arousal and anxiety	• Motivate learner to an optimal arousal level; provide non-threatening learning environment
	• Attention and fatigue	• Avoid practicing new skills when fatigued
	• Boredom	• Introduce new drills to coach same skill

Once information has been sensed by various receptors (exteroceptive or proprioceptive), we must then process this information and decide how to respond appropriately. We have a well-developed system that allows us to do this. Information passes through several successive stages of processing (stimulus identification, response selection, and response programming), after which a decision can be made, depending on the information we are given. Reaction time, anticipation, and level of arousal are some of the factors that affect our abilities to respond quickly and accurately to various stimuli.

Our abilities to process information are also

Figure 17.7 What system of motor control is required for: **A.** threading a needle; **B.** figure skating; **C.** sailing; **D.** baseball batting; **E.** soccer; **F.** horseshoe throwing; **G.** rock climbing?

dependent on concentration, attention, and memory. Because our attention capacities are limited, we cannot attend to all the stimuli that exist in the environment around us. Therefore, it is important to focus attention on information that is most appropriate to the situation, as well as have the ability to shift or broaden this attention as it becomes necessary. In closely contested competitions, concentration can be the defining difference between victory and defeat.

Without memory processes, every movement we attempted would be a new one – we would be forced to re-learn numerous skills and movements. Luckily, memory allows us to store, retrieve, and utilize information from past experiences as we need it. Although memory is not always accessed with success, the potential for a limitless amount of information to be stored in long-term memory exists, which acts towards effectively improving future movement performances.

Some of the responses we make in fact result from feedback received through receptors throughout the body that continually update the central nervous system as to how the action is being executed. A closed-loop control system contends that, through feedback mechanisms, responses can be changed and altered even during a movement in order to achieve the desired movement outcome. An open-loop control system is based mainly on motor programs that define movements before they occur and are executed automatically, without feedback. Each theory has its own advantages and disadvantages, and is more accurate for describing different types of skills.

Key Words

Absolute refractory period	Feedback	Receptive segment
Action potential	Information processing	Relative refractory period
Afferent neurons	Interneuron	Response programming stage
All-or-none law	Membrane potential	Response selection stage
Axon	Motor neuron	Sensory neuron
Cell body	Myelin sheath	Stimulus identification stage
Central nervous system (CNS)	Neuron	Synapse
Closed-loop control	Nodes of Ranvier	Terminal endings
Conductive segment	Open-loop control	Transmissive segment
Dendrites	Peripheral nervous system	
Depolarization	(PNS)	
Efferent neurons	Polarization	

Discussion Questions

1. What name is given to a nerve cell? What are its major components?

2. Differentiate between afferent and efferent transmission of information.

3. List and briefly describe the three functional regions comprising most nerve cells.

4. Describe the process involved during a change in membrane potential. Why are ions important in the process?

5. Explain the *all-or-none law* as it relates to synaptic transmission.

6. Identify and describe the three information processing stages through which information must pass before a movement is executed.

7. Discuss the major differences between open-loop and closed-loop control. Briefly discuss the advantages of each.

8. For the two information processing mechanisms discussed in this chapter, provide examples of limitations and subsequent instruction strategies to overcome these limitations.

A Career in Coaching

NAME: Mark Temple

OCCUPATION: Director of Swimming and Head Coach, Mississauga Aquatic Club; Canadian and Olympic Coach

EDUCATION: BPHE, University of Toronto
MBA, MSBA, University of Southern California

What does the coach of a community-based swimming club do?

My role function has three key aspects. First, I use my leadership skills and knowledge experience to articulate and implement the vision and mission of the swimming club on behalf of a volunteer board of directors and the general membership. Second, within the business operations I must recruit and develop a skilled coaching staff for all competitive levels of community swimmers. Third, I design the training programs that, over time, will allow the community's competitive swimmers to develop as student athletes to a world top-50 level. For the most successful student athletes, I coach them to the world championships and Olympic Games.

What skills are required to be a professional coach?

First and foremost you must have a passion and enthusiasm for pursuing goals. The pursuit of excellence is in the process. The coach's primary task is to develop favorable situations so the athletes experience success in graded levels of stress. You must demonstrate a successful combination of leadership style and knowledge of human motivations. The successful coach is a great communicator and possesses extensive knowledge of skill acquisition, sport science, and program design.

How did your studies in physical and health education benefit your career?

I was already coaching when I entered the BPHE program at the University of Toronto. From my previous engineering studies and continued coaching, I developed a fascination for human physiology and performance so I enrolled in every physiology course I could, read every medical school text book, and delved into the psychology of the impossible. I did a master's level study in leadership theory in one of my electives. This eclectic education prepared me to ask good questions and be mentored by some of the world's finest coaches and sport scientists. I now prepare training programs for Olympic hopefuls. If you have the will to succeed, then continual learning and advanced education can greatly benefit your career.

What do you enjoy most about your profession?

I enjoy watching student athletes strive to master difficult skills and fitness challenges in their pursuit of being the best they can be in a highly competitive environment. Their individual performances are an inspiration to everyone about dreaming the goal and mastering the psychology of the impossible.

What career advice would you give to students interested in amateur club coaching?

Mentoring is key. Learn from the most successful leaders within your area. Visit them. Interview them. Coaching swimming and being a teacher is a terrific combination of professional balance until your success allows you to take on a full-time position as a coach. Being a teacher would refine your teaching skills by working with the appropriate age groups involved in club sports.

What advice would you give to students entering this field?

Coaching is about a portfolio of lifelong success. Your product is the student athlete. In many respects the profession is akin to farming. One cannot cram for a successful harvest. There is a time to plant, to measure and nurture, and then, only then, the harvest. Then, each year, you begin the process again – one eye on the horizon and one eye on the next step.

In This Chapter:

Skill Acquisition Process   436
    Starting the Learning Process at a Young Age   436
    Providing Sufficient Learning Time   437
    Being Taught by Qualified Instructors   437
    Following the Right Progression   437
    Using Good and Scaled-down Equipment   437

Stages of Learning a Skill   438
    Cognitive or Understanding Stage   438
    Associative or Practice Stage   438
    Autonomous or Application Stage   438

Information Feedback for Skill Learning   441
    Feedback Classifications   441
    Motivational Properties of Feedback   445
    Minimizing Feedback Dependency   446
    Information Feedback Questions and Answers   447

Transfer in Motor Learning   448
    Types of Transfer   449
    Popular Transfer Strategies   451

Designing Effective Practice   455
    Conditions of Practice   456
    Massed Versus Distributed Practice   456
    Grouping for Practice   457

Effects of Motivation on Learning   458

Summary   458

CHAPTER 18

Motor Learning in Practice: Skill Acquisition Processes

After completing this chapter you should be able to:

- explain the skill acquisition process;

- describe the stages of learning a skill;

- describe the types of feedback and their roles in skill learning;

- apply motor learning principles to teach a skill;

- describe the types of transfer and apply transfer principles to learning a skill;

- use effective practice methods when designing a learning environment.

Distinct changes that occur as a skill is learned and developed are easy to detect, because the execution becomes swifter and more fluid and demands much less attention. Your own experiences provide an example of how motor skills change and develop. Your first steps may not have been perfectly executed, but look at you now, walking with the best of them. Certainly, your early attempts at playing the piano, serving a tennis ball, or shooting a basketball were not worthy of acclaim; but with practice and guidance, major improvements undoubtedly followed.

Skill Acquisition Process

Before individuals can become skilled in any activity, they must first acquire a basic movement repertoire, consisting of fundamental movement skills. The important questions to ask here concern the best time and conditions under which *movement intelligence* (discussed in Chapter 16) may be acquired (Figure 18.1). Research and practice have identified several factors that affect the development of an individual's movement intelligence: beginning at a young age, providing sufficient learning time, being taught by qualified instructors, following the right progression, and using good equipment. These factors are discussed in more detail in this section.

Starting the Learning Process at a Young Age

Education involving movement skills should begin at a young age, even as early as the preschool

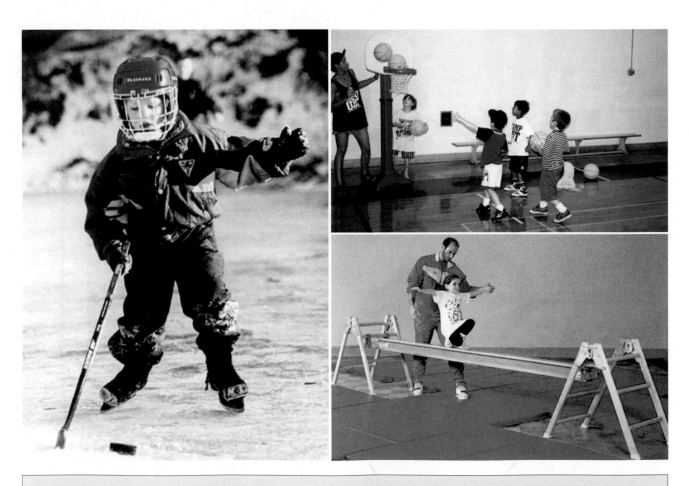

Figure 18.1 Getting started early and using scaled-down equipment are two of the most important factors in developing movement intelligence.

years. Developing basic skills such as walking, throwing, catching, climbing, etc. early on allows a child to incorporate these skills (which are the basis for numerous other activities) effectively into a repertoire of motor skills. Because movement patterns are still being established in young children, it is important to teach skills correctly the first time to avoid the development of bad habits early.

Providing Sufficient Learning Time

A large amount of time during the school day is traditionally dedicated to the acquisition of the more important cognitive skills (for example, linguistic and mathematical). Similarly, in order to improve an individual's motor skill development, sufficient time must be allotted to participating in physical activities that enhance movement skills. Without physical experience, skills cannot be learned effectively and maintained.

Being Taught by Qualified Instructors

Instructors, physical educators, and coaches must be properly trained and have experience with teaching physical activity in order to teach movement skills. But too commonly, unqualified staff are given the task in schools, community programs, and sports camps. Students deserve the best level of instruction available.

Following the Right Progression

Choosing the right progression to follow has a direct influence on acquisition of movement skills. In other words, the organized action and the sequence of drills ensure that skills are easier to grasp. For example, you might introduce children to baseball by playing tee-ball (which simplifies the game), and slowly incorporating a live pitcher for batting (slow-pitch first), etc. The skills learned

Figure 18.2 When learning to ride a bicycle, beginners often start out with a tricycle or training wheels before graduating to the two-wheel version.

from simpler tasks can then be effectively transferred to more complex tasks (Figure 18.2).

Using Good and Scaled-down Equipment

The quality of equipment available for teaching movement skills is also important for effective learning. Safe, appropriate, and well-maintained equipment makes learning most effective for students. For example, children have different needs from teenagers or adults. Equipment that is scaled down to their size (e.g., lower basketball hoops, smaller basketball and soccer balls, smaller soccer nets, lighter baseball bats, etc.) is essential (Figure 18.3).

Figure 18.3 Scaled-down equipment for children is a must for proper skill learning. How would you feel in an environment where everything was twice its normal size?

Many other factors in addition to the ones identified previously have an impact on the teaching and acquisition of motor skills. This chapter will review several related topics in order to provide a broad-based perspective on the skill acquisition process.

Stages of Learning a Skill

Research and practice have identified three general stages in learning a skill. We will outline the changes that occur as motor learning takes place and the important features that are unique to each stage (Figure 18.4). The three stages are the cognitive stage, the associative stage, and the autonomous stage.

Cognitive or Understanding Stage

This first stage, the **cognitive** or **understanding stage**, begins when the task is first introduced to the learner. As the skill is completely new, the first major goal for the learner is to determine cognitively the general shape of the particular skill and the goals to be achieved. Questions concerning what, when, and how predominate at this early stage as the learner tries to get a feel for the activity. Because much of the early ideas and instructions are verbally transmitted to the learner, this stage is sometimes referred to as the **verbal stage**.

Instruction, demonstrations, films, videos, and vivid descriptions serve to convey the general idea of the skill to the learner. Some learners even verbally guide themselves through skills by engaging in self-talk. Giving themselves some verbal reminders as they attempt a skill for the first time offers security, and begins to instill the major ideas associated with performing the skill.

For example, a beginner in gymnastics may remind herself to tuck her head on the forward roll, or to stay balanced on the beam. However, such a procedure demands concentration, and does not allow other information to be processed simultaneously. But during this initial stage, verbal activity can give the learner a rough idea of what the skill is all about. In fact, it can also facilitate rapid learning and bring about considerable improvement.

Although performance at this stage may be slow, jerky, highly variable, and even awkward at times, it serves as a foundation on which a learner can build.

Associative or Practice Stage

With some practice, the learner can move to the second stage of learning, the **associative** or **practice stage**. This stage is focused on performing and refining the skill by organizing more appropriate movement patterns. Now that most of the stimuli related to the skill have been identified and defined, a greater amount of concentration can be directed to refining details.

For example, the learner can experiment with how timing can be improved by using environmental cues, as well as how movements can become more efficient and executed with increased speed. Practice allows the learner to make certain movements more automatic and controlled. The motor programs introduced in Chapter 16 can begin to develop skills that are specific to particular actions, and make movements more fluid and consistent. Variability of performance from one attempt to another also begins to decrease. As performers discover what constitutes an effective performance, their confidence increases.

Performance improves rapidly at this stage. Self-talk diminishes considerably and anticipation and consistency continue to improve. The ability of learners to detect some of their own errors in performing various skills represents an important development at this stage. Generally, the associative stage usually lasts longer than the cognitive stage for most individuals.

Autonomous or Application Stage

In the final **autonomous** or **application stage**,

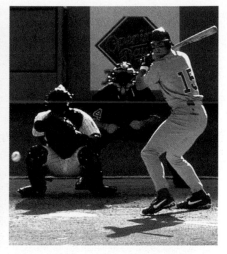

Cognitive Stage: The task is first introduced. Performance may be initially slow, jerky, and awkward.

Associative Stage: Focus is on refining smaller details. Greater consistency and control is evident.

Autonomous Stage: Attention demands are reduced as movements become automatic.

Figure 18.4 Many changes take place as learners move from one learning stage to another.

movements have become almost automatic and very proficient. Attention demands are dramatically reduced, providing an opportunity to focus on other aspects of performance, such as creativity and strategy. The ability to analyze environmental stimuli is enhanced during this advanced stage, and relevant cues are quickly detected with increased accuracy.

At the peak of their careers, professional hockey players are clearly operating in the autonomous stage. Their hockey skills are so well developed from years of practice and experience that they are able to concentrate on creative plays on the ice that often seem impossible to the average player.

It is equally remarkable to see a refined pianist play with speed and fluidity, but also with creative or imaginative flair. Such performances are the result of a great deal of practice and dedication. Performance improvements during this stage, however, are relatively slow because the learner has already reached such a high level of proficiency before the stage begins. This is not to say that learning stops here, because other less obvious gains (such as a reduction in mental effort

Application of Learning Stages to Coaching Basketball

Stage 1:

Cognitive Stage

Players are introduced to basic basketball skills, such as dribbling, passing, shooting, etc., and perform them under simplified, undemanding conditions, initially while standing still and later while moving.

Stage 2:

Associative Stage

After much practice the individual skills become more refined and are performed with fewer errors that are increasingly self-detected and self-corrected. This ability is based on gradual development of muscle feeling that generates intrinsic feedback discussed in the next section. Gradually, the coach introduces skill variations according to game demands. Variations may focus on movement speed (ball or player), distance, movement direction, etc. Scoring is attempted at higher speeds, from different distances, from different angles, and, if necessary, from both left and right directions.

Game-specific combinations in which several game elements are combined into a more demanding practice are gradually incorporated into training. Initially, the coach chooses combination elements/plays that occur immediately before or after the skill just learned. Then the easiest forms are chosen and are practiced in more demanding complex game forms. For example, when practicing dribbling, the ball can first be passed to a player in a standing position, then while running; and later, after dribbling, the ball can be played to another player.

In order to strengthen technical skills, the coach may then gradually introduce opponents, whose impact is guided by the coach. Initially the skill is practiced with inanimate opponents (objects such as cones, chairs, etc) and then with passive opponents (players). Players have to learn to take an opponent into account. The passive opponent eventually turns into a semi-active opponent who agitates a player but still lets him or her finish the exercise. Players now have to broaden all technical skills in order to be successful.

The demands on a player become higher when the opponent becomes active, not only trying to disturb the flow of movement, but also to hinder it. At this point, tactical training becomes important and is incorporated into practice gradually.

Stage 3:

Autonomous Stage

The players' skills have become almost automatic or habitual. They have learned how to carry out the various skills and combinations of movements without much thinking, thus freeing their attention for other more tactical or creative aspects of the game. The goal of practice becomes learning how to apply the technical elements learned and complex combinations in a game situation within a determined tactical framework.

In the autonomous stage, basketball players' movements become spontaneous. Controlling their movements requires no attention or mental effort. This freed-up attention enables them to observe their opponents and teammates, consider tactical aspects of the game, and anticipate their own actions.

required for skill execution and of anxiety and an improvement in techniques) may result.

Information Feedback for Skill Learning

When we practice motor skills we are continually receiving information that is related to our movements, both during the performance and as a result of it. This constitutes **feedback** in the true sense. In motor learning literature it is often known as **information feedback**.

Research and practitioners have established that feedback plays a strong role in motivating, reinforcing, and shaping or regulating behaviour in a skill learning environment. Feedback informs the learner about significant strengths or weaknesses that may have been detected during performance. Without it, practice and, in turn,

Does Practice Make Perfect?

It may be said that practice alone does not make perfect, but practice with appropriate feedback does.

learning become far less effective.

There are various types of feedback and the following section will highlight effective strategies instructors may use when providing feedback to learners.

Feedback Classifications

Feedback is intrinsic or extrinsic and can be further subdivided into knowledge of performance and knowledge of results. These concepts are summarized in Figure 18.5.

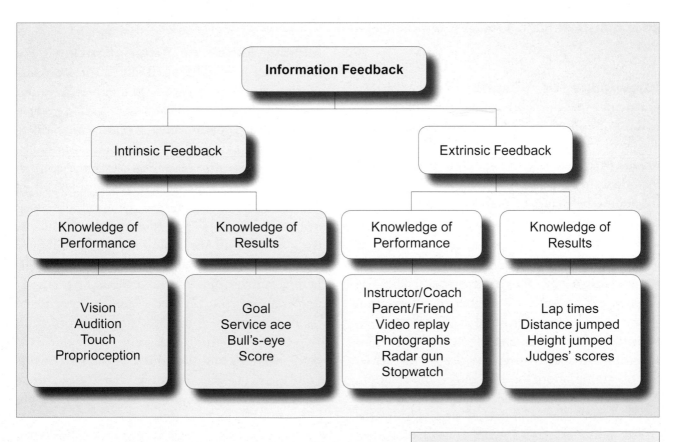

Figure 18.5 Information feedback family.

The "Secret" Language of the Muscles

Seasoned athletes can tell how good their performance was, almost as well as a panel of judges, by instinct, an infallible comprehensive measuring system. "On my first try I knew deep down that it was a good jump as far as rhythm and take-off. But the second try was even better, more powerful especially. I really noticed it." Good long and triple jumpers or even discus or javelin throwers can often tell with great accuracy how far they have jumped or thrown, without looking of course, if they "felt" the jump or throw properly.

Experienced athletes "measure" and judge the quality of their movements using those stimuli that are present in their bodies during execution of the movement – the *muscle feeling*. But even more important, the execution of these movements can be controlled by the information obtained from these stimuli within the closed-loop model discussed in Chapter 17.

Intrinsic Feedback

Information that is provided as a natural consequence of performing an action is considered **intrinsic feedback**. For example, when you throw a dart, you can feel your arm extend, you can see the dart fly through the air, and you can hear it make contact with the board as it hits the bull's-eye.

Knowledge of Results   When you are practicing free-throw shooting the success (or failure) of your shots provides intrinsic feedback. This constitutes an example of **knowledge of results (KR)** feedback. Other examples of this type include seeing the dart hit the bull's-eye, watching the tennis ball land in the opponent's court, or covering an excellent distance in a 12-minute walk/run test.

Knowledge of Performance   The feel of your arm extension is related to information about your performance and is thus known as **knowledge of performance (KP)** feedback. This type of feedback involves the use of the senses for obtaining more or less direct information. Examples include the fine finger sensations felt when playing the piano (feeling of touch), or the crowd noise associated with college basketball games (audio sensation), or the pull in your

shoulders when you are pulling on the oar as part of a crew. These sensations are related to the muscle feeling that athletes experience.

Particularly in the second learning stage many of these movements are relatively easy to detect directly, without the need for verbal instruction from the instructor or coach.

Muscle Sense or Proprioception   For any activity, several hundred muscles are normally involved in a highly specialized interplay. Without a well-developed **muscle sense**, or a good **muscle feeling**, as it is often called in sports, any athlete would have difficulty performing optimally. Without this sense, mastering any movement or even trying to execute movements already learned would be almost impossible.

This muscle sense, the intrinsic feedback, is the sum of all the sensations that result from every movement of all the limbs in the body. In the muscles, tendons, and joints of the body numerous receptors, called "spindles" because of their appearance, constantly supply information about the position of each joint, i.e., about fixed body positions and the course of the movements (Table 18.1). The stimuli that cause these movements are the result of pressure and tension in the muscles and tendons.

The muscle feeling is not alone, however, in gathering information about movement

Table 18.1 Perception of balance, turning motion, muscle sensation, and touch.

Stimulus	Receptor/Sensory Organ	Information Received
Gravity, straight body motion	Vestibule in the inner ear **Sense of balance**	Body position in space (balanced or out of balance), quick up and down movements, forward and backward body motion **Feeling of balance**
Body moving in direction other than straight	Semicircular canal in inner ear **Sense of turning motion**	Turning body motion in all three physical planes: sagittal (twists, pirouettes), transverse (rolls), frontal (cartwheels) **Feeling of turning motion**
Muscle expansion and contraction	Muscle, tendon, and joint spindles **Muscle sense**	Positioning and movement of parts of the body (arms and legs, bent or stretched, raised or at right angles; weight, light to heavy) **Muscle feeling**
Effects of solids, liquids, etc.	Free nerve endings in skin **Sense of touch**	Surface qualities (sports apparatus slippery or with good grip, surface even or uneven), shape and size of objects, pain **Feeling of touch and pressure**

sequences. With every movement that is taken other sensory organ receptors are stimulated simultaneously. Muscle feeling works in close collaboration with the sense of touch and the sense governing balance, and of course with sight. In conjunction especially with the sense of touch, the muscle feeling, often referred to as **kinesthetic sense**, gives an indication of the strength, force, speed, duration, direction, and extent of any movement (Table 18.1).

Development of Muscle Feeling Muscle feeling will be unclear and obscure at first. During the first learning stage, the moving muscles send contradictory bits of information to our brains. The beginner does not have the capacity to become aware of the signals coming from muscles, tendons, and joints. Nothing is interpreted properly. Without extensive practice in the second learning stage, this type of perception is rather blurred and obscured.

Beginners tend to use visual feedback more than their muscle feeling to guide their performance. Novice basketball players learning how to dribble a ball will feel that they absolutely must watch the movements of their hands or feet and the ball. Gradually, after much practice in the second learning stage, it will dawn on them that they can rely more and more on intrinsic feedback – sensations coming from the muscles in their hands and feet, which are becoming more and more trained.

Extrinsic Feedback

In contrast to intrinsic feedback, **extrinsic feedback** refers to information that is provided to the learner by an external source at the outcome of a performance. Such sources of information encompass a suggestion offered by a coach or instructor, a judge's score, video replays, and so on. Therefore, this feedback, also known as **augmented feedback**, provides information above and beyond what is naturally available to the learner. Drawing on the previous basketball example, the teacher may notice that you are not using your legs enough during the shot, or that you are not following through on the shot – suggestions you can use to correct and refine your skill.

This type of feedback may also be controlled. You and/or the teacher or coach can choose when, in what form, as well as how often to provide such feedback. Different activities and different learners require varying levels of information feedback. This allows teachers or coaches to adapt to the particular situation by creating an environment that is more conducive to learning and accommodating these differences.

Every physical education class offers unique challenges, so it is up to teachers to identify the level of skill they are dealing with, and how much and what type of feedback is required. Again, extrinsic feedback is subdivided into knowledge of results and knowledge of performance feedback.

A Picture Is Worth More Than a Thousand Words....

The use of video replays in teaching or coaching environments is one of the most effective types of information feedback an instructor can provide.

The various video cameras of today are small and easy to use and feature small monitors for delivery of instantaneous feedback. It is vivid and accurate, and very much appreciated by students and athletes alike. However, as the video replay provides a lot of information, the instructor must be able to direct the learner to examine only the selected features of the movement. A picture can definitely be worth a thousand words.

Positive KP – Negative KR Situation

Unlike KR, it is important to note that KP does not necessarily provide information concerning movement success in achieving the intended goal; instead, it serves to highlight information about correctness of movement patterns that were actually produced by the learner. A basketball player might correctly execute a foul shot in practice (positive KP), but may miss the shot (negative KR), or vice versa. In other words, a movement can be performed the way it was intended and still not achieve its goal.

Knowledge of Results The general goal of feedback is to provide information to performers about the proficiency with which they move and act. More specifically, *knowledge of results (KR)* is information, usually verbalized, concerning the degree of success of a response with respect to the intended behavioural or environmental goal.

In football, if your goal was to kick a field goal through the goal posts, KR represents that information you receive concerning your success at that task. This information might seem insignificant because such information becomes redundant with intrinsic feedback that would occur naturally. Undoubtedly, KR is not effective when certain outcomes are obvious – the basketball player who misses a shot does not need to be told that the ball did not go into the basket.

However, when performance outcomes are less obvious, the role of KR is important for learning, and indeed, becomes essential for future performances. In activities involving judging, such as gymnastics, diving, and dancing, athletes must wait for their scores before they can learn how well they performed. And it may take weeks or months before the students obtain knowledge about their performance in certain tasks, in the form of a grade. For other activities like shooting and archery, knowledge about where the target was hit is not always possible to discern immediately, so a coach or teacher must provide the essential information.

Knowledge of Performance *Knowledge of performance (KP)* type of feedback provides information concerning the correctness of a particular movement and is commonly extrinsic in being used by teachers and coaches. For example, a batting coach might suggest that a player is taking the eye off the ball, or that the swing used was a little late. This kind of information gives the player something to consider – and to improve – over successive attempts.

Terminology Alert!

In keeping with the use of the term by most motor learning scientists, "feedback" from this point on will refer to *extrinsic feedback* as it has been defined earlier.

Motivational Properties of Feedback

Extrinsic or augmented feedback serves to motivate the learner, and supplies reinforcement for both correct and incorrect movements. As a student, you can appreciate the value of receiving information about how well you have performed, especially if that information is positive. But perhaps it is more important for motor learning to receive feedback that highlights errors in patterns of action. Correction of these errors is important if performance is to be modified for improved future performance.

This is why a skilled instructor is important. A skilled instructor is able to point out errors, reinforce correct actions, and guide the learner to improved performance as errors are held to a minimum.

Physical educators have an important task in motivating their students to learn new skills and to ensure that these skills are taught appropriately. Movements that are learned early on have the greatest impression on students, so information feedback must be given in order to develop the proper movement skills the first time around.

Information feedback by teacher or coach fulfills a valuable motivational role and is thus one of the vital links in the information processing model presented in Chapter 17.

Minimizing Feedback Dependency

Both instructor and players may notice that feedback that is too frequent can lead to learner dependency, serving as a crutch. Skills are executed well when feedback is present, but suffer when they must be performed independently. Research supports this common observation. Providing continuous feedback over an extended period may not be ideal for the learner, but occasional feedback tends to enhance learning.

Various strategies can be used to minimize the dependency produced by feedback.

Faded Feedback

Faded feedback advocates providing feedback at very high frequencies early on in practice when it is most important that the proper movement pattern be established. In order to prevent learner dependency, feedback can then gradually be reduced or faded as skills begin to develop. When a higher degree of skill has been reached, players develop an ability to detect some of their own errors in performing various tasks, and removing feedback on a few trials does not have a detrimental

effect on performance.

This method allows a teacher or coach to assess the needs of each individual learner, and tailor feedback to respect individual differences. But it is important to recognize that, while feedback is essential to the development of skills, the performance that is the goal of such skills must be executed independently of such feedback.

Bandwidth Feedback

The potential for dependency produced through repeated feedback can also be reduced by what is called bandwidth feedback. This method has the instructor deliver feedback only when errors fall outside some defined range of correctness.

For example, a karate instructor might provide a student with feedback about stance or limb position during a punch or kick only if it falls outside some specified range, and allow trials that fall within this range to pass without remark. For many activities, a little leeway can make a significant difference to performance.

Research has identified several advantages to bandwidth feedback. First, this procedure eventually produces faded feedback because as skill increases, more movements fall within the band, reducing the need for feedback later.

Second, learners receive positive reinforcement for actions that fall into the band as a result of not receiving feedback.

Finally, learners are not encouraged to change movements on each trial, thereby developing consistency of execution.

The bandwidth feedback range changes across various levels of performance. Because professional athletes require high precision, their coaches or mentors apply an extremely narrow bandwidth feedback range. For lesser skilled athletes, instructors use wider ranges (Figure 18.6).

Summary Feedback

Using summary feedback a teacher or coach provides feedback several times during practice, but only after a certain number of trials have been completed. For example, a tennis instructor might make summary KP comments concerning the

Figure 18.6 A. The bandwidth range of feedback for beginners tends to be much wider than for professionals. **B.** The bandwidth range of feedback is quite narrow for professional athletes.

back and forward swing of the racquet only after every 10 serves.

Like bandwidth feedback, summary feedback serves to block a learner's tendency to correct every movement, thus generating consistency. Summary feedback also serves to avoid overloading a performer's information processing capacity, discussed in Chapter 17.

Many other types of feedback exist, with varying degrees of effectiveness, and its importance to motor learning cannot be overstated.

Information Feedback Questions and Answers

Let us summarize some of the most important principles of effective feedback for teachers and coaches.

When in the learning process is information feedback needed most?

Feedback is required throughout the learning process, but is particularly vital *early*, especially during the cognitive and associative stages of learning. Later in training, however, after the learner has gained experience and developed an internalized model of the skill, an instructor can apply faded, bandwidth, or summary feedback before withdrawing feedback altogether.

How much feedback is necessary?

The discussion about information processing in Chapter 17 should help answer this question. A player's ability to process information can easily be overloaded, particularly when learning new skills. Most players can effectively concentrate on only a limited number of tasks, usually just one. Only later, when a novel task has become more familiar, can a player shift attention to other tasks or other requirements of the movement or play. Intense but selective instruction from a teacher or coach experienced during the early stages of development can ensure progress at an optimal rate. In the end, successful development requires balanced feedback.

Avoid Overload

To avoid overloading the learner's information processing capacities, an effective instructor will provide one important piece of information feedback at a time.

How precise should feedback be?

Motor learning research shows that precise and specific coaching generates better results. Instructors must formulate a precise standard for each task or play and develop a trained eye in order to provide precise information to students about errors and how to correct them.

Figure 18.7 demonstrates the effectiveness of precise (i.e., prescriptive) KP in comparison with some general (descriptive) verbal encouragement. More precise feedback should be withheld until the students have had enough practice on a task to benefit from detailed information. During the early stages of learning, it may be more appropriate to provide more general (descriptive)

information about the students' performance until their skill level or knowledge of the skill's dynamics improves.

What is the best timing for information feedback?

Our short-term memory bank (discussed in Chapter 17) is very susceptible to loss of information. Generally, then, the greater the delay in giving a learner information about performance, the less effect the given information has. Immediate instruction is more beneficial to the development of skills than the provision of information feedback at the end of a lesson, when the students are ready to leave the gym.

Transfer in Motor Learning

We often practice certain skills hoping that learning achieved on that task will be of some use

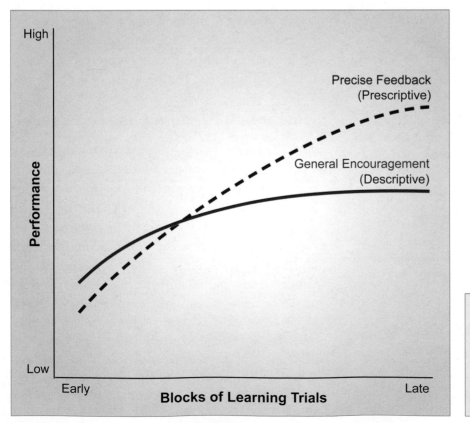

Figure 18.7 Research has shown that general verbal encouragements may be helpful during the initial stages of learning but are detrimental to development of a skill in the long run.

Prescriptive vs. Descriptive Feedback

During activity classes where you learn new skills, your teacher will use both prescriptive and descriptive feedback. A **descriptive feedback** statement indicates something you did, right or wrong, whereas a **prescriptive feedback** statement provides you with precise correction statements about how to improve your movements on subsequent trials.

Some examples from your badminton activity class are provided below.

Descriptive Feedback

- You were better last time.
- There was no follow-through.
- Be more careful with your footwork.
- Watch your timing.

Prescriptive Feedback

- Drive the shot deep like you did last time.
- Snap your wrist more on the follow-through.
- Stay on your toes when receiving the serve.
- Keep your eye on the birdie during the smash.

---

on some other task. This is the general idea behind the **transfer of learning**, and is an important instructional concept in physical education and skill learning. Transfer involves learning that can occur on a **criterion task** (i.e., the present goal of learning in an activity class) as a result of practicing some other task (i.e., previous skill learning experiences). Teachers and coaches can organize practices and instructional periods to facilitate such transfer of learning from one skill to another.

Identical Elements Theory

Transfer of learning is most efficient when both tasks share common elements. Those elements that are similar or identical to other elements in a learning situation will positively aid the learner, while dissimilar elements will hinder the transfer of learning.

Types of Transfer

The transfer of learning between two tasks generally increases as the similarity between them increases, but some important differences may prove significant. This leads to distinguishing among various types of transfer such as negative and positive transfer and near and far transfer.

Positive Transfer

Positive transfer occurs, for example, when players are taught various fundamental movement skills that are later applied to play various games. Consider the numerous lead-up games and drills that basketball coaches put their players through – practicing free throws, lay-ups, and offensive plays, as well as defensive strategies. Practicing these drills will only be effective if the transfer from the drill to the actual basketball game (the criterion task) is strong or positive. Similar drills are used in many other sports. Drills and lead-up games are really a means to another goal.

Negative Transfer

Negative transfer is not common. Nevertheless, it is essential that learners avoid activities that may transfer negatively to the criterion task when performance is critical.

Table 18.2 presents examples of positive and negative transfer across several activities.

Near Transfer

When the learning goal is a task that is relatively similar to the training task, **near transfer** is desired. In other words, the activity being practiced is different yet still very similar to the criterion task. The volleyball coach who has his or her team practice various plays in preparation

Table 18.2 Factors involved in the potential transfer between various activities.

Factors Affecting Transfer	Positive Transfer Example	Negative Transfer Example
Movement Responses/ Patterns • Skill elements • Technique • Equipment	• Tennis and badminton both involve play with racquets, a net, and similar shot variations on a bounded court	• Tennis uses a ball and requires a firm wrist/grip, while badminton uses a birdie and requires a looser wrist/grip
Psychomotor Demands • Balance • Reaction and movement times • Anticipation	• Rowing, kayaking, and canoeing are carried out on the water and require similar levels of dynamic balance and coordination	• Gymnasts on the balance beam require a high degree of static balance, while surfers or skiers depend largely on dynamic balance on a variable surface
Cognitive Demands • Strategy • Tactics • Rules	• Basketball and handball are team sports geared towards scoring as many points as possible while limiting scoring by the opponent	• Handball has a crease around the goal and limits player travel with the ball, while basketball allows players to dribble on any part of the court
Biomotor Demands • Explosive power, strength • Endurance and fitness • Quickness or speed	• Sprinters and long jumpers both possess well-developed explosive power in the legs to achieve maximum performance	• Soccer is played continuously over two long halves and requires endurance, while hockey involves playing short shifts over three shorter periods
Psychological Demands • Concentration/attention • Patience • Staying power	• Archery and darts both require a narrow focus of attention and the ability to stay calm and composed under pressure	• Hockey goalies shift attention depending on how the play develops, while participants in judo or karate must be alert and vigilant at all times

for their next match does not have the actual opponent to compete against, but hopes that the practicing of these plays will transfer positively to the actual match. Although many unexpected events will occur during the match, the team will be prepared to execute the plays they practiced when the opportunity presents itself. Transfer of learning in this case is fairly specific and closely approximates the ultimate situation in which the skills learned in practice are to be applied.

Far Transfer

In other situations, a teacher may only be interested in providing learners with more general capabilities for a wider variety of skills. This is called **far transfer** because the transfer of learning occurs from one task to another very different task or setting. In this case, the goal of practice is more general, and the effectiveness of the practiced skill in the present is not as significant as the extent to which these skills transfer to future activities.

This idea is best applied when a player is just beginning to learn a skill. Consider children who are learning how to execute an overhand throw effectively. This general overhand pattern underlies a multitude of other activities including throwing a baseball, throwing a football, serving in tennis, and spiking a volleyball (Figure 18.8). The child who is having fun just throwing rocks into the lake is already on the way to acquiring numerous other motor skills involving throwing movement patterns.

Figure 18.8 Using the ideas from Table 18.2, how many and what kinds of similarities can you identify in the two series of pictures above?

Another example is learning to jump, run, and skate; the ability to perform these skills effectively in practice is not as important as their execution at some future time when these general capabilities will be used to play basketball, play ice hockey, participate in track and field, and so on. If some class of movements shares the same general pattern, the learner will most likely be able to transfer this learning to other movements of the same class.

Popular Transfer Strategies

The most common transfer strategies used by instructors are based on positive transfer, and include the use of simulators, slow-motion practice, drills and training devices for abilities training, simplification, part practice, training machines, and mental rehearsal. These strategies are discussed in this section.

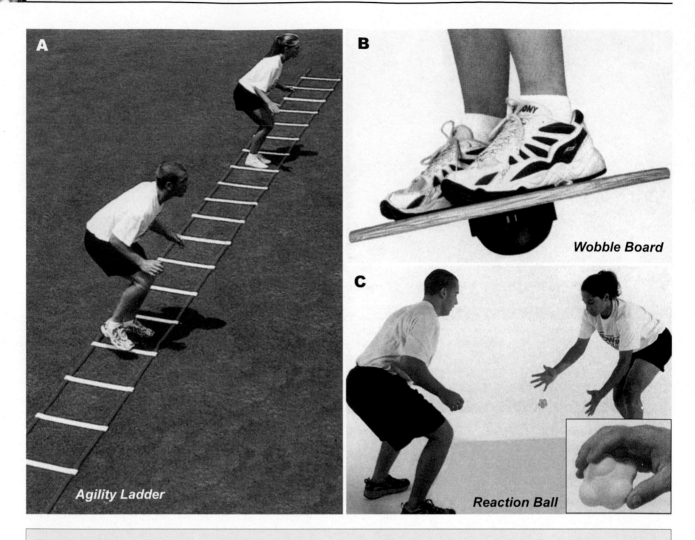

A Agility Ladder

B Wobble Board

C Reaction Ball

Figure 18.9 Examples of inexpensive devices designed for perceptual motor training. **A.** Foot quickness, agility, and coordination. **B.** Balance and coordination. **C.** Reaction time and hand–eye coordination.

Training Machines and Simulators

Recent advances in technology have generated numerous training machines and **simulators** that closely mimic certain or almost all the features of real-world tasks. Rowing and bicycle ergometers and ball-throwing machines (for baseball, volleyball, soccer, tennis, football, etc.), for example, can be important parts of instructional programs. The overall goal of simulation is the expected positive transfer of learning from the simulator to the target skill.

The effectiveness of using a simulator depends upon its ability to simulate not only the motor elements of the target game, but also its perceptual, conceptual (tactical), and biomotor (i.e., strength,

speed, endurance, etc.) elements. Many simulators do so as they provide sport-specific virtual reality learning and/or practice experiences.

For example, professional baseball batters use computerized pitching machines that throw pinpoint fastballs, curves, and changeups at random. In advanced tennis academies the ball machines clone tennis serves (and other strokes) so they appear to come from the racquet of a computer-generated opponent on a video screen. While some of these simulators are very expensive there are many cheaper versions on the market that are used in school activity programs and clubs (Figure 18.9).

When athletes train on strength and fitness machines such as Nautilus and Universal Gym,

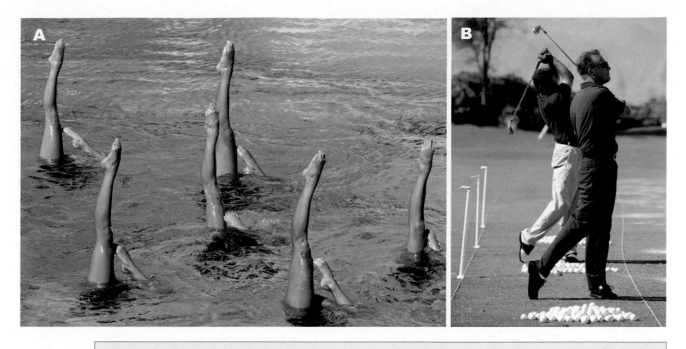

Figure 18.10 Some skills are developed more effectively with **A.** part practice or **B.** whole practice.

they expect a positive transfer to take place to the specific demands of their respective sports.

Whole Versus Part Practice

Many complex motor skills can be divided into discrete components for independent **part practice**. The eventual goal of part practice is to integrate these isolated units into one fluid performance. For instance, performing a gymnastics routine would almost surely require that it be broken down into components – there are far too many aspects involved in the skill to be mastered all at once. This is true of sports such as basketball and football as well. The important question is whether practicing the isolated components of an activity can be beneficial to learning and performance and whether the proficiency thus gained can be transferred to the task as a whole. Of course, effectiveness of part practice depends on the activity (Figure 18.10).

Part Practice   Part practice tends to be more effective for serial skills and for tasks that are relatively long in duration. The gymnast who must put together a set of routines in proper sequence

may practice each activity separately to facilitate learning. But this will be effective only as long as the actions of one part do not interact strongly with those of the next part. In other words, part practice will be more effective than whole practice when the components of the skill are relatively independent of each other; as the interaction

Simplification

A child practicing three-ball juggling by first using scarves is learning through **simplification**, i.e., a practice method in which difficulty of the target skill is significantly reduced. Any type of slow-motion practice falls into this category. The use of a tee in baseball practice and the use of ball-throwing machines in a variety of sports are other examples of simplification practice.

among task components increases, the effectiveness of part practice decreases dramatically.

Part practice can involve further segmentation. Segmentation is very effective for actions in which several tasks must be linked together. **Segmentation** or **progressive part practice** involves either a forward or backward chaining. In **forward chaining** the first part of a skill is practiced first to some criterion level before introducing the second part and so on. This method is particularly popular among track and field coaches and dance instructors. In **backward chaining** the last segment is learned first. For example, an athlete practicing the discus throw by first working on just the toss, and then combining the toss and one turn is using the progressive part method.

Whole Practice While part practice may be effective for serial skills of long duration, practicing parts of a discrete task separately offers minimal transfer to the whole skill. This is especially true of actions that are rapid, where components will most likely interact intensely. Some skills are more effective when performed as a whole because practicing their component parts changes the character of the skills. Practicing fast programmed actions, such as a golf swing, in parts may even have a negative impact on learning. Early use of part practice in developing a skill can be beneficial for identifying the major components of the particular skill, but it is best to begin using **whole practice** as soon as it can be performed with some degree of success.

Lead up Activities and Drills

Lead-up activities and drills to develop movement patterns, speed, balance, and visual skills popular with teachers and coaches are rarely of interest in themselves but are only a means of transferring these skills to their target sporting activity.

Experience from coaching basketball has determined that starting and stopping, turning, evading and faking, and skipping and jumping drills are an effective means of practice for the game of basketball. Passing, shooting, dribbling, and faking drills in soccer training are designed for the same purpose, and drills in football involve stepping through tires and speed ladders to increase football-specific movements.

Figure 18.9 presents several drills and types of equipment that can be used to develop core skills. While research has yet to confirm the usefulness of such practice, the experiences of the teachers and coaches are positive.

Mental Rehearsal

Another form of practice that may be useful to the learner is **mental rehearsal**. Can learners really gain benefits by simply thinking about the skills they are learning? Much evidence has demonstrated that mental rehearsal of the performance of a skill in the absence of any overt physical movement, referred to as **mental practice**, may generate positively transferable motor learning.

Mental practice generally involves constructing model situations and going through the motions

---

Who Benefits Most From Mental Practice?

Injured athletes in particular have found many benefits in mental rehearsing techniques. Unable to physically maintain their usual training regimen, these athletes can use mental practice to keep "active" even while the body may not physically be capable of performing.

Mental practice is particularly important in sports where the number of repetitions during a practice session is limited to only a very few repetitions. Ski jumping, bobsledding, luge, and skiing all fall into this category of sports.

Mental Imagery

Mental imagery is a special type of mental rehearsal. There are two types of mental imagery, the internal and external.

Internal: Performers see, feel, hear, and taste through their own senses. When you experience an action internally, you see the action as if with an internal video camera. You see, for example, the ball traveling towards you as a performer.

External: When you stand back mentally from yourself in performing a skill, you witness your performance externally. It is as if you are a spectator sitting in the stands watching yourself.

Kinds of Imagery

Visual: picturing the activity or event in your mind; visualizing yourself performing the task proficiently and with confidence.

Kinesthetic: the movement associated with a task: feeling the contact with your equipment, opposing players, the field, the playing area.

Gustatory: tastes connected with an activity: the water, sweat.

Olfactory: smells linked with performance: chalk, grass, leather, chlorine.

Auditory: the sounds associated with performance: hearing the sound of the ball making contact with your racquet, the splash of the water as you dive into the pool, your skate blade on the ice, the bat hitting the ball, etc.

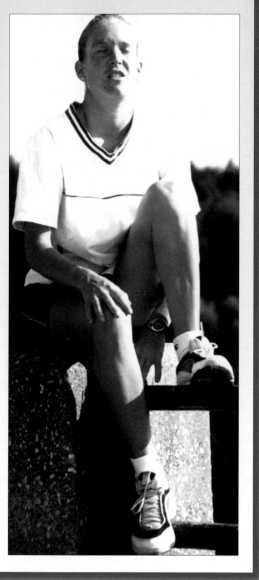

of what will actually be done later. Rehearsing the steps mentally, and going through the sequential actions can offer some genuine benefits. Mental rehearsal can be done at just about any time, requires no apparatus, and can accommodate a large group of learners. Although mental practice alone should not replace actual physical experience with the skill, it is a useful supplement in developing timing and rhythm, and aiding in concentration and preparation for competition. As well, it consolidates specific movement patterns and gives the athlete an overall competitive edge.

Mental rehearsal may also be an effective way to stay on top of skills between physical practice trials.

Designing Effective Practice

Without practice there is no skill learning. Practice allows movement patterns to become more automatic and coordinated as motor programs develop and attention demands are reduced. The conditions necessary for practice, however, are much debated.

Conditions of Practice

How can the time spent in practice best be scheduled to enhance learning? Common experience might suggest that practicing one skill repeatedly without interruption by other activities is the best way to ensure that the learner acquires a particular skill. Other researchers and coaches argue the converse.

Blocked Practice

Consider the coach who wants a tennis player to practice ground strokes, volleys, and serves in the same practice session. Would it be more effective for the player to practice all trials of one task (e.g., serving) before continuing with the next task (e.g., volleying), and so on? This type of practice schedule is called **blocked practice**, where a given task is practiced on many consecutive trials before setting about to the next task. This has been the traditional method adopted by most instructors. In volleyball, for example, you have spiking drills, bumping drills, and volleying drills, all designed to allow the learner to concentrate on one task at a time until it is well learned. This schedule also enables learners to correct specific problems and refine their skills one at a time, especially early on in practice.

Random Practice

This approach views the presentation of tasks somewhat differently. In **random practice**, the ordering of tasks is randomized so that tasks from different classes are mixed throughout the practice period. Thus a tennis player might practice serving on the first trial, and proceed to ground strokes next, without repeating the same skill over and over again. Of course, a situation in which a learner does not practice the same task on two consecutive trials would represent an extreme version of random practice.

Blocked Before Random

Teachers and coaches know from their experience that giving learners the opportunity to practice a specific task many times is necessary for effective realization of the skill. Especially early in practice when correct habits should be formed, learners need to become familiar with the tasks being presented, and repeating specific movement patterns allows players to become proficient and confident.

Once a skill has become more developed, and a higher level of proficiency attained, random practice will be very effective in generating long-term learning and in meeting skill-specific demands.

Massed Versus Distributed Practice

In preparing a practice schedule, instructors must decide on specific amounts of practice and rest to be incorporated into a single practice period. Two considerations will influence their decision.

Massed Practice

A schedule in which the amount of rest between practice trials is short relative to the trial length is described as **massed practice**. An example might be 5 seconds of rest (or no rest at all) for a practice trial lasting 60 seconds. This type of continuous practice may be used for performing lay-up drills in basketball, where you are continually moving, either shooting or rebounding the ball, or for playing overhead smashes in badminton without interruption.

Distributed Practice

Practice that allows for more rest between trials relative to the trial length is considered **distributed practice**. In this case, the rest period may last as long as the trial itself.

Massed practice, then, generally allows for less rest between trials than distributed practice which allows more.

The effects of these types of practice on both physical and mental fatigue are consequently different. For any given number of practice trials, reducing the amount of rest between trials will also reduce the amount of time the body and central nervous system have to recover from physical and mental fatigue. This tends to have a negative effect on the level of performance attained on successive trials, particularly in situations where players are required to learn new skills or movement patterns. It should be noted, however, that there is no single optimal practice–rest ratio for all learning tasks; differences seem to exist for discrete and continuous tasks.

Skill Characteristics and Scheduling For short discrete tasks such as throwing, shooting, or kicking that may last only a fraction of a second, reducing the rest between practice trials generally has no effect on learning or performance, and may even provide a slight benefit. The reduction of rest between trials in practicing continuous skills, by contrast, has a negative impact, principally because of the effect of fatigue on performance. The increased time required to recover from fatigue during some tasks suggests that rest periods should be increased for continuous activities such as swimming and cycling. While massed practice appears to degrade performance, effects on learn-ing are less significant. Overall, fatigue is not a significant variable in learning, although it does affect performance.

Grouping for Practice

Dividing players for practice makes for efficient organization. Students can be grouped according to their individual capacity to perform certain activities, thereby creating an equitable environment. **Grouping for practice** is designed to make learning suitable for everyone involved. You yourself have probably been involved in a situation where your skill level was used to determine where you fit into a specific group. When you take that first swimming class, you are considered a beginner, an intermediate, or an advanced swimmer, and each group receives different instructions according to this designation.

But what criterion should be used? It is generally accepted that grouping for practice should be based on the learners' skill levels, rather than a subjective determination of their underlying abilities. But instructors must consider several other factors, such as maturity level and previous experience, as well as level of physical fitness when making such distinctions.

Providing instruction to learners with a common level of proficiency may mean having

Distinction Between Learning and Performance

Learning has traditionally been defined as a relatively permanent change in behaviour due to practice or experience. It is related to any permanent change in movement intelligence (the vast store of fundamental and specialized movement skills, as defined in Chapter 16). Although learning cannot be observed directly, it is reflected in one's performance which is always measurable. Achieved time, the height jumped, the points scored, the score awarded, etc. are all examples of performance measures. A change in performance is an indirect indication that learning has occurred. However, note that learning is not the only factor that has an influence on performance. Numerous other factors such as motivation, presence or absence of quality feedback, and fatigue all affect performance.

groups of different ages and of both sexes. While this may seem fair and equitable, it may not always be easily arranged. Further, some members of the group may feel isolated or resentful if they are placed in a category that says "you're not good enough."

Grouping for practice may not provide the answer for everyone. Being put into a group with others of a similar level of skill seems ideal for learning to occur. But if all the students in a class were to be treated equally, could those individuals with less developed skills benefit from the great proficiency of their peers? Or would those with a higher skill level taunt and exclude their less skilled counterparts? What do you think?

Effects of Motivation on Learning

While the general purpose of practice – to develop proficiency in the execution of a skill – may be obvious to coaches and teachers, it is not always as clear to learners. Some form of motivation is necessary in such cases. Until the learner has been motivated, effective learning is unlikely to occur.

It's a Fact!

An athlete who is motivated makes more of an effort during practice, can practice for longer periods of time, and learns more in the end.

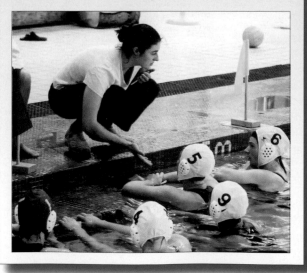

An instructor plays an important role in motivating his or her students. Whether it is through motivational feedback, encouraging learners to set goals, providing excellent demonstrations, or using visual aids, an instructor needs to deliver effective instructions that keep learners involved.

According to the **law of effect**, success and failure can significantly influence learning. Praising learners serves to keep them motivated and gives them a reason to work harder and to improve. Positive feedback will act as a stimulant, and will go a long way towards avoiding monotony that leaves learners lacking interest.

The Law of Effect

The *law of effect* states that organisms tend to repeat responses that are rewarded and to avoid responses that are not rewarded or are punished.

Summary

From the time we are born, we are continually adding to and enhancing our repertoire of skills. As skills become better learned, actions become swifter, smoother, and more accurate, and demand much less attention. But acquiring basic movement skills is achieved most effectively under certain conditions: beginning at a young age, with sufficient time, good equipment, qualified instructors, and an appropriate program. Developing your movement intelligence is just as important as developing your cognitive intelligence early on in life under proper conditions.

There are three stages of learning skills: cognitive, associative, and autonomous stages. At each stage, different problems are overcome as the skills become more developed and require less conscious effort.

Numerous factors affect motor learning and performance, such as the conditions of practice (blocked versus random), the feedback provided, and learning capacity.

Whole or part practice may be effective for discrete and serial tasks respectively; massed practice is recommended for activities in which fatigue is not a major concern. Distributed practice schedules allow for more rest to combat the possibility of greater fatigue.

Mental rehearsal of skills offers another method of practice especially for individuals who are injured. It may also be effective in eliminating fears and anxieties, allow you to stay on top of skills between physical practice trials, as well as help you build confidence for future performances.

Designing effective practice is also critical to developing skills and improving performance. Before beginning, instructors should seek to increase motivation and interest in the activity among learners through various techniques. Once practice begins, instructors or coaches must make several decisions that will maximize learning and performance.

Key Words

Associative (practice) stage
Augmented feedback
Autonomous (application)
  stage
Backward chaining
Bandwidth feedback
Blocked practice
Cognitive (understanding)
  stage
Criterion task
Descriptive feedback
Distributed practice
Extrinsic feedback
Faded feedback

Far transfer
Forward chaining
Grouping for practice
Information feedback
Intrinsic feedback
Kinesthetic sense
Knowledge of performance
  (KP)
Knowledge of results (KR)
Law of effect
Massed practice
Mental imagery
Mental rehearsal (practice)
Muscle sense (muscle feeling)

Near transfer
Negative transfer
Part practice
Positive transfer
Prescriptive feedback
Random practice
Segmentation (progressive
  part practice)
Simplification
Simulator
Summary feedback
Transfer of learning
Whole practice

Discussion Questions

1. List four factors that influence the acquisition of movement intelligence.

2. Identify the three stages of learning a skill. What are the important features of each?

3. What are the essential differences between blocked and random practice? Describe an activity that would benefit from each method of practice.

4. How does extrinsic feedback differ from intrinsic feedback? Give examples of each.

5. Describe two methods that may be used to reduce the dependency-producing effects of feedback in learning a skill.

6. What are the differences between near and far transfer? Provide an example of the use of transfer as an important practice goal.

7. What considerations must be made when designing effective practice? When is part practice most effective? How can mental practice offer benefits to performance?

8. Differentiate between segmentation and simplification practice.

9. How can mental rehearsal help learning or performance?

10. What is mental imagery? Who benefits most from it?

Physical Activity and Sport in Society

- **Physical Activity and Sport Issues**

- **Society, Culture, and Sport**

- **Career Opportunities in Physical and Health Education**

In This Chapter:

Aggression and Violence in Sport *465*
    What Causes Aggressive Behaviour in Sport? *466*

Cheating in Sport *467*
    The Sport Ethic and Deviance in Sport *468*
    Athlete Recruiting *469*
    Academic Cheating *469*
    Cheating in Games *469*
    Performance-enhancing Drugs *469*
    Sexual Harassment *470*

Gender and Sport *471*
    Access to Sport for Women *472*

Race and Ethnicity in Sport *474*
    The Black Athlete *475*
    Other Victims of Discrimination *478*

Physical Activity and Sport Trends *483*
    Health and Fitness Concerns Will Continue to Increase *483*
    Groups Seeking Alternative Sports *483*
    Spectators and Spectator Sports *485*
    Virtual Sports *486*

Summary *486*

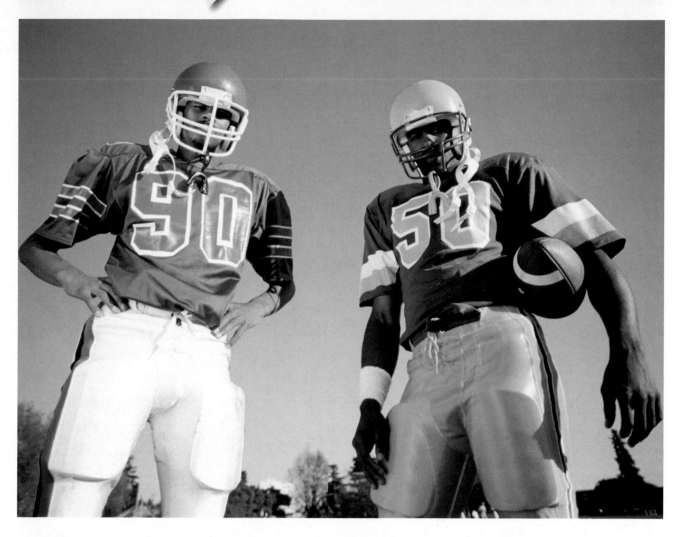

CHAPTER 19

Physical Activity and Sport Issues

After completing this chapter you should be able to:

- identify the major issues and controversies in the field of sport sociology;

- examine the impact of our "win at all cost" philosophy on the sport participant's behaviour;

- foster a greater awareness of the needs of diverse groups in our community;

- examine personal attitudes and values critically as they relate to modern day sport and physical activity.

Modern sport, in many ways, reflects modern society. In North America, we are obsessed with the idea of winning at all costs. We strive to get ahead and, in the process, often resort to questionable behaviours to achieve that end. Some people cheat on their taxes, while others undermine their co-workers to get that all-important promotion. We read of instances of road rage after a worker has experienced a frustrating day at the office. Some people turn to drug abuse.

Numerous parallels can be found in modern sport. A famous NFL football coach was once quoted as saying, "Losing is a little like dying." What kind of effect does this philosophy have on sport behaviour? What are some of the negative connotations of trying to win at all costs? What issues and controversies are most problematic in our modern day sport culture?

The discipline of sport sociology has tackled these and many other similar questions. **Sport sociology** studies sports as parts of social and cultural life. For example, why have sports in particular groups been organized in certain ways? And how are sports related to important spheres of social life, such as politics, the economy, family, education, and the media? These and similar questions reflect the focus of this field of study. It has examined the problem of aggression and violence in sport, cheating, the use of performance-enhancing drugs, gender issues, equal access for participants, and diversity issues. What have we learned from this extensive research base? Is the overall nature of modern day sport improving, or is it getting worse? In this chapter, we will attempt to answer these questions by examining some of the most important topics in sport sociology. At the conclusion of the chapter, you should have a deeper understanding of the nature of North American sport.

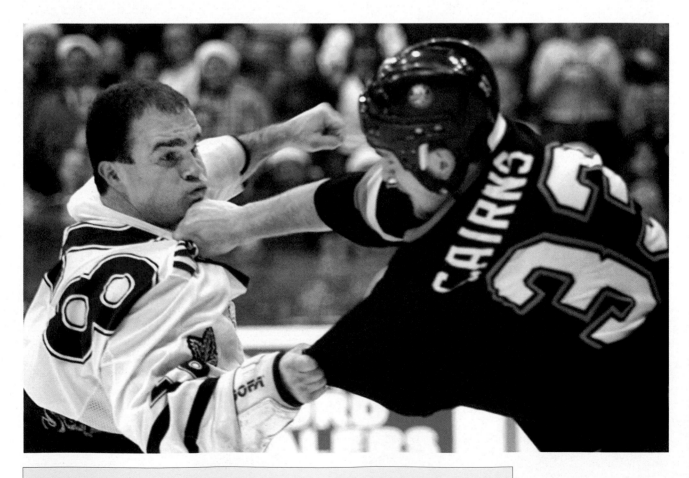

Figure 19.1 Sometimes athletes become a little "testy" during a heated contest.

Table 19.1 NHL suspensions for hockey violence.

Suspension	Description of the Violent Incident
82 games	Marty McSorley of the Boston Bruins knocked out Vancouver's Donald Brashear by slashing him in the head with his stick (February 2000).
23 games	Gordie Dwyer of Tampa Bay for leaving the penalty box to fight with Washington players (September 2000).
21 games	Dale Hunter of Washington for a blind-sided check on Pierre Turgeon of the New York Islanders after a goal in a playoff game (May 1993).
20 games	Tom Lysiak of Chicago for intentionally tripping a linesman (October 1983).
20 games	Brad May of Phoenix for hitting Steve Heinze of Columbus on the nose with his stick (November 2000).

Aggression and Violence in Sport

Few topics in sport sociology have received as much attention as that of aggression and violence. The evening news provides numerous examples of societal violence, from sectarian strife around the globe, to terrorist attacks and routine murders. The sports news isn't much better. Hockey, Canada's national sport, provides us with many notable examples (Figure 19.1). In fact, the National Hockey League (NHL) has handed out a variety of player suspensions for violent behaviour. Table 19.1 summarizes only five recent incidents.

Consider in particular the incident surrounding Tie Domi of the Toronto Maple Leafs: In the waning seconds of Game 4 in the NHL playoffs in 2001, Domi elbowed Scott Niedermayer of the New Jersey Devils. Domi received a 10-game suspension for elbowing, and was fined $1,000. As it turned out, because the Leafs were eliminated from the playoffs, Domi served an 8-game suspension at the beginning of the next season, and was fined $164,000 from his $1.68 million salary.

The violence is by no means limited to hockey. In 1995, Houston Rockets guard Vernon Maxwell climbed into the stands to hit an abusive fan during a basketball game in Portland. In 2000, New York Yankee Roger Clemens threw a jagged piece from a broken bat at Mike Piazza during a baseball playoff game. On Thursday, September 19, 2002, first base coach Tom Gamboa of the Kansas City Royals was attacked by two fans at Comisky Park in Chicago. He was slammed to the ground by the bare-chested father and his son, and was pummeled repeatedly. Teammates rushed to his aid and Gamboa escaped with only a few cuts and a bruised cheek. Examples such as these can be found in almost every sport.

Before exploring the reasons for this aggressive behaviour in sport, it is important to define our terms clearly and succinctly. **Violence** is a term that is usually used to refer to extreme examples of aggression. Aggressive behaviour is subdivided into three distinct components. **Hostile aggression** occurs when the primary goal is the injury of another athlete. The intent is to cause bodily or psychological harm, and has nothing to do with the outcome of the contest. Anger is usually involved. Hostile aggression is usually performed outside the rules of the game. **Instrumental aggression**, on the other hand, has the primary goal of achieving some external reward, such as contest victory. No anger is involved with instrumental aggression. Instrumental aggression is usually within the rules of the contest. Finally, **assertive behaviour** is a term that is often confused with aggression. Assertive behaviour requires increased effort and energy expenditure. There is no anger involved, and there is no intent to harm an opponent.

What Causes Aggressive Behaviour in Sport?

Several causes of aggressive behaviour have been proposed. Let's look at the most popular and likely instigators of aggression.

Parents and Coaches

Many times parents and coaches encourage aggressive behaviour without knowing it. Verbal comments such as "that was some fight," or "Bob can really take care of himself" give the impression that aggression is acceptable. Similarly, demonstrating interest in televised sporting event fights has the same effect.

> **Appropriate Action:** Every effort should be made to convey a negative reaction to aggression.

Outcome of the Contest and League Standing

Research consistently demonstrates that more aggression occurs after a losing contest. Players are frustrated, and often resort to aggressive behaviour. In a related fashion, teams that are lower in the league standing usually demonstrate more aggressive behaviour. Once again, the source of such aggression is frustration. Moreover, since winning the league championship appears out of the question, players believe there is little to lose by behaving aggressively.

> **Appropriate Action:** Coaches need to refocus the team's effort into more productive channels, such as a new game plan or reducing the number of turnovers.

Point Spread

Closely related to outcome and league standing, the point spread of a contest can also be a factor. The larger the point spread, the more aggression occurs. This is likely because the game is perceived to be out of reach, so taking a penalty will not likely affect the outcome of the contest.

> **Appropriate Action:** Coaches and players could take this opportunity to try out a new play that has been worked on in practice. Since the game is already out of reach, nothing can be lost by trying a new strategy. By employing this technique, players will not focus on the point spread or experience the resulting frustration; this will in turn reduce the tendency to resort to aggression.

Physical Contact

The nature of certain sports tends to encourage aggressive behaviour. Sports in which a good deal of physical contact occurs, such as body checks and tackles, tend to result in more aggression. One possible explanation for this is the perceived intent of the opponent. If a player believes that an opponent intends bodily harm, there is an increased likelihood that aggression will occur.

> **Appropriate Action:** Coaches should encourage athletes to respond with increased effort rather than aggressive acts. By having athletes focus their attention on greater intensity, it is less likely that they will devote their attention to aggressive responses. This increases the chances of victory – the ultimate way to get back at an opponent!

Figure 19.2 Fans play an important role in the expression of aggression by athletes.

Home Versus Away Games and Fan Reaction

Research across several sports reveals that more aggression occurs when a team plays away from home. Many writers have linked this finding to fan reaction (Figure 19.2). When a team plays an away game, the crowd they encounter is usually unfriendly and hostile. The verbal taunts and jeering from the crowd may anger the visiting team. This anger often manifests itself in aggressive behaviour.

Appropriate Action: Coaches and players must learn to "tune out" this fan reaction and focus on the game plan. Athletes should respond to this verbal taunting by applying maximum effort, and concentrating on technique. Invite them to use positive self-statements, such as "Way to go! You have really got the crowd's attention now – keep your mind on your game plan, and the crowd can suffer the consequences."

A variety of causes of aggression have been outlined in this section. Often several of these interact together to produce aggressive behaviour. Coaches, athletes, and parents need to be aware of these instigators, and should use the recommendations presented in this section to reduce aggression in sport.

Cheating in Sport

Cheating is inevitable when there is an overemphasis on winning. Slashing, high sticking, or an excessive body check in hockey are all examples where creating injuries can help you win a contest – if you don't get caught. Cheating can be defined as behaviour aimed at getting around the rules or breaking them. Why do athletes engage in this form of behaviour? One major researcher in sport sociology suggests that cheating results from the sport ethic. Let's examine the meaning of the sport ethic and how it results in deviant behaviour.

The Sport Ethic and Deviance in Sport

The **sport ethic** is a cluster of norms that many individuals in power and performance sports have accepted as the definition of an athlete. Four specific norms constitute the sport ethic.

Sacrificing for the Game

An athlete makes sacrifices for the game. Above all, an athlete must love the game, and meet the demands of competition without question. This spirit emphasizes that athletes must make sacrifices and be willing to pay the price to play their sports (Figure 19.3).

Striving for Distinction

An athlete strives for distinction. The Olympic motto "Citius, Altius, Fortius" (swifter, higher, stronger) captures the meaning of this norm. Being an athlete requires constant improvement and the pursuit of perfection.

Accepting Risks

An athlete accepts risks and plays through pain. Pressure, pain, or fear are never sufficient reasons for abandoning athletic goals. To move up the competitive pyramid, it is necessary to overcome the fear and challenge of competition and accept the increasing risk of failure and injury.

Accepting No Limit

An athlete accepts no limit in the pursuit of possibilities. This dream and the obligation to pursue it without question are all that matter. An athlete's very identity is bound up with the belief that sport is an arena of human endeavour in which anything is possible, as long as an individual is dedicated enough.

These four norms, which make up the sport ethic, are deeply rooted in the culture of today's

Figure 19.3 No individual personifies sacrificing for the sport and accepting risks more than Silken Laumann.

successful athletes. It is conformity to these norms that makes sport participation unique. However, deviance (or cheating) occurs when the norms of the sport ethic are accepted without question. When this happens, a variety of deviant behaviours occur. We will now turn our attention to the most popular forms of sport deviance.

Athlete Recruitment

Rules are often bent if not broken in order to sign promising talent. For example, highly sought-after athletes have "found" envelopes with large quantities of money in their lockers. This technique has been one way to "get around" the rules regarding athletic scholarships.

Similarly, some institutions will "ignore" the required admission standards if the application comes from a highly recruited athlete. In these situations, more deserving candidates may be cheated out of their rightful admission to a college or university of their choice.

Academic Cheating

Over the years, there have been several highly publicized cases of high-profile student athletes who have had their course work written by "academic support" staff. For the most part, these cases occurred in high-profile revenue-producing intercollegiate programs. These athletes supposedly felt intense pressure to keep up their academic averages so that they would be allowed to continue participating in their sport. However, in this they are no different from other students. The intense pressure to maintain a certain grade point average certainly has the potential to cause an athlete or any student to consider cheating.

Cheating in Games

In most cases, cheating in games involves trying to get away with as much as possible. One common form of cheating involves the modification of equipment. For example, fencing competitions have been rewired to allow certain athletes to achieve higher scores. Baseball hitters have been fined for using cork-filled bats. Baseball pitchers often "doctor" the ball by putting saliva, Vaseline, or any other foreign substance on the ball. Other pitchers have used a nail file to scuff the ball. In both cases, this causes an erratic flight of the pitched ball, and provides an unfair advantage to the pitcher. Basketball players use the slightest amount of physical contact to throw off an opponent's jump shot. Some coaches actually teach this technique, to be used when the player is out of the referee's sight lines. Once again, all of these behaviours are done to increase the chance of ultimate victory.

Performance-enhancing Drugs

Apparently, many athletes enjoy competitive sports so much that they will do whatever it takes to live up to the expectations of their coaches and fellow athletes. In reality, what this means is that as long as some athletes are willing to take performance-enhancing drugs to gain the winning edge, others will conclude that they must use similar substances just to stay competitive. When an athlete feels the pressure to win is overwhelming, then the temptation to use the "miracle pill" is considerable.

The most notable example for Canadians is the Ben Johnson tragedy. In 1988, Ben Johnson won the gold medal for Canada in the 100-metre dash at the Seoul Olympics. His time for the event, 9.79 seconds, set a new Olympic and world record. However, news that Johnson tested positive for drug use (anabolic steroids) three days later shocked Canada and the world. The subsequent Dubin Inquiry and Johnson's ultimate admission became the centre of the worldwide controversy over the use of performance-enhancing substances in sport (Figure 19.4).

A wide range of performance-enhancing drugs has been used to gain an unfair advantage in competitive sport. **Amphetamines** have been used to increase muscle tension, heart rate, and blood pressure. Athletes take these to "get up"

Figure 19.4 Ben Johnson and Charlie Francis became household names in 1988 because of the anabolic steroid issue and ensuing Dubin Inquiry.

for the big contest. **Cocaine** has also been used as a stimulant, and to conquer the fear of major competitions. **Rectal injections** of air have been used to increase swimmers' buoyancy. **Alkalines** have been used to neutralize the accumulation of acids in the bloodstream during physical exertion (the burn). **Blood doping** involves removing 1,200 cc of blood in advance, and then replacing just the red cells to increase the oxygen-carrying capacity of the blood. **Beta-adrenergic receptors** (e.g., propranolol, librium, valium) are sometimes used by archers, ski jumpers, and trap shooters to slow down the heart and steady the hands.

Unfortunately, performance-enhancing drugs are not only illegal according to the International Olympic Committee, but also have serious health side effects for athletes (addiction, gonadal atrophy, nervous tension, high blood pressure, premature

balding, decreased sperm count, stunted growth, excessive body hair, gastrointestinal cramping, and disruption of the menstrual cycle). For example, Steve Courson from the Pittsburgh Steelers took steroids. This helped make him one of the NFL's best offensive linemen and one of the world's strongest men. They also likely contributed to the severe heart disease that now threatens his life. Courson has required a heart transplant to survive.

Athletes must be counselled to stay drug-free, and seek alternative positive techniques to achieve the winning edge.

Sexual Harassment

The issue of sexual harassment also needs to be addressed. Back in 1997, Canadians became acutely aware of this problem in sport. Graham James pleaded guilty in January, 1997, to sexual harassment. He was the former coach of the Swift Current Broncos, a hockey team, and was sentenced to three-and-a-half years in prison for sexually abusing two of his players on numerous occasions. Just days later, Sheldon Kennedy, at that time a player with the NHL's Boston Bruins, held a press conference to announce that he had been one of the victims. Sexual abuse has clearly become a major concern in modern day sports.

Gender and Sport

One hundred years ago, women around the world were not allowed to vote, own property, get the educational training they desired, or work in their chosen field. During much of the nineteenth century, a woman was defined almost exclusively by her biology as a reproducing organism. In addition, women were frightened into believing that participation in any form of active physical exercise might very well destroy their ability to have children.

This repression of female sexuality was also reflected in the attitudes towards physical activity.

The expectation of women athletes was that they should be "lady-like" and feminine. For example, bicycling was viewed as an "indecent practice," swimming "smacked of depravity," and athletics was viewed as a "corrupting influence for a well brought-up girl." Mildred "Babe" Didrikson Zaharias, an American athlete, was consistently viewed and described as a "tomboy." Many other specially gifted athletic women were labeled "Amazons."

In the latter part of the nineteenth century, sports such as tennis, golf, badminton, skating, netball, gymnastics, swimming, and athletics became possible as they did not threaten their relationship with men. But throughout the nineteenth century and the early part of the twentieth century, women were expected to wear corsets, long sleeves, long dresses, and stockings while playing sports (Figure 19.5). Obviously, clothing of this nature was not conducive to efficient athletic performance – a fact that was not lost on the male sport authorities of the time. In fact, the founder of the modern Olympic movement, Baron Pierre de Coubertin, stated in 1902 that the only task that women should have in the Olympics was the crowning of men with garlands.

Figure 19.5 Women have made tremendous advancements in sport over the past 100 years.

Figure 19.6 Women now participate at competitive levels that rival their male counterparts, and they bring the same level of dedication and skill.

Access to Sport for Women

The single most dramatic change in the world of sport over the past generation surely has to be the increased participation of women. Despite resistance in some countries, women now have access to a variety of school, community, and club programs that did not exist approximately 30 years ago (Figure 19.6). What has brought about this dramatic change of events? The following important factors are considered responsible for the much needed increase in the participation of women in amateur and professional sport.

New Opportunities

Much of the increased participation in sport among girls and women today has resulted from new opportunities available to them. The teams and programs that have developed since the late 1970s have allowed women to discover and cultivate interests that were largely unheard of in the past. Although it can be argued that females still don't receive an equal share of sport resources in most organizations and communities, their increased participation numbers can still be traced to the development of new opportunities. For the most part, these new opportunities have resulted from some form of political pressure or equal-rights legislation, or individual leadership defying the majority point of view.

Political Pressure and Equal Rights Legislation

In the early 1980s in Canada, women's groups pressured for investigations of sport opportunities. In 1984, a major study on equal opportunities in athletics found that funding, opportunities, and facilities were not the same for women and men in Ontario universities and colleges. The following paragraphs summarize the major findings:

- At most colleges and universities, intramural activities were offered on a male-only, female-only, and co-ed basis. In addition, at most colleges and universities, more activities were offered only to men than only to women.

- The participation statistics for intramural activities revealed a greater participation rate for men than for women. In many colleges and universities, women were allowed to participate on men's teams if the same activity was not offered to women. However, men were not allowed to participate on women's teams.

- Greater resources were dedicated to sporting activities for men than for women. An unequal portion of the intramural budget was found to be allocated to activities for men.

- In intercollegiate sports, more programs were available to men at the indoor level. In 1982-1983, approximately twice as many men as women were participating in inter-college sports. In 1984, 64 percent of inter-university athletes were male.

Three years later, a 1987 survey conducted by the Ontario Commission on Inter-university Athletics (OCIA) reported that 64 percent of inter-university athletes were still male. Today, more women enjoy equal access to sports in our college and university systems. However, the sports in which women excel are not usually promoted as mass sports. In addition, the financial reward for women at the top of their sport is still less than it is for men.

The Global Women's Rights Movement

The global women's rights movement over the past 30 years has repeatedly emphasized that women realize their full potential as human beings when they are given the opportunity to develop their intellectual *and* physical abilities. This position has encouraged women of all ages to pursue their interest in sports. It has also led to the creation of new interests among those who, in the past, never would have considered participating in sports. The women's movement has also played a role in redefining occupational and family roles for women. This in turn has provided more women with the time and resources they need to participate in sport.

Lobbying efforts by women's rights groups led to the inclusion of statements related to sports and physical education in the official **Platform for Action** of the United Nations' Fourth World Conference on Women, held in Beijing, China, in 1996. These statements called for new and increased efforts to provide sport and physical education opportunities. The statements also invited new efforts to promote the education, health, and human rights of girls and women in countries around the world. Today, this movement has developed into a widely accepted global effort to promote and guarantee equal access to sport and physical activity to women around the world.

The Expanding Health and Fitness Movement

Since the mid-1970s, a great deal of research

has emphasized the many benefits of regular participation in physical activity. This increased awareness has encouraged girls and women to seek out more opportunities to participate in sport. Well-toned muscles and cardiovascular fitness are no longer seen as desirable only by men. More women are pursuing the goal of developing physical strength and sport competence.

Increased Media Coverage of Women in Sports

Although women's sports are still not given the media coverage provided men's sports, girls now have greater opportunity to watch women's sports on television, and to read about their accomplishments in magazines and newspapers (Figure 19.7). This encourages them to be active athletes themselves. One notable example is when Nadia Comaneci became the first gymnast ever to score a perfect 10.0 in the Olympic Games. In fact, she is credited with seven perfect scores at the 1976 Summer Olympics in Montréal, Canada. In

Figure 19.7 Canadian Hayley Wickenheiser made headlines in 2003 when she became the first woman to play and register a point in a men's second division hockey league in Finland.

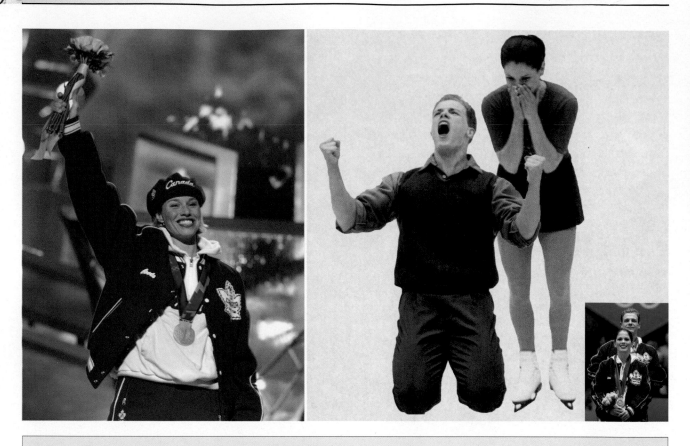

Figure 19.8 Catriona Le May Doan, along with Jamie Salé and David Pelletier, captured the hearts of Canadians at the Salt Lake City Olympic Winter Games in 2002.

total, she left Montréal with three gold medals, one silver medal, and one bronze. For more on this topic, see Chapter 20.

Consider the interest in soccer that developed in the USA after the national women's soccer team won the World Cup in 1999. The media coverage of that event, and the emergence of Mia Hamm and Brandi Chastain as national heros, were powerful and inspirational images for girls and women around the world.

From a Canadian perspective, two examples are especially noteworthy (Figure 19.8). In Salt Lake City in 2002 at the Winter Olympic Games, Catriona Le May Doan won a gold medal in the women's 500-metre speedskating event. And, on Monday, February 11, 2002, Jamie Salé and David Pelletier won a silver medal in the pairs skating event. A public outcry over judging irregularities forced the International Olympic Committee to award them a gold medal four days later.

To sum up, these factors have collectively fostered increased interest and participation in sport among women. It has also driven home the point that gender equity in sports is an important and worthwhile goal.

Race and Ethnicity in Sport

Before discussing race, ethnicity, and minority groups in sport, it is necessary to define these terms clearly.

Generally speaking, **race** refers to a category of people who are regarded as socially distinct because they share genetically transmitted traits believed to be important to people with power in society. In other words, race involves reference to physical traits, but is ultimately based on the meanings that people have given to those particular physical traits.

Ethnicity is different from race in that it refers to the cultural heritage of a specific group of people. Ethnicity is not based on genetically determined traits, but rather characteristics associated with cultural traditions and background. An ethnic group consists of individuals who share a particular way of life, including norms, attitudes, and values.

Lastly, a **minority group** is a sociological term that refers to a socially identified group of people who experience discrimination and suffer social disadvantages because of discrimination. A minority group does not have to be a racial or an ethnic group, and not all racial or ethnic groups are minority groups. For example, whites in Canada could be considered a racial group, but they would not be a minority group unless some other racial group had the power to discriminate against them.

The Black Athlete

Today, when we look at North American professional baseball, basketball, and football teams, we see many non-white athletes. Until quite recently, however, this was not the case. Originally, in the United States, only white athletes were allowed to play on major league baseball teams. Black athletes were forced to play in "Negro Leagues," where there were fewer jobs, lower pay, and often dangerous conditions. At that time, discrimination on the basis of colour was not illegal.

Jackie Robinson was the first black baseball player to play in the major leagues and thus became the first to "break the colour barrier" (see box *How Would You Feel?*). The team was the Brooklyn Dodgers and the year was 1946. Players like Robinson, and their wives, had to stay in hotels separate from their teammates, because many such hotels barred blacks. Robinson also suffered the embarrassment of being forced to eat behind screens in some restaurants so as not to offend white customers. At other restaurants, where blacks were not allowed, Robinson had to wait in the bus while his teammates ate their meals.

Unfortunately, without enforceable laws, racist attitudes remained widespread. This racism spilled over into the game itself. Robinson was verbally taunted regularly. He received death threats in the mail. Pitchers threw balls at his head consistently. This practice continued for many years. When Frank Robinson joined the Cincinnati Reds in 1956, he immediately became a popular target, getting hit by opposing pitchers 20 times in his first year. In spite of this blatant racism, black players persisted and continued to press for better conditions and greater representation.

Research reveals that steady progress has been made over the years in three of the most popular North American professional sports, baseball, basketball, and football (Table 19.2). Clearly, there has been a significant increase in black athlete representation in these three professional sports as well as others (Figure 19.9). However, it is revealing that this same research shows that in the NFL (football) and NBA (basketball), 100

How Would You Feel?

Put yourself in Jackie Robinson's position. How would you feel if you had to stay in a separate hotel, and eat behind a screen in a restaurant or all by yourself in the team bus? How would you like to receive death threats, and be purposely targeted by opposing players? Would you have persisted like Jackie Robinson, or would you have called it quits? Ask yourself this question: "How would you have felt to be Jackie Robinson?"

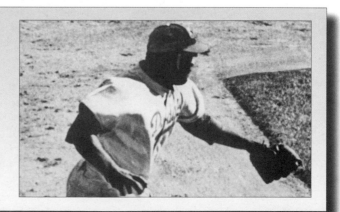

Sister Act

Serena Williams was awesome in defeating her sister Venus 6-4, 6-3 in the 2002 U.S. Open final. After winning the last three major finals, she proceeded to Australia in January 2003 looking for the tennis Grand Slam. Venus was the number one player just 12 months previously. Between them, it has been very difficult for others to win a major tournament in recent years. The impact of these sisters on women's tennis remains to be seen, but it is suspected that their impact will not only increase interest in women's tennis, but will also open the door to more black athlete involvement. Venus became the first black woman to hold the world number one ranking in February, 2002.

Table 19.2 Black athlete representation trends in three professional sports.

Baseball		Basketball		Football	
Year	%	Year	%	Year	%
1954	7	1956	14	1954	5
1967	11	1968	28	1962	30
1978	17	1975	42	1970	56
1980	22	1982	49	1980	75
1985	20	1985	54	1985	75
1998	15	1998	65	1998	77

Note: In the above table, % represents percentage of the total professional athletes in the specific sport.

Anson Carter

Willie O'Ree

Jarome Iginla

Figure 19.9 Willie O'Ree made his NHL debut with the Boston Bruins on January 18, 1958, at the age of 21. He didn't score a goal or register an assist, but he made history just by stepping on the ice. He was the first black athlete to play in the NHL. Since that time, many more black athletes have chosen to lace up the skates. Currently, 19 black athletes (approximately 3% of players) play in the NHL. Canadians will identify with prominent names in professional hockey, such as retired goaltender Grant Fuhr, Jarome Iginla, Anson Carter, Mike Grier, Donald Brashear, and goaltenders Kevin Weekes and Fred Brathwaite. All of these individuals portray how black athletes have truly "raised the bar" in athletic performance.

percent of the team owners are white, while in MLB (baseball), 97 percent of the team owners are white. Those in power in these sports remain white, and the possibility of unequal access in these sports continues.

Other Victims of Discrimination

Over the years, a large proportion of the research on discrimination has focused on the black athlete. More recently, however, other minority groups have been receiving increased attention. In this section, we will provide a brief overview of other minorities who have felt the sting of discrimination.

Canada's First Nations

In the period before and just after the arrival of the Europeans in Canada, native games and sports were associated with four main categories: mortuary practices, sickness, climatic conditions, and fertility. Respectively, these were activities

Jordin Tootoo

Figure 19.10 Canada's Jordin Tootoo is a rising star worth watching. This young Inuit played at the 2003 World Junior Hockey Championships in Halifax, and is destined for the NHL after being drafted by the NHL's Nashville Predators in 2001.

aimed at promoting tribal unity, healing and group help, rain dances, and celebrating births and good harvests. The most popular sports during this time period were foot racing, archery, swimming, ball games, and lacrosse.

Today, the main concerns of native people in Canada with regard to sport, fitness, and recreation focus on equity and cultural tradition. By most social indicators (income, housing, health, education, etc.), native people in Canada are often at the bottom of the social ladder. A lack of financial resources and sport facilities, isolation from sports events, limited coaching opportunities, as well as little support and encouragement all add to this problem.

Cultural concerns, on the other hand, focus on the traditions and values of native society and that sport should reflect those values. Special events, such as lacrosse or snow snake, and the value of inclusion and sharing as opposed to competition, are important considerations for native people.

Although the needs and values of Canada's native people with regard to sport and physical activity have been largely ignored, there is now some indication that Sport Canada will address this issue in the near future (Figure 19.10).

The Arctic Winter Games The inaugural Arctic Winter Games were hosted by Yellowknife in 1970. More than 500 athletes participated in these games. Athletes from the Northwest Territories, Yukon, and Alaska came together for the purpose of social interchange, cultural exhibition, and competitions in a variety of sports (Figure 19.11).

Since 1970, the Arctic Winter Games have been held every two years, and since their inception, have more than tripled in size, expanding to include large contingents from Greenland, Chukotka (Russia), Magadan (Russia), Alberta North, Nunavut (Eastern Northwest Territories), and Nunavik (Arctic Québec). The event has also evolved in recent years to highlight a cultural program that showcases the unique skills and attributes of northern performers and artists.

The primary objectives of the Arctic Winter

The one-hand reach competition

The one-foot high-kick competition or "aquaorik"

Sled dog race

Figure 19.11 Since their inception in Yellowknife in 1970, the Arctic Winter Games have included games that test athletes' endurance, strength, and patience, reflecting the necessary qualities for survival in the harsh environment of the North.

Games are to involve as many athletes as possible, and to provide a competitive exchange below the elite level of competition. The 2002 Games were co-hosted by Nunavut and Greenland. These Winter Games involved 17 different sports, including alpine skiing, arctic sports/Inuit and Deme games (Greenland), badminton, cross-country skiing, indoor soccer, snowboarding, snowshoeing, table tennis, volleyball, arctic sports/ Inuit and Deme games (Nunavut), basketball, curling, dog mushing, gymnastics, ice hockey, speedskating, and wrestling.

Disabilities and Sport

The sheer level of determination and commitment shown by athletes with disabilities has highlighted attention on their segregation within the world of sport (Figure 19.12). In recent years, there has been a major change in social attitudes towards those who cannot participate in "regular" sports. Not that long ago, people spoke of these individuals as "crippled" or "handicapped." In July, 1983, the Canadian Human Rights Code substituted the term "disability" for "physical handicap." Disability is defined as "any previous or existing mental or physical disability, disfigurement, and previous or existing dependence on alcohol or a drug." However, sport organizations still distinguish between physical and mental disabilities.

Many disabled athletes have spent many years fund-raising simply to get their achievements recognized. Before Terry Fox and Rick Hansen, the media paid very little attention to the amazing dedication of disabled athletes. In 1980, Terry Fox inaugurated his "Marathon of Hope" to raise Canadian awareness for the need to find a cure for cancer (see Chapter 20, Society, Culture, and Sport). Fox had recently had his right leg amputated six inches above his knee because of bone cancer. Although Fox had hoped to run all the way across Canada, his journey was unfortunately halted after 5,342 km when he arrived in Thunder Bay, Ontario. Cancer had spread to his lungs and he was unable to continue. Even so, Fox succeeded in raising $24.17 million for cancer research. In addition, his gutsy performance captured the imagination of an entire nation.

Rick Hansen was another athlete who brought major attention to the cause of disabled athletes. A truck accident at the age of 15 left Hansen with both legs paralyzed. Hansen immediately decided he was not going to let this interfere with his love of sports. Hansen is probably best known for his 25,000-mile wheelchair tour around the world. The idea behind the "Man in Motion World Tour" was to raise $10 million for spinal cord research, rehabilitation, and wheelchair sports. A second purpose was to raise awareness of the potential of disabled persons. In addition to this extraordinary accomplishment, Hansen set five world track records and one Pan Am Games

Chantal Petitclerc

Figure 19.12 Athletes with disabilities have certainly excelled in terms of athletic accomplishments.

record; won 12 track gold at the BC Games; gold, silver, and bronze medals at the 1980 wheelchair Olympics; British Columbia wheelchair tennis singles titles; and much more. Rick Hansen truly epitomizes the courage and determination potential of disabled athletes.

Largely in part due to these two courageous individuals, the Canadian media and the public are paying more attention to achievements of disabled athletes. An increasing number of events are being offered to persons with disabilities. Wheelchair skiing, basketball, high jumping, and many other sports now involve disabled competitors. In 1986, the federal government passed **Bill C-62**, which required all federally regulated companies with 100 employees or more to promote the hiring of disabled individuals. As more access ramps are built to allow persons with disabilities to become independent, we also see more sports becoming available to them. These tremendous changes have come about as a result of the efforts of disabled athletes, disabled adults, and other interest groups.

Gay Athletes and the Gay Games

The gay community has also fought discrimination in many areas, including sport. Because an individual's social status, family bonds, and even livelihood could be at risk, it has taken great courage for gay people to identify themselves publicly. For the most part, professional sport has defined itself as being male, heterosexual, and homophobic (hostile towards homosexuals). In fact, the first North American gay athlete to say publicly that he was gay was Dave Kopay in 1976. Kopay was a football player in the NFL.

In 1982, the Gay Games were formed to enable gay athletes to participate in their own culturally defined sports and athletics (Table 19.3). The key philosophy of these Games was participation, support, inclusiveness, and the enjoyment of physical movement. All sports are open to women and men of all athletic abilities. This philosophy is exactly the opposite of conventional international competitions, which stress exclusion and rankings. In 1990, the Gay Games III Sport and Cultural

Table 19.3 History of the Gay Games Sport and Cultural Festival.

Games	Location	Year
I	San Francisco, CA	1982
II	San Francisco, CA	1986
III	Vancouver, BC	1990
IV	New York, NY	1994
V	Amsterdam, Netherlands	1998
VI	Sydney, Australia	2002
VII	Montréal, PQ	2006

Festival was held in Canada for the first time in Vancouver, British Columbia. This event received support from many sectors of society.

Since their inception in 1982, the Gay Games have continued to grow. The fifth quadrennial Gay Games in Amsterdam involved more than 15,000 competitors from nearly 70 nations and 200,000 spectators. The most recent Games held in Sydney, Australia, in November 2002 also proved to be a huge success, featuring over

11,500 athletes, 3,000 volunteers, 800 international accredited media, 2,000 cultural festival participants, 45 sports venues, 31 sports, and nine days of conferences and workshops.

The Gay Games are slated to return to Canada, as Montréal, Québec, will host the seventh quadrennial Gay Games Sport and Cultural Festival in 2006.

The growing success of the Games has allowed gay and lesbian athletes to continue to form sport groups and teams that provide enjoyable experiences and enrichment in their social lives.

GAY GAMES® VII
Sports and Cultural Festival
Montréal
Rendez-Vous 2006

Older Adults in Sport

Increasingly, restrictions on participation in sport and physical activity on the basis of age are also being questioned (Figure 19.13). Aging involves biological and physiological changes, but the relationship between aging and participation in sport depends on the social interpretation of those changes. Around the turn of the twentieth century, developmental theory stressed that development occurs predominantly during childhood and adolescence. For this reason, sport and physical activity programs were created and sponsored for the young, not for older people. Theory at that time suggested older individuals were already

Figure 19.13 Older adults are now entering the picture and showing that they still have what it takes to be competitive and enjoy participation and competition.

"grown up," and their characters could no longer be shaped.

Medical professionals at that time also discouraged an aging population from engaging in sport and physical activity, believing that strenuous activity could put too much strain on the heart and other muscles in older individuals. Although this did not prevent all older individuals from participating in physical activity, it did serve to curb the establishment of organized sport programs for this segment of the population.

As the average age of the population in most societies continues to increase, older people represent an increasingly larger part of the world's population. Since this trend has developed, there has been a growing interest in sports and physical activities that do not involve intimidation, use of physical force, and the risk of physical injuries.

Older people are more likely to see sports as social activities. They are also interested in making participation more inclusive than exclusive. Seniors are now forming groups to compete at the local, national, and international levels. The activities range from power walking in malls to highly skilled sports such as gymnastics and athletics.

The Masters Games, for example, attract older adults from around the world to compete at the highest levels across most sports. Athletes may be as young as 27 in some events, and participate in categories up to 90 years of age.

The first World Masters Games were held in Toronto in 1985. By 1994, in Brisbane, this competition grew to the point where it became the largest international sporting competition ever held, with some 24,000 athletes from 71 nations competing. The following Games held in Portland in 1998 drew only 11,000 participants because of exorbitant entry fees. Edmonton, Canada, has been chosen to host the 2006 World Masters Games.

The idea of regular physical activity as part of an overall lifestyle has replaced the notion that physical activity diminishes as we grow older. For this reason, the future will see more "senior" sport leagues, where rules are modified to emphasize

the joy of movement, social connections, and the challenge of controlled competition. But we will also see an increased emphasis on physical activities such as walking, hiking, athletics, and weight training, taken very seriously but performed in social settings that focus on personal health and fitness rather than the setting of personal records.

Physical Activity and Sport Trends

Other important trends will have an impact on the future of physical activity and sport. These are explored briefly starting below.

Health and Fitness Concerns Will Continue to Increase

As health care programs and policies around the world increasingly emphasize illness prevention rather than treatment, society will continue to become more aware of health and fitness issues (see Chapter 1, Introduction to Health and Wellness). The wellness movement currently evolving in Canada and the rest of North America will encourage a greater number of individuals to forsake power and performance sports and to increase their involvement in participation sports. Health and fitness considerations will also be aggressively promoted in the physical education curriculum in schools, colleges, and universities. Less attention will be paid to traditional performance sports and more emphasis will be placed on teaching physical activities that involve lifetime skills, such as walking, jogging, aerobics, swimming, cross-country skiing, golf, and tennis.

Groups Seeking Alternative Sports

Sport participants who reject traditional performance sports will look increasingly to alternative sports (Figure 19.14). High school students will continue to form their own sport

Figure 19.14 Alternative sports are enjoying increased participation and media coverage.

groups and play games on their own rather than accept the constraints of playing on varsity teams. If schools don't successfully organize their sport programs for the future, more and more students will look outside the school for alternative sporting activities.

Some unique sport cultures have developed around a variety of alternative sports. Two studies involving skateboarders and snowboarders in Colorado found that many young participants in these sports resisted attempts to turn their sports into a commercialized, competitive form. Other alternative sports such as windsurfing, parasailing, mountain biking, rock climbing, and orienteering have also caught on with a number of young people. Indeed, their popularity has made some of these sports, such as snowboarding, Olympic events.

In summary, people will continue to seek alternatives to traditional power and performance sports. How to maintain these alternative sports as overall participation continues to increase will present a challenge.

Spectators and Spectator Sports

Unfortunately, an increasing number of people will continue to watch more sports while participating less themselves. As a result, obesity rates in Canada will soar even higher. Statistics Canada has reported that the percentage of Canadians considered to be obese has increased from 13 percent to 15 percent during the six-year period from 1994-95 to 2000-01. The number of obese adults increased 24 percent over that period. An increased interest in professional sports has also resulted in ever higher salaries of professional athletes, as shown in Table 19.4.

The sports that people choose to watch may be the result of unexpected shifts in interest. For example, more people may tune in to soccer, while fewer watch baseball, as many fans are becoming increasingly less forgiving of the number of work stoppages or strikes that have continued to occur in major league baseball. Attendance numbers and television viewership reports are markedly lower

Table 19.4 The Toronto Maple Leafs' and Toronto Raptors' salaries (top 10 players for each club) expressed in millions.*

Toronto Maple Leafs		Toronto Raptors	
Mats Sundin	$14.2	Antonio Davis	$18.9
Ed Belfour	$10.2	Vince Carter	$15.8
Alexander Mogilny	$8.7	Hakeem Olajuwon	$9.0
Bryan McCabe	$4.5	Alvin Williams	$8.4
Robert Svehla	$4.5	Jerome Williams	$8.3
Jyrki Lumme	$4.3	Lamond Murray	$6.5
Robert Reichel	$4.3	Lindsey Hunter	$4.7
Gary Roberts	$3.9	Eric Montross	$4.3
Shayne Corson	$3.9	Nate Huffman	$2.4
Mikael Renberg	$3.2	Michael Bradley	$1.9

* *Toronto Star (2002), November 15, D3.*

since the last strike. It is also likely that people will watch a wider range of different sports, such as fishing channels for retired people and alternative sports for the younger generation.

Virtual Sports

Television and the internet will help to shape how sports are imagined, created, and played in many societies around the world. This increased exposure has the potential to cause participants to question their choices in sports and physical activities and to seek more attractive alternatives.

In a somewhat different fashion, the internet will likely continue to recruit new fans in a variety of fantasy leagues, where the fans have the opportunity to construct teams, choose players, and qualify for prizes if their team does well. Video games will provide sophisticated new virtual sports where, for a few dollars, the player will be able to play golf with Tiger Woods, bat against Roger Clemens, play soccer with Mia Hamm, or raft down the Colorado river. Although exciting, these virtual games are likely to lower actual physical participation rates even further.

Summary

In this chapter, we examined the alarming occurrence of aggression and various forms of cheating in sports. The issues of equal access to participation and diversity considerations were emphasized using several examples. Specifically, gender, ethnic minority status, disability, and diversity were discussed in terms of their impact in the past and on the current situation in sport. Finally, we examined likely future participation trends based on current societal values.

Key Words

Assertive behaviour	Instrumental aggression	Sport ethic
Ethnicity	Minority group	Sport sociology
Hostile aggression	Race	Violence

Discussion Questions

1. What are some examples of instrumental aggression, hostile aggression, and assertive behaviour that you have viewed in sports?

2. List, with a brief description, instances of cheating you have witnessed, either at your high school, at local sports, or in professional sports.

3. Do you feel the sport ethic has benefited or hindered Canadian sport in terms of the cheating problem? Explain your answer.

4. What instances of sexual harassment have you witnessed in your years of sport participation? How would you explain these occurrences? What caused them, and how were they handled?

5. What effect has the increased coverage of women in sports in the media had on Canadian sports? Provide specific examples.

6. Who is your favourite black athlete in sports history, and why do you feel this way?

7. Who is your favourite female athlete in sports history, and why do you feel this way?

8. What future physical activity trends do you predict? Explain why you feel this way.

9. From your own personal perspective, are today's professional athletes worth the money they earn? Explain your viewpoint in detail.

The Skills to Exceed All Odds

NAME: Peter Burwash
OCCUPATION: Chairman, Peter Burwash International (PBI)
EDUCATION: BPHE, University of Toronto (Physical and Health Education)

Peter graduated from the University of Toronto with the opportunity to fulfill his lifelong dream – to play in the NHL. After playing four successful seasons for the university, he was drafted by the St. Louis Blues. With only several weeks to prepare, Peter went about practice as he went about all of his life endeavours, with fury and energy. But after a freak accident, he found himself lying on the ice, paralyzed form the waist down. Peter had been checked into the boards and caught the edge of a slightly open penalty box door with his spine. Luckily, his condition was temporary, but while wondering whether he would ever walk again, Peter vowed to give up the sport. He immediately drove 5,200 kilometres to his parents' house back in Toronto, where he caught a plane the next day and began a new dream.

While playing hockey and studying physical education and health at the University of Toronto, Peter also played and excelled in tennis. With the experience of three consecutive Canadian Collegiate Championships, Peter entered a tournament in the French Riviera circuit and won his first match. He continued to follow the circuit, but playing tennis for a living wasn't quite that easy. After spending most of his money on plane tickets to get to Europe, he was living on a budget of 15 cents a day. From tournament to tournament Peter slept on other players' floors and ate scraps from dinners of those who could afford them. He was also playing against the top players in the world and had to make up for his lesser talent with heart. But with multiple scars and bone chips from headlong dives, Peter survived until Wimbledon. He had become known as the "Flying Canadian" and was acknowledged for his tremendous efforts and determination. When he returned home after the final tournament, he had received monetary gifts that, in combination with his hard work, ensured the future of his career.

What He's Doing Today

- entrepreneur: started PBI (Peter Burwash International), an international network of traveling tennis coaches
- coached in 135 countries
- invented wheelchair tennis
- developed triple awareness
- started tennis in prisons
- brought tennis to soldiers in the Vietnam war

- author of books on tennis, motivation, health, and leadership
- motivational speaker for corporations
- TV and radio appearances

How PHE Got Him Here

- learned discipline and structure
- gained knowledge of anatomy and physiology, helping him understand sports nutrition and the body
- learned flexibility and adaptability skills
- feels comfortable speaking in front of people
- can work comfortably with others
- knows how to teach according to the situation and students

What is the benefit of having a PHE degree in your field?

In the field of business, it is critical to be able to speak to people in their terms. As a graduate from the field of physical and health education I have the ability to adapt my communication skills to meet the needs of the situation. In a medical setting, my understanding of science and technology allows me to speak to doctors, physiotherapists, and nurses. In a business setting, I am able to communicate to entrepreneurs, secretaries, and CEOs because of my background in administration and organizational behaviour. It is my experience in physical education that has allowed me to become flexible as a person. Furthermore, being a graduate of the physical education program has taught me the skills of a successful leader. Discipline, commitment, and self-motivation are critical.

What do you like about what you do?

I am able to travel the world and meet the most amazing people. Nelson Mandela comes to mind. He is a man of great strength and had the ability to mobilize hundreds of thousands of people.

What is the most valuable life lesson that you have learned through your endeavours?

My experiences and travels have taught me that the most important thing in life is simplicity. When life is simple everything comes together. You can have everything in the world and be unhappy, but when you lead a simple life with only the necessities, life can be beautiful.

In This Chapter:

Brief History of Sport in Canada *490*
    Early Canada (1600-1850) *490*
    Victorian Period (1850-1920) *491*
    Emergence of Sport as a Commodity (1920-1960) *491*
    Sport and the Canadian State (1960-Present) *492*

Brief History of the Olympic Games *492*

Sport and Canadian Culture *497*
    A Quest for Excitement *500*
    Sports Are Appealing *500*
    Sport's Cultural Significance *500*

Canadian Athlete Role Models *501*

The Business of Sport *505*
    Professional Sport in North America *506*
    Amateur Sport in Canada *507*
    Sport Sponsorship *507*

Sport as a Spectacle *511*
    Television *512*
    Newspapers *512*
    Books and Magazines *513*
    Radio *514*
    Film and Video *514*
    The Internet *515*

Being an Informed Consumer *515*
    Factors Influencing Student Participation *515*
    The Benefits of School and Community Physical Activity *517*
    The Importance of Being an Informed Consumer *517*

Summary *519*

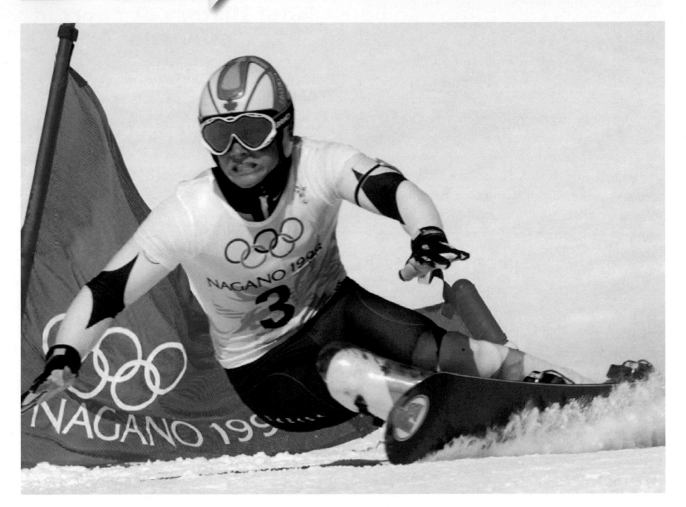

Society, Culture, and Sport

After completing this chapter you should be able to:

- provide a brief history of the development of physical activity and sport in Canada;

- describe the history of the Olympic movement;

- discuss the accomplishments of some of Canada's sports heroes;

- explain how the commercialization of sport in modern society has evolved, and how it impacts the consumer.

Society, culture, and sport are deeply interrelated. To understand this complex relationship, it is necessary to examine the historical underpinnings of sport in the modern world and in Canada, in particular.

Canada provides a variety of competitive and recreational opportunities for all who are interested, from our school systems through community, provincial, national, and even international sport governing bodies. Canadian athletes have achieved national and worldwide recognition in an extraordinary range of sports (see Canada's Summer and Winter Olympics medal count in Table 20.2, page 500).

But in Canada, as elsewhere in the world, sport is part of the social and cultural matrix. Indeed, sport is no longer just sport, but it is also big business. Enormous sums of money are spent and made in both amateur and professional sport. Sponsors are happy to lend their corporate logos and financial support to both athletes and competitions.

Brief History of Sport in Canada

The history of sport in Canada can be divided into four periods for the purpose of this survey.

Early Canada (1600-1850)

Canada's history can be traced back much further than its traditional origin when Champlain, the founder of New France, erected the first building at Québec. Aboriginal peoples, including the Inuit, Iroquois, Algonquins, the Plains Indians, and many tribes along the Pacific coast, were already here and greatly outnumbered the 3,215 white inhabitants of New France in 1665. Games were important to early native cultures. For the most part, they were focused around ceremonial and religious practices, the transmission of cultural values to the young, or the teaching of survival skills. But with one notable exception,

Figure 20.1 Baggataway, now known as lacrosse, enjoyed great popularity in early Canada.

baggataway, now known as lacrosse (Figure 20.1), early colonists were more interested in survival than they were in games.

In 1763, the Treaty of Paris saw France yield its colony to England. With the fall of New France, wealthy British military officers who had come from private schools brought with them their own sporting traditions, in activities as diverse as cricket, horse racing, fox hunting, and snowshoeing. Rural farmers and settlers, by contrast, did not have the resources or time to enjoy a comparable level of sporting activity. The sporting clubs that did evolve, such as the group of Scottish merchants who formed the Montréal Curling Club on January 22, 1807, were motivated by social considerations.

Victorian Period (1850-1920)

The period from the mid-nineteenth century to the end of World War I was marked by extensive political, economic, and demographic changes in Canadian society. By the end of World War I, an industrialized society had emerged, with rapid urbanization. Industrialization brought with it not only technological change, such as the railway, telegraph, and mass press, but also the whole new concept of free time. The reduced work week, half-holidays on Saturday, and recognition of the Sabbath paved the way for the conditions needed for the development of sport in a modern society.

The main focus of early Canadian sports was predominantly social in nature. There were no leagues or competitions, and there were few common rules for the events that did take place. This changed dramatically, however, during the remainder of the century. In Montréal in 1860, there were 24 clubs in 4 sports (snowshoeing, curling, lacrosse, and cricket). By 1894, this number had grown to 234 clubs in 15 sports. By this time, leagues, regularly scheduled competitions, and standardized rules had developed.

The last decade of the nineteenth century, and continuing until the First World War, was marked by increased promotion of both participatory and spectator sports.

Emergence of Sport as a Commodity (1920-1960)

After World War I, it was inconceivable to most Canadians that in only 20 years they would be engaged in another world war. No one imagined that World War II would end the poverty and unemployment of the Great Depression. The period following World War II and continuing throughout the 1950s was accompanied by economic prosperity, rapid technological change, and tremendous population growth, largely due to immigration. By 1960, Canada was a different nation. Sport was also forever changed. Sports were no longer just seen as community endeavours. Television made an appearance in the early 1950s, and transformed the coverage of both amateur and professional sport. Indeed, sport became part of our national identity (Figure 20.2).

This period also marked the commercial expansion of sport. Take hockey, Canada's national sport, as an example. When organized hockey first appeared, local rink owners booked the games and kept over 50 percent of the profit. The emergence of professional hockey changed this picture. Organizers now were responsible for hiring the players and renting the arena, and kept the difference between expenses and profits for themselves. This marked the foundation of the National Hockey League in 1917. Commercial hockey prospered over community teams, and the

Figure 20.2 When hockey first appeared in Canada, it had an entirely different look than it does today.

people who formed the hockey cartel were ready to welcome, in addition to teams from Toronto, Montréal, Ottawa, and Hamilton, the first American franchise, the Boston Bruins, in 1924. Teams from New York, Chicago, Detroit, and Pittsburgh were added to the list so that by the start of the 1924 season, the NHL had 10 teams playing in two divisions. This evolution from community sport to commercialization epitomizes the changes that occurred during this era.

Sport and the Canadian State (1960-Present)

The role of government and politics in Canadian sport can be traced back to the Dominion Rifle Association, formed in 1869. This organization received government support because it was thought to have the potential to improve Canada's militia. An excellent recent study suggests that several factors contributed to this marriage of convenience between sports and politics.

First, in the years after World War II, there was a call for the government to improve labour and welfare legislation. Leaders in the world of sport began calling for similar improvements in the sporting domain.

Second, sport leaders became increasingly more accepting of government involvement after World War II. This was in marked contrast to the claims of government interference that had occurred prior to this time.

Third, in the late 1950s, Canada's performance in international sports was at an all-time low. When John Diefenbaker of the Conservative Party became prime minister in 1957, he publicly stated that athletic achievement in Canada could give a significant boost to national pride. This created a more favourable political climate for the development of sport in Canada. When the Duke of Edinburgh rebuked Canadians for their low fitness level in a speech to the Canadian Medical Association in 1961, the scene was set for the passage of **Bill C-131**, the **Fitness and Amateur Sport Act**.

Bill C-131

The *Fitness and Amateur Sport Act (Bill C-131)* marked the first time the federal government was officially committed to the promotion and development of fitness and amateur sport. The funding was administered by the Department of National Health and Welfare. Initially, the funds were quite small by today's standards. In 1961, $29,641 was spent, but by 1967-68, the amount had risen to $3,655,413. Today, the amount is in excess of $5 million.

This Bill eventually resulted in $5 million in annual funding for administrative structure, personnel, provincial and federal cost-sharing agreements, grants for sports governing bodies, the initiation of the **Canada Games** (Table 20.1), and research grants and scholarships for physical education specialists. From this point onward, amateur sport would have to work closely in conjunction with the Canadian state.

The Canada Games

The Canada Games have historically been staged in smaller Canadian centres in order to leave behind a legacy of training and competition facilities, as well as trained sports enthusiasts.

Brief History of the Olympic Games

The Sydney Olympics in 2000 showed how much the Olympics have changed since the first modern Games in Athens in 1896. Following is a capsule summary of each of these Olympic Games.

Athens, 1896

A wealthy businessman bailed out the Greek government when it did not have the finances to pay for the Games. Thirteen countries, including

Table 20.1 The Canada Games (1967-2001).

Winter	Summer
1967 - Québec City, Québec	1969 - Halifax-Dartmouth, Nova Scotia
1971 - Saskatoon, Saskatchewan	1973 - New Westminster-Burnaby, BC
1975 - Lethbridge, Alberta	1977 - St. John's, Newfoundland
1979 - Brandon, Manitoba	1981 - Thunder Bay, Ontario
1983 - Saguenay-Lac-St-Jean, Québec	1985 - Saint John, New Brunswick
1987 - Cape Breton, Nova Scotia	1989 - Saskatoon, Saskatchewan
1991 - Charlottetown, PEI	1993 - Kamloops, BC
1995 - Grande Prairie, Alberta	1997 - Brandon, Manitoba
1999 - Corner Brook, Newfoundland	2001 - London, Ontario

Australia, Austria, Britain, Bulgaria, Chile, Denmark, France, Germany, Hungary, Sweden, Switzerland, USA, and Greece, participated. The Games consisted of nine sports, and involved 311 male participants.

Paris, 1900

Held at the same time as the Paris Universal Exhibition, these Games were a near disaster. They were poorly organized, and received little attention, although 13 new sports were added. Women, significantly, competed in golf and tennis.

St. Louis, 1904

Once again, these Games were held at the same time as the World Fair. At these Olympics, only 12 countries took part, and the majority of the competitors were American.

London, 1908

The use of well-established rules governing specific sports returned some pride to the Games, but the all-British judges caused considerable animosity among the various teams.

Stockholm, 1912

In contrast to the previous Games, these Olympics were well organized and involved twice as many competitors. In total, 2,490 male athletes and 57 female athletes participated in the Games. Women participated in swimming. No incidents or protests occurred.

The Modern Olympics

Baron Pierre de Coubertin is credited with the idea of beginning the modern Olympic Games. In his late 20s, he wanted athleticism and fitness to be an everyday part of life. For this reason, he devoted his time to bringing back the long-dead Olympic Games. When the Greek government frowned at the potential expense, de Coubertin persuaded the leader of Greece to lead a fund-raising campaign to bring the Games to Athens. Although the 1900 Paris Games were a near disaster, he persisted in his efforts, and the movement developed. In 1936, he was nominated for the Nobel Peace Prize, but was not selected. He died of a stroke at the age of 74 on September 2, 1937. He requested in his will that his heart be removed from his body and buried at Olympia in Greece. This wish was carried out.

1914-1918

Because of World War I, these Olympics were cancelled.

Antwerp, 1920

Belgium hosted these Games soon after recovering from the First World War. Twenty-nine countries participated, but Germany, Austria, Hungary, Bulgaria, and Turkey were not allowed to participate. Many competitors had experienced suffering and hardship during the war.

Paris, 1924

These Olympics were marked by a large increase in the number of countries taking part (there were 44). This resulted in many more competitors (3,092) than had been involved in the past.

Amsterdam, 1928

Women participated in athletics (Figure 20.3) and gymnastics at these Games, although several women collapsed at the end of the 800-metre event. Forty-eight countries took part.

Los Angeles, 1932

Travel costs reduced the number of participants at these Olympics. Many more spectators attended the events, including over 100,000 at the opening ceremonies. The first Olympic village was built to accommodate participants.

Berlin, 1936

The persecution of Jews and other groups had begun in Germany under the rule of Hitler's Nazi party. Surprisingly, the International Olympic Committee still insisted that the Games take place. Hitler used the Games for propaganda purposes, hoping to show the world the superiority of the German race. Jesse Owens, a black athlete from the USA, foiled Hitler's plans by winning four gold medals. Hitler congratulated the German medal winners but did not mention Jesse Owens.

1939-1945

The Second World War caused the cancellation of these Olympics.

London, 1948

These Games were held in a blitzed city still reeling from the exhausting effects of the war. Fifty-nine countries and 4,500 competitors were involved, although Germany, Japan, and the Soviet Union did not attend.

Helsinki, 1952

With Germany's continued absence, these were known as the "Friendly Games." After a 40-year absence, the Soviet Union once again participated. These Olympic Games saw the beginnings of the East–West rivalry that still exists.

Figure 20.3 Early track and field uniforms worn at the Olympic Games have little in common with today's aerodynamic designs.

Melbourne, 1956

These Games were marked by unexpected events and political turmoil. Strict quarantine laws prevented foreign horses from entering the country. This nearly led to the Games being withdrawn from Melbourne. After much debate, it was decided the equestrian events would be held in Stockholm, Sweden. This marked the only time in the history of the modern Games that all events weren't held in the same state or region. Spain and Holland withdrew because the Soviet Union had invaded Hungary just prior to the Games. China withdrew because Taiwan took part, and Egypt and Lebanon pulled out because of fighting in the Suez Canal. East and West Germany combined into one team.

Rome, 1960

No political problems occurred, although an all-white team represented South Africa, in keeping with its apartheid policy. The events were viewed across the globe on television. A Danish cyclist died after using drugs to improve his performance.

Tokyo, 1964

The 1964 Olympic Games were marred by the absence of South Africa, Indonesia, and North Korea. South Africa was banned from these Games because of the country's apartheid policy. Both Indonesia and North Korea voluntarily withdrew their teams from competition when several of their contestants were found to be disqualified (those athletes who had participated in the New Emerging Forces Games in Jakarta in 1963 were not allowed to participate in the Olympic Games). The event still turned out to be very successful (and expensive), with 94 countries taking part.

Mexico City, 1968

East and West Germany entered as separate teams. A demonstration against poverty and the cost of the Olympic Games was violently broken up, and many people were killed. Drug tests took place for the first time. During the medal ceremonies, black American athletes staged a protest against inequality and injustice in the treatment of Blacks in the United States. South Africa was barred from competition once again.

Munich, 1972

These Olympics were brilliantly staged from a technical perspective, but several serious problems greatly marred the Games. Black American athletes once again protested during the medal ceremonies, while the Rhodesian team was sent home because it was believed the country had been racist in selecting its (all white) team. Palestinian terrorists killed several Israeli athletes and officials. As a result, some teams and many individual competitors decided to leave the Games.

Montréal, 1976

The Montréal Olympics were extremely costly and there was heavy security involved. French Canadians were vocally upset because Queen Elizabeth II opened the Games. Canada recognized only the Peoples' Republic of China; Taiwan was consequently forced to withdraw from competition. Black African countries boycotted the Games. Thirty-two nations walked out of the Olympic village when the International Olympic Committee (IOC) refused to ban New Zealand because its national rugby team was touring racially segregated South Africa.

Moscow, 1980

Although these Games were successfully organized, and 81 teams took part, there was a boycott by Western countries, spearheaded by the United States. The boycott seriously reduced attendance by participating countries. With the Soviets occupying Afghanistan, and unable to persuade the IOC to cancel or move the Summer Games from Moscow, President Jimmy Carter pressured the U.S. Olympic Committee to withdraw officially in April, 1980. As a result, many other Western governments followed suit and withheld athletes from participation. In total, only 81 nations competed in these Games. Security was very heavy.

Los Angeles, 1984

These Olympic Games were probably the most commercialized to date. Extensive marketing and sponsorship were involved in the Hollywood showmanship. The Games turned an enormous financial profit, with 140 countries participating. The Soviet Union, Cuba, and most East European countries boycotted the event. In total, 13 communist allies joined the boycott in a "payback" for Moscow. Romania was the only Warsaw Pact country to come to Los Angeles. Libya withdrew after two of its journalists were refused entry.

Seoul, 1988

These Games were also superbly organized and turned a huge profit. No boycotts, disruptions, or political protests took place. However, on a sombre note for Canadians, Ben Johnson, after winning the 100-metre final in world record time, was disqualified for using a banned substance (anabolic steroids). Professional tennis players were allowed to compete for the first time.

Barcelona, 1992

These Olympics were entirely peaceful, and without incident. The Soviet Union was replaced by a "unified team" and some independent countries. Germany competed as one country instead of fielding an East and West team. Athletes from Yugoslavia and Slovenia took part either as independent competitors or as a part of Croatia's team. The USA "Dream Team," composed of professional athletes, participated in basketball.

Atlanta, 1996

Almost every country participated in these Games: there were 197 countries and 10,788 athletes involved. The Soviet Union had been replaced by the Russian Federation and several former Soviet Union regions now competed as independent countries. Despite extreme security, a small bomb was detonated in a public square.

Sydney, 2000

Sydney will be a hard act to follow for the next Olympics in Athens in 2004, as well as the already tainted site of Beijing in 2008. The Games were flawlessly organized and went off without a hitch (Figure 20.4). No incidents marred these Games, and the closing ceremonies were a spectacle for the

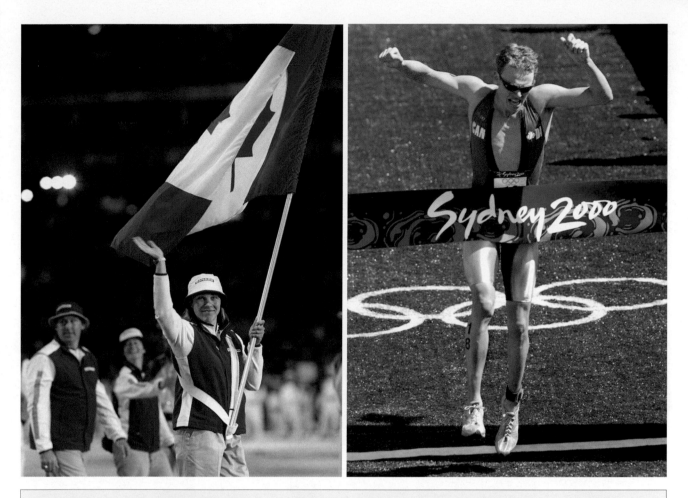

Figure 20.4 Sydney, Australia, lived up to its billing as a perfect site for the Olympic Games, and produced many memorable moments for Canadians.

ages. A total of 10,651 athletes competed in 300 events.

The modern Olympic Games have survived more than 100 years, two World Wars, boycotts, bombs, killings, and numerous political demonstrations (Figure 20.5). The Atlanta bomb is the sole blemish since the Seoul Olympics in 1988. It appears that a new era of sporting peace has evolved. Undoubtedly, security will still be on high alert for the next Games.

Sport and Canadian Culture

When Canada hosted the 1976 Olympics in Montréal, they were accompanied by many other cultural activities, such as art displays, music, and drama. This organization of activities indicated that the Games were seen as a **cultural event** as well as an arena for athletic accomplishment. This viewpoint runs in direct opposition to those who feel that sport and culture are antithetical, and should not even be used in the same sentence. Most people would agree, however, that sport and Canadian culture are intricately intertwined in many significant ways.

Why is sport such an important aspect of popular culture, not just in Canada but in other developed countries around the world? **Culture** can be broadly defined as the ways of life people create in any given society. Culture is not something that is imposed upon a group, but is a creation of people interacting with one another. The relationship between sport and culture can be explained by three theories.

Figure 20.5 Official Summer and Winter Olympic Games posters (1896-2002), as well as logos for the upcoming Summer Games in Athens, Greece, 2004, and Winter Games in Torino, Italy, 2006. The Winter Olympic Games are much smaller in comparison to the Summer Olympic Games, with fewer countries involved. Canada has enjoyed success in both the Summer and Winter Olympic Games, especially in recent years, as shown by the medal count in Table 20.2.

Table 20.2 Canada's Summer and Winter Olympics medal count.

Summer Games	Gold	Silver	Bronze
Paris, 1900	1	0	1
St. Louis, 1904	4	1	0
London, 1908	3	3	10
Stockholm, 1912	3	2	2
Antwerp, 1920	3	3	3
Paris, 1924	0	3	1
Amsterdam, 1928	4	4	7
Los Angeles, 1932	2	5	8
Berlin, 1936	1	3	5
London, 1948	0	1	2
Helsinki, 1952	1	2	0
Melbourne, 1956	2	1	3
Rome, 1960	0	1	0
Tokyo, 1964	1	2	1
Mexico City, 1968	1	3	1
Munich, 1972	0	2	3
Montréal, 1976	0	5	6
Moscow, 1980	Boycott – Did Not Compete		
Los Angeles, 1984	10	18	16
Seoul, 1988	3	2	5
Barcelona, 1992	7	4	7
Atlanta, 1996	3	11	8
Sydney, 2000	3	3	8

Winter Games	Gold	Silver	Bronze
Chamonix, 1924	1	0	0
St. Moritz, 1928	1	0	0
Garmisch-Partenkirchen, 1936	0	1	0
St. Moritz, 1948	2	0	1
Oslo, 1952	1	0	1
Cortina d'Ampezzo, 1956	0	1	2
Squaw Valley, 1960	2	1	1
Innsbruck, 1964	1	0	2
Grenoble, 1968	1	1	1
Sapporo, 1972	0	1	0
Innsbruck, 1976	1	1	1
Lake Placid, 1980	0	1	1
Sarajevo, 1984	2	1	1
Calgary, 1988	0	2	3
Albertville, 1992	2	3	2
Lillehammer, 1994	3	6	4
Nagano, 1998	6	5	4
Salt Lake City, 2002	6	3	8

A Quest for Excitement

Most sport sociologists agree that sport, whether for participants or spectators, appeals to our quest for excitement in otherwise somewhat uneventful lives. Sport offers physical challenge and psychological risks that are unavailable or hard to find in contemporary society. For example, when is Canada more galvanized than when our national team plays in the Olympics or World Championships (Table 20.3), or when Stanley Cup fever arrives each spring?

Sports Are Appealing

Every one of us has an appreciation of the tremendous physical skills that are required to participate in high-level sports. The amazing accomplishments of the elite athletes in any sport are certainly comprehensible to the adult or child who has attempted the same activity. As children grow, they continue to master the general skills of speed, strength, coordination, balance, and dexterity in games and play. These memories remain with us the rest of our lives.

Sport's Cultural Significance

Sport has cultural significance because of our need for the development of social identification and rivalries. We all feel the need to be part of a collective whole, and identify with our collective accomplishments. Students reading this text were not even born when the first Canada–Soviet hockey confrontation, called the "Summit Series," took place in 1972. When Paul Henderson (see box *The Spectacular Summit Series*) scored the series-winning goal in the last minute of play in the final and deciding eighth game, the entire nation breathed a collective sigh of relief. We celebrated the victory but, more importantly, we celebrated how Canadian individualism succeeded over the Soviet Union's communist regime.

This series reaffirmed our collective belief that Canada is indeed a unique nation, with an individual sense of identity. Many students can identify with this event, having just enjoyed the same excitement and pride when our Canadian men's and women's hockey teams won double gold at the Winter Olympics in Salt Lake City, 2002. Sport indeed is a significant part of Canadian culture (Table 20.3). It speaks volumes about who we are and how we feel about ourselves.

Canadian Athlete Role Models

Although an entire book could be devoted easily to Canadian athletes who stand out historically

The Spectacular Summit Series

Paul Henderson was the undisputed hero of the 1972 Summit Series. After four games, all played on home soil, Canada trailed the series with one win, two losses, and a tie. Then, Team Canada lost the first game in Moscow, 5-4. From this point onward, it was all Paul Henderson. He scored the game winner in Game 6, then did the same thing in Game 7, with a highlight-reel goal that he calls the best goal he's ever scored. Then came the one for which he will always be remembered. On September 28, 1972, in Moscow's Luzhniki Arena, Henderson scored what remains the most famous goal in Canadian hockey history. With only 34 seconds remaining in the deciding eighth game, he directed a rebound past Vladislav Tretiak to give Canada a dramatic come-from-behind 6-5 victory. The series captured the imagination of our nation. In the year 2002, Team Canada was voted "The Team of the Century" by a panel of sports writers.

Table 20.3 Canadian women's team at hockey world championships.

Women's World Hockey Championships		
Year	Final Score	Place
1990	CAN 5 - USA 2	1st
1992	CAN 8 - USA 0	1st
1994	CAN 6 - USA 3	1st
1997	CAN 4 - USA 3 (OT)	1st
1999	CAN 3 - USA 1	1st
2000	CAN 3 - USA 2	1st
2001	CAN 3 - USA 2	1st

as significant role models, we will focus on just a select few of these athletes who have made special contributions. The brief capsule summaries and boxes starting below present a wide range of accomplishments that range from sports excellence to significant sociological contributions to Canadian sport, all of which have served to shape sport in Canada and around the world.

Tom Longboat

Tom Longboat was born in 1884 on the Six Nations Reserve near Brantford, Ontario. Longboat shocked North America when he won the Boston Marathon in 1907. His time for the race was 2 hours and 24 minutes, a full 5 minutes faster than the previous record set in 1901. This was even more remarkable because the event took place in rain, sleet, and slush. Longboat instantly became a legend and Canada's national sport hero. He was considered the best runner in the world at that time.

Bill Crothers

Bill Crothers fought for honesty in sport. In the 1960s, he was considered one of the best middle distance runners in the world. In the 1964 Tokyo Olympics, he won a gold medal in the 800-metre race. Of equal significance was his devotion to crusading for drug-free sport. Crothers testified at the Dubin Inquiry in 1989.

Fergie Jenkins

Fergie Jenkins, originally from Chatham, Ontario, is the first Canadian to be inducted into the Baseball Hall of Fame in Cooperstown, N.Y., because of his accomplishments as a baseball pitcher. When Jenkins went to play baseball in the southern United States in the early 1960s, he found life very different from that in Ontario. Black athletes were not even allowed to eat in restaurants, but rather had teammates bring them food. Jenkins persevered to become the sole Canadian in Major League Baseball's Hall of Fame.

Basketball's Beginnings

When asked to design an indoor sport for the physical education students at the YMCA one winter, **James Naismith** nailed up two peach baskets, and a whole new game was born. James Naismith was a sports innovator and the inventor of basketball.

Naismith wrote down the original rules of the game on two typewritten pages in December 1891 and posted them in the gym at the YMCA International Training School in Springfield, Massachusetts, shortly before the first game ever played. The Naismith Memorial Basketball Hall of Fame stands in Springfield as a tribute to Naismith and the game he invented.

Nancy Greene

Nancy Greene's fearless skiing technique made her the "tiger of the slopes." Her storied career saw her win the World Cup of Skiing in 1967 and 1968, as well as gold and silver Olympic medals. Nancy started racing at 14, and two years later was chosen to the Canadian Olympic team for the 1960 Olympics at Squaw Valley. She was the first woman skier to do extensive weight training

Nancy Greene

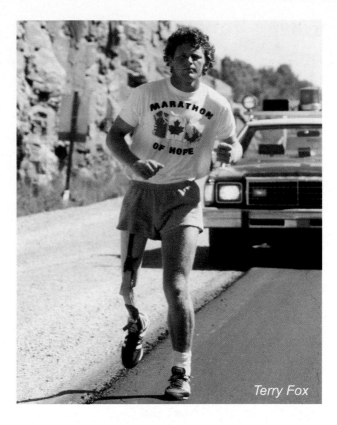

Terry Fox

to strengthen her legs. In 1968 she was named Canada's female athlete of the year, the best overall Canadian athlete of the year (Lou Marsh Trophy), and Canada's woman of the year. In addition to these accolades, she also received the Order of Canada. Over 30 years after her retirement, the Canadian Press named her the Canadian Female Athlete of the Century.

Paul Henderson

Paul Henderson became an instant Canadian hockey hero when he scored the winning goal to beat the Soviet Union in the classic "Summit Series" of 1972 (see box *The Spectacular Summit Series*). This was the first showdown between the best hockey players in the USSR and Canada. The series lasted eight games, and Canada needed to win the last game to claim victory for the series. Paul Henderson made this happen when he scored the winning goal in the last minute of play.

Terry Fox

Terry Fox, a disabled athlete, won Canada's heart when he embarked on the "Marathon of Hope" to raise money for cancer research. Fox's right leg had been amputated six inches above his knee, but undeterred he set out to run across Canada. He made it as far as Thunder Bay, Ontario, when he had a relapse, and was forced to abandon his quest. However, he did succeed in raising $24.17 million for cancer research. To this day, he remains an inspiration to all who know his story.

Rick Hansen

Rick Hansen is a disabled athlete. With both legs paralyzed, he embarked on his odyssey. He captained his wheelchair team to three national volleyball titles and participated in many marathons and basketball championships. He is best known for his 25,000-mile wheelchair tour around the world. His "Man in Motion World Tour" raised $10 million for spinal cord research.

Rick Hansen

Wayne Gretzky

Known as "The Great One," Gretzky had fun as the whole world watched. Born in Brantford, Ontario, in 1961, Wayne went on to dominate and re-write the NHL hockey record books. He set almost unsurpassable records in goals scored and assists in any one season, in addition to other records too numerable to present in this chapter. He remains a true Canadian sports hero.

Silken Laumann

In spite of her world ranking, Laumann was never well-known because rowing has never been one of television's glamour sports. Plagued by chronic back problems and a pinched sciatic nerve, ongoing physiotherapy and prudent training helped her win a second Pan American Games gold medal at the 1987 Games in Indianapolis. At Lausanne in 1991, she set a world record in the 2,000-metre sculls in a time of 7 minutes 22.41 seconds. She also won a gold medal in the World Championships in Vienna.

Silken Laumann

Myriam Bédard

Until Myriam Bédard, no Canadian had ever stood on the Olympic podium in a biathlon event. Bédard didn't start competing until she was 16, but from then on, her rise to stardom was spectacular. She finished second in the overall World Cup standings in 1991, then, in 1992 at the Winter Olympics in Albertville, France, she captured her

first medal, a bronze. During the following year, she won a gold and silver medal at the World Championships, finishing second in the overall World Cup standings. Then, at the 1994 Winter Olympics in Lillehammer, she became the first Canadian woman to win two Winter Olympic gold medals, making her the obvious choice for the Lou Marsh Trophy, awarded to Canada's outstanding athlete of the year.

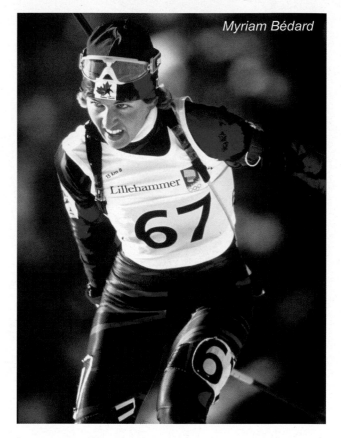

Myriam Bédard

Donovan Bailey

After the Ben Johnson tragedy in the 1988 Seoul Olympics, Donovan Bailey restored Canadian pride in track and field by winning gold medals in the 100-metre dash, as well as the 4 x 100-metre relay in the 1996 Olympics in Atlanta.

Marnie McBean and Kathleen Heddle

These two exceptional athletes represent Canada's most decorated summer Olympians, and as such

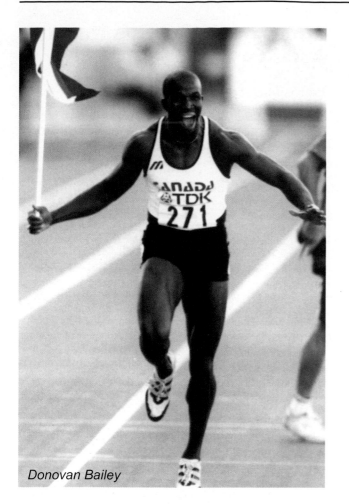

Donovan Bailey

deserve to be recognized accordingly. In the 1992 Olympic Games in Barcelona, these rowers won two gold medals in the women's straight pair and the women's eight competitions. Then, at the 1996 Olympic Games in Atlanta, they won a third gold medal, and later added a bronze. This third career gold medal was the largest number of Olympic gold medals won by any Canadian in the century. After the awards ceremony for this medal, as these exceptional competitors were getting ready for their next event, a reporter asked the two rowers if they had planned on making Canadian sport history. "No," they answered. "We didn't even realize it until you told us." Such is the character of legends.

The Business of Sport

The commercialization of sport has increased steadily since the 1950s. But sports have never been more commercialized than they are today. Economic factors now dominate major decisions about sport. An editor at Financial World, a major

Medal for McBean

Marnie McBean was the recipient of the 2002 *Thomas Keller Medal* awarded by the International Rowing Federation (FISA). The highest honour in the sport of rowing, the medal is presented to recognize an exceptional rowing career as well as exemplary sportsmanship.

McBean excelled in both sweep rowing and sculling, and she is *the only woman* to have ever won World Championships and Olympic medals in all boat classes for women: eights, fours, pairs, single sculls, double sculls, and quad sculls. She was a member of the Canadian national rowing team from 1989 until 2000 when a back injury forced her to withdraw from the Sydney Olympic Games. During her rowing career, the Toronto native won a total of 12 World and Olympic medals.

The 18-carat gold Thomas Keller Medal was presented to McBean by Dominic Keller, son of the late Thomas Keller, at the awards ceremony of the 2002 FISA World Rowing Championships in Seville, Spain.

Marnie McBean surrounded by Dominic Keller (l) and FISA president Denis Oswald (r).

economics magazine, has shown that sports is not simply another big business – it is one of the fastest growing industries in the USA.

It is true that success in sport today is measured by gate receipts and revenues from sales of concessions, licensing fees, merchandise, media rights, and internet hits. Athletes themselves are evaluated in terms of endorsement potential and being "fan friendly." In fact, an athlete's popularity often depends on a symbiotic tie to a corporate name (Figure 20.6). Golfer Tiger Woods, for example, earns approximately $40 million per year to endorse Nike.

The economic conditions that allow corporate business to thrive are also the same conditions necessary to the survival of commercial sport. Commercial sport grows and prospers best under four specific conditions: (1) a market economy, where material rewards are highly valued; (2) societies with large, densely populated cities, and hence with greater numbers of spectators; (3) regions with a relatively high standard of living and good transportation network and whose inhabitants have discretionary cash and free time; and (4) large amounts of capital, public or private, which can be used to build and maintain stadiums and arenas.

Professional Sport in North America

Professional sport in North America is often privately owned. The owners of most sports teams, including the top franchises in the NFL (National Football League), NBA (National Basketball Association), NHL (National Hockey League), and MLB (Major League of Baseball), are comprised of individuals or small partnerships. Those who own minor league teams in North America, both individuals and groups, rarely make money, and in fact are lucky to break even. Over the years, four football leagues, a few soccer leagues, a hockey league, a team tennis league, and many basketball teams and soccer teams have gone out of business. Building and maintaining a competitive franchise in today's market is extremely difficult and takes a lot of dedicated time, money, and effort.

Ownership of the top North American professional franchises is much different from ownership at other levels of professional sport. In 2000, franchise prices ranged from approximately $100 million to $700 million. Owners are large corporations, wealthy partnerships, or individuals who have millions or even billions of dollars (Figure 20.7).

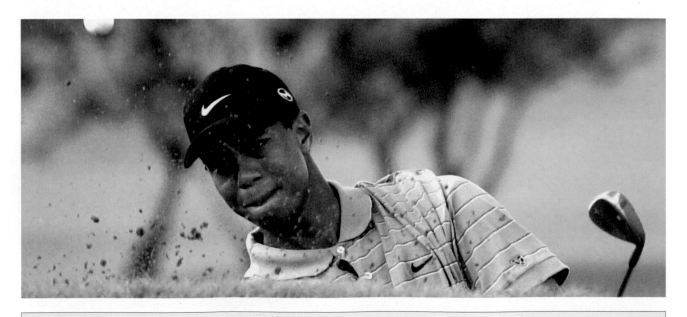

Figure 20.6 The irrefutable link between sport and business has become very lucrative for top performers in their respective sports.

Figure 20.7 Only large cities can afford to host major sport franchises and build elaborate competition venues, such as the SkyDome in Toronto.

Amateur Sport in Canada

Amateur athletes do not make a salary, and participate for the love of the game. Amateur sports do not have owners, but they do have governing bodies that control, promote, and sanction these athletes. These centralized sport authorities administer sports in most countries. These groups work with the national governing bodies of individual sports. Together, they have control over athletes, events, and revenues. In our country, Sport Canada and the Canadian Olympic Association are examples of these centralized authorities. Together, they develop the rules and policies that govern the national sport organizations in Canada, such as *Row Canada*, the *Canadian Track and Field Association*, or the *Badminton Association of Canada*. The organizational structure of the sport community in Canada is illustrated in Figure 20.8.

Sport Sponsorship

The distinction between professional and amateur athletes can also be seen in the area of **sponsorship**. Sports sponsorship is an agreement between a commercial company and an individual, team, or sport. The athletes agree that in return for money, they will advertise the names of the sponsors. They do this with clothing lines, corporate logos on their equipment, TV advertisements, and choice of commodities.

In terms of professional sport, we have already mentioned Tiger Woods' lucrative endorsement of Nike products. Hockey teams, baseball teams, and soccer teams throughout Canada are besieged with advertising slogans in their arenas, courts, and fields. The detailed arrangements of the advertising are worked out by the potential sponsors and the athlete or team. The bottom line is that professional teams and athletes make millions, and even billions of dollars from corporate sponsorships.

Amateur sports also benefit greatly from sponsorship. This sponsorship takes many forms. A growing number of university athletic departments have contracts with major sponsors, such as Nike, Reebok, Pepsi, Coca-Cola, and others. At the University of Toronto, for example, the varsity athletic program is sponsored by Coca-Cola and Gatorade (Figure 20.9). Seven Canadian Universities, including McMaster, Guelph, and

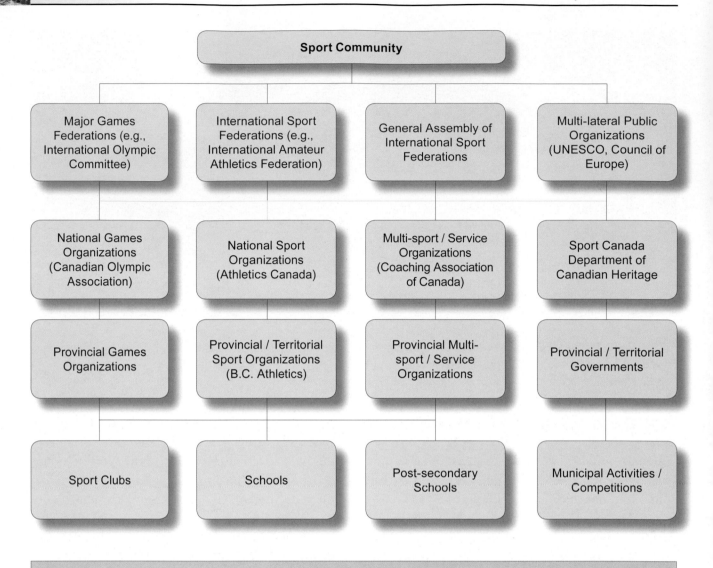

The Canadian Sport System

The sport system in Canada is made up of a number of organizations that provide sport programming and services at the national, provincial/territorial, and municipal level. These groups serve either individual sports (single sport organizations) or cater to numerous sports sharing common needs (multi-sport and multi-service organizations). Basketball Canada would be an example of the former, while the Coaching Association of Canada and the Canadian Wheelchair Sport Association are examples of the latter.

These organizations receive financial support from governments according to the scope of their programs and services. For example, a local amateur swim club may be funded by the municipality and participant fees, whereas the organization responsible for the national swim team competing internationally would be eligible to receive federal government funding. National sport organizations also obtain corporate financing through sponsorship agreements and generate revenue themselves through other sources including fund-raising and membership fees.

National Sport Organizations (NSOs) are members of **International Sport Federations (ISFs)** that establish the rules of the sport and, among other things, determine where their respective international competitions will be held. National Games Organizations, such as the Canadian Olympic Association, belong to international games organizations like the International Olympic Committee (IOC), which are the franchise holders for major games.

Figure 20.8 The sport community in Canada has a complex and diversified organizational structure.

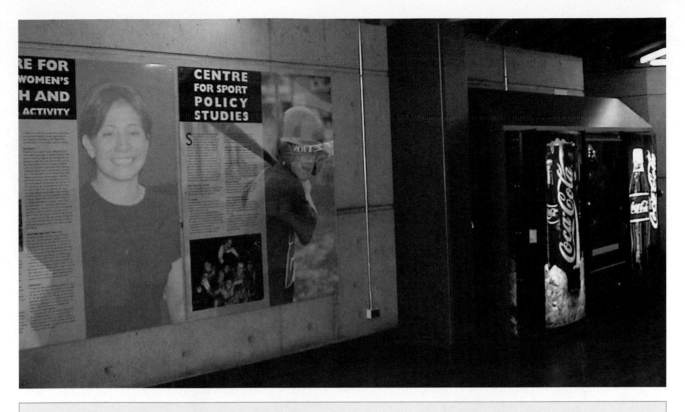

Figure 20.9 Coca-Cola vending machines sit conspicuously beside a poster describing the Centre for Sport Policy Studies at the University of Toronto.

Waterloo, have exclusive deals with Coca-Cola. One significant ethical problem that results from this marriage occurs when the legal contract requires the athlete or team to wear only certain products or drink only certain beverages on the bench or at half-time. What do you do when this happens? Some universities have taken the sponsor's product, poured it down the drain, and substituted a supplement that the research says best aids the athlete.

When a company looks at the possibility of sponsoring a sport or sporting event, it must consider several questions:

- Can the product be tied to the sport successfully?

- Is there sufficient public interest in the sport?

- Is there wide publicity in various media for the sport?

- Will the sport, team, or individual be seen on television?

- Will events draw large numbers of spectators?

- What are the chances this team or individual will win the title, championship, etc?

Advantages and Disadvantages of Sport Sponsorship

With professional teams and athletes, the potential advantages and disadvantages of sponsorship are determined by the bottom line – is money made or lost? The answer to this question determines whether the sponsorship will continue or be terminated.

The question becomes a little more complex in the case of amateur sports. Sponsorship allows amateur athletes or a team to give up their jobs and train full time; it covers day-to-day living expenses, pays for athletic clothing and equipment, and for the cost of training and competition.

The principal disadvantage of sponsorship is that once it is accepted, athletes and teams come to rely on it. Sudden withdrawal of the sponsorship brings with it financial problems and uncertainty. This provides the sponsor with a powerful influence over sport.

The control sponsors exercise can be even more pervasive. For example, sponsors have been known to request changes in the time-outs involved for that sport in order that they may have sufficient time to advertise their product over a television commercial break. These changes are often not in the best interests of the athlete or sport.

Finally, some sports have little TV appeal, and for this reason attract little sponsorship (Figure 20.10).

How It All Works

Sponsorships last for an agreed period of time, sometimes for several months and also for a number of years. Athletes, teams, and sponsors sign legal agreements. Neither party is permitted to pull out quickly if things go wrong. Poor sporting behaviour or problems in the personal lives of athletes may bring bad publicity to a sponsor. A sponsor may be linked to unethical practices. In either case, this legal agreement is difficult to terminate, so it is very important to select the correct athlete, team, or sponsor at the outset. Having said this, however, sport sponsorship continues to increase. This indicates that companies, athletes, and teams find it mutually beneficial.

The Nature of the Sponsor

A final, important consideration involves the nature of the sponsor. Should companies that sell

Figure 20.10 Most amateur sports do not attract corporate sponsors due to their low television appeal.

Figure 20.11 How many advertisements can you spot on these athletes and their equipment?

tobacco products, alcohol, and different foods that pose a health risk to society be allowed to sponsor sports? Many universities in Canada and the USA are no longer willing to sign agreements with these companies. In fact, several Canadian universities, such as the University of Toronto, have specific committees to consider sponsorship questions of this nature. The same cannot be said for professional sport (Figure 20.11). Many franchises are sponsored by precisely such organizations. This type of sponsorship remains an ethical dilemma. However, the legal issues involved were underlined in 1997, when the federal government passed Bill C-71, banning tobacco sponsorship for all sports and cultural events.

Sport as a Spectacle

In the previous section, we saw how sport has become commercialized and evolved into a big business. This trend has been accompanied by a variety of spin-off effects that are directly related to, and in some ways caused by, the media. Newspapers, magazines, books, radio, television, movies, and the internet pervade, and to a large extent, influence Canadian culture.

The different forms of media provide information, interpretation, and entertainment. When more than one of these are provided simultaneously, entertainment goals are likely to take prece-

Table 20.4 Top 10 U.S. network telecasts by household (1961-2000).

Program	Date	Average U.S. Audience
1. M*A*S*H (special)	2/28/83	60.2 million
2. Winter Olympics	2/23/94	45.7 million
3. Super Bowl XXX	1/28/96	44.2 million
4. Super Bowl XXXII	1/25/98	43.6 million
5. Super Bowl XXXIV	1/30/00	43.6 million
6. Super Bowl XXVIII	1/30/94	42.9 million
7. Cheers	1/20/93	42.4 million
8. Super Bowl XXXI	1/26/97	42.0 million
9. Super Bowl XXVII	1/31/93	42.0 million
10. Winter Olympics	2/25/94	41.5 million

Source: Based on data from A.C. Nielson as of April 30, 2000.

dence over information and interpretation goals. In other words, the media is interested in entertainment, and entertainment knows what sells. Let's now turn our attention to the different forms of media and briefly examine their relationships with sport.

Television

A writer for the New York Times once memorably described televised sports as a form of **sportainment**, the equivalent of a television movie that purports to be based on a true story. Nevertheless, sport on television is all pervasive. For example, in 2000, ESPN's three channels transmitted sports coverage to more than 150 countries in more than 12 languages. Sports also account for a growing proportion of income made from the sales of commercial time by television companies. Over the past two decades, they have paid rapidly escalating amounts of money for television broadcast rights for particular sports. NBC, for example, inked a $5.7 billion deal for exclusive U.S. rights to seven Olympic Games from 2000 through to 2012 (see box *Olympic Games – The Biggest Sporting Spectacle and Business on Earth*).

In the year 2001, the NFL paid $2.3 billion,

the NBA paid $660 million, MLB paid $420 million, and the NHL paid $120 million. Television companies feel these big expenditures are justified because sporting events are the most popular weekend television programs. This is why one full minute of advertising during the Super Bowl costs in excess of $1 million.

A look at Table 20.4 indicates the tremendous popularity of sports viewing. Although these figures are from the USA, it is estimated that Canadian viewership would rank in a similar fashion, although the actual figures would be reduced dramatically to reflect the fact that Canada has approximately one-tenth of the population of the United States of America.

Newspapers

At the beginning of the twentieth century, the single sports page in newspapers consisted of notices of upcoming events, a short piece about races or college games, and scores of local contests. By the late 1920s, that page had expanded into the sports "section," similar to the one with which we are familiar. Today, the coverage devoted to sports has grown to account for almost 25 percent of the major city dailies in North America. In fact, in most North American newspapers, more daily

Olympic Games – The Biggest Sporting Spectacle and Business on Earth

The executives of the major U.S. networks liken the Olympics to eight Super Bowls spread over 17 days. They believe the Olympic Games are the only show on earth that puts the entire family in front of the television at the same time.

Television coverage for the Olympics began in the United States in 1960 – a mere 15 hours of total coverage from Squaw Valley, California. Since then, the Games have grown to include wall-to-wall coverage valued at billions of dollars. The table below shows the amounts of money the International Olympic Committee (IOC) has been able to garner from U.S. networks from 1960 to the present.

Summer Games			Winter Games		
Year	Location, Network	Contract Value (U.S. $)	Year	Location, Network	Contract Value (U.S. $)
1960	Rome, CBS	$394,000	1960	Squaw Valley, CBS	$50,000
1964	Tokyo, NBC	$1.5 M	1964	Innsbruck, ABC	$597,000
1968	Mexico City, ABC	$4.5 M	1968	Grenoble, ABC	$2.5 M
1972	Munich, ABC	$7.5 M	1972	Sapporo, NBC	$6.4 M
1976	Montréal, ABC	$25 M	1976	Innsbruck, ABC	$10 M
1980	Moscow, NBC	$87 M	1980	Lake Placid, ABC	$15.5 M
1984	Los Angeles, ABC	$225 M	1984	Sarajevo, ABC	$91.5 M
1988	Seoul, NBC	$300 M	1988	Calgary, ABC	$309 M
1992	Barcelona, NBC	$401 M	1992	Albertville, CBS	$243 M
1996	Atlanta, NBC	$456 M	1994	Lillehammer, CBS	$300 M
2000	Sydney, NBC	$705 M	1998	Nagano, CBS	$375 M
2004	Athens, NBC	$793 M	2002	Salt Lake City, NBC	$545 M
2008	Beijing, NBC	$894 M	2006	Turin, NBC	$613 M
2012	Location TBA, NBC	$1.181 B	2010	Vancouver, NBC	$1.018 B

coverage is devoted to sports than any other topic, including politics or business. It is estimated that the sports section accounts for at least one-third of total circulation, and a large part of the advertising revenues for large city newspapers, whose daily readership numbers in the millions.

Books and Magazines

If you walk into any variety store, you will find literally dozens of magazines about sport (Figure 20.12). The reading ranges from major activities like hockey, football, baseball, basketball, and tennis to minority sports, such as the triathlon. These magazines document the biographies of today's superstars, provide up-to-date statistics, offer pages of pictures, and all forms of news about particular sports. For some reason, magazines about sports in general are harder to find, and traditionally have not done well in terms of sales.

If you explore bookstores, such as Chapters or Indigo in Canada, you will also find a large number of books devoted to individual and team sports. In many instances, these books are

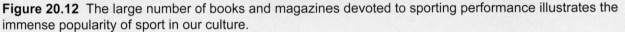

Figure 20.12 The large number of books and magazines devoted to sporting performance illustrates the immense popularity of sport in our culture.

biographies or autobiographies about classic or contemporary sports heroes. These books are published in great detail, and get very personal. Coaching and training books make up the next largest category of sales. Novels based on sport are much harder to find.

Radio

Before television, radio was the principal medium for reporting events live. Radio commentators described the action in a game instantaneously and in such vivid detail that the listener thought he or she was right there, watching it take place. Radio is a more economical medium for broadcasting because it involves a smaller number of producers and announcers than does television. For the listener, radios cost less and are much more mobile than televisions. This means that the listener can do other things at the same time

as listening to a sporting event. This is a very important consideration when the sport takes an extended time to complete, which is the case with hockey, baseball, basketball, and football games, as well as tennis matches.

Film and Video

Because sports are dramatic, and full of winners and losers, they should be especially suited to films and videos. Surprisingly, this is not the case. In 1996, the top five sports films were said to be, in order, *Hoop Dreams* (1995, basketball), *Raging Bull* (1980, boxing), *The Club* (1980, Australian football), *The Hustler* (1961, pool), and *Slap Shot* (1977, ice hockey). Today, video collections of great sporting moments remain very popular. Instructional videos for improving personal performance and coaching expertise also remain quite popular.

The Internet

The internet is unique from the other media forms in that it allows the consumer to access information at the time of his or her choosing. It is not limited to sequential programming. In the case of sport, most people use the internet as an extension of the existing media. Fans can link to team sites and listen to the game audio in the event that local radio stations do not cover the contest. They can go online to view game statistics and read commentary to complement what they have just read in the newspaper or seen on television. Other individuals may choose to join **fantasy leagues**, where they select team members for a given sport, then track their team's "performance" against other internet participants. Unlike other media forms, the internet provides virtual access to almost unlimited information from around the world that is potentially free from control of large media companies. This provides a relatively "unedited" version of sports reality.

In summary, sports and the media have come to depend on each other in many ways. Although they could survive without each other, both would be radically changed by the other's absence. For example, commercial sports would not be so widespread, and there would probably be less emphasis on high-level competitive sport. However, it is also likely that this would not translate into increased participation rates in the general population. Without exposure to sports and physical activity through the media, people would probably place a lower priority on these activities.

Being an Informed Consumer

In the previous sections, we have looked at Canadian sport history, the relationship between sport as a business, the impact of sport as a spectacle, and how all this relates to professional and amateur athletes. At this point, let us turn our attention to the question as to how sport commercialism, as well as our rich sports history, impacts on us as individual consumers. Just as corporations want to control athletes and sports teams, they also have a financial interest in the average Canadian citizen, and more relevant to this chapter, the Canadian high school student.

Factors Influencing Student Participation

Research indicates that people make decisions to participate in sports for different reasons at different points in their lives. This research suggests that the issues considered by a high school student who makes a decision about sports participation will be different from the issues considered by an adult, such as one of the teachers. Participation in sport and physical activity is linked to how the individual perceives the cultural importance of sports, and the impact of playing sports, with general social acceptance and the achievement of personal goals.

Obviously, the physical activity trends referred to in Chapter 19 play a significant role in our choice of active involvement. In addition, there are several other factors that influence our choices in terms of participation. For example, the physical education teacher and coach play a large role in our perception about the value of physical activity and sports. Quite often, students are either "turned on" to or "turned off" of active participation by these significant individuals in the school environment.

Many individuals have gone on to lifelong involvement in physical activity and sports due to the proper learning environment. By contrast, many people completely forsake physical activity because of negative school experiences. In addition, almost every high school student has one or more Canadian athletes whom he or she idolizes. Earlier in this chapter, we looked at 13 significant Canadian athlete role models. Every person reading this chapter would like to add several more names to that list. The major point to remember is that each and every one of us

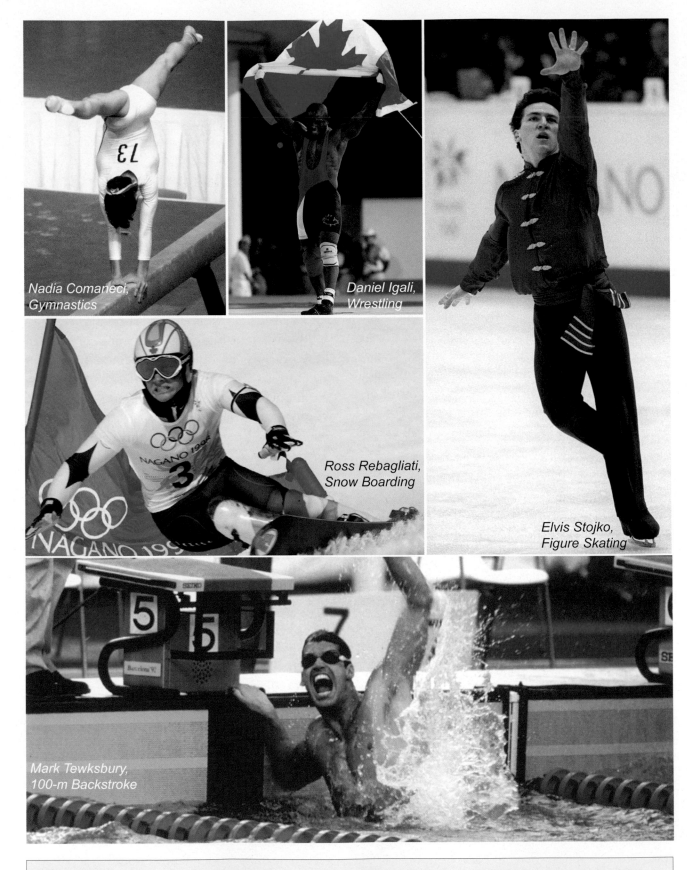

Nadia Comaneci, Gymnastics

Daniel Igali, Wrestling

Ross Rebagliati, Snow Boarding

Elvis Stojko, Figure Skating

Mark Tewksbury, 100-m Backstroke

Figure 20.13 Some very special athletes have had a dramatic impact on participation rates around the world.

has been touched by a Canadian athlete or team that has caught our attention (Figure 20.13). This emotional "link" has drawn us to further participation in the sport or physical activity of our choice.

The effect of Nadia Comaneci on gymnastics represents a valid example. Nadia was the first person ever to score a perfect 10.0 in Olympic history. In fact, she received seven of them at the 1976 Summer Games in Montréal. This remarkable athlete left the Games with three gold medals, one silver medal, and one bronze medal. This unprecedented performance resulted in significantly more interest in women's gymnastics around the world.

Finally, in the sections on the business of sport and sport as a spectacle, we saw how commercial interests and the various forms of media influence our perceptions of sport and physical activity. We are continuously inundated by media depictions of sport. We also see advertisements and programs that tout the value of regular physical activity. All of these exposures have an impact on our perception of physical activity. As an informed consumer, we need to carefully analyze the messages we receive, and put them in the proper perspective of what we want out of our personal lives.

The Benefits of School and Community Physical Activity

The benefits of participating in sports and physical activity are numerous. Regular participation results in improved fitness levels. More specifically, regular exercise is associated with improved cardiovascular conditioning, increased strength and muscular endurance, improved flexibility, and a lower percentage of body fat. This in turn leads to lower hospitalization costs to the government over the long term, since many major medical expenses are related to chronic degenerative conditions that are associated with inactivity. Research also indicates that regular involvement in physical activity of any kind is often associated with improved self-esteem and overall mood. These things taken in conjunction usually lead to greater overall

acceptance by one's peers. For more on the effects of physical activity, see Chapters 3-6.

Along a somewhat different line, varsity sports play a huge role in the development of school spirit. Few things bring a school together more than a big game or track meet against an arch rival. School pride is on the line, and emotions often run high. It is also refreshing to see teachers and students together, cheering on the home team. These situations go a long way in improving cohesion among faculty and students alike.

The Importance of Being an Informed Consumer

With all this talk about the business of sport and how sport has become increasingly commercialized, we need to reflect on how these cultural trends affect us. If we tune in to the different media forms, we will almost always feel the need to buy more and better sports and exercise equipment. After all, advertisers want to make money, so we are told that what we currently have comes up far short.

Technology

Technology continues to change sports, as it does other aspects of our lives (Figure 20.14). For example, in terms of equipment, tennis players hit with greater power when using larger racquets made of graphite, and strung more tightly. Golfers are said to have a distinct advantage when they play with clubs that have titanium heads, graphite shafts, and larger sweet spots. The introduction of the flexible fibreglass pole many years ago completely changed pole vaulting. Sprinting times are electronically controlled, and gauges are available to measure wind speed to ensure integrity of performances and past records. The gun and starting blocks are linked to detect false starts. The "cyclops" machine in tennis measures whether a serve is in or out.

Again, however, we need to ask ourselves whether these changes matter to us personally. If your goal is to become an elite athlete, then these

Figure 20.14 The technology of sporting goods equipment and design has resulted in much improved performance in sports.

changes take on added significance. To the average consumer, however, they are quite irrelevant. Taking the tennis and golf changes, for example, it is important to remember that it takes many years with any type of equipment to become competent at these sports. The choice of racquet or clubs will make little, if any, difference to your performance. For this reason, it is probably best to go with the less expensive equipment until that time when you are ready to advance to the next level.

Clothing

Another category that warrants attention is sports and physical activity clothing. Improved materials allow clothing to dissipate more heat for distance athletes, and make them more rain- and windproof for athletes participating in prolonged events, and more aerodynamic for any events related

to attaining high speed. Sports shoes have been designed for each specific exercise and sporting

Figure 20.15 Have you ever considered who pays for today's professional athletes' salaries? Where is the money coming from? Does it come from you, by choosing to attend professional sporting events? Do you mind paying $200 for a pair of shoes endorsed by your favourite player? The professionals are very grateful.

event. These shoes are tested biomechanically for maximum performance and durability. What is the difference between a $40 and a $200 pair of sports shoes? About $160 would be the best answer. Unless you are able to participate and compete at the highest levels, you will probably receive little benefit from all of these technological advances (Figure 20.15). The best thing to remember is that regular involvement in physical activity, regardless of equipment, is still one of the best ways to get fit, feel better about yourself, and have fun!

Summary

In this chapter, we traced a brief history of physical activity and sport in Canada, and looked at a brief retrospective of the Olympic Games. We then reflected on some of our most significant Canadian sports role models and summarized their accomplishments. The chapter also provided a brief analysis of the relationship between sport and culture in Canada. Sport is an important aspect of culture, both in Canada and around the world. It offers excitement and a chance to identify with others who share our interests and goals.

But sport has also become a business and a spectacle. In recent years, professional sports have evolved into a multi-million dollar industry. Many companies now sponsor professional and amateur athletes in exchange for endorsements of their products. This arrangement is especially beneficial for amateur athletes because it covers expenses and allows them to train full time.

The media has played a large part in the emergence of sport as an entertainment leader. Factors such as increased television and newspaper coverage have placed sport front and centre in our society and in our culture. Finally, the chapter looked at the impact of our sports history and the current sports trends on us as individuals, especially as they related to participation habits, school involvement, and the importance of being an informed consumer.

Key Words

Baggataway	Fantasy leagues	Sponsorship
Canada Games	Fitness and Amateur Sport	Sportainment
Culture	Act	

Discussion Questions

1. From the perspective of sport psychology, which of the Olympic Games summarized in this chapter do you feel has had the most significance? Justify your answer.

2. How has the role of sport in society changed in Canada over the years? Do you feel this change is beneficial or detrimental? Explain.

3. What do you feel is the role of sport and physical activity in the high school culture? Is the influence good or bad? Why?

4. What individual or individuals do you feel had the most impact on your decision to participate or not to participate in sports and physical activity? What made you feel this way?

5. Provide a brief description of which media form has had a significant impact on you in terms of your involvement in sports and physical activity. Why?

6. In your own words, explain the importance of being an informed consumer in the sports and physical activity domain.

7. Who is your favourite Canadian athlete role model? What is it about this person that makes him or her your top choice?

8. Share with your classmates a time in your life when you feel your decision to purchase a piece of athletic equipment may have been affected by advertising in the media. Try to recall how this media exposure made you feel about your purchase. In retrospect, do you feel you made the correct decision? Why or why not?

9. Have you benefited personally from any of the technological advances in sporting goods equipment? Explain your answer.

A Career in Sport Administration

NAME: Chris Rudge
OCCUPATION: CEO and Secretary General of COC
EDUCATION: BPHE, University of Toronto

What do you do?

I am currently the CEO and secretary general of the Canadian Olympic Committee (COC). My job generally entails coordinating the activities of the Olympic movement in Canada. These include raising funds from the private sector, maintaining government relations, managing the process of getting the teams to the Pan Am and Olympic Games, advocating for improved sport systems in Canada, sharing with all Canadians the values of Olympism through education programs and Olympic academies, and working with the international sport communities and the International Olympic Committee (IOC) to further the interests of Canadian sport on the world stage.

My numerous careers have included being president of Canada, Europe, and Latin America for the world's largest printing company as well as a member of the office of the CEO. I have owned and sold companies, worked in the publishing business, played and managed in professional sport (lacrosse), and taught physical education for 10 years in Toronto.

Why did you choose this career?

I've always had a basic philosophy of not wanting to be sorry for what I didn't do. My interests are extensive and eclectic, and I've always basically believed I could do anything I set my mind to. As I built my life I tried to choose careers that would both utilize my previous experiences as well as open new doors for growth. In that sense I have always made sure that I kept many doors open, and this allowed me a multitude of options when I decided to pursue change. In a sense change is a stimulant to me.... I need to find new mountains to climb regularly.

How did studies in physical and health education benefit your career?

I think you take many things from any learning environment, many of which you don't even realize that you are incorporating into your skill set at the time. Most of my metaphors in business and leadership came from sport. Virtually anything I have ever accomplished has been as a result of the commitment, passion, skill, and motivation of the people I've been fortunate enough to lead and work with. These things I learned in my younger years in sport and were reinforced during my studies at the University of Toronto. Business is a game.... You have a team, the others guys have a team, throw out the ball and play

by the rules. Understanding the game and developing strategies and tactics that seize the opportunity while maximizing the talent of your players will ultimately lead to success. I think that academic studies married with discipline-specific programs gave us broader insights into a wide range of life skills.

What other career options are available to students graduating from physical and health education?

I think career options are limited only by your imagination and drive. Clearly the professions require specific academic training and skill sets, and there is nothing preventing physical and health education grads from moving into these areas. Beyond that anything is possible.

What career advice would you give to students?

Pay attention to the following and you can't fail: (1) No matter what you do, be the best you can be. Never do a mediocre job just because you're waiting for something else to come along.... It won't. Talent and commitment are easily recognized and usually rewarded. (2) Look after today's job and tomorrow's job will take care of itself. Climb the stairs one step at a time. (3) Keep as many doors open as possible. When you see opportunity, move to it with conviction. (4) Find a mentor. A mentor will not only teach you but will also move you forward as his or her career advances. (5) Don't be afraid to ask questions or to say "I don't know." You won't learn if you are not inquisitive. (6) Don't worry about failure.... We all trip up occasionally. The measure of your character is how you handle adversity. Anyone can handle success.

What do you enjoy most about what you do or have done?

I enjoy the constant stimulation of learning new things about life, people, and myself. I still don't know what I'm going to do when I grow up!

In This Chapter:

What's in a Name? Diversity of University Physical Education Programs *524*

Career Opportunities for University Physical and Health Education Graduates *526*
    Teaching Careers *526*
    Health Sciences Careers *526*
    Fitness Careers *528*
    Sport and Recreation Administration Careers *528*
    Coaching Careers *528*
    Exercise Sciences Careers *530*
    Other Careers *530*

Enhancing Your Career Possibilities *530*
    The Diversification of Physical Education *532*

Summary *534*

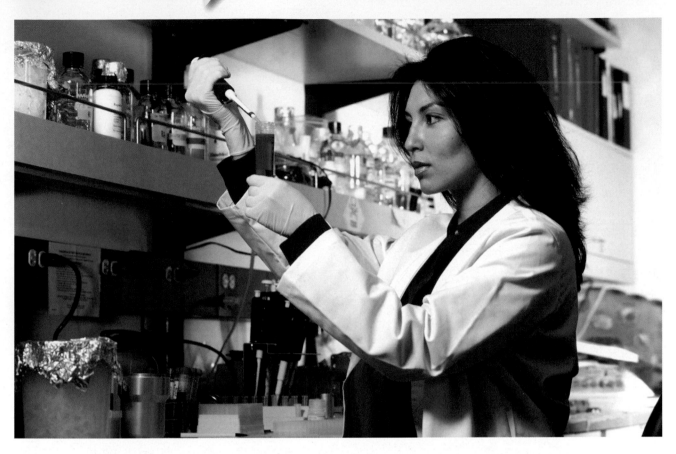

Career Opportunities in Physical and Health Education

After completing this chapter you should be able to:

- describe the diversity of university programs in physical education;

- identify career opportunities available to physical and health education graduates;

- describe the role of physical and health education in today's society.

Notions based on outdated stereotypes sometimes make physical education out to be a field for "dumb jocks." In addition, when people think about careers in physical and health education, visions of their high school P.E. teachers often come to mind. However, secondary school teaching represents but one of many opportunities available to university graduates in physical and health education. Completion of a university degree in physical and health education (or related field) can provide you with the foundation for numerous further career options such as sports medicine/medical doctor, physiotherapy, business and sport administration, community health, fitness consulting, and many other areas not directly related to physical and health education.

The increased emphasis on physical activity in today's society as a means to better health as well as improved business productivity has meant a corresponding expansion of career possibilities in a variety of fields.

The diverse positions filled by university physical and health education graduates are a continuing reminder that the old stereotypes and caricatures are fast disappearing. This chapter will survey the diverse learning and career opportunities available in physical education and health-related fields.

What's in a Name? Diversity of University Physical Education Programs

In order to pursue a productive career in fields related to physical and health education it is usually necessary to complete at least an undergraduate university degree. At one time, all Canadian university physical education programs where known by that name. This is because most such university departments were initially formed (between about 1940-1970) primarily to train those planning on teaching physical education in elementary and secondary schools.

Since then a huge evolution has occurred in the diversity of knowledge and its application in the field. This includes major developments in areas such as exercise physiology and biochemistry; sports medicine and exercise rehabilitation; fitness, nutrition, and health; sport psychology; biomechanics and applied ergonomics; sport and recreation administration; and fitness for elderly, disabled, or very young populations as well as advanced training and coaching techniques for elite athletes. This vast expansion of the scope of the discipline has also resulted in the growth of new and exciting areas for employment for graduates.

With the evolution of this expansion has come diversification and partial fragmentation of Canadian university physical and health education programs. None of these university programs is geared entirely to train physical education teachers, although many programs still do this as part of their mandate. And to avoid a narrow association of physical education with training for the school system, many university programs have over the past 20 years changed their name. Of the 36 Canadian universities listed in Table 21.1 that offer "physical and health education" related programs, 25 (or 69 percent) no longer include "physical education" as part of their name. Some of the names that physical and health education has evolved into include "**kinesiology**," "**human kinetics**," "**kinanthropology**," "**exercise sciences**," and "**human biology**" (Table 21.1).

In the 1960s most university physical education programs were also somehow associated (to a greater or lesser extent) with the university athletics departments. By the late 1990s this had also changed significantly. While some university physical education programs are still administratively linked to athletics, most others are administratively separate, part of faculties of science, or have been combined in some way with other university health science oriented programs, such as physiotherapy and nursing. These developments reflect the continuing evolution of the discipline and its widening contribution to and impact on Canadian society.

Table 21.1 University physical education programs across the country.

Name of Program	University
School of Human Kinetics and Recreation	Memorial University of Newfoundland (NFLD)
Department of Human Kinetics	St. Francis Xavier University (NS)
School of Health and Human Performance	Dalhousie University (NS)
School of Recreation Management & Kinesiology	Acadia University (NS)
École de kinésiologie et de récréologie	Université de Moncton (NB)
Faculty of Kinesiology	University of New Brunswick (NB)
Département d'éducation physique	Université Laval (PQ)
Département de kinésiologie	Université de Montréal (PQ)
Département des sciences de l'activité physique	Université de Québec à Trois-Rivières (PQ)
Department of Exercise Science	Concordia University (PQ)
Department of Kinanthropology	University of Quebec at Montreal (PQ)
Department of Kinesiology and Physical Education	McGill University (PQ)
Faculté d'éducation physique et sportive	Université de Sherbrooke (PQ)
Department of Kinesiology	McMaster University (ON)
Department of Kinesiology	University of Waterloo (ON)
Department of Kinesiology & Physical Education	Wilfrid Laurier University (ON)
Department of Physical Education Faculty of Applied Health Sciences	Brock University (ON)
Faculty of Human Kinetics	University of Windsor (ON)
Faculty of Physical Education and Health	University of Toronto (ON)
School of Human Kinetics	Laurentian University (ON)
School of Human Kinetics	University of Ottawa (ON)
School of Kinesiology	Lakehead University (ON)
School of Kinesiology	University of Western Ontario (ON)
School of Kinesiology and Health Science	York University (ON)
School of Physical and Health Education	Queen's University (ON)
Faculty of Physical Education and Recreation Studies	University of Manitoba (MB)
Physical Activity and Sport Studies	University of Winnipeg (MB)
College of Kinesiology	University of Saskatchewan (SK)
Faculty of Kinesiology and Health Studies	University of Regina (SK)
Department of Kinesiology and Physical Education	University of Lethbridge (AB)
Faculty of Kinesiology	University of Calgary (AB)
Faculty of Physical Education & Recreation	University of Alberta (AB)
Department of Human Kinetics	Trinity Western University (BC)
School of Human Kinetics	University of British Columbia (BC)
School of Kinesiology	Simon Fraser University (BC)
School of Physical Education	University of Victoria (BC)

Whether university programs are called physical and health education, kinesiology, or by some other related term, most deal primarily with various aspects of the study of human movement. Some programs specialize in the more scientific or quantitative aspects of this study, others more in health and fitness areas, and still others in recreation and leisure, etc. Some offer sports, fitness, and coaching practicals, others more laboratory experiences, and still others things such as co-op sport administration placements. However, most Canadian university programs are diverse and comprehensive enough to allow for study in many of these areas along with the development of various student interests. The name of a program alone will not always distinguish its specialization since many "physical education" programs also deal heavily with the health science or biomechanics of physical activity and many "kinesiology" programs may offer practical courses such as basketball or sport administration. Only by more closely investigating and comparing the full array of a university program's offerings can potential students decide which program is right for their interests.

Career Opportunities for University Physical and Health Education Graduates

Teaching Careers

Traditionally, the majority of university physical and health education graduates has gone on to become elementary or high school teachers. In Ontario one becomes a certified teacher after completing an undergraduate degree followed by a Bachelor of Education degree from a university college of education. A survey at the University of Toronto revealed that over 50 percent of the graduates from the School of Physical and Health Education in the early 1980s had entered teaching careers. By the late 1990s the prospects

for teaching careers for graduates of physical and health education and related programs had greatly diminished. Not only was the competition for places in colleges of education more intense, most Canadian school boards were greatly reducing their hiring. A cursory look at employment of kinesiology and physical education graduates of Wilfrid Laurier University in the mid-1990s shows that no more than about 10-20 percent of them had careers in teaching after graduation. Recently this trend has again reversed itself with many more opportunities currently available in teachers colleges and in teaching careers as many older teachers retire and the number of school-age children again begins to climb. It is difficult to predict whether this current trend will continue when present high school students are ready to enter the work force.

While teaching will remain a rewarding career option for some, many other graduates are availing themselves of the various other job opportunities that have become available to physical and health education graduates over the past 20-30 years.

Health Sciences Careers

Many physical and health education graduates are now opting for careers in the health sciences. These include professions such as medical doctor, chiropractor, physiotherapist, podiatrist, clinical kinesiologist, athletic therapist, clinical exercise therapist, massage therapist, and many others.

Many of these careers require further study after completion of an undergraduate physical and health education or related degree. However, the undergraduate physical education curriculum now provides the necessary preparation for entry (at times with advanced standing) into the other areas through courses in human anatomy and physiology, sports medicine, athletic injuries, community health, and biomechanics.

In addition, undergraduates in physical education often learn practical interpersonal and client/patient relationship skills, thus further aiding their career prospects in these expanding areas.

A Career in Physiotherapy

NAME: Joan Mlynarczyk
OCCUPATION: Sports Physiotherapy Specialist
EDUCATION: MA, BPHE, BSc PT, CATC

What careers have you pursued since graduating?

Following my undergraduate education, and through my experiences as a varsity athlete, I became interested in sports medicine. I specialized in athletic training during my master's in physical and health education, became a certified athletic therapist, and then pursued a degree in physiotherapy. As a physiotherapist and certified athletic therapist, I worked with university varsity athletes during the academic season, and traveled with our Olympic and National women's basketball team during the summer months. As an athletic therapist I have been appointed to over eight major Games medical teams, including the 1992 Summer Olympics. Currently, I own a private physiotherapy clinic called Osteopathy and Physiotherapy Specialists. I also hold a faculty appointment at McMaster University, and teach undergraduate physiotherapy students. I am also working towards a PhD in exercise science and biomechanics.

What do you enjoy most about your job(s)?

I definitely enjoy the variety and diversity. I enjoy treating and caring for athletes. I also enjoy the team approach to injury management, having other key practitioners with similar interests collaborating. Most of all, I enjoy the opportunity to continuously evolve, learn, and develop clinical and professional skills, to share this information with others as an educator, and to take good care of my patients using evidence-based and well-thought-out methods and treatment approaches.

What other career options are open to students who are interested in sports injury management?

Combining your physical education training with virtually any health care profession will make you more specialized to assess and treat athletes. Currently, the Sports Medicine Council of Canada sends physiotherapists, athletic therapists, and medical doctors to major Games as a part of the Canadian Medical Team. National teams also work closely with massage therapists, osteopaths, psychotherapists, strength and fitness trainers, as well as nutritionists.

Why did you choose a career in sports physiotherapy?

As a varsity basketball player, I sustained a significant injury to my hamstring muscle, which took several months to rehabilitate. I became fascinated by the whole process. While respecting the stages of healing, I had to keep myself as physically fit and as mentally ready as possible. This required a progressive program and good communication among coach, doctor, and athletic therapist.

What are the future job prospects in this area?

Excellent. There is an endless number of positions available for those who do good work. The characteristics I look for in employees in my clinic are good interpersonal skills, a passion and enthusiasm for their work, and a keen desire to continually improve their knowledge and skills through continuing courses and interests. I believe these characteristics will make people successful in anything they do.

What advice do you have for students who may be interested in sports physiotherapy?

A degree in physical and health education is beneficial. Expose yourself to volunteer work or work placements in one of the various health care professions, and try to gain as much information as possible about your area of interest. Most physiotherapists, athletic therapists, and physicians would be willing to spend some time answering your specific questions.

What salary range can be expected in this field?

Well, that would depend on the setting. Generally, physiotherapists will have a higher salary range than athletic therapists, and physicians higher salaries than physiotherapists. The highest salary opportunities for physiotherapists and athletic therapists are in private practice. Other environments such as hospitals, universities, and/or professional sports are more secure, but sometimes less financially rewarding. These other settings will be far more rewarding in other ways.

Graduates with strong backgrounds in health have also recently been finding employment with community health promotion and research organizations. Often these jobs require applicants to have a master's degree in health or exercise science and some research or health promotion experience.

The marketing of exercise and sports-related protective and corrective equipment such as braces, orthotics, nutritional supplements, and acute sports injury management equipment also continues to expand. Numerous stores specializing in this niche market, and employing physical education graduates, have recently opened up across Canada and growth in this area is expected to continue.

Fitness Careers

Since the late 1990s fitness is fast becoming a career choice for an increasing number of physical and health education graduates. The Canadian fitness industry continues to expand and opportunities related to fitness assessment, instruction, programming, administration, and sales are currently growing. Many graduates are finding full- and part-time employment as fitness instructors/programmers with fitness clubs, community centres, and YM- and YWCAs. Still others have become instructors and programmers for special populations such as the elderly in chronic care, and personal trainers for busy executives or master athletes. And in response to studies which have demonstrated increased productivity and decreased sick time for physically active individuals, many large corporations have also set up and staffed in-house fitness facilities for employee use.

Many physical educators are now also in sport administration. Physical and health education graduates have found careers in sports equipment sales, as well as in the business side of sports/fitness equipment manufacturing and distribution. These often overlooked career possibilities may best suit students with some marketing or sport administration emphasis in their undergraduate

physical education programs as well as practical work experience.

Sport and Recreation Administration Careers

Amateur sport remains another strong area of employment for physical education graduates. While much of Canadian amateur sport is still volunteer based, most Canadian sports governing organizations are administered professionally both at the provincial and national levels. Although it is often helpful for potential employees to have a background in the sport itself, organizations continue to employ physical education graduates with work experience and education in administration.

There are also growing opportunities in administration and marketing with professional, semi-professional, and junior sports teams and organizations. Other related employment opportunities include facilities management (i.e., stadiums, recreation complexes), sports camp administration, and intramural administration in universities and colleges.

Careers in the recreation and leisure field continue to expand, especially in non-traditional areas. One of these areas, and in which some university programs specialize, is outdoor adventure and tourism such as white water rafting, canoe touring, skiing, and mountaineering. University programs that emphasize recreation and leisure administration also prepare graduates for careers in the recreation hotel/tourist industry and local tourism, camping, and recreation promotion. These are all potential growth areas for employment opportunities for physical education students.

Coaching Careers

Graduates of physical and health education programs have traditionally been employed in coaching young and elite athletes. Many coaching positions in Canada involve volunteer or part-time work. However, some sports, particularly

A Career in Fitness

NAME: Susan S. Lee

OCCUPATION: Personal Trainer-Manager
Executive Director, Canadian
Personal Trainers Network
Program Manager, University of
Toronto Athletic Centre

EDUCATION: Harbord Collegiate (Secondary
School)
BPHE, University of Toronto
(Bachelor of Physical and Health
Education)
MPE, University of British Columbia
(Master in Physical Education)

What do you do?

I work in the field of personal training as the executive director of the Canadian Personal Trainers Network (CPTN), an organization which specializes in education, certification, leadership, and advocacy for fitness professionals. Since 1993, I have provided leadership for the development of a national certification program for personal trainers, and specialty workshops (such as The Art and Science of Personal Training, Golf Conditioning Specialist, Post-Rehabilitation Functional Training, Nutrition 101, and Pilates Mat and Ballwork Specialist). At the University of Toronto Athletic Centre, I implemented and supervise the personal training program which services the students, staff, faculty, and community members.

What is unique about your roles?

I am often viewed as a resource person for the fitness and personal training industries. I have had the opportunity to develop curriculum for new workshops and technical manuals for the industry. I co-authored a book entitled *Business Strategies for Personal Training*. I am often quoted by the media as a result of interviews for magazines and newspapers. I speak on fitness and personal training at national and international conferences, allowing me to share my insights with international audiences in China, Australia, Canada, and the U.S.

How did studies in physical and health education benefit your career choice?

My university degrees provided me with a solid foundation in the theoretical frameworks and practical applications of physical and health education. The combination of a strong academic background and broad work experiences provided me with the confidence to pursue my professional career. My education has allowed me to develop new products and services for the fitness industry, and to become a leader and mentor for novice personal trainers.

What are the future prospects in the field?

Personal training is becoming a popular career choice for individuals who enjoy physical activity and want to share this enthusiasm with others. The demand for personal training is on the rise as a result of the aging population, as well as concerns about the rise in obesity among children, youth, and adults. Physical activity through personal training will be one career to address the health needs of the general population.

What career advice would you give to students interested in this field?

Students interested in personal training will need a solid background in physical and health education through university or college, or personal training workshops. Most trainers now become certified with a reputable organization to identify themselves as quality trainers. The public is looking for well-educated personal trainers. To succeed in the industry, learn about cardiorespiratory, strength training, and flexibility training techniques. Excellent communication skills are required as well. You can practice your communication skills through public speaking and develop your interpersonal skills by working on projects with peers or participating on a sports team. To be an entrepreneur in the industry, business courses will provide you with the skills to become successful in your own personal training business.

What do you enjoy most about your profession?

I enjoy meeting people and learning about their unique needs and interests, and then being able to provide them with an exercise program and the professional support to reach their goals. I often find myself training people for the sport of life. I am in the business of improving people's quality of life by helping them become stronger and more confident through physical activity. A sedentary client who can be transformed into an active one is one of my greatest rewards.

those with large club bases such as figure skating, swimming, and gymnastics, do employ relatively large numbers of full-time coaches throughout Canada. Squash and tennis clubs also tend to employ full-time "pros" to coach elite and recreational members. As well as having considerable background in the sport as successful competitors themselves, many of these coaches are also graduates of university physical and health education programs. In the education system, many of the coaches of school teams are employed as full-time physical education teachers.

Exercise Sciences Careers

Upon completion of an undergraduate degree in physical and health education, some students choose to pursue further education in the form of master's and/or doctoral (PhD) studies. For some of these individuals there are employment opportunities as university professors, researchers, or laboratory technicians in the wide array of exercise sciences. For others, there are increasing opportunities in areas related to community health promotion and research with private or public organizations or as independent consultants.

Community colleges which offer fitness- and health-related courses also have employment opportunities for these individuals. Although these areas require between two to six years of further university education beyond the undergraduate degree, the employment rewards can be very fulfilling.

It should be noted that in an increasingly competitive marketplace, some students find that they are more marketable in some of the previously discussed areas if in addition to a bachelor's degree in physical and health education, they have completed a graduate degree in an area related to their employment objectives.

Other Careers

Graduates from physical and health education programs have been exposed to a wide variety of courses in the arts and sciences, and like other university graduates, can market themselves for the wide array of employment opportunities available to any university graduate.

Several areas of employment, although not directly related to physical and health education, also tend to attract graduates of these programs. Over the last 20-30 years, many graduates have found employment as police officers, fire fighters, and ambulance attendants because of the physical and interpersonal skills required in these careers. However, all these jobs require further training beyond a physical and health education degree.

Sales and marketing careers have also been popular alternatives for physical education graduates. In particular, the insurance industry and the pharmaceutical and textbook sales areas have in the past been successful career alternatives for physical education specialists. In fact many business-related career alternatives have been successfully followed by graduates of physical and health education with special skills and interests. Some of these include careers in computer software design, law, translation, and various entrepreneurial endeavours.

Enhancing Your Career Possibilities

As in any field, having an appropriate university degree is only one of many often necessary attributes. To increase one's marketability, a student should be encouraged to gain as much work and practical experience as possible. This is often accomplished by volunteer work, summer or part-time employment, or through university cooperative education (co-op) programs.

In selecting volunteer or employment opportunities students should try to involve themselves in activities that are as closely related to their future career goals as possible. A focused approach to career planning and enhancement is usually more successful than drifting through your education without any set plan.

A Career in Coaching

NAME: Mike Locicero
OCCUPATION: President, Just Goaltending Inc., Concord, Ontario; Goaltending Training Specialist and Business Entrepreneur
BACKGROUND: Emery College, Ontario (Secondary School) Humber College 1977-86, professional hockey player (2nd and 3rd level goaltender, German Hockey League; 1st division goaltender, Italian Hockey League)

What do you do?

I operate a facility and a program that specializes in training the physical and mental aspects of goaltending. I run goaltending training camps throughout the summer, and I work one on one with goalies throughout the year.

Why is your program unique?

Unlike most other sports, such as golf or gymnastics, goaltending has never been broken down and analyzed systematically. But we have created a program that does precisely this. We work with goalies on an individual basis both on the ice and in a puck shooting range. We use a procedure that minimizes trial and error, and we train goalies on three components: skating, form, and net. We want to develop "thinking" goaltenders by promoting learning, understanding, and finally, application. Usually we see a dramatic improvement in two and a half hours of training.

What was your motivation for starting "Just Goaltending"?

I enjoyed the years I spent playing hockey in Europe, but I often wondered what I would do once it all ended. Every summer I returned to Canada, and when I was 19, I bought my first puck shooting machine. So I would take on three or four hockey players each summer and train them at goaltending. One summer my cousin suggested that I start a goaltending school, and from that point on, I operated a summer camp for goalies. In 1986 I retired from hockey and opened a permanent training facility.

Was it difficult to start the business?

When I first started "Just Goaltending," I maintained a second job until the business became lucrative. Our reputation has been established by word of mouth alone, so it has taken a lot of work to get where we are now.

Did you have problems making the transition from athletics to business?

As an elite athlete, you are relieved of all responsibility. Somebody takes care of your accommodations and travel, and all you must do is show up on time for practices and games. I was very dedicated to training, but it took me five years to become responsible in the "real world" outside of hockey. I had to learn how to survive. I had to dedicate myself to my business and make it work. I knew it was not going to be an easy transition, but having the business certainly made it easier. Unlike many of the guys I played with, I had something to look forward to, and something new to focus on.

What do you like best about your job?

Watching kids improve and develop right before my eyes. I see them thinking and making adjustments and corrections before I even open my mouth. I love sharing in their joy when they succeed. I get more satisfaction from working one on one with a goalie than I ever would from working with an entire hockey team. Goaltending is my first love.

What career advice do you give your students?

Respect the time you give to the sport, but realize that the limelight is only temporary. Although hockey is there for you today, it probably won't be there to pay the bills when you're older. I see a lot of young players failing to prepare themselves for retirement, so I stress the importance of an education. Play it smart and enjoy it while you can.

Summer practice on the artificial ice at "Just Goaltending."

The Diversification of Physical Education

The past several decades have seen a significant diversification of the role of physical and health education in Canadian society. Career possibilities for physical educators have extended beyond the traditional ones of teacher and coach and now include various aspects of health practice and promotion, sport and leisure administration, fitness instruction and administration, exercise science research, and various business possibilities related to sport, health, fitness, and leisure.

Numerous other career possibilities more peripherally related to physical and health education such as law enforcement and financial sales and management are increasingly attractive to physical and health education graduates, due in part to their unique skills. These changes reflect the diversification of the physical and health education discipline as well as changes in the activity patterns and needs of Canadians.

Health, fitness, recreation, and leisure have become integrated into many more facets of today's business as well as the private lifestyles of Canadians. Awareness of the relationship of

A Career in Sport Administration

NAME: Anne Zavaros
OCCUPATION: Assistant Facilities Manager of Athletic Centre
EDUCATION: BA, University of Waterloo (Recreation with a business option in the co-op program)

What do you do?

I oversee the provision of services to all Faculty programs and Athletic Centre members, i.e., athletic equipment set-up for all programs and special events, towel and laundry service, and other day-to-day customer service. I hire, train, supervise, and schedule staff. I assist with facilities budget administration and monitoring specifically related to small facility renovations and maintenance, equipment purchase and maintenance, towel and laundry budgets.

What is unique about your job?

Working with students. Students are a pleasure to work with. Young people making a career in physical education, health, and recreation are enthusiastic and eager to work and learn in this environment.

Why did you choose a career in sport administration?

I followed my heart. I was a provincially ranked tennis and badminton player and also taught both sports and coached badminton at the university level. My love of sports and athletics simply made me want to make a career of it. I wanted to share my knowledge of sport and to promote athletics and a healthy lifestyle.

What do you enjoy most about your profession?

There is never a dull moment. Our ever-changing calendar of programs and special events provides a daily challenge. The job is a physically active position, not a "desk job," which appeals to me very much.

What career advice would you give to students interested in entering this field?

Do as much as you can to get "hands-on" experience. Network and meet other professionals in the field and keep in touch with them. Learn as much as you can and never stop learning throughout your career. Love what you do!

A Career in Business

NAME: Tom E.S. Wright
OCCUPATION: Commissioner, Canadian Football League (CFL)
EDUCATION: Upper Canada College (secondary school)
BPHE, University of Toronto (Physical and Health Education)
MBA, York University (Marketing and Finance)

What do you do?

The commissioner of the Canadian Football League is basically the chief executive officer of the league. Even though football is a game, in order for the CFL to succeed it must be run as a business. Apart from managing the business of the CFL, I work very closely with the owners and governors of our nine member clubs to help ensure that their teams are successful while building the game of football in Canada. I also represent the league in our relationship with government, amateur sport, other professional leagues, and of course the media.

What is unique about your job?

There are not that many professional sport leagues in North America let alone Canada, so to be the commissioner of one is rather unique. While I work for a league that competes against other sports properties and entertainment businesses, the people I work for also compete against each other. Believe me, that makes it unique.

Why did you want to be the commissioner of the Canadian Football League?

I am as passionate about our country as I am about sport. In Canada, there are precious few things that connect our country and unite our communities like the Canadian Football League and the Grey Cup. I also am able to marry my vocation with my avocation. That makes me a pretty lucky guy.

How did studies in physical and health education benefit your career choice?

After my BPHE degree, I decided to take my MBA and pursue a career in the business of sport. While the MBA was important for a business career, the more valuable lessons were learned while taking my BPHE. Time management, discipline, teamwork, leadership, and resourcefulness were all skills learned during my four years at the University of Toronto. As you can imagine from the list, not all of them were learned in the classroom.

What do you enjoy most about your profession?

The people, the challenge, and the fun. The people that I meet across our country reflect the diversity of our nation. They are passionate, they are interesting, and they are strong willed. They are as insightful as they are opinionated and they are terrific people to work with. In terms of challenge, with the benefit of the rear view mirror the most rewarding times in my life have been the most challenging. And in the end, it's important to have fun. Each of us will spend more than half of our waking life working, so it is easy to see the importance of having fun and enjoying what you do.

What career advice would you give to students interested in entering this field?

Be patient and trust your instincts. Good things happen to good people and in the world of business, it is more like a marathon than a sprint. It is equally important to believe in yourself and have confidence in your abilities. Nobody knows better what makes you tick than the person on the other side of the mirror. Don't spend time being that which you're not. Recognize your strengths and live through them.

fitness, health, and productivity has increased significantly among the general public as well as among business interests. The diversification of physical education as a discipline is partially a reflection of these trends.

Summary

This chapter illustrates how educational and career opportunities in physical and health education and related disciplines have become much more diverse over the last several decades. This reflects both the expanding perspective of the physical and health education discipline as well as its impact on and reaction to trends in Canadian society.

At one time, university physical education programs were designed primarily to train teach-

ers for elementary and secondary schools. Now teaching is only one of a variety of challenging and rewarding careers available in the field of physical and health education. Many graduates use their physical education background as a stepping stone to a career in the health sciences, such as medicine, chiropractic, physiotherapy, athletic therapy, and massage therapy. The growing fitness industry is also a popular employment choice, along with recreation and sport administration. Of course, coaching is always an option for physical education graduates.

University programs have evolved to accommodate this increased diversification of physical education. Expanding career opportunities for students trained in physical and health education or related disciplines indicate a bright future for the field and those pursuing its study.

Key Words

Exercise science   Kinanthropology
Human kinetics   Kinesiology

Discussion Questions

1. Which physical and health education career areas appear to be growing at present?

2. Which physical and health education career areas appear to have fewer opportunities than in the past?

3. How do the terms kinesiology and exercise science relate to physical and health education?

4. How do the diverse employment prospects for physical and health education graduates reflect trends in Canadian society?

Beyond the Gym Class

- **Introduction to Research Methods**

- **Introduction to Statistical Concepts**

In This Chapter:

Research Defined *538*
    How Is Research Useful to Me? *538*

The Scientific Method *540*

Validity of Research *542*
    Internal Validity *542*
    External Validity *542*

Types of Research *542*
    Field Versus Laboratory Research *542*
    Basic Versus Applied Research *542*

Characteristics of the Researcher *543*
    Open-mindedness *543*
    Knowledge *543*
    Intellectual Curiosity *543*
    Perseverance *544*
    Honesty *544*

Ethics in Human Participant Research *544*
    Rights of the Participants *544*

Preparing a Research Project *546*
    Obtaining References *546*
    The Art of Research Writing *546*

Writing the Research Report *547*
    Title *547*
    Abstract *547*
    Introduction *547*
    Statement of Research Hypothesis *548*
    Review of Literature *549*
    Methods *549*
    Results *549*
    Discussion *549*
    Summary *550*
    References *550*

Poster Presentations *551*

Summary *551*

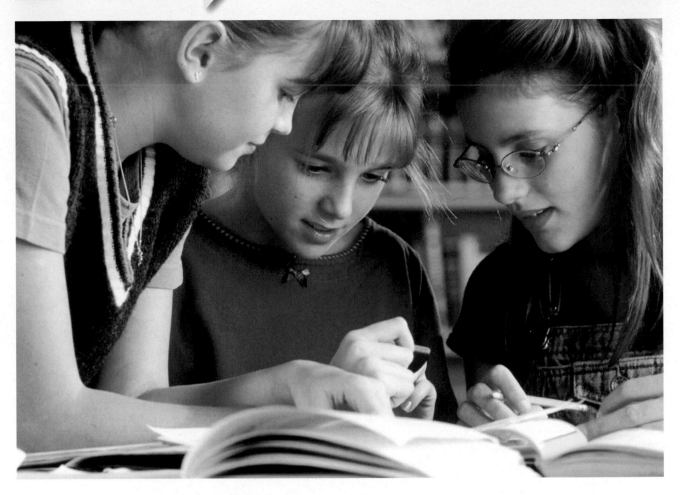

CHAPTER 22

Introduction to Research Methods

After completing this chapter you should be able to:

- describe the purposes and importance of research;

- explain the various research methods and concepts;

- describe the ethics in human participant research;

- demonstrate skills for writing and presenting a research project.

Research is an integral part of the modern world in which we live, yet many misconceptions persist that have characterized research as dull and impractical. The mere mention of the word invokes fear and loathing among students. But research and statistics (Chapter 23) are poorly understood by many people, and their value is often underrated. Television, radio, newspapers, and magazines are continually bombarding us with research in some form or another, and we take for granted the vast information that is presented to us daily.

It seems that nearly everything we do is based in some way on research that has been or is presently being done. Whether we make decisions concerning who we should vote for, what we should eat, how much we should exercise, what soap we should buy, or whether or not we should drink alcohol, these are informed decisions made with the aid of research.

Although we may not fully appreciate the degree to which research pervades modern societies, it cannot be disputed that we live in a world driven by statistics and research. Just imagine what it would be like to go through life without knowing what effect smoking has on your health, or how effective a certain medical procedure is before an operation. This chapter will highlight the significance of research and various research methods and concepts.

Research Defined

What exactly is research? When many people think of research, visions of scientists in lab coats conducting complex experiments involving dangerous chemicals come to mind. But research is much more far reaching than this narrow characterization might lead you to believe. Research can be defined as a logical, methodical procedure for solving problems and discovering knowledge. Stated simply, it is a means by which information is gathered to develop new knowledge, and provide a basis for decision making. It is

essential to a wide range of activities.

Coaches may like to know what practice schedule will be most effective for their athletes; doctors may want to discover better ways to treat certain medical conditions; parents may want to know when they should introduce their children to physical activity and sport; and as a student, you may wish to determine which university you should attend and the field of study you should pursue. A knowledgeable understanding of the relevant issues would prove essential to making an informed decision in each case.

How Is Research Useful to Me?

If we are to be productive and effective professionals, it is important to stay on top of current knowledge and research. But research may be compromised in several ways. Consider the case of advertising. Companies will frequently boast that their product clearly outperforms those of its competitors. But such claims are often misleading and even false. Critical understanding of what makes research legitimate and identifying the limitations of a study therefore can be important.

Being able to distinguish fact from fiction in research allows us to make decisions with confidence. A decision to buy low-fat foods will be based not on celebrity endorsement, but on the numerous legitimate studies that have shown that diets high in fat are linked to increased risk of heart disease.

A critical understanding of research procedures will also have an impact on other areas of your life. You may begin to question so-called facts presented in the media, and gain a new perspective on the use of selective information. You may also discover that you become more productive as your ability to gather and use appropriate information increases (Figure 22.1).

In an age dominated by a knowledge explosion, and a continually expanding information superhighway, the ability to access information quickly and effectively has become a much valued skill. Researching in the library

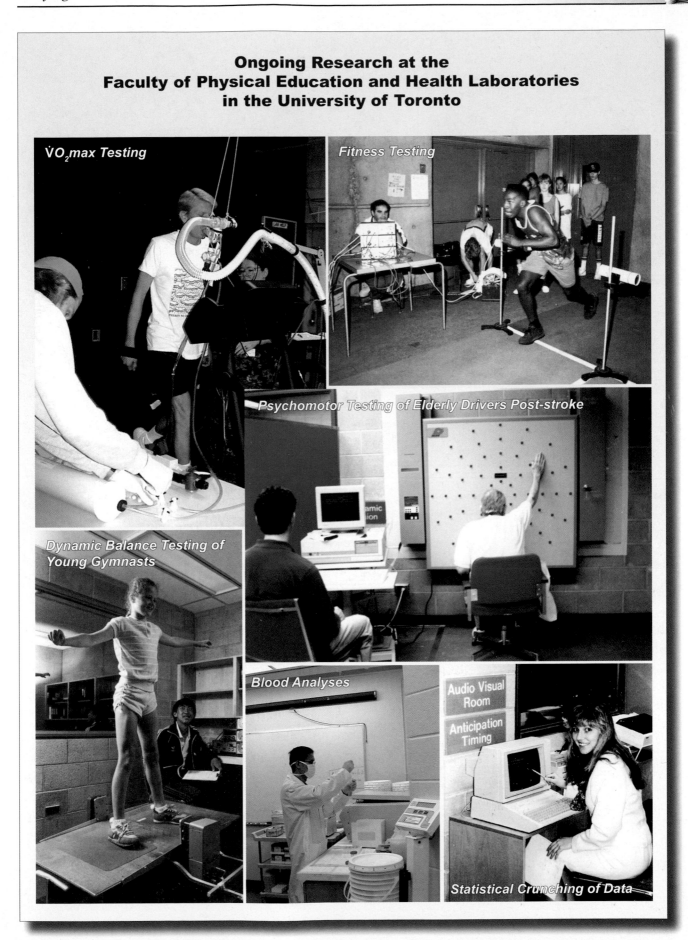

Ongoing Research at the
Faculty of Physical Education and Health Laboratories
in the University of Toronto

$\dot{V}O_2max$ Testing

Fitness Testing

Psychomotor Testing of Elderly Drivers Post-stroke

Dynamic Balance Testing of Young Gymnasts

Blood Analyses

Audio Visual Room

Anticipation Timing

Statistical Crunching of Data

Figure 22.1 Research in training methods provides answers about how much, how often, at what intensity, and what kind of exercise produces an optimal exercise/training effect.

need not cause anxiety or prove discouraging. An organized approach to a subject or issue can make a world of difference. All you require is the desire to learn, and the ability to apply a general method and to carry it out to its logical end.

The Scientific Method

Many researchers use the **scientific method**, which involves logical organization in answering questions and interpreting data. This approach can be applied to just about any problem, and provides a useful outline to follow when tackling a research question. It involves several important steps that must be followed. The following example involving the value of the Dynavision board (Figure 22.2) in the training of visual skills

and speed of reaction in athletes will illustrate the steps involved in the scientific method.

- *State the problem.* Does training on the Dynavision board improve visual skills and reactions for hockey goaltending performance?

- *State a testable hypothesis.* Dynavision board training over a considerable period will improve goaltending performance.

- *Plan the methods to be used in carrying out the study.* Who are the participants? What will their ages be? Sex? Experience? How many training sessions will be involved? What measurements will be made? How and when will measurements be made? What apparatus will be required? What statistics will be used?

- *Carry out the study.* The participants will

follow the prescribed procedures set out by the researcher.

- *Analyze the data using appropriate statistics.*

- *State the conclusions of the study.* There is a positive correlation between improvement in Dynavision performance and ball-stopping ability of the participant.

- *State a new research question.*

The scientific method is based on logical organization and clearly defined measurement techniques. Consequently, data may be collected in a manner that makes results more accurate and dependable. However, many researchers may have a pre-existing idea about what they would like to find in their results, and this bias may affect conclusions drawn from the study.

For example, the manufacturers of the Dynavision board would certainly hope that the apparatus would prove beneficial to improving goaltending performance, while researchers may not be inclined to find the same result. Results that show slight improvements may be meaningful to the inventor of a piece of equipment on the one hand, and statistically insignificant to a researcher who has no vested interest in it.

The scientific method, while the most logical and organized approach, is not the only type of research practiced. Other less scientific methods, such as trial and error and tradition, are also common. In fact, many of the decisions we make in our daily lives are based on such methods. When it comes to choosing what food to buy, we often base our decisions on our senses (I like the taste), tradition (I've always bought this brand), or other subjective factors (I feel good when I eat it). Advertisers prey on this by making products more colourful and aesthetically pleasing to the eye. While we may be aware of the advertisers' tactics, we would probably be surprised by the impact they have on the decisions we make. It would seem that

Figure 22.2 The Dynavision board has been used in many applied research studies at the University of Toronto, Faculty of Physical Education and Health.

if celebrities tell us that the shoes they endorse are of special quality, our decision to buy their shoes is an easy one. However, the scientific method would probably lead to the best information in most situations; trying out several shoes for yourself for your own unique needs would presumably yield a better decision in the end.

Validity of Research

The value of research depends on its validity. There are two types of research validity, internal and external.

Internal Validity

Internal validity refers to the overall quality and design of the research including the accuracy of measurements made, the statistics used, and the effect of limitations and constraints. Under ideal conditions, internal validity should be high, so that research questions can be tested reliably and findings can be replicated to reflect accurate results.

External Validity

A study's generalizability, or potential application of its results, is termed **external validity**. Although there is no statistical value given to quantify it, external validity describes the degree to which the results of a study can be used under different conditions. For example, if a study is done to determine the effects of caffeine on teenage boys, could the results of that study be used to describe women as well? How about older men and women?

The more the results can be generalized to other conditions or populations, the more externally valid a study is deemed to be. Different research questions obviously will be dealt with differently, so the varying levels of internal and external validity will depend on what the research study hopes to accomplish.

Types of Research

Different types of research have their advantages as well as disadvantages. A distinction can be made between field and laboratory research.

Field Versus Laboratory Research

Field research, as its name suggests, is done out in the field, outside of the tight controls of a laboratory environment. It is performed in the so-called real world where a limited number of variables are manipulated. Examples would include research done in schools, parks, hockey arenas, swimming pools, hospitals, and classrooms.

Laboratory research differs in that it is conducted in a highly controlled environment that gives the researcher greater control over an experiment (Figure 22.3). Such control improves the soundness of the research, and thus results in higher internal validity. However, field research often allows for more application of results (external validity) than laboratory research because it is performed in an environment that more closely resembles the conditions of the outside world. It is clear that both types of research offer benefits as well as limitations.

Basic Versus Applied Research

The distinction between basic and applied research is not clear-cut; however, the essential difference lies in the degree of specificity of the research question being explored.

Basic research is research that is performed without a specific purpose in mind, being conducted for gaining knowledge alone. For example, a physical education teacher may decide to have students play a new game that they have never been taught before to discover how they respond to the game.

Applied research is conducted with a specific

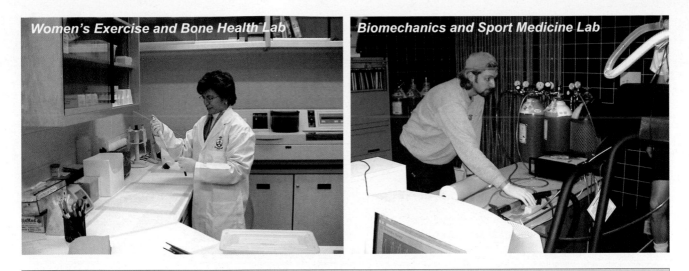

Figure 22.3 Laboratory research studies at the University of Toronto's Faculty of Physical Education and Health are conducted in highly controlled environments.

purpose in mind. Consider the hockey coach who wants to know if training on a Dynavision reaction board will improve his goalie's performance in the net (Figure 22.2).

Both types of research, however, exist on a continuum, and neither necessarily represents an extreme. While the teacher may have introduced the new game without any specific purpose in mind, she may come to discover that the game is well liked, improves fitness levels of participants, and allows for more involvement from all the students. By making these observations, the physical education teacher may choose to play the game more often and recommend it to other instructors – a significant application.

Characteristics of the Researcher

Obviously, some researchers are more competent than others. Understanding what constitutes a capable researcher may help you along the path to successful researching in your own pursuits. This section describes several important characteristics a researcher must possess: open-mindedness, knowledge, intellectual curiosity, perseverance, and honesty.

Open-mindedness

First, researchers must be **open-minded**. This would include being open to asking new questions, exploring possible explanations for results, and not being satisfied by traditional strategies and findings.

Knowledge

Second, **knowledge** in a particular subject area is beneficial, because the researcher with such knowledge can ask the right questions, identify the concerns that exist, as well as avoid known limitations and potential constraints. While knowledge is an advantage, the desire to learn more is also an important trait when conducting research.

Intellectual Curiosity

Third, the researcher must possess **intellectual curiosity**. This entails having the desire to learn more by reading and forging imaginative connections between the various types of information. Curiosity serves to heighten interest in a specific area and allows research to make greater strides than it might if confined to a narrow rule-bound perspective.

Perseverance

Fourth, an able researcher will have **perseverance**, continuing on in the face of adversity. Some experiments do not lead to the expected results but open doors to new approaches.

Honesty

Finally, a dependable researcher must be **honest**. Developing accurate knowledge is a goal of every area of study, but dishonesty about method, data, or results can greatly impede such a goal. Therefore, researchers have a duty to present their findings clearly and honestly, without an attempt to mislead or unjustly influence others with incomplete information.

Ethics in Human Participant Research

Much of what researchers know today has been obtained by extensive research involving human participants. However, certain conditions need to be observed. Individuals participating in studies have the right to a safe environment and to humane and professional treatment. In fact, every university and hospital has a panel of experts called an **institutional review board (IRB)**, which judges the quality and safety of studies before they can be performed.

Rights of the Participants

The general research rights of all human participants are outlined as follows.

Informed Consent

First, a potential participant must give **informed consent**. This decision should be based on sufficient information and comprehension of a study. Often, this involves a potential participant reading and signing a written document (consent form, Figure 22.4) that outlines the details of the

study clearly and completely. The form should include background information about why the study is being conducted, an explanation of the procedures, potential risks or discomforts that may arise, potential benefits, as well as the rights of participants to withdraw at any time. After reading this form and having any questions answered by the researcher(s), clearing up any possible questions, the participant should have sufficient knowledge to make an informed decision about his or her own participation.

Confidentiality

Another right of the participant is **confidentiality** and anonymity. This implies that observations made during the study should be kept as confidential as possible.

Safe Treatment

All participants in a research study deserve **safe, professional treatment**. Measurements should be made competently and in a way that respects the participant's dignity. The participant must also be confident that potential risks and discomforts will be minimized and unnecessary risks avoided.

What Do You Think?

When human participants are involved in a study, they are assured a safe and quality environment and may end their involvement at any time.

Animals used in studies, on the other hand, really have no say in their fate, and many would argue that animals should be given the same considerations. What do you think?

Knowledge of Results

The last right of the human research participant is the **knowledge of results**. After the participant's

General Consent Form

I hereby consent to participate in a study, under the supervision of John Smith of the Faculty of Physical Education and Health at the University of Toronto, involving the use of the following apparatus (circle and initial one or more):

1. Dynavision Apparatus

2. Minnesota Manual Dexterity Test

3. Pursuit Rotor Test

4. Ring Replacement Test

5. Dynamic Balance Stabilometer Apparatus

6. Bassin Anticipation Timer

The equipment has been shown and described to me. I am fully aware of the minimal risks involved with this/these apparatus in each of the tests in which I have decided to participate. I have been fully advised of the purposes and potential benefits of the experiment.

The experimenter has my consent to use data derived from my performance in any research report which may result from the study. I understand that my anonymity is guaranteed in all reports.

I am aware that my participation is completely voluntary, and that I have the right to terminate my participation at any time during the study, and to retrieve or destroy the data from my participation up to the time of my withdrawal.

I have read all of the above conditions.

_____   _____
Date   Signature of Participant

_____
Signature of Witness

If you have any questions about your participation, please feel free to contact Dr. J. Smith at (416) 555-5055.

Figure 22.4 Example of a general consent form used in the Psychomotor Laboratory of the Faculty of Physical Education and Health at the University of Toronto.

performance is completed and the information gathered, the investigator still has a professional obligation to provide the participant with feedback about the results, and the general outcome of the study when such information becomes available.

Preparing a Research Project

Putting together a good research paper or project takes a lot of time and dedicated effort. But before you begin it is advisable to review existing literature covering controversies, methods, and participants used in the past. Recommendations made by other researchers should be undertaken as well. This will provide the necessary background for successful research.

Obtaining References

References you will use are either primary or secondary in nature. **Primary references** refer to an original book, article, or report, while **secondary references** are those in which the original work is described or cited by someone other than the author of the original work. It goes without saying that primary references provide more precise information as it comes directly from the original author. Secondary references (such as those in most textbooks), on the other hand, cite other works and thus may be affected by the bias transferred from author to reader. Therefore, secondary references should only be used in research projects when primary sources are not available.

Library Search

Retrieving information for research can be intimidating for the student. But it need not be because libraries are well equipped to make doing research quick and efficient. Not only are there bibliographies, indexes, and research reviews available to locate information on specific topics, but in today's world of expanding technology, computerized information retrieval is becoming increasingly widespread. Some of the computer database indexes (such as Sport Discus) that are now available allow information to be accessed with speed and updated periodically with ease. Numerous journals exist that have specific information on health, physical education, and recreation, making it an easier task to do effective research on these topics.

Once you have sufficiently researched your topic of interest and you have a relatively strong grasp of the subject, it is time to start writing the research project. Anyone who is considering writing a research proposal would be advised to plan well in advance before beginning the writing process.

The Art of Research Writing

Obviously, research writing involves more than just getting words down on paper that make sense. The researcher must consider that good writing is clear, concise, unambiguous, and makes reading more enjoyable. Therefore, any writer should make an honest attempt to treat the writing of a research paper as an art. This means planning ahead, developing an outline, keeping a dictionary and thesaurus handy, reviewing several times, and avoiding plagiarism completely. Now that virtually all word processing programs are equipped with spelling and/or grammar checks, simple errors of spelling and grammar reflect poorly on a piece of writing. Use the spell check before submitting any piece of work – but remember that there is no substitute for careful proofreading.

Your choice of words is also critical to the outcome of the project. Errors involving tense, abbreviations, and the misuse of words serve to lower the quality of your writing. The key to effective writing is to keep it simple. Don't try to impress readers by using polysyllabic words that you don't understand or don't know. Avoid wordiness and the use of jargon whenever possible. A concise, well-argued research paper will capture and hold interest longer than one that rambles or is unnecessarily difficult to follow.

Writing the Research Report

The researcher must understand the many steps that must be taken and the various components involved in writing a research paper. A brief outline of what is required follows.

Title

The **title** of a paper may seem insignificant on the surface, but it reveals some very important information. The title should indicate precisely the subject of the paper. This way, potential readers will be able to determine whether or not the study is related to their interests or needs.

Since computer searches for related information are often based on identifying key words in titles, a comprehensive title can make searching for information easier for others as well as encourage citation and use of a study. Because titles must convey such important information, they are typically 10 to 15 words long, neither too broad nor obscure. A title should be understandable to readers, and get to the point as quickly as possible. It would be a good idea to consult journals and other resources in the library for examples before committing to a title.

Abstract

The **abstract** serves as a short, concisely worded summary of what the study is about, its intended purpose, the participants involved, the method of investigation used, results obtained, as well as some general conclusions drawn from the study. An abstract should be brief, and is generally limited to about 100 to 150 words. To make it distinguishable from the rest of the paper, abstracts tend to appear in journal articles below the title in italics or bold print.

Introduction

The introduction to any piece of writing is often very important to its overall effectiveness. The

---

Select Journals in Health, Physical Education, and Recreation (HPER)

- *Adapted Physical Activity Quarterly*

- *American Journal of Health Promotion*

- *International Journal of Sport Biomechanics*

- *International Review of Sport Sociology*

- *Journal of Philosophy of Sport*

- *Journal of Physical Education, Recreation & Dance*

- *Journal of Sport Psychology*

- *Journal of Sports Medicine and Physical Fitness*

- *Medicine and Science in Sports and Exercise*

- *Perceptual and Motor Skills*

- *Quest*

- *Research Quarterly for Exercise and Sport*

Sample Abstracts

EFFECT OF EXERCISE ON SIMPLE REACTION TIMES OF RECREATIONAL ATHLETES

T. McMorris, P. Keen
Centre for Sports Sciences, West Sussex Institute of Higher Education

Abstract. *To examine the effect of moderate and fatiguing exercise on the simple reaction times of recreational athletes, 12 subjects took a simple reaction time test while at rest and while cycling on a Monark cycle ergometer at 70% and 100% of maximum workload. To estimate 70% and 100% of maximum workload, the subjects underwent a standard incremental test until exhaustion, defined as subjects not being able to maintain the required pedal rate of 70 rpm. Simple reaction time during maximal exercise was significantly slower than in the other two conditions, which did not differ significantly from one another. Heart rate and rate of perceived exertion differed significantly for all three conditions.*

PHYSIOLOGICAL AND ANTHROPOMETRIC PROFILES OF ELITE PREPUBESCENT TENNIS PLAYERS

T. Buti, B. Elliott, A. Morton
Department of Human Movement and Recreation Studies, University of Western Australia

Abstract. *Eight male and eight female elite prepubescent tennis players were tested to determine their anthropometric and physiological profiles. No significant differences between girls and boys were found for height, weight, bone widths, girth measures, $\dot{V}O_2$max, anaerobic power, flexibility, muscular endurance, and grip strength in preferred and non-preferrred hands. The girls had a significantly higher level of fat as measured by sum of skinfold thicknesses. Both boys and girls had a significantly higher grip strength in preferred than non-preferred hands.*

introduction should present the general problem under consideration, and clearly reveal the value of the study. Its main purpose is to justify the need for the study, and to describe how it will highlight the topic under examination. This can be accomplished by providing a brief outline of the existing relevant literature that highlights conflicts, concerns, and controversies surrounding the topic of interest. Further, relevant terms and techniques to be used in the paper should be distinctly described or defined for clarity.

Once the broad context for the paper has been established, it is important that the discussion be narrowed down to the specific aspect being examined in the present study. The last sentence of the introduction might begin: "The purpose of this study is to …" or "The present study is being carried out in order to …" In order to bridge the gap between the general topic and the methods by which the question will be investigated, key phrases such as these can clearly impart the purpose of the study to the reader.

Statement of Research Hypothesis

The **research hypothesis** of your study is a general statement that summarizes, in a few sentences, the overall purpose of your study or what the expected outcome is. This statement should disclose to the reader what your study proposes to find through scientific investigation. An example might be: "It is hypothesized that swimmers will have faster simple reaction times than hockey players." This statement would let the reader know that the researcher would expect swimmers to have faster simple reaction times than hockey players after conducting the study. Stating a research hypothesis, however, does not necessitate the word "hypothesis" being mentioned because it is often implied by the purpose of the study itself.

Review of Literature

This section of a research paper is written in the past tense because you are providing the reader with a background highlighting what has already been done in the area you are studying, including findings and methods used. A **review of literature** should summarize what previous studies have found related to your study, and to lay the groundwork for your own hypothesis. The process of writing this review can also help you to narrow your focus of study, and upon completion of this section, the specific purpose of your study should become clear to you, as well as to the reader.

A review of literature should be based *primarily* on recent research articles that reflect the most current ideas and findings in the area. A review might be interpreted by many students as simply summarizing one study per paragraph. While it would certainly be easier to organize a review of literature this way, the intended purpose of such a review is to analyze the literature critically, rather than just listing the results and conclusions of other studies. Instead of taking this approach, this section should be organized around common concepts or themes that arise throughout various articles. This can prove challenging, especially if the topic is not thoroughly familiar, but it can also help provide a deeper understanding of the topic.

Methods

Knowledge of the method used in a study is essential if readers are to interpret the findings presented appropriately. The section on **methods** should therefore contain information regarding how the study was conducted, providing enough detail to allow the reader to replicate the experiment. While the description must be precise and complete, it must also be as compact as possible. The section should include the number and descriptions of the participants involved (e.g., age, sex, experience), how measurements were made, what apparatus was involved, the procedure followed (usually chronological), and any statistical analyses performed.

Results

In this section of the research report, the data stands on its own; interpretation is reserved for the discussion section. Consequently, the **results** are often brief and presented as concisely as possible. This section often begins by making reference to the relevant data in some summarized form such as tables, figures, and graphs – this simplifies large amounts of data, allowing the reader to follow the obtained results comprehensively and to extract key information more efficiently. It is often stated here whether the hypothesis was accepted or rejected based on the appropriate statistics.

Although knowledge about commonly used statistics is helpful in assessing the reliability of results, we will not examine such statistics in detail here. Still, each graph and table used to display statistical results should be numbered and provided with an accurate caption describing its purpose. Also, the axes of graphs should be clearly labeled with an accompanying key (i.e., independent variables on the x-axis and dependent variables on the y-axis; see Chapter 23 for further details).

Discussion

The **discussion** section serves an important role by interpreting the results and linking them to the general problem outlined in the introduction. It attempts to explain the findings of the study and to put them into perspective by comparing the results to those produced by other studies. Since findings may be in accordance with or contrary to those of other studies, an analysis is often necessary. For example, this section might answer the question why your study did not yield the significant results obtained by another research study examining the same question.

Limitations of the Study

Another component to the discussion is a presentation of the **limitations** of the study. Some aspects of the study may have been affected by extraneous variables, affected by short duration, or the number and type of participants may not have been ideal, and so on. These limitations are not always directly laid out, however, and a reader must often scrutinize the study for them. However, an honest review of the limitations of research can do much to further the collective enterprise of knowledge.

Implications of the Study

This discussion section may also elaborate any **implications** the study may have. For example, if a study showed that a specific simulator significantly improved the golf performance of amateurs over a period of training, coaches may be inclined to use the simulator or recommend it to other instructors. Applying the results of research studies to real-world experiences is essentially the reason most research is conducted. But researchers must be careful about applying the findings of a single study to other conditions (recall the criterion of external validity in research). Consider the example above – because the simulator improved amateurs' golf games, does that mean that younger golfers will necessarily benefit? What about professionals? Therefore, the application of results to other participants and conditions may be limited to those conditions that most closely resemble the original study.

Recommendations

Finally, this section may suggest **recommendations** or improvements to the current study that may be helpful to others who read the paper. Suggestions might include variations in the participants used (e.g., age, sex), alternative methods of measurement or experimental design, or changes in the length of the study. Overall, the main purpose of the discussion is to comment on the general problem with which you started with respect to the experimental results.

Summary

The **summary** concludes the research report. It provides a brief overview of the need for the study, statement of the problem, methods, and main findings.

References

It is important to provide a list of all references with your paper to indicate the sources for your information. Providing references is part of your professional obligation. It is essential to the integrity and honesty of all research.

Referencing in the Text

There are many styles of **referencing**. The style commonly used by many researchers in the Health, Physical Education, and Recreation (HPER) fields is the one recommended by the American Psychological Association (APA). When citing a reference in the text in this style, the author's last name and the date of publication of the reference are included in parentheses. For example: "It was first stated by Magill (1979) …" or "It was reported (Magill, 1979) that ….." This style is relatively easy to use because no numbering is involved and changes are easy to make if references are added or deleted as the paper is being prepared. It is important to keep the citation close to the text to which it relates, whether it be at the end or in the middle of a sentence.

Reference Section

The **references** cited in the text should be gathered at the end of the paper in a bibliography or reference section. The list of articles and books used is organized alphabetically by author, using the APA style. If the same author has written more than one item referred to, these are listed in chronological order by date of publication. Examples are provided in the box *Examples of Referencing APA Style* for a journal article, a book, and a chapter in an edited book; for more details on referencing, refer to the APA manual (1994).

Researchers should take time to reference data in order to avoid errors and to ensure accuracy. All sources of ideas, direct quotations, paraphrasing,

Examples of Referencing APA Style

- *Journal Article*

Mokha, R., Kaur, G., & Sidhu, L. S. (1992). Effect of training on the reaction time of Indian hockey players. *Journal of Sports Medicine and Physical Fitness, 32*(4), 428-431.

- *Book*

Pollock, M. L., Wilmore, J. H., & Fox, S. M. (1984). *Exercise in health and disease: Evaluation and prescription for prevention and rehabilitation.* Philadelphia: W. B. Saunders.

- *Chapter in an Edited Book*

Carron, A. V., Brawley, L. R., & Windemeyer, W. N. (1998). The measurement of cohesion in sport. In J. L. Duda (Ed.), *Advances in sport and exercise psychology measurement* (pp. 213-226). Morgantown, WV: Fitness Information Technology.

and evidence must be fully documented. Take the time to cite from primary references whenever possible, and double-check your references.

Poster Presentations

There are other ways of presenting the results of a research study. The **poster** method provides one example that is especially helpful to students.

The same major sections that compose a research paper (e.g., title, abstract, introduction, methods, etc.) should also be included when research is presented in a poster format. But this method allows you more scope, and lends itself especially to those individuals who have a sense of imagination and creativity. Not only can such a project be easier to complete, more visually appealing, and fun to put together, but it also makes viewing and discussing the research easier. A well-organized poster that makes good use of space, colour, and creativity and flows coherently from one point to the next is an excellent vehicle for presenting research.

There are certain points to keep in mind when preparing a poster to present your research most effectively.

1. It is important first of all to have a clear and bold title to catch the reader's attention.

2. Because the poster may be viewed from a distance, it is a good idea to keep the font or typeface dark and relatively large for clarity. This includes fonts for tables, illustrations, photographs, and legends.

3. Make sure you keep all tables and figures simple and uncluttered to enhance their visual effectiveness.

4. Use strong visual contrast to enable readers to distinguish among various colours and symbols (many people may have some degree of colour blindness).

In general, use your imagination. Don't be limited by traditional materials and symbols to create your display, and put thought into presenting your research by emphasizing the most important points and eliminating unnecessary detail that may tire the eyes of readers.

Summary

Research, the logical and methodical procedure for solving problems and discovering knowledge,

Preparing a Poster Presentation

It is extremely important to present your work in a clear and concise manner. When one considers the amount of time and energy that goes into preparing a research project, to have effective communication dashed by an incomprehensible poster presentation would be a missed opportunity for both the presenter and the target audience. Attention is invariably drawn to posters with a crisp, clean design and a snappy title. Keep the following guidelines in mind when developing a poster presentation of your own.

1. On a large display board surface, the title and author(s) should be displayed prominently across the top border with large lettering. Subheadings should be proportionately smaller. A combination of capital and lower-case letters works better for material other than headings and subheadings. It should be obvious where to start inspecting the poster and where to go next – generally, right to left, top to bottom. You may even consider numbering sections or using arrows.

2. Poster displays must include the **ABSTRACT** (in the upper left hand corner) and other **TEXT NARRATIVE**. Depending on the focus of the research, one also typically includes some or all of the **TABLES**, **FIGURES**, **ILLUSTRATIONS**, **PHOTOGRAPHS**, and **LEGENDS**. Choose large type or print fonts and points that can be viewed from a short distance. One example that works well is a Times font in 18 point.

3. There are many effective materials to use for your display, ranging from paper, to paper and photographs mounted on thin poster board, to having the entire display printed on a scroll. Avoid mounting material of thick or heavy backing, as push pins will be unable to secure it effectively to display boards.

4. Include and arrange your material so a coherent and straight-forward story is told without your presence. Emphasize the most important points and avoid overwhelming the viewer with too much detail. Leave some open space in the design. A tightly packed space will tire the eye quickly and cause viewers to walk away. Some specific recommendations include:

- In the **INTRODUCTION**, briefly summarize the necessary background that led to this work, clearly identify the purpose or specific aims of the present research, and identify the questions asked or hypothesis(es) tested.

- Provide sufficient detail of the **EXPERIMENTAL DESIGN** and the **METHODS** employed to do the work, including the number and necessary demographics of the participants studied (if applicable).

- **RESULTS** can be effectively presented with tables, figures, illustrations, and/or photographs. Make each stand on its own so the viewer does not have to refer elsewhere on the display to understand the important message(s) being presented. For each table, figure, etc., a clear **INTERPRETIVE LEGEND** will go a long way in highlighting and *briefly* discussing the essential points.

- In the **SUMMARY** and **CONCLUSIONS** *briefly* discuss the main points of your work.

- Include an **ACKNOWLEDGEMENTS** section to identify individuals who have contributed significantly but who are not listed as authors.

5. In addition to large and dark lettering, keep these other fundamentals in mind:

- Keep tables and figures simple and uncluttered.

- Strong visual contrast is a must. Many people have difficulty distinguishing closely related colours, such as green from blue, or among shades of a primary colour, particularly against incompatible background colours. Up to 10 percent of the people who view your work will have some degree of colour blindness.

- Most graphic computer software programs have innumerable options for colour and symbol shape. Although many are great options, many others may be ineffective when printed. Try a few out before settling with a choice. Depending on your specific needs, there is much to be said for using large and unique symbols or shading patterns to distinguish groups and conditions, with a more sparing use of colour to make these distinctions.

Using a poster to present your research projects and other work and assignments is not only fun and informative, but also makes your work more interesting and visually appealing – for everyone. Keep it simple by emphasizing the most important points. The effective use of colour, space, and your own unique design can go a long way in capturing and holding the attention of potential viewers. Use your imagination and creativity to get your message across. Make your work speak for itself!

is an integral part of the world in which we live. It allows us to gather information and develop new knowledge, and enhances our ability to make informed decisions. We are continually bombarded by research findings in the media on a daily basis, but research and statistics still carry an aura of dullness and impracticality.

Staying on top of the current knowledge is vital to success in any field. The ability to separate fact from fiction in research and to identify the limitations of a study, and how it may be applied, is the result of understanding how research is written and conducted.

The scientific method is more logical and organized than other ways of investigating a topic. Methods based on trial and error, tradition, or on subjective factors are less scientific. Knowing what constitutes good research is important in evaluating what we read, hear, or watch. Issues of internal and external validity, the type of research conducted, and the research design used can all

have a great impact on the results of a study.

To be competent and effective, researchers should be open-minded and knowledgeable, have intellectual curiosity and perseverance, and be honest at all times. Also, participants involved in studies have several rights that should be respected by all researchers. They have the right to informed consent, confidentiality and anonymity, and an assurance that their privacy will be respected and their safety guaranteed. The results of any study in which they participate should also be communicated to them.

An effective research paper has several components: a comprehensive title, abstract, introduction, statement of research hypothesis, review of literature, an overview of the method used, results, discussion, and references. Each section has many points that must be included for completeness and accuracy, and it is important to understand the goal of each section.

Key Words

Abstract	Informed consent	Primary reference
Applied research	Institutional review board	Research
Basic research	(IRB)	Research hypothesis
External validity	Internal validity	Scientific method
Field research	Laboratory research	Secondary reference

Discussion Questions

1. What is research? Using the scientific method, devise your own study outline.

2. Describe two types of research and provide an example of each.

3. What characteristics make a good researcher? Explain.

4. What are the major components of a research paper? Describe any two in detail.

A Career Working in Active Living for People with Disabilities

NAME: Patti Longmuir
OCCUPATION: Inclusive Active Living Research Consultant
EDUCATION: BPHE, University of Toronto (Physical and Health Education) MSc, University of Toronto (Community Health and Exercise Science)

What does an inclusive active living research consultant do?

My job is to find ways for people to participate in active living, regardless of a disability. For example, I may be asked to find a way for a person with quadriplegia to play tennis. I then design a research project, apply for grants, and hire and train a group of research assistants. I am also responsible for the publication and documentation of the research results. I may also be involved in testing new devices and prostheses which have been developed for the use of people with disabilities in recreational settings. Teaching physical activity professionals about the research results is also part of my job.

Why did you choose a career in recreation for people with disabilities?

My first exposure to people with disabilities was in junior high school. I was involved in an acting group that performed for children with disabilities. After our performance, I would meet and talk with the kids. During high school I volunteered for a recreation program at a local hospital, and got involved in recreational and competitive swimming for people with disabilities. By the end of high school I was convinced that I wanted to get into a profession that would help people with disabilities participate in recreational activities.

What do you like most about your job?

The diversity. Every day is different and challenging. I am constantly challenged by totally new and varied research problems.

In addition to research, what other career options are open to students who are interested in active living and people with disabilities?

There are many. Some options include teaching physical education classes to students with disabilities, performing fitness and nutritional appraisals, engineering and designing devices to assist people with disabilities, supervising and teaching community membership programs (weight training, aerobics, swimming, etc.), and full- and part-time coaching.

How are the future job prospects within this area?

Excellent. The medical and rehabilitation professions are becoming more aware of the importance of active living for people with disabilities. Yet very few people have both a physical education background and a knowledge of how to help people with different abilities. In addition, as people with disabilities become more integrated into our communities, recreation centres will require staff who can meet their needs. In 10 years I don't think there will be a field in physical education where you will never encounter a person with a disability.

What advice do you have for students who may be interested in active living for people with disabilities?

Stay broad-based in your course selections. Career opportunities are going to become less specialized and require people who can help people both with and without disabilities. I also highly recommend volunteer work. This helps students to become comfortable with people who have different abilities, and to overcome the fear component of working with people with disabilities.

In This Chapter:

Levels of Measurement *558*
    Nominal Level *558*
    Ordinal Level *558*
    Interval Level *558*
    Ratio Level *560*

Types of Statistics *560*
    Parametric Statistics *560*
    Nonparametric Statistics *560*
    Descriptive Statistics *560*
    Inferential Statistics *560*

Research Design and Hypothesis Testing *561*
    Independent and Dependent Variables *561*
    Hypothesis Testing *562*
    Sampling Procedures *563*

Organizing and Displaying Data *564*
    Frequency Distribution *564*
    Graphs *565*
    Bar Graphs *567*
    Pie Charts *567*

Measures of Central Tendency *568*
    The Mean *568*
    The Median *569*
    The Mode *569*

Percentiles *569*

Correlation *570*
    Positive and Negative Correlations *570*
    Scatter Plots *572*

Summary *573*

CHAPTER 23

Introduction to Statistical Concepts

After completing this chapter you should be able to:

- define various statistical methods and concepts;

- discuss the value and purposes of statistics;

- interpret basic statistical results;

- organize and display various data in a usable format.

The negative connotations that plague it make statistics a subject of considerable anxiety for many students. But statistics, like the research from which they spring, have a bearing on all facets of life. **Statistics**, the study of the summary, analysis, and evaluation of data, is perhaps the most vital tool for research. Its primary function is to extract from a large amount of data a numerical value that reveals a trait about the data under examination. Careful statistical analysis of data produces precise results. As such it is closely tied to the scientific method of research.

We should dispel one particular misconception at the onset. Statistical analysis does not require extensive knowledge in engineering or advanced mathematics. On the contrary, most statistics can be calculated using simple arithmetic. If you can add, subtract, multiply, divide, find a square and square root on a calculator, you can incorporate statistics into your research. Working with equations can be equated to reading a map – once the signs and symbols are well understood, it's just a matter of following the right path to the desired destination or end result. Further, computer software packages now exist that have made calculating statistics easier than ever.

Levels of Measurement

On its own a number tells us very little. Does the number 99 refer to the number on Wayne Gretzky's uniform? Your placing in a marathon race? A temperature reading? Levels of measurement allow us to know something about the complexity of the numbers we gain from research, and give us a way of describing the data – an important fact when choosing the correct statistical procedures to use (Table 23.1).

Nominal Level

Nominal level data are the least complex because they only provide information about a difference. Consider the numbers on sports uniforms –

number 23 is different from 99, which is different from 66. This basic information indicates a difference, but not much else. Nominal levels are also associated with categories of data. For example, when respondents to a poll are asked to name the television channel they watch most frequently, they might respond "3," "15," or "30." These numbers really only serve to group the responses into categories, and cannot be subjected to any arithmetic operations, such as addition, subtraction, multiplication, or division.

Ordinal Level

Ordinal level data also indicate a difference, but go further in showing the direction of the difference. In other words, they demonstrate rank – for example, when an athlete finishes third in a marathon race. This tells you that she did better than the person who finished fourth, and not as well as the runner who placed second, and so on. We are given more information than with nominal data, but we still do not know the amount of difference between each because there is no equality of units. The athlete who placed fourth may have been only tenths of a second away from third place, while the winner could have won by more than a minute.

When university committees rank scholarship candidates for overall merit, this is done using an ordinal scale. Percentile scores (discussed later) are another example of ordinal measurements, which often are used in reporting test results to students, since they too provide rank information.

Interval Level

Interval level data have the same properties of ordinal data with the added characteristic of equality of units. This means that we know about difference, the direction of difference, and the amount of difference in equal units. A Celsius temperature scale provides a good illustration of this type of data. For example, 10 degrees is warmer than 8 degrees by 2 degrees, but cooler than 12 degrees by 2 degrees. We can say with

Table 23.1 The levels of measurement.

Level	Permissible Statistical Procedures	Examples
Nominal • numbers are used to name, identify, or classify	• statistical procedures based on counting	
Ordinal • numbers indicate rank or order	• interpretations of "greater than" or "less than"	
Interval • intervals or distances between each number are known, but it is not known how far any of them are from zero	• addition and subtraction • statistical techniques based on these arithmetical operations are possible	
Ratio • each number can be thought of as a distance measured from zero	• there are no limitations regarding the use of any arithmetical or statistical techniques	

confidence that the difference between 8 and 10 degrees is the same as that between 10 and 12 degrees.

Interval level data do not have a true zero point; therefore, such data can only be added or subtracted, but not divided. Division always presupposes the existence of an exact zero point.

Ratio Level

Ratio level data are the most complex of the levels of measurement. This level has all the properties of the interval level, but also an absolute zero point, which represents the absence of the trait being measured. Examples of variables with meaningful absolute zero points include weight, distance, time, and loudness.

Absolute Zero

Temperature does not fall into the ratio category because at zero degrees Celsius temperature still exists; if you doubt this, try going outside in a T-shirt or shorts on a zero-degree day.

We cannot say, for instance, that 20 degrees is twice as hot as 10 degrees (although it is 10 degrees warmer) because the zero point on the Celsius scale is not an absolute zero (the absolute zero point for temperature is –273 degrees Celsius).

Absolute zero points allow statements such as 10 metres is one fifth as long as 50 metres, 15 kilograms is three times as heavy as 5 kilograms, or 30 seconds is three times as long as 10 seconds. Such comparisons can only be accurately made about ratio level data.

Types of Statistics

Statistics can be classified as parametric or nonparametric in nature. Depending on what purpose the statistic will fulfill, statistics may also be described as descriptive or inferential. These concepts are described in this section.

Parametric Statistics

Parametric statistics are used when the data involved are interval or ratio level. These data are considered *continuous* because they may be measured with increasingly greater precision, depending on the accuracy of the measuring instrument. For example, time can be measured in milliseconds, seconds, minutes, hours, weeks, decades, and so on.

Nonparametric Statistics

When data are nominal or ordinal in nature nonparametric statistics are used. These nominal and ordinal data are considered *discrete* because observations are limited to certain numbers, usually whole values. For example, when we count people for a survey, whole numbers must be used because we cannot have a fraction of a person; similarly, the number of field goals kicked during a football game cannot be three and a half since half a field goal does not exist. Various statistics fall into these two general categories, some of which will be discussed later.

Descriptive Statistics

Descriptive statistics involve measurements that are used to describe current events or conditions without generalizing the statistics to other conditions or groups. For example, your basketball free-throw shooting percentage, or your accumulated academic average could be considered descriptive (Figure 23.1 A).

Inferential Statistics

Inferential statistics are used to make inferences predictions, or generalizations from a small group to a larger group. In order to evaluate the physical fitness level of the entire school versus the national norms, one need only obtain a sample that is representative of the students in order to make an estimation of the student body's relative fitness (Figure 23.1 B). Since smaller groups are

Figure 23.1 A. Free-throw shooting percentage is considered a descriptive statistic. **B.** Fitness test scores of a small sample are examples of inferential statistics.

more economical for the purposes of research, inferential statistics are invaluable.

Research Design and Hypothesis Testing

The main purpose of research is to answer questions and to solve problems. A research process that involves the manipulation of events or variables to solve a problem is called an **experimental design**. In an experiment, at least two groups are normally involved: one subjected to the experimenter's manipulation (**experimental group**), and the other which is not subjected to such manipulation (**control group**).

In a study conducted to determine whether a certain sports drink (e.g., Gatorade) aids endurance athletes, the experimental group would consume the drink during training, while the control group would just drink water as usual. In this study, the researcher attempts to vary the drink and observes the effect of this variation on the responses of the participants. A lot of research is based on such designs, and this will be our focus here.

Independent and Dependent Variables

A research study that is based on the scientific method involves at least two variables. The first, the **independent variable**, is controlled by the researcher in order to determine the effect on some behaviour. The **dependent variable** is the behaviour that is measured to determine if it is affected by the independent variable.

Another example may be useful to further illustrate this distinction. In a study that looks at the effects of practice on the level of skill achieved in gymnastics, the amount of practice

Table 23.2 Examples of independent and dependent variables used in physical education experiments.

Independent Variables

- training time per session

- number of training sessions per week

- number of repetitions per set

- number of sets per session

- intensity of exercise per unit of time

- type of diet

- training method used

- type of practice method

- age, sex, or other demographic variable

- motivational technique

- medicine or drug

Dependent Variables

- distance thrown or jumped

- reaction time

- running time

- weight lifted

- self-confidence or self-concept score

- improvement in skill performance

- number of errors committed

- achieved accuracy

- academic record

- percentage of improvement

- aggressive behaviour

(e.g., two hours, one hour, half an hour) would be the independent variable (controlled by the researcher), and achieved skill level would represent the dependent variable (the behaviour), which is partially dependent on the amount of practice time. The researcher attempts to discover what effect the amount of practice exerts on one's ability to improve a given level of skill in individuals who are otherwise similar.

Other common independent and dependent variables in physical education and sport are presented in Table 23.2.

Hypothesis Testing

In our discussion on writing a research project (see Chapter 22), we introduced the *research hypothesis*, which predicts relationships among variables based on prior research. In an experimental design, a hypothesis is usually stated in a way that allows the data to be analyzed statistically to determine if the hypothesis should be accepted. But the ultimate basis for such testing is the **null hypothesis**, which predicts that *no* relationship or *no* difference will exist between the experimental and control groups involved in a study. In other words, a null hypothesis challenges a research hypothesis.

Examining the relationship between televised sporting violence and youth aggression, the null hypothesis might be: "Viewing televised sporting violence and aggression among youth are not significantly related." If the null hypothesis is found statistically to be true, this means the original research hypothesis is false (the variables are not significantly related); likewise, a null hypothesis that is rejected indicates that the initial research hypothesis is correct (the variables are significantly related). In other words, if the probability is small that the null form is true, then we reject it in favour of the research hypothesis; if the reverse is true, the null hypothesis must be accepted, and a new research experiment must be proposed. A rejected null hypothesis suggests that a difference or relationship does exist among the variables being studied at an acceptable level of confidence.

Sampling Procedures

When researchers ask questions, they conduct their research with the aim of helping us make predictions about a larger group (the population) than just those involved in the study itself. To do so, researchers often measure only a portion, or fraction, of the population being examined, called a **sample**. While a **population** is composed of persons, places, or things that share at least one common characteristic (e.g., all the 10-year-old boys in a given school), a sample is a representative subset containing the essential characteristics of that population. Data collected on the sample can then be generalized to estimate the characteristics of the population.

Populations can be large, and it is often impractical and financially unfeasible to measure all variables for each member. Sampling is thus essential. However, measuring 2,000 members versus 100 members of a population of 20,000 (number of spectators at centre court at the U.S. Open; Figure 23.2) would reflect a more accurate representation of the population. The larger the sample, the more accurately it will represent the population, and the smaller the error in prediction. Therefore, researchers must try to maximize their sample size, sometimes while working within tight financial and time constraints.

How to Select a Sample

Not all samples are statistically useful, however. Suppose a study is done on balance among high school students. Can the results be generalized to other adults in general? Probably not, because high school students are younger on average and are likely more active, and so on.

A sample must be random in order to be truly representative. In a **random sample** each member of the population has an equal opportunity of being selected. Balloting, for example, would conform well to this requirement. Random sampling is unbiased and more likely to represent the population under consideration.

Figure 23.2 How would you study the income level of spectators attending the U.S. Open tennis tournament?

What Do You Think?

Researchers often gather data from a select group of individuals to help make predictions about a larger population to which the group belongs.

Selecting the members of a school's volleyball team to represent the fitness level of an entire school population would not be considered a random (or representative) sample. Such a limited group may have characteristics that differ from the rest of the population, leading to a potentially biased sample.

Why do you think a volleyball team in this case would not represent the most representative sample? How would you go about selecting a better sample for your school?

Organizing and Displaying Data

When research studies are conducted and data are collected, a lot of information is gathered. However, before any real conclusions can be drawn from the research, the raw data must be organized systematically. Tables, graphs, histograms, and other visual aids are among the clearest and most effective ways of presenting both the information you have gathered and the results of your research.

Frequency Distribution

When raw values are presented in no particular order, interpretation of the data is difficult. One way of organizing data into a usable format is its **frequency distribution.** Different types of distributions exist, but in each case, a distribution of data serves to provide a quick indication of the values you are dealing with (see Table 23.3).

For example, physical education teachers may wish to place data on selected fitness scores of 15 grade 11 students into a **rank order distribution** from highest to lowest for statistical analysis.

The extreme scores (highest and lowest values) and variability in the scores can thus be easily identifiable (Table 23.3 A).

If the number of students to be tested is relatively large (two or more grade 11 classes), their scores can be arranged in a **simple frequency distribution** (Table 23.3 B) or **grouped frequency distribution** (Table 23.3 C), where performances are arranged into non-overlapping segments called **class intervals**. Intervals are equal in length, thereby aiding the comparison between the frequencies of any two intervals.

The number of observations falling into any interval is called the **class frequency (f)**. For the first interval, f is 11, obtained from the tally. The **tally** is a convenient way of keeping track of a set of observations (Table 23.3 C).

Frequency tables often include other features, such as **relative frequency**, which represents the relative percentage of total cases falling within any class interval. It is obtained by dividing the number of cases in the class interval by the total number of cases and multiplying by 100. For example, in Table 23.3 C, the relative frequency of the first class, 21-25 push-ups, is $(11/79)100 = 13.9$ percent (or rounded to 14 percent). This value indicates the total percentage of total cases that fall into a given class interval.

Table 23.3 Frequency distributions of push-up scores for grade 11 students. **A.** Rank order. **B.** Simple frequency. **C.** Grouped frequency.

A

X (no. of push-ups)
24
22
20
18
18
18
17
15
13
13
13
5
5
4
2

N (number of scores) = 15
H (highest score) = 24
L (lowest score) = 2
R (range) = (24 − 2) = 22

B

X	f (frequency)
24	1
23	2
22	4
21	4
20	4
19	2
18	5
17	5
16	8
15	9
14	12
13	6
12	7
11	2
10	5
9	1
8	2

N (number of scores) = 79
H (highest score) = 24
L (lowest score) = 8
R (range) = (24 − 8) = 16

C

X	Tally	f	Relative Frequency (%)
21 – 25	ЖЖ ЖЖ I	11	14
16 – 20	ЖЖ ЖЖ ЖЖ ЖЖ IIII	24	30
11 – 15	ЖЖ ЖЖ ЖЖ ЖЖ ЖЖ ЖЖ ЖЖ I	36	46
6 – 10	ЖЖ III	8	10
1 – 5		0	0
		N = 79	100

Graphs

While tables are useful tools for organizing data, particularly for determining the limits of the data, graphs can provide distinct advantages in displaying information. **Graphs** are useful for making comparisons and identifying trends.

Basic line graphs and curves follow a simple form. All graphs show data along the x-axis (abscissa, horizontal axis) and the y-axis (ordinate, vertical axis) (Figure 23.3).

The graph shows the relationship between values plotted on the vertical and horizontal axes. The dependent variable, which changes in a way that is related to another variable (e.g., performance), is normally plotted on the y-axis, while the independent variable (e.g., number of practice sessions), which is controlled in an experiment, is plotted on the x-axis. Graphs allow us to quickly see trends in the data that may not

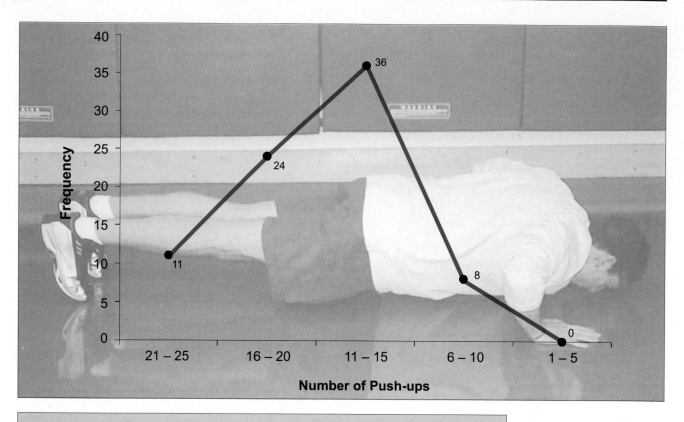

Figure 23.3 Graph or frequency polygon for push-up scores from Table 23.3 C.

Figure 23.4 Number of chin-ups performed by four participants who trained once a week (participant 1), twice a week (participant 2), three times a week (participant 3), and four times a week (participant 4).

have been apparent in a table, such as improved performance as a result of increased practice (Figure 23.4).

Although data points are conventionally connected with a line, this is not necessarily the best way to illustrate a relationship. When a consistent relationship is suspected between variables, a **line of best fit** or an **ellipse** is more appropriate (see Figure 23.8). This line travels through the data as close to most of the points as possible. This line of best fit allows predictions to be made about values of the dependent variable that are unknown. Although statistical techniques exist for computing such lines, doing so by sight is often adequate.

Bar Graphs

Bar graphs or **histograms** are another simple but effective means of presenting data that are similar and where comparison is desired. The bars on the x-axis represent the performance categories, groups, or participants, while the height of each bar is determined by the frequency of a particular group or participant (Figure 23.5).

If you wanted to graph the average heights of eighth-grade students, the various heights would be labeled along the x-axis, while the frequency of these values would be along the y-axis, indicated by the height of the bars. The graph allows you to see the bars side-by-side so that you can visualize the comparison easily.

Pie Charts

A popular way to display data arranged in categories is in a **pie chart**, a circle divided into wedges that correspond to the percentage

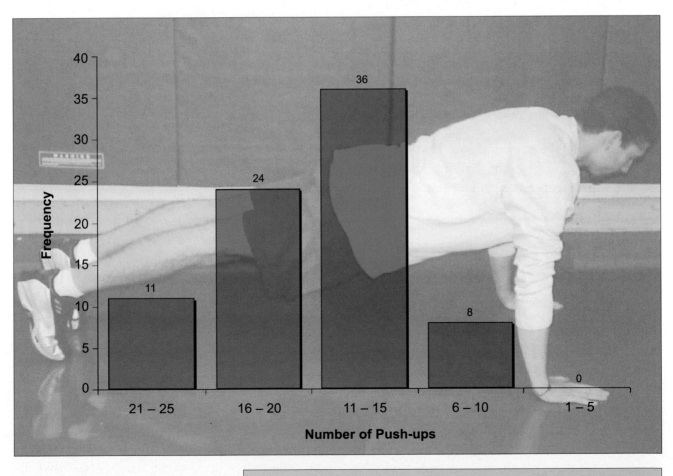

Figure 23.5 Bar graph showing push-up scores from Table 23.3 C.

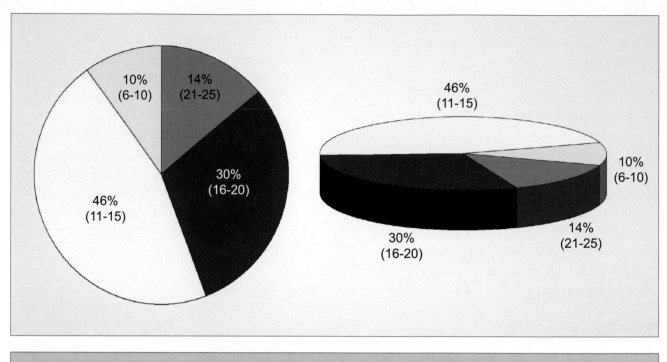

Figure 23.6 Pie chart showing the relative frequency and number of push-ups performed by grade 11 students from Table 23.3 C.

frequencies of the distribution (Figure 23.6). Pie charts are useful in conveying data across a small number of categories.

Even this brief introduction to a complex subject will have served its purpose if it has demonstrated that raw data on its own is of limited value and that the significance emerges only through organization and display.

Measures of Central Tendency

Recall that statistics allow single meaningful values to be extracted from a large amount of data. **Measures of central tendency** are no exception; they describe the central characteristics of a set of data and are the most representative of all the values in a distribution. They allow a given score to be compared to those scores that typify the middle of a distribution of data. The three statistical measures of central tendency are the mean, the median, and the mode.

The Mean

We are all familiar with the use of means in our everyday lives. The **mean** is the arithmetic *average* of a distribution of scores (the customary symbols are *M* or *X*), and is the measure of central tendency most commonly used. The mean is used when the data are interval or ratio level.

The mean is calculated by summing all the observations (scores) in the sample and dividing by the number of observations (scores). The calculated mean from Table 23.3 A is 13.8.

The use of means in sports is obviously important for calculating baseball batting averages, basketball points-per-game averages, and so on. These calculations consider the number of scores involved as well as their value, giving each score weight relative to other scores in the data distribution.

The mean tends to be regarded as the most reliable measure of the three measures of central tendency. The mean, however, is vulnerable to extreme scores in a set of data. Scores that are *significantly* higher or lower than other scores will pull the mean towards that extreme, leading to potentially misleading average values.

Consider the following distribution of scores representing the number of push-ups performed by a class of students: 100, 25, 22, 20, 20, 19, 18. Most individuals in the class scored in the same general range, but one individual, a highly trained gymnast, was able to do 100 push-ups; the mean here would be inflated by this one atypical score ($M = 224/7 = 32$).

The atypically low or high scores, called **outliers**, pull the average towards that extreme. In this case, the median would be of more value.

The Median

Stated simply, the **median** score in a distribution is the middle score that divides the data in half (designated by ***MED***). It is the point in a distribution where 50 percent of the scores lie above and below. The median is often used when the data are ordinal in nature. Therefore, before determining the median for a set of data, the scores must be put in a rank order distribution (highest to lowest or lowest to highest).

When the number of scores in a distribution is odd, the median is the exact middle score (15 in Table 23.3 A), while the median for an even number of scores falls between two scores. In the following odd number of scores in the distribution: 11, 9, 7, 7, 6, 5, 3, 2, 2, the median is 6 (the middle score in the range); an even number of scores in the distribution: 11, 9, 7, 7, 6, 5, 3, 2 has a median of 6.5 (falling between scores 6 and 7).

This method tends to be used when there are not many tied scores, or when a distribution has a small total number of scores. Further, unlike the mean, the median is not affected by outliers (extreme atypical scores). Again, for the example involving the number of push-ups performed by a class of students (100, 25, 22, 20, 20, 19, 18), the median value would be 20, despite the outlying score of 100. Therefore, in this case the median more accurately represents the group's performance as a whole.

The Mode

This measure of central tendency is not used very often because it does not take into account extreme scores, the number of scores, or their relation to the middle of the set of data. The **mode** is simply the score that occurs most frequently in a distribution. When data has been arranged in a rank order distribution, the mode may be obtained by plain inspection, without any calculation. It is possible to have two or more scores that have the same frequency (18 and 13 in Table 23.3 A); in this case, the distribution has more than one mode, and is called **bi-** or **multimodal**.

Percentiles

Percentiles are especially useful in interpreting data that may be difficult to appreciate in its raw form. Sportscasters commonly use percentages to describe data such as a team's free-throw shooting accuracy, because this information in its raw form does not allow quick comparisons to be made with other teams. It is certainly more useful to know that a team is shooting 75 percent, than to be told they have made 510 out of 680 attempted shots (Table 23.4).

In statistics, a **percentile** is defined as a **standard score**. It is a point or position on a continuous scale of 100 theoretical divisions such that a certain fraction of the population of raw scores lies at or below that point. In other words, the percentile rank of a score indicates the percentage of all scores that lie below a given score and conversely, the percentage of all scores that lie above it.

We are often interested in how our scores rank relative to other individuals, or groups. Your percentile score on a given test will indicate how you compare with the other raw scores in the set of data.

For example, if you performed a total of 50 sit-ups on a muscular endurance test, which we will assume is the 80th percentile, this would mean that 80 percent of the relevant comparison group

Table 23.4 Sample statistical scouting report on a visiting basketball team.

Statistics	Per Game Average
Points	74.5
Field Goal Percentage	.433
Three-point Percentage	.386
Three Pointers Attempted	19.9
Free-throw Percentage	.647
Total Rebounds	37.7
Offensive Rebounds	14.0
Assists	16.8
Steals	7.9
Turnovers	16.0
Blocks	2.2

performed 50 or fewer sit-ups, and only 20 percent performed a larger number. This would tell us that your level of muscular endurance is equal to or better than that of 80 percent of individuals in the particular population. Therefore, percentile scores provide more information than raw data alone.

Percentiles can also allow comparisons between sets of data based on different units of measurement. Consider the athlete who wants to choose which of two sports (sprinting and diving) she should pursue based on her performance. A time of 14 seconds in the 100-metre sprint and an average score of 7.4 in a diving event seem incomparable. But if the raw scores are converted into percentiles, they may be directly compared. Let's assume that a score of 14 seconds in the 100-metre sprint is the 63rd percentile, and that a score of 7.4 in diving is the 90th percentile; we can say with confidence that this athlete would be better off pursuing diving rather than sprinting.

Correlation

When two measures obtained on the same object conform in such a way that it is possible to predict one measure from the other, they are said to be correlated. Correlations are valuable statistical tools researchers can use to examine two or more variables. **Correlations** provide a quantitative means of measuring the extent to which two variables are associated or related. How are height and weight related? Or strength and weight among varsity athletes? Or your IQ (Intelligence Quotient) and academic success? The answers to these questions may be obtained by performing a statistical analysis using correlations.

Correlation is also significant for **prediction**. Once a correlation has been established between two variables, one variable may be used to predict the other. Consider the relationship between heart disease and fat intake. In order to stay healthy for a longer period of time, we can predict that eating lower-fat foods will help reduce the risk of heart disease later in life.

Positive and Negative Correlations

A calculated **correlation coefficient (*r*)** is a number that shows the direction and degree of relationship between two measures. Correlations can be

Can You Solve This?

What is the correlation between the following pairs of variables? Circle your answer.

	Positive (P)	Negative (N)	Zero (Z)
• Hoight and weight	P	N	Z
• Hours spent watching television and swimming sprint speed	P	N	Z
• Arm length and softball throw for distance	P	N	Z
• $\dot{V}O_2$max and placing in a cross-country meet	P	N	Z
• Standing long jump and vertical jump scores	P	N	Z
• Golf score and tennis serving accuracy	P	N	Z

positive or negative depending on the variables involved. For perfect positive correlations, $r = +1.00$; for perfect negative correlations, $r = -1.00$. For variables that show no correlation, $r = 0$.

A **positive correlation** between variables exists when the increase in one variable entails a corresponding increase in the other. An example is the relationship between an athlete's weight and maximal strength – as weight increases, so does strength (Figure 23.7 A).

Other relationships may exhibit the characteristics of a **negative correlation**: as one variable increases, the other tends to decrease. For example, an individual's education level and smoking are negatively correlated, as are age of adults and maximal strength. A negative correlation also exists between achieved times in the 1,500-metre run and maximal oxygen uptake ($\dot{V}O_2$max): the higher the $\dot{V}O_2$max, the better (lower) the running times (Figure 23.7 B).

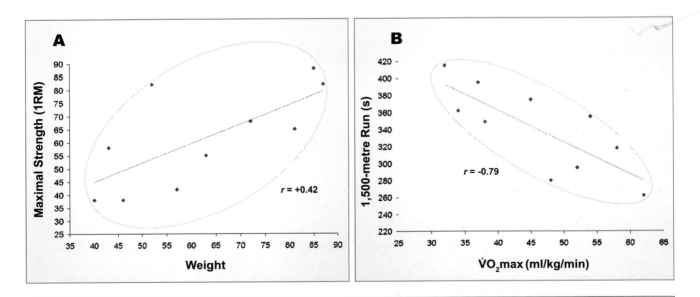

Figure 23.7 Examples of correlations between two variables among 10 participants. **A.** Positive correlation. **B.** Negative correlation.

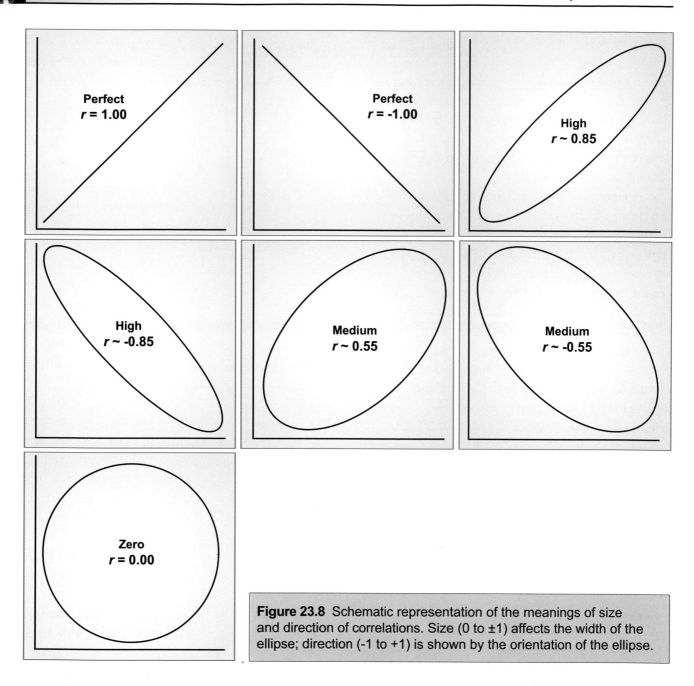

Figure 23.8 Schematic representation of the meanings of size and direction of correlations. Size (0 to ±1) affects the width of the ellipse; direction (-1 to +1) is shown by the orientation of the ellipse.

In summary, these examples demonstrate that the raw materials required to compute a correlation coefficient are two measures for a single object or individual. The correlation coefficient itself is a number between -1.00 and +1.00 and the sign of the coefficient expresses the direction of the relationship.

Scatter Plots

In determining correlations, the various relationships are often displayed in a **scatter plot** (or **scattergram**), in which values of one variable are shown on the horizontal axis and values of the other on the vertical axis. Examples of positive and negative correlation scatter plots are presented in Figure 23.7 A and B. When the data on such a graph run diagonally upward from left to right, the correlation is positive, while data running downward from left to right indicate a negative correlation.

As described earlier, a line of best fit can be drawn through the points to indicate the general trend of the data. Data that are very closely clustered to the line of best fit indicate a high degree of correlation, while moderate correlations will show a greater amount of spread in the data. Data that are weakly correlated will show no apparent pattern. A perfect correlation is represented by a perfectly straight line through the data, although because of human variability, this is virtually impossible.

The closer the points in a scatter plot come to falling on the line of best fit, the closer *r* will be to ±1.00. This information, provided as a result of calculated correlations, allows us to note how closely two variables are related with some accuracy.

An ellipse that surrounds or embraces all data in a scattergram may also be used as an effective visual display of the relationship between two variables. The orientation of the ellipse from SW to NE in Figure 23.7 A indicates a moderately high positive correlation, whereas the ellipse's orientation from NW to SE in Figure 23.7 B indicates a relatively high negative correlation.

In general, the narrower the ellipse encompassing the points in a scattergram, the higher the correlation. A circle indicates zero correlation between variables, while a straight line indicates a perfect correlation. These relationships are shown in Figure 23.8.

Relationship Versus Cause and Effect

It is important to note, however, that a correlation does not indicate a causal relationship. In other words, just because one variable is related to the other, does not mean that it causes changes in the other. For example, we must be careful not to assume that because the incidence of cardiovascular disease is related to fat intake, eating fat causes heart disease. A correlation only indicates that the two variables are related.

Summary

Statistics is the study of the summary, analysis, and evaluation of data, and is a vital tool for research. Statistics allow us to extract from a large amount of data a numerical value that reveals a trait about the data under examination. Descriptive statistics describe current events or conditions, such as goals-against average or academic grades. Inferential statistics are used to make predictions or generalizations from a small group to a larger group.

The main purpose of research is to answer questions and to solve problems. In any research experiment, at least two groups are usually involved. The experimental group is subjected to the manipulation of the tester; the response of this group is compared with that of the control group. During testing, the researcher controls a specific element – known as the independent variable – to determine its effect on some behaviour. The dependent variable is the behaviour that is measured.

Clear and effective means of representing results include tables, graphs, histograms, and pie charts. Statistical techniques such as correlations, percentiles, and measures of central tendency are very precise, providing us with important insight into various research problems and questions.

Key Words

Bar graph (histogram)	Experimental design	Inferential statistics
Class frequency	Experimental group	Interval level
Class interval	Frequency distribution	Line of best fit
Control group	Graphs	Mean
Correlation	Grouped frequency	Median
Dependent variable	distribution	Mode
Descriptive statistics	Independent variable	Negative correlation

Nominal level
Nonparametric statistics
Null hypothesis
Ordinal level
Parametric statistics
Percentile

Pie chart
Population
Positive correlation
Random sample
Rank order distribution
Ratio level

Relative frequency
Sample
Scatter plot (scattergram)
Simple frequency distribution
Tally

Discussion Questions

1. Identify the three levels of measurement and give an example of each.

2. How do independent and dependent variables differ? Give an example.

3. Why is random sampling important for conducting research?

4. What does a correlation tell you? Differentiate between positive and negative correlations.

References and Suggested Readings

CHAPTER 1
Introduction to Health and Wellness

DeMarco, T., & Sidney, K. (1990). Enhancing children's participation in physical activity. *The Education Digest*, 55(6), 59-61.

Edwards, P. (1993). Self-esteem, sport and physical activity (Vol. 1, No. 1). *Canadian Association for the Advancement of Women and Sport and Physical Activity*. Gloucester, ON.

Evans, J., & Roberts, G. C. (1987). Physical competence and the development of children's peer relations. *Quest, 39*, 23-35.

Evans, R., Barer, M., & Marmor, T. (1994). *Why are some people healthy and others not? The determinants of health of populations*. New York, NY: Aldine de Gruyter.

Ontario Physical and Health Education Association (1997). *Healthy active living standards for physical and health education in Ontario, grades 1-9*. Available through OPHEA at 1185 Eglinton Ave. E., Suite 501, North York, Ontario, Canada, M3C 3C6.

CHAPTER 2
Human Anatomy: The Pieces of the Body Puzzle

Akesson, E. J., Loeb, J. A., & Wilson-Pauwels, L. (1990). *Core textbook of anatomy* (2nd ed.). Philadelphia, PA: J.B. Lippincott Company.

Moore, K. L., & Dalley, A. F. (1999). *Clinically oriented anatomy* (4th ed.). New York, NY: Lippincott Williams & Wilkins.

Williams, P. L., & Warwick, R. (1986). *Gray's anatomy* (36th ed.). Edinburgh: Churchill Livingstone.

CHAPTER 3
Muscle Structure and Function

Bompa, T. O. (1999). *Periodization: Theory and methodology of training* (4th ed.). Champaign, IL: Human Kinetics.

Hartmann, J., & Tunnemann, H. (2001). *Fitness and strength training for all sports*. Toronto, ON: Sport Books Publisher.

McArdle, W. D., Katch, F. I., & Katch, V. L. (1991). *Exercise physiology: Energy, nutrition, and human performance* (3rd ed.). Philadelphia, PA: Lea & Febiger.

Shea, C. H., & Wright, D. L. (1997). *An introduction to human movement: The sciences of physical education*. Needham Heights, MA: Allyn & Bacon.

Vander, A. J., Sherman, J. H., & Luciano, D. S. (1994). *Human physiology* (6th ed.). New York, NY: McGraw-Hill Inc.

CHAPTER 4
Muscles at Work

Baechle, T. R., & Earle, R. W. (2000). *Essentials of strength training and conditioning*. Champaign, IL: Human Kinetics.

Bompa, T. O. (1999). *Periodization: Theory and methodology of training* (4th ed.). Champaign, IL: Human Kinetics.

Hartmann, J., & Tunnemann, H. (2001). *Fitness and strength training for all sports*. Toronto, ON: Sport Books Publisher.

Scholich, M. (1999). *Circuit training for all sports*. Toronto: Sport Books Publisher.

Shea, C. H., & Wright, D. L. (1997). *An introduction to human movement: The sciences of physical education*. Needham Heights, MA: Allyn & Bacon.

CHAPTER 5
Energy for Muscular Activity

Baechle, T. R., & Earle, R. W. (2000). *Essentials of strength training and conditioning*. Champaign, IL: Human Kinetics.

Bompa, T. O. (1999). *Periodization: Theory and methodology of training* (4th ed.). Champaign, IL: Human Kinetics.

McArdle, W. D., Katch, F. I., & Katch, V. L. (1991). *Exercise physiology: Energy, nutrition, and human performance* (3rd ed.). Philadelphia, PA: Lea & Febiger.

Shea, C. H., & Wright, D. L. (1997). *An introduction to human movement: The sciences of physical education*. Needham Heights, MA: Allyn & Bacon.

CHAPTER 6
The Heart and Lungs at Work

Guyton, A. C. H. (1998). *Textbook of medical physiology – Pocket companion* (1st ed.). Philadelphia, PA: W.B. Saunders Company.

McArdle, W. D., Katch, F.I., Katch, V.L. (1991). *Exercise physiology: Energy, nutrition, and human performance* (3rd ed.). Philadelphia, PA: Lea & Febiger.

Oscai, L. B., Williams, B. T., & Hertig, B. A. (1968). Effect of exercise on blood volume. *J Appl Physiol, 24*, 622-624.

Suter, E., Hoppeler, H., Claassen, H., Billeter, R., Aebi, U., Horber, F., Jaeger, P., & Marti, B. (1995). Ultrastructural modification of human skeletal muscle tissue with 6-month moderate-intensity exercise training. *International Journal of Sports Medicine, 16*, 160-166.

CHAPTER 7
How Do I Move? The Science of Biomechanics

Coh, M., & Jost, B. (2000). *Biomechanical characteristics of selected sports.* Faculty of Sport, University of Ljubljana, Ljubljana: Institute of Kinesiology.

Ecker, T. (1996). *Basic track and field biomechanics* (2nd ed.). Mountain View, CA: Tafnews Press.

Hall, S. J. (1999). *Basic biomechanics.* Boston, MA: McGraw-Hill Publishing.

Kreighbaum, E., & Barthels, K. M. (1996). *Biomechanics: A qualitative approach for studying human movement* (3rd ed.). New York, NY: Macmillan Publishing Company.

Winter, D. A. (1990). *Biomechanics and motor control of human movement* (2nd ed.). Toronto, ON: John Wiley & Sons.

CHAPTER 8
Out of Harm's Way: Sport Injuries

Anderson, M., & Hall, S. J. (1997). *Fundamentals of sports injury management.* Baltimore, MD: Williams & Wilkins.

Hall, S. J. (1999). *Basic biomechanics.* Boston, MA: McGraw-Hill Publishing.

Hammer, W. I. (1999). *Functional soft tissue examination and treatment.* Baltimore, MD: Aspen Publications.

Magee, D. J. (1997). *Orthopedic physical assessment.* Toronto, ON: W.B. Saunders Company.

CHAPTER 9
Physical Fitness

Baechle, T. R., & Earle, R. W. (2000). *Essentials of strength training and conditioning.* Champaign, IL: Human Kinetics.

Bompa, T. O. (1999). *Periodization: Theory and methodology of training.* Champaign, IL: Human Kinetics.

Hartmann, J., & Tunnemann, H. (2001). *Fitness and strength training for all sports.* Toronto, ON: Sport Books Publisher.

Scholich, M. (1999). *Circuit training for all sports.* Toronto, ON: Sport Books Publisher.

CHAPTER 10
Evaluation in Physical and Health Education

Berg, K. E., & Latin, R. W. (1994). *Essentials of modern research methods in health, physical education, and recreation.* Englewood Cliffs, NJ: Prentice Hall.

The Canadian physical activity, fitness & lifestyle appraisal. (1996). Ottawa: Canadian Society for Exercise Physiology.

Johnson, B. L., & Nelson, J. K. (1986). *Practical measurements for evaluation in physical education* (4th ed.). New York, NY: Macmillan Publishing Company.

Morrow, Jr., J. R., Jackson, A. W., Disch, J. G., & Mood, D. P. (1995). *Measurement and evaluation in human performance.* Champaign, IL: Human Kinetics.

CHAPTER 11
The Nutritional Connection

Gastelu, D., & Hatfield, F. (1997). *Dynamic nutrition for maximum performance: A complex nutritional guide for peak sports performance.* Garden City, NY: Avery Publishing.

Guthrie, H. (1989). *Introductory nutrition* (7th ed.). St. Louis, MO: Mosby-Year Book.

Health and Welfare Canada. (1990). *Action towards healthy eating – Canada's guidelines for healthy eating and recommended strategies for implementation.* Report of the Communications/Implementation Committee. Health and Welfare Canada.

Health and Welfare Canada. (1990). *Nutrition recommendations: Report of the scientific review committee.* Health and Welfare Canada, Cat. No. H49-42/199E.

Health and Welfare Canada. (1992). *Canada's food guide to healthy eating.* Ministry of Supply Services Canada, ISBN 0-662-19648-1.

Insel, P. M., & Roth, W. T. (1994). *Core concepts in health* (7th ed.). Mountain View, CA: Mayfield Publishing Company.

Payne, W. A., & Hahn, D. B. (1992). *Understanding your health* (3rd ed.). St. Louis, MO: Mosby-Year Book.

CHAPTER 12
Weight Management: Finding a Healthy Balance

Fedyck, H., Nadolny, D., & Cremasco, J. (1985). Eat well, live well. *Ontario Dietetic Association.*

Insel, P. M., & Roth, W. T. (1994). *Core concepts in health* (7th ed.). Mountain View, CA: Mayfield Publishing Company.

Payne, W. A., & Hahn, D. B. (1992). *Understanding your health* (3rd ed.). St. Louis, MO: Mosby-Year Book.

Woodside, D. B., & Garfinkel, P. E. (1989). An overview of the eating disorders: Anorexia nervosa and bulimia nervosa, *N.I.N. Review, 8*, 1-4.

CHAPTER 13
Substance Use and Abuse

Antonio, J., & Stout, J. R. (2002). *Supplements for endurance athletes*. Champaign, IL: Human Kinetics.

Antonio, J., & Stout, J. R. (2002). *Supplements for strength-power athletes*. Champaign, IL: Human Kinetics.

Harland, B. F. (2000). Caffeine and nutrition. *Nutrition, 16* (7-8), 522-526.

McArdle, W. D., Katch, F. I., & Katch, V. L. (1999). *Sports and exercise nutrition*. Baltimore, MD: Lippincott Williams & Wilkins.

Shils, et al. (1999). *Modern nutrition in health and disease.* (9th ed.). Baltimore, MD: Lippincott Williams & Wilkins.

CHAPTER 14
The Mental Side of Human Performance

Courneya, K. S., & Carron, A. V. (1992). The home advantage in sport competitions: A literature review. *Journal of Sport and Exercise Psychology, 14*, 13-27.

Cox, R. H. (2002). *Sport psychology: Concepts and applications* (5th ed.). New York, NY: McGraw-Hill.

Irving, P. G., & Goldstein, S. R. (1990). Effect of home-field advantage on peak performance of baseball pitchers. *Journal of Sport Behavior, 13,* 23-2.

Leith, L. M. (2003). *The psychology of coaching team sports: A self-help guide.* Toronto, ON: Sport Books Publisher.

Nideffer, R. M. (1995). *Focus for success.* San Diego, CA: Enhanced Performance Services.

Van Raalte, J. L., Brewer, B. W., Lewis, B. P., Linder, D. E., Wildman, G., & Kozimor, J. (1995). Cork! The effects of positive and negative self-talk on dart throwing performance. *Journal of Sport Behavior, 18*, 51-57.

Williams, J. M. (2001). *Applied sport psychology: Personal growth to peak performance* (4th ed.). Mountain View, CA: Mayfield Publishing Company.

CHAPTER 15
Growth and Development

Bloom, B. (1985). *Developing talent in young people.* New York, NY: Ballantine Books.

Canadian Association of Sport Sciences National Fitness Appraisal Certification and Accreditation Program and Fitness Canada. (1987). *Canadian standardized test of fitness interpretation and counselling manual,* Ottawa.

Klavora, P., & Gaudin, D. (1990). *Talent in children: Can we do better?* Proceedings of IV Congress of Sport Pedagogues of Yugoslavia and International Symposium.

Konzak, B., Konzak, M., & Konzak, S. (1999). Girl power: Self-defense for teens. Toronto, ON: Sport Books Publisher.

Payne, V., & Isaacs, L. (1991). *Human motor development: A lifespan approach.* Mountain View, CA: Mayfield Publishing Company.

Ratnesar, R. (2000, August 14). Changing stripes. *Time, 156*, 43-45.

Shephard, R. J. (1985). Long-term studies of physical activity in children. In R. A. Binkhorst et al. (Eds.), *Children and exercise XI* (pp. 252-259). Champaign, IL: Human Kinetics.

Swift, E. M. (1997, February 24). Kid stuff. *Sports Illustrated,* 29-31.

CHAPTER 16
Movement Intelligence: A Vast Store of Skills

Fleishman, E. A. (1972). On the relation between abilities, learning, and human performance. *American Psychologist, 27*, 1017-1032.

Guthrie, E. R. (1952). *The psychology of learning.* New York, NY: Harper & Row.

Magill, R. A. (1993). *Motor learning: Concepts and applications.* Madison, WI: WCB Brown and Benchmark Publishers.

Robb, M. D. (1972). *The dynamics of motor-skill acquisition.* Englewood Cliffs, NJ: Prentice Hall.

Schmidt, R. A., & Wrisberg, C. A. (2000). *Motor learning and performance.* Champaign, IL: Human Kinetics.

Shea, C. H., Shebilske, W. L., & Worchel, S. (1993). *Motor learning and control.* Englewood Cliffs, NJ: Prentice Hall.

CHAPTER 17
Information Processing in Motor Learning

Adams, J. A. (1971). A closed-loop theory of motor learning. *Journal of Motor Behavior, 3,* 111-150.

Carola, R., Harley, J. P., & Noback, C. R. (1992). *Human anatomy.* New York, NY: McGraw-Hill.

Reilly, R. (1996, February 19). I was just a pawn! *Sports Illustrated,* 96.

Schmidt, R. A. (1991). *Motor learning and performance.* Champaign, IL: Human Kinetics.

Schubert, F. (1988). *Psychology from start to finish.* Toronto, ON: Sport Books Publisher.

Shea, C. H., Shebilske, W. L., & Worchel, S. (1993). *Motor learning and control.* Englewood Cliffs, NJ: Prentice Hall.

CHAPTER 18
Motor Learning in Practice: Skill Acquisition

Fitts, P. M. (1964). Perceptual-motor skills learning. In A. W. Melton (Ed.), *Categories of human learning* (pp. 243-285). New York, NY: Academic Press.

Magill, R. A. (1998). *Motor learning: Concepts and applications.* Boston, MA: WCB McGraw-Hill.

Schmidt, R. A., & Wrisberg, C. A. (2000). *Motor learning and performance.* Champaign, IL: Human Kinetics.

Schubert, F. (1998). *Psychology from start to finish.* Toronto, ON: Sport Books Publisher.

Shea, C. H., Shebilske, W. L., & Worchel, S. (1993). *Motor learning and control.* Englewood Cliffs, NJ: Prentice Hall.

Thorndike, E. L. (1927). The law of effect. *American Journal of Psychology, 39,* 212-222.

CHAPTER 19
Physical Activity and Sport Issues

Beal, B. (1995). Disqualifying the official: An exploration of social resistance through the subculture of skateboarding. *Sociology of Sport Journal, 12*(13): 252-267.

Brooks, D., & Althouse, R. (Eds.). (1999). *Racism in college athletics: The African-American athletes' experience* (2nd ed.). Morgantown, WV: Fitness Information Technology.

Coakley, J. (1986). *Sport in society.* Toronto, ON: Times Mirror/Mosely College Publishing.

Coakley, J. (2001). *Sport in society: Issues and controversies* (7th ed.). New York, NY: McGraw-Hill.

Cox, R. H. (2002). *Sport psychology: Concepts and applications* (5th ed.). New York, NY: McGraw-Hill.

Crissey, J. (1999). *Corporate cooptation of sport: The case of snowboarding.* Unpublished thesis, Colorado State University, FL: Collins Publishers.

Eitzen, D. (1999). *Fair and foul: Beyond the myths and paradoxes of sport.* Lanham, MD: Rowman & Littlefield.

Fasting, K. (1996, July). *40,000 female runners: The Grete Waitz run – Sport culture and counter-culture.* Paper presented at the International Pre-Olympic Scientific Conference, Dallas, Texas.

Fausto-Sterling, A. (2000). *Sexing the body: Gender politics and the construction of sexuality.* New York, NY: Basic Books.

Lapchick, R. E., & Mathews, K. (2000). *Racial and gender report card (for 1998).* Boston, MA: Center for the Study of Sport in Society (Northeastern University).

Leith, L. M. (2003). *The psychology of coaching team sports: A self-help guide.* Toronto, ON: Sport Books Publisher.

MacIntosh, D. (1989). Female participation in Ontario inter-university sport programs. *CAHPER Journal, 7,* 1-20.

Sopinka, J. (1984). *Can I play? The report of the task force on equal opportunity in athletics in 11 schools and universities.* Ottawa, ON: Government of Canada.

Young, K. (2001). Sport and violence. In J. Coakley & E. Dunning (Eds.). *Handbook of sports studies,* (pp. 382-407). London, GB: Sage.

CHAPTER 20
Society, Culture, and Sport

Jennings, A., & Sambrook, C. (2000). *The great Olympic swindle: When the world wanted its Games back.* London, GB: Simon & Schuster.

Kidd, B. (1988). The philosophy of excellence: Olympic performances, class power, and the Canadian State. In P. J. Galasso (Ed.), *Philosophy of sport and physical activity: Issues and concepts* (pp. 11-31). Toronto, ON: Canadian Scholars Press.

Lavoie, M. (2000). Economics and sport. In J. Coakley & E. Dunning (Eds.), *Handbook of sports studies* (pp. 157-170). London, GB: Sage.

Leith, L. M. (1998). *Exercising your way to better mental health.* Morgantown, WV: Fitness Information Technology, Inc.

Lowes, M. (1999). *Inside the sports pages: Work routines, professional ideologies, and the manufacture of sports news.* Toronto, ON: University of Toronto.

McDaniel, S., & Sullivan, C. (1998). Extending the sports experience: Mediations in cyberspace. In L. Wenner (Ed.), *Mediasport*, 266-281. New York, NY: Routledge.

Ozanian, M. (1995, February). Following the money. *Financial World, 164*(4): 27-31.

Porterfield, K. (1999). Late to the line: Starting sport competition as an adult. In J. Coakley & P. Donnelly (Eds.), *Inside sports* (pp. 37-45). London, GB: Routledge.

Wilson, S. (1988). *Politics and leisure.* London, GB: Unwin Hyman.

CHAPTER 21
Career Opportunities in PHE

Bouchard, C., McPherson, B. D., & Taylor, A. W. (Eds.). (1992). *Physical activity sciences.* Windsor, ON: Human Kinetics.

Freeman, W. H. (1997). *Physical education and sport in a changing society* (5th ed.). Boston, MA: Allyn & Bacon.

Tiidus, P. M., & Leatt, P. (1986). Employment patterns for graduates of physical and health education at the University of Toronto, 1979-1983. *CAHPER Journal, 52,* 50-51.

CHAPTER 22
Introduction to Research Methods

American Psychological Association [APA] (1994). *Publication manual of the American Psychological Association* (4th ed.). Washington, DC: American Psychological Association.

Berg, K. E., & Latin, R. W. (1994). *Essentials of modern research methods in health, physical education, and recreation.* Englewood Cliffs, NJ: Prentice Hall.

Vincent, W. J. (1995). *Statistics in kinesiology.* Champaign, IL: Human Kinetics.

CHAPTER 23
Introduction to Statistical Concepts

Berg, K. E., & Latin, R. W. (1994). *Essentials of modern research methods in health, physical education, and recreation.* Englewood Cliffs, NJ: Prentice Hall.

Vincent, W. J. (1995). *Statistics in kinesiology.* Champaign, IL: Human Kinetics.

Key Words Index

A

Abduction, *23*
Absolute refractory period, *421*
Absolute strength, *243*
Absolute V̇O₂max, *204*
Absorption, *263*
Abstract, *547*
Acceleration, *132*
Achievement, *234*
Achievement motivation, *348*
Actin, *65*
Action potential, *111, 420*
Action–reaction, *147*
Active flexibility, *206*
Activity cross training, *226*
Acute mountain sickness (AMS), *125*
Addiction, *318*
Adduction, *23*
Adenosine diphosphate (ADP), *96*
Adenosine triphosphate (ATP), *96*
Aerobic cross training, *224*
Aerobic metabolism, *104*
Aerobic power (V̇O₂max), *203*
Aerodynamics, *151*
Afferent neurons, *417*
Agility, *254*
Agonist, *64*
Agonist–antagonist training, *200*
Alcohol, *321*
All-around athlete, *397*
All-or-none law, *420*
All-or-none principle, *71*
Altitude, *124*
Alveoli, *118*
Amenorrhea, *312*
Amino acid, *267*
Amylase, *263*
Anabolic steroids, *323, 326*
Anaerobic alactic, *98*
Anaerobic glycolysis, *100*
Anaerobic lactic, *98*
Anaerobic metabolism, *104*
Anaerobic threshold, *100, 227*
Anatomical position, *19*
Angle of attack, *154*
Angular acceleration, *132*
Angular displacement, *132*
Angular kinetics, *159*

Angular motion (rotation), *136*
Angular velocity, *132*
Anorexia nervosa, *310*
Antagonist, *64*
Anterior (ventral), *19*
Anterior cruciate tear, *175*
Antioxidant, *272*
Anxiety, *343*
Apoptosis, *91*
Appendicular skeleton, *25*
Applied research, *542*
Arousal, *343*
Arterial–venous oxygen (a–v O₂) difference, *116*
Arteriole, *115*
Artery, *114*
Assertive behaviour, *466*
Associative (practice) stage, *438*
ATP re-synthesis, *96*
Attribution theory, *351*
Augmented feedback, *444*
Autonomous (application) stage, *438*
Auxotonic contraction, *80*
Axial skeleton, *25*
Axis of rotation, *135*
Axon, *418*

B

Backward chaining, *454*
Baggataway, *491*
Balance, *157*
Ball and socket joint, *34*
Bandwidth feedback, *446*
Bar graph (histogram), *567*
Basal metabolic rate (BMR), *298*
Basic research, *542*
Becoming, *4*
Being, *4*
Belonging, *4*
Bending, *172*
Bernoulli's principle, *154*
Bile, *265*
Bile salts, *265*
Binge eating disorder (BED), *311*
Bioelectrical impedance analysis (BIA), *302*
Biological adaptation, *74*
Biological age, *386*

Biomechanics, *130*
Blocked practice, *456*
Blood doping, *328*
Bod-Pod, *302*
Body composition, *208, 300*
Body mass index (BMI), *302*
Bohr effect, *124*
Boundary layer, *152*
Breath sound check, *227*
Bronchiole, *119*
Bronchus, *119*
Bulimia nervosa, *310*
Bursitis, *184*

C

Caffeine, *319*
Caloric balance, *296*
Calorie, *266*
Canada Games, *492*
Cannabis, *323*
Capillary, *115*
Carbohydrate, *270*
Carbohydrate loading, *290, 324*
Cardiac muscle, *62*
Cardiac output, *112, 377*
Cardiorespiratory (cardiovascular) endurance, *203*
Cell body, *418*
Central nervous system (CNS), *416*
Centre of mass (gravity), *143*
Childhood, *369*
Cholesterol, *269*
Chronological age, *386*
Circuit training, *216*
Circumduction, *23*
Class frequency, *564*
Class interval, *564*
Closed skill, *405*
Closed-loop control, *425*
Cognitive (understanding) stage, *438*
Cognitive state anxiety, *343*
Competitive State Anxiety Inventory–II (CSAI–II), *345*
Collagen, *205*
Complementary proteins, *267*
Complete dislocation, *179*
Complete protein, *267*
Composite diagram, *134*

Compound fracture, *181*
Compression, *172*
Concentric contraction, *83*
Concussion, *181*
Conduction zone, *118*
Conductive segment, *419*
Condyloid (knuckle) joint, *34*
Conservation of angular
   momentum, *160*
Continuous training, *221*
Control group, *561*
Contusion, *174*
Cori cycle, *105*
Correlation, *570*
Creatine, *326*
Creeping obesity, *307*
Criterion task, *449*
Critical (sensitive) periods,
   366
Cross bridge formation, *67*
Cryotherapy, *173*
Culture, *497*
Curvilinear motion, *135*

D

Deep, *19*
Deformation, *170*
Dendrites, *418*
Dependent variable, *561*
Depolarization, *420*
Depressants, *323*
Descriptive feedback, *449*
Descriptive statistics, *560*
Diagnosis, *233*
Diaphragm, *120*
Diastole, *111*
Dietary supplements, *318*
Digestion, *263*
Digestive system, *263*
Disaccharide, *270*
Disordered eating, *312*
Displacement, *132*
Distal, *19*
Distress, *343*
Distributed practice, *456*
Dorsiflexion, *23*
Drag, *152*
Drugs, *318*
Dual energy x-ray
   absorptiometry (DEXA), *302*
Dynamic (ballistic) stretching,
   206
Dynamic contraction, *80*
Dynamic equilibrium, *157*

E

Early childhood, *369*
Early specialization, *386*
Eccentric contraction, *83*
Ectomorph, *304, 371*
Efferent neurons, *417*
Elastic region, *171*
Elastin, *205*
Emotional arousal, *351*
Emotional health, *2*
Endomorph, *304, 371*
Endurance training, *221*
Energy balance equation, *296*
Environmental health, *2*
Enzyme, *100*
Ephedra, *328*
Epidural haemorrhage, *28*
Equilibrium, *157*
Ergogenic aids, *291, 323*
Erythropoietin (EPO), *116, 328*
Esophagus, *263*
Essential amino acids, *267*
Essential fat (EF), *301*
Essential nutrients, *266*
Ethnicity, *475*
Eustress, *343*
Eversion, *23*
Executive program, *402*
Exercise, *198*
Exercise science, *524*
Experimental design, *561*
Experimental group, *561*
Expiration, *120*
Explosive load increase, *214*
Extension, *20*
External validity, *542*
Extrinsic feedback, *444*

F

Faded feedback, *446*
Fantasy leagues, *515*
Far transfer, *450*
Fartlek, *221*
Fast twitch (FT) fibre, *69*
Fat-soluble vitamins, *272*
Fear of failure, *348*
Feedback, *423*
Female athlete triad (FAT), *311*
Fibroblastic repair phase, *173*
Field research, *542*
Field test, *236*
Fight or flight, *343*
First class lever, *140*

Fitness and Amateur Sport
   Act, *492*
Fixator, *64*
Flat bone, *24*
Flexibility, *205, 251*
Flexion, *20*
Forward chaining, *454*
Free radicals, *272*
Frequency distribution, *564*
Frontal (coronal) plane, *20*
Fulcrum, *138*

G

Gallbladder, *266*
Gas diffusion, *122*
Gastrointestinal tract, *263*
General coordination abilities,
   399
General motion, *136*
Generalized (dynamic) motor
   program (GMP), *394*
Gluconeogenesis, *100*
Glycogen, *271*
Glycolytic system, *98*
Gradual load increase, *214*
Graphs, *565*
Gravitational hypothesis, *341*
Gravity, *133*
Grip dynamometer, *243*
Grouped frequency
   distribution, *564*
Grouping for practice, *457*

H

Habituation, *318*
Hallucinogens, *323*
Health, *2*
Heart rate, *113, 377*
Hematocrit, *116*
Hemoglobin, *116*
High energy (immediate)
   phosphate system, *98*
Hinge (ginglymus) joint, *34*
Hostile aggression, *465*
Human anatomy, *18*
Human kinetics, *524*
Hydrochloric acid, *265*
Hydrodynamics, *151*
Hydrogenation, *269*
Hydrostatic weighing, *302*
Hyperthermia (heat stroke),
   125
Hyperventilation, *124*

I

Impact, *145*
Impulse, *145*
Incomplete protein, *267*
Independent variable, *561*
Inertia, *143*
Infancy, *367*
Inferential statistics, *560*
Inferior, *19*
Inferior vena cava, *111*
Inflammatory response phase, *173*
Information feedback, *441*
Information processing, *423*
Informed consent, *544*
Insertion, *42, 63*
Insoluble fibre, *271*
Inspiration, *120*
Institutional review board (IRB), *544*
Instrumental aggression, *466*
Inter-muscle coordination, *72*
Internal validity, *542*
Interneuron, *418*
Interval level, *558*
Intra-muscle coordination, *72*
Intrinsic feedback, *442*
Intrinsic motivation, *348*
Inversion, *23*
Inverted U, *346*
Involuntary muscle, *62*
Irregular bone, *24*
Isokinetic contraction, *82*
Isometric contraction, *80*
Isotonic contraction, *81*

K

Kilocalorie, *266*
Kinanthropology, *524*
Kinematics, *132*
Kinesiology, *524*
Kinesthetic sense, *444*
Kinetics, *133*
Knowledge of performance (KP), *442*
Knowledge of results (KR), *442*
Kreb's cycle, *105*

L

Laboratory research, *542*
Laboratory test, *236*

Lactic acid, *100*
Lactic acid system, *100*
Laminar flow, *152*
Large intestine, *266*
Late childhood, *369*
Late specialization, *386*
Lateral, *19*
Lateral (external) rotation, *23*
Lateral ankle sprain, *179*
Lateral epicondylitis, *184*
Law of effect, *458*
Lean body mass (LBM), *301*
Left atrium, *110*
Left ventricle, *110*
Lever, *139*
Lift force, *151*
Line of best fit, *567*
Linear motion, *135*
Lipid, *268*
Little league elbow, *372*
Liver, *265*
Load, *170*
Locus of control, *352*
Long bone, *24*

m

Macronutrients, *274*
Magnus effect, *155*
Magnus force, *155*
Mass, *143*
Massed practice, *456*
Maturation–remodeling phase, *174*
Maximal (absolute) strength, *87*
Maximal aerobic power ($\dot{V}O_2$max), *106, 117*
Maximal oxygen consumption ($\dot{V}O_2$max), *236*
Mean, *568*
Medial, *19*
Medial (internal) rotation, *23*
Medial epicondylitis, *184*
Median, *569*
Median (midsagittal) plane, *20*
Membrane potential, *420*
Mental health, *2*
Mental imagery, *455*
Mental rehearsal (practice), *454*
Mesomorph, *304, 371*
Micronutrients, *274*
Mid-childhood, *369*
Minerals, *274*

Minority group, *475*
Mitochondria, *105*
Mode, *569*
Moment arm, *139*
Moment of force (torque), *138*
Moment of inertia, *143*
Momentum, *145*
Monosaccharide, *270*
Monounsaturated fat, *268*
Motility, *263*
Motivation, *234, 348*
Motive to achieve success, *348*
Motor end plate, *70*
Motor neuron, *417*
Motor program, *393*
Motor unit, *70*
Movement intelligence, *393*
Muscle biopsy, *70*
Muscle fibre, *64*
Muscle force deficit, *72*
Muscle sense (muscle feeling), *442*
Muscular endurance, *87, 200, 247*
Muscular endurance cross training, *224*
Muscular strength, *200*
Myelin sheath, *418*
Myofibril, *64*
Myofilament, *64*
Myosin, *65*

n

Near transfer, *449*
Negative correlation, *571*
Negative transfer, *449*
Net force, *141*
Neurons, *417*
Newton's first law, *144*
Newton's second law, *145*
Newton's third law, *147*
Nicotine, *321*
Nodes of Ranvier, *418*
Nominal level, *558*
Nonparametric statistics, *560*
Norms, *234*
Null hypothesis, *562*
Nutrition, *266*

O

Obesity, *306*
One repetition maximum (1RM), *87, 243*

Open skill, *407*
Open-loop control, *427*
Opiates, *323*
Ordinal level, *558*
Origin, *42, 63*
Osteoporosis, *312*
Oxidative phosphorylation, *98*
Oxygen system, *104*

P

Parabolic path, *147*
Parameter, *394*
Parametric statistics, *560*
Part practice, *453*
Partial dislocation, *179*
Participatory modeling, *350*
Particle model, *133*
Passive flexibility, *206*
Patellar tendonitis, *184*
Pepsin, *265*
Percent body fat, *302*
Percentile, *569*
Perceptual motor abilities, *398*
Periodization of training
   principle, *214*
Peripheral nervous system
   (PNS), *416*
Peristalsis, *263*
Personality, *338*
Personality states, *340*
Personality traits, *340*
Physical activity, *198*
Physical fitness, *198*
Physical health, *2*
Physical proficiency abilities,
   398
Pie chart, *567*
Pivot joint, *34*
Placement, *233*
Plane (gliding) joint, *34*
Plantar flexion, *23*
Plasma, *116*
Plastic region, *171*
Plyocentric contraction, *83*
Polarization, *420*
Polysaccharide, *271*
Polyunsaturated fat, *268*
Population, *563*
Positive correlation, *571*
Positive imagery, *347*
Positive self-talk, *347*
Positive training effect, *171*
Positive transfer, *449*
Posterior (dorsal), *19*

Power, *87, 200, 244*
Pre-competitive anxiety, *345*
Prediction, *233*
Prescriptive feedback, *449*
PRICE, *173*
Primary reference, *546*
Prime mover, *04*
Profile (form) drag, *152*
Profile of Mood States
   (POMS), *340*
Program evaluation, *234*
Progressive muscular
   relaxation (PMR), *347*
Progressive resistance
   (overload) principle, *213*
Projectile, *147*
Pronation, *23*
Prone, *19*
Proprioception, *179*
Proprioceptive neuromuscular
   facilitation (PNF) stretching,
   206
Protein, *267*
Proximal, *19*
Psychomotor ability, *208*
Pyruvate, *100*

Q

Qualitative analysis, *132, 162*
Quantitative analysis, *130*

R

Race, *474*
Random practice, *456*
Random sample, *563*
Range, *149*
Rank order distribution, *564*
Ratio level, *560*
Readiness, *367*
Receptive segment, *419*
Recommended Daily Intake
   (RDI), *277*
Recommended Nutrient Intake
   (RNI), *277*
Rectilinear motion, *135*
Red blood cell (erythrocyte),
   116
Rehabilitation, *171*
Relative frequency, *564*
Relative refractory period, *421*
Relative strength, *85*
Relative $\dot{V}O_2$max, *205*
Reliability, *235*

Repetition maximum (RM), *89*
Research, *538*
Research hypothesis, *548*
Respiratory zone, *118*
Response programming
   stage, *423*
Response selection stage, *423*
Response uncertainty, *407*
Reticulocytes, *116*
Reversibility principle, *214*
Right atrium, *110*
Right ventricle, *110*
Rigid body segment model,
   135
Rivalry, *355*

S

Saddle joint, *34*
Sagittal plane, *20*
Saliva, *263*
Sample, *563*
Sarcolemma, *64*
Sarcomere, *65*
Sarcopenia, *91*
Saturated fat, *268*
Scalar quantity, *141*
Scatter plot (scattergram), *572*
Scientific method, *540*
Second class lever, *140*
Secondary reference, *546*
Secretion, *263*
Segmentation (progressive
   part practice), *454*
Self-confidence cycle, *383*
Self-efficacy, *349*
Sensory neuron, *417*
Sesamoid bone, *24*
Shear, *172*
Shin splints, *187*
Short bone, *24*
Shoulder impingement, *187*
Simple fracture, *181*
Simple frequency distribution,
   564
Simplification, *453*
Simulator, *452*
Sinus node, *110*
Skeletal muscle, *62*
Skill, *401*
Skill as a task, *401*
Skill as quality of
   performance, *401*
Skinfold calipers, *301*
Skinfold measurement, *240*

Skin-friction (surface) drag, 152
Sliding filament theory, 65
Slow long distance (SLD) training, 221
Slow twitch (ST) fibre, 69
Small intestine, 265
Smooth muscle, 62
Social facilitation, 355
Social health, 2
Soluble fibre, 271
Somatic state anxiety, 345
Somatotype, 371
Spatial uncertainty, 407
Specificity of exercise principle, 214
Speed–strength, 87
Spiritual health, 2
Sponsorship, 507
Sport ethic, 468
Sport sociology, 464
Sportainment, 512
Sprain, 175
Stability, 157, 352
Stacking, 326
Static contraction, 78
Static equilibrium, 157
Static stretching, 206
Station training, 216
Stick figure model, 134
Stimulants, 323
Stimulus identification stage, 423
Stomach, 263
Storage fat (SF), 301
Strain, 175
Strength, 243
Strength endurance, 87
Stress, 171, 343
Stress fracture, 187
Striated muscle, 64
Stroke volume, 113, 377

Subluxation, 179
Submaximal static contraction, 78
Subroutine, 402
Successful performance, 350
Summary feedback, 446
Superficial, 19
Superior, 19
Superior vena cava, 111
Supination, 23
Supine, 19
Synapse, 420
Synergist, 64
Synovial joint, 34
Systole, 111

T

Tactical uncertainty, 409
Talk test, 227
Tally, 564
Temporal patterning, 405
Temporal uncertainty, 409
Tendon, 62
Tendonitis, 184
Tension, 172
Terminal bronchiole, 118
Terminal endings, 418
Third class lever, 140
Torsion, 172
Total body fat (TBF), 301
Total body mass (TBM), 301
Trachea, 118
Training frequency, 209
Training intensity, 209
Training time, 209
Training volume, 209
Trait anxiety, 343
Trans fatty acid, 269
Transfer of learning, 449
Translation, 135
Transmissive segment, 419

Transverse (horizontal) plane, 20
Treatment, 171
Triglyceride, 268
Turbulent flow, 152

U

Ultimate failure, 171

V

Validity, 235
Valve, 115
Vector, 141
Vector quantity, 141
Vegetarian, 285
Vein, 115
Velocity, 132, 136
Ventilation, 120
Ventilatory threshold, 227
Venule, 115
Verbal persuasion, 351
Vicarious experience, 350
Violence, 465
Vitamins, 272
Voluntary muscle, 62

W

Water-soluble vitamins, 272
Wellness, 2
White blood cell, 116
Whole practice, 454
World Anti-Doping Agency (WADA), 329

Y

Yield-level point, 171

Credits

Pictures were reproduced with permission from the Faculty of Physical Education and Health, University of Toronto.
Photo credits: Rob Allen, Lewko Hryhorijiw, Kristina Ristoka.

Additional photography provided by Canadian Press, Corbis/Magma Photo Inc., Stan J. Czerniec, Firstlight, PK Photo, Maifith Design Inc., PhotoDisc, Niko Slana, Sports Illustrated, Sportverlag, Toronto Star, VEB Georg Thieme.

Every effort has been made to acknowledge correctly and contact the source and/or copyright holder of each picture, and Sport Books Publisher apologizes for any unintentional errors or omissions which will be corrected in future editions of this book.

	Pages
Canadian Press	xi, xiii, 73 (decathlete Michael Smith), 84, 88 (weightlifter), 129, 131, 138 (pushing bobsled), 141, 153 (Figure 7.14 D), 161 (Figure 7.21 C), 185 (baseball pitcher), 207, 319 (rower Silken Laumann), 323, 342 (Wayne Gretzky Figure 14.3), 350, 384, 430 (Figure 17.7 B), 473, 474, 477 (Figure 19.9: Anson Carter and Jarome Iginla), 478, 479 (dog sled race), 480, 489, 495 (Figure 20.3: bottom image), 497, 500 (background Donovan Bailey, Table 20.2), 501, 502, 503 (Nancy Greene, Terry Fox), 504, 506, 511 (Figure 20.11, race car and driver Jacques Villeneuve), 516, 518 (Figure 20.15), 559 (Gretzky jersey).
Maifith Design Inc.	19, 21, 22, 34 (joint types), 35, 66, 111 (heart), 114, 115, 116, 120, 128, 134 (Figure 7.2 C), 136, 138 (3D images), 139, 151, 154 (Figure 7.15), 157, 218-219, 265, 297, 419, 420.
Corbis/Magma Photo Inc.	cover, 12 (doctors), 28 (soccer header), 46 (butterfly swimmer), 49 (biceps curl), 60, 79 (tug of war), 92 (Figure 4.12), 147, 153 (Figure 7.14 C), 188 (butterfly swimmer), 191, 197, 199 (background muscular strength), 295, 299 (students walking, house cleaning), 303 (background image, Figure 12.5), 317, 337, 361, 363, 365, 369 (Figure 15.4), 372, 373, 375, 376, 381, 388 (Figure 15.13), 390, 391, 428, 429, 430 (Figure 17.7 E, F, G), 437 (Figure 18.2), 439 (Figure 18.4: left baseball image, right soccer image), 453 (Figure 18.10 A), 482 (Figure 19.13: weightlifting, karate, golf), 484 (Figure 19.14: snow boarder, skate boarder, wind surfer), 522, 536, 537, 544, 547, 556, 557, 559 (dice, phone number pad, man with thermometer, man with pocket watch).
Firstlight	42 (boy eating chocolate), 272, 277, 283, 286, 289, 291 (Figure 11.13), 294, 296 (Figure 12.1: right image), 307, 311, 371, 388 (sandwich).
Niko Slana	ii, iii, 7, 18, 48 (kayaker), 50 (pole vaulter), 53 (sprint start), 56 (javelin throw), 57 (cross-country skier), 64, 65 (gymnast), 68 (mountain biker, basketball player), 71 (high jumper), 79 (gymnast, skier, judo athletes, shooter), 90, 91, 92 (wall climber), 95, 97, 102 (rower), 119 (skier), 137 (kids wrestling), 146 (soccer player), 148, 153 (Figure 7.14 A), 154 (ski jumper), 158 (Figure 7.19 B, D, F), 159, 165, 168, 170, 177 (tennis player), 181 (Figure 8.7), 183 (tennis player), 189 (runner), 190 (Figure 8.10), 199 (background psychomotor ability), 201, 204 (left image), 205 (gymnast), 208, 210, 290 (gymnast), 291 (tennis player, Figure 11.12), 313, 327 (long jumper, high jumper), 328 (skiers), 330, 331, 332, 333, 339 (soccer player, tennis player), 345, 346, 351 (Figure 14.9), 360, 362, 366, 385, 386, 387, 392, 394, 398, 399, 400, 406 (dancers, rhythmic gymnast, equestrian), 408 (judo athletes), 410 (images Figure 16.11), 411, 426, 430 (Figure 17.7 C), 434, 436 (hockey player), 439 (Figure 18.4 middle soccer image), 442, 450, 482 (Figure 19.13 tennis player), 484 (Figure 19.14 rock climber), 570.
PK Photo	vi (Anderson, Lam, Skonieczny, Wells), 42 (smiling women), 68 (elbow flexion angles), 113 (Figure 6.4), 125, 140, 166, 174 (drugs), 175, 194, 203 (rowers), 204 (right image), 225, 226 (rower), 235, 240, 241, 243 (background image, Table 10.5), 245 (background images Table 10.6), 247, 249, 250 (Figure 10.12 A), 251 (Figure 10.14), 252 (background images Table 10.13), 255 (background image, Table 10.16), 256 (background image, Table 10.17), 288, 302 (Figure 12.4 B), 306, 321 (alcoholic beverages), 324, 401, 403, 425, 430 (Figure 17.7 A), 433, 436 (young basketball players), 447 (Figure 18.6 A), 455, 487, 509, 514, 522, 527, 529, 531, 532, 535, 539, 543, 553, 561 (Figure 23.1 B), 566, 567.
PhotoDisc	xiv, 1, 2, 3 (background images), 4, 5, 6, 11 (cyclists), 15, 17, 51 (walker), 61, 76, 77, 82, 94, 108, 109, 117 (rock climber), 123 (mountain biker), 124, 132, 158 (Figure 7.19 E), 169, 176, 185 (golfer), 186 (basketball players), 190 (Figure 8.11), 195, 199 (background flexibility), 212, 230, 231, 232, 233, 234, 237, 248 (background image, Table 10.8), 299 (skiing, cycling, tennis), 300, 312 (runner, Figure 12.12), 336, 339 (archer), 341, 380, 395, 406 (swimmers, darts), 408 (football, baseball, rugby), 414, 435, 440, 445, 453 (Figure 18.10 B), 461, 462, 463, 484 (Figure 19.14: dirt biker), 488, 540.
Stan J. Czerniec	vi (Maione), 81, 113 (Figure 6.3), 178, 179 (basketball players), 180 (one-legged balance, ankle strengthening exercises), 183 (exercises), 185 (forearm flexor exercise), 186 (exercises), 188 (exercises), 189 (exercises), 199 (background muscular endurance, body composition), 202, 206, 207 (top image in box, Figure 9.9), 211, 239, 242, 243 (grip dynamometer), 245 (Figure 10.8), 246, 248 (Figure 10.11), 250 (Figure 10.12 B), 251 (Figure 10.13), 252 (Figure 10.15), 253, 254, 255 (Figure 10.18), 257.
Sports Illustrated	9, 143, 162, 203 (cross-country skiing), 348, 364, 369 (figure skater), 437 (basketball player).
Sportverlag	26, 27, 44, 45, 73 (inset images), 244 (background image in box).
Toronto Star	264, 464.
University of Toronto	v (students), vi (De Souza, Goode, Klavora, Leith, Locke), 351 (Figure 14.10), 439 (Figure 18.4 left soccer image), 458, 467, 472, 561 (Figure 23.1 A).
VEB Georg Thieme	24 (background images, Table 2.1), 25, 26, 27, 28 (skulls, Figure 2.8), 29, 30, 31, 32, 33, 34 (background image box), 36, 37, 38, 39, 40, 41 (bones and joints of the foot, Figure 2.20), 43, 44, 45, 46 (muscles of the pectoral girdle, Figure 2.26), 47, 48 (lateral muscles of the scapula–humeral region, Figure 2.28), 49 (muscles of the right arm and forearm, Figure 2.29), 50 (muscles of the pelvic girdle, Figure 2.30), 51 (posterior muscles of the pelvic girdle, Figure 2.31), 52, 53 (muscles of the leg, Figure 2.33), 54, 55 (deep muscles of the abdomen, Figure 2.35), 177-189 (anatomical images).

THREE COMPANIONS TO
FOUNDATIONS OF EXERCISE SCIENCE

EXERCISE SCIENCE
TEACHER'S GUIDE
STUDYING HUMAN MOVEMENT AND HEALTH

A. ANDERSON
T. HARKER
P. KLAVORA
R. WAKELIN

EXERCISE SCIENCE
STUDENT WORKBOOK
STUDYING HUMAN MOVEMENT AND HEALTH

P. KLAVORA
P. MAIONE

1. Teacher's Guide
2. Student Workbook
3. Graphics Package